Scale (km)

0   10   20   30

The Breeding Birds of North-East Scotland

An atlas of the breeding birds of Aberdeen, Aberdeenshire and Moray

Including part of the Cairngorms National Park

Edited by Ian Francis and Martin Cook

Photographic editor: Harry Scott

2011

With the support of
Scottish Natural Heritage, Forestry Commission Scotland, Cairngorms National Park Authority,
RSPB Scotland, Aberdeenshire Council and East Grampian Coastal Partnership

Designed and produced by:
Pica Design, 51 Charlton Crescent, Aboyne, Aberdeenshire AB34 5GN.
Email: picades@ifb.co.uk

Front cover Ptarmigan photographs:
(top) Stob Binnein, May 2000. © *Stuart Rae* **(lower left)** Glas Maol, May 2009. © *Ed Duthie*
(lower middle) Beinn Sgulaird, May 2010. © *Stuart Rae* **(lower right)** Creag an Leth-choin, June 2009. © *Paul Bingham*

Back cover photographs:
(top) Goldeneye, Deeside, May 2011. © *Harry Scott* **(mid-left)** Snow Bunting, Ben Macdui, June 2009. © *Paul Bingham*
(mid-right) Guillemot, Crawton, June 2009. © *Ed Duthie* **(lower left)** Oystercatcher, Ballater, April 2007. © *John Chapman*
(lower right) Slavonian Grebe, Speyside, July 2006. © *Dave Pullan*

Ordnance Survey base map data: Reproduced by permission of Ordnance Survey on behalf of HMSO.
© Crown Copyright 2009. All rights reserved. Ordnance Survey licence number 100049442.

Topographic data used in the atlas base maps is copyright Intermap Technologies Inc. 2009. All Rights Reserved.

Satellite imagery (end cover):
© Planet Observer - www.planetobserver.com - All rights reserved.

AC7

This publication should be cited as:
Francis, I. and Cook, M. 2011. (eds.).
The Breeding Birds of North-East Scotland.
Scottish Ornithologists' Club, Aberdeen.

A section from this publication should be cited as in the example below:
Marquiss, M. 2011. *Sparrowhawk.* pp. 140–141 in Francis, I. and Cook, M. (eds.)
The Breeding Birds of North-East Scotland. Scottish Ornithologists' Club, Aberdeen.

© 2011 Ian Francis and Martin Cook

First published in 2011 by Scottish Ornithologists' Club.

ISBN 978-0-9561126-3-7

Further information about the project can be found at www.nescotlandbirdatlas.org.uk

Any profits from the sale of this book will be held in a specific fund
by the Scottish Ornithologists' Club (Grampian Branch)
and will be used for future local ornithological projects,
in agreement with major funding partners.

Printed and bound in China through Asia Pacific Offset Ltd
www.asiapacificoffset.com

Gold East Paper is strictly committed to the wood used in paper
manufacturing originating from sustainable forests

Contents

Foreword

This 500-page book is the most impressive single result from the multiple endeavours of North-East birdwatchers in the last century, mainly since 1970. When I became interested in birds as an Aberdeenshire schoolboy in 1942, the sole birdwatcher in the Turriff district was the headmaster, who in younger days had collected eggs but in retirement did not search for birds. Since then, the increases in distribution and abundance of North-East birdwatchers have massively exceeded those of most of the bird species they observe.

An early spark was the Scottish Ornithologists' Club, which in 1947 started an Aberdeen branch. By 1974, observers sent records for an annual typed *North-East Scotland Bird Report*. A book with maps appeared in 1990 on *The Birds of North-East Scotland* (excluding Moray), and hard on its heels in 1992 there came *The Birds of Moray and Nairn* by Martin Cook. Both paved the way for the current book, stimulating its editors to a more comprehensive aim.

Each of the 153 species that have been confirmed breeding is given a separate account, illustrated in colour by maps and photographs. Sixty authors wrote these species accounts, and many photographers contributed pictures illustrating aspects of breeding for each species. In the fieldwork 348 people took part, 258 from Aberdeenshire, 67 from Moray and 23 from outside, spending almost 17,000 hours. Editors Ian Francis and Martin Cook state, 'in short, our atlas effort represents a phenomenal amount of work and stands as a testament to the enthusiasm of local birdwatchers'.

As one of the 60 authors I can vouch for it also being testament to the editors' unceasing commitment, attention to detail, abiding obsession with the task, and knack for inspiring others into action, all crucial ingredients for excellence in teamwork. The editors, despite not being raised locally, have evinced the most enduring intense interest in the North-East's birds and their conservation.

The 2011 book is much more than an atlas. For each species one finds not just maps of distribution, but also detailed text on changes in distribution and abundance over the years. General chapters on habitats and land use, distribution changes, and conservation will be of wide interest as a valuable historical record. The book will be a sound reference for birdwatchers and others, in the North-East and beyond.

It highlights the splendid variety of North-East Scotland, from its wonderful seaboard through farmland, woodland and town to river, loch, moor, and alpine land. This variety, and the richness of the birds that make their homes and rear their young here, are signals of the quality of the North-East's environment. There is much to be proud of, and in this Foreword I stress positive aspects. There are a few negative aspects, with declines of farmland birds from subsidised agriculture and open-country birds from grant-aided afforestation, and with illegal persecution of protected raptors on some private estates. The authors do not shirk from identifying such ills. Ending them requires politicians to act decisively in the public interest, and this book will be a reliable benchmark for that process.

The land, the wildlife, the folk are what make the North-East special. That land and that wildlife now depend on the folk to care for them. Let this book help in that selfless aim.

Adam Watson

Crathes, March 2011

Plate i. Dotterel, Cairn Gorm plateau, May 2008. © *Derek McGinn*

Summary

This atlas of breeding birds covers North-East Scotland - the local authority areas of Moray, Aberdeenshire and Aberdeen City, and includes almost half of the Cairngorms National Park. It maps the distributions of all birds that showed evidence of breeding during the period 2002–06, and also makes comparisons with earlier atlases, both local (1981–84) and national (1968–72 and 1988–91). It is the first 'repeated' local breeding bird atlas for any area in Scotland. Where possible, information on breeding birds has been updated to 2009.

The mapping unit is the tetrad - 2x2 km squares of the national grid - and the 2,340 surveyed make this the largest tetrad atlas ever undertaken, covering almost 4% of the UK land area and 11% of Scotland. The level of participation in the atlas was very high, with almost 350 observers taking part. Sixty of these also wrote the species accounts, and 62 photographers contributed a wide range of images illustrating breeding activity, a distinctive feature of this atlas. Almost 117,000 records were submitted during the course of the project.

During 2002–06, 189 species showed some evidence of at least possibly breeding, and 153 species were confirmed to have done so. The number of 'new' breeding species outnumbered those lost since previous atlases, more species showed evidence of an increase in their breeding range than showed a decrease, and more species appeared to have increased in numbers than decreased. However, these conclusions were certainly influenced by varying levels of observer effort and coverage, which it was not possible to quantify fully. Despite this, circumstantial evidence reinforces the conclusion that the breeding ranges (and populations) of many species have increased over the past four decades, and probably more species now breed in North-East Scotland than ever before. It is also clear, though, that some species are declining, with much reduced ranges, and these tend to be birds that are 'red-listed' at a national level.

For each species, its habitat, breeding biology, local breeding status and distribution are summarised. An estimate of breeding population is provided, along with evidence for change in distribution and numbers. The geography and habitat context in which our breeding birds are found is described in some detail, as are the main influences on their distribution and trends in numbers - the issues that are critical to bird conservation.

Most of the records from the atlas have been uploaded to the National Biodiversity Network and are publicly available, and we invite anyone to use the information in further analyses.

North-East Scotland Breeding Bird Atlas 2002–06 - some summary statistics

Atlas process:
- Land area: 8,686 km^2 (11% of Scotland's and 3.6% of UK's land areas)
- Number of tetrads covered: 2,340 (=116 whole or part 10-km squares)
- Number of records submitted: Total all records 116,878; non-duplicated records of maximum breeding status = 82,231
- Detailed breakdown of records
  - 'Confirmed Breeding'   32,319 (39%)
  - 'Probable Breeding'   23,538 (29%)
  - 'Possible Breeding'   22,738 (28%)
  - 'Observed, not breeding'   3,636 (4%)
- 80,783 records deposited with NBN; 1,448 confidential records excluded from this and held by the editors
- Number of observers participating: 348
- 33% of records collected by top 10 recorders; 47% by top 20
- Estimated 17,000 hours of observer effort; average of 7.7 survey hours per tetrad
- 60 species authors and 62 photographers helped with the production of the atlas.

Breeding Bird Atlas results:
- Number of species that at least possibly bred in atlas period: 189
- Number of species confirmed breeding: 153
- Most widespread species: Chaffinch, Wren, Meadow Pipit, Woodpigeon, Willow Warbler
- Most numerous species: Wren, Siskin, Chaffinch, Meadow Pipit and Blackbird.
- Species showing greatest increases in range since 1981–84 (evidence from two methods and low influence of observer effort): Buzzard, Stonechat, Great Spotted Woodpecker, Blackcap, Red-legged Partridge, Jay
- Species showing greatest decreases in range since 1981–84 (using two methods): Lapwing, Yellowhammer, Hooded Crow, Redshank, Rook, Corn Bunting, Curlew

North-East Scotland holds:
- 1% or more of the European breeding population of 14 species (e.g. Scottish Crossbill, Guillemot, Oystercatcher)
- 10% or more of the UK breeding population of 22 species (e.g. Ptarmigan, Crested Tit, Goldeneye)
- 20% or more of the Scottish breeding population of 31 species (e.g. Sandwich Tern, Corn Bunting, Tree Sparrow)

Introduction

Almost 30 years have passed since fieldwork began for the pioneering '*Birds of North-East Scotland*' atlas (Buckland *et al.* 1990). The recording period for this spanned 1981–1984 and breeding evidence for all bird species was located in each of 395 recording units, in what is now the area formed by the local authorities of Aberdeenshire and Aberdeen City. This ground-breaking book remains unique in its breadth and depth of coverage of all aspects of the distribution and occurrence of birds in this area throughout the year.

Many changes have taken place since then in the numbers and distribution of breeding birds. Following discussions between local ornithologists and representatives of different clubs and organisations, it was decided to attempt a new breeding bird atlas, 20 years on from the first, with fieldwork beginning in 2002 and spanning a five-year period up to 2006. The new atlas was run by an informal committee of local birdwatchers from the Scottish Ornithologists' Club Grampian branch and the Moray Bird Club.

This new *Breeding Birds of North-East Scotland* therefore covers a different overall area to the first, but shares the same geographic term. It includes Moray, which has not been subject to a local breeding bird atlas previously and, although 'North-East Scotland' may be slightly confusing in this context, we adopted it in the absence of any other satisfactory shorthand way of describing the area. The atlas covers what was the former Grampian local government region, which existed from 1974 to 1996. Nowadays, three local authorities cover this same area - Aberdeen City, Aberdeenshire and Moray, which together form a rather unwieldy grouping of names. The term 'Grampian' is still used by the police, fire and health services but it is gradually falling into disuse. The wider 'North-East Scotland' as defined here is used by some newer bodies such the Biodiversity Action Plan partnership and Flood Alleviation Group and is perhaps in the ascendancy. In addition, the creation of the Cairngorms National Park in 2003 produced another overlapping administration, and almost half of the national park falls within our area. Given this situation, we hope that our terminology clarifies rather than confuses further!

Previous substantial accounts of birds in the area were published in the 19th and early 20th centuries by Gordon (1844), MacGillivray (1855), St John (1863), Edward (1856–1860 - included more accessibly in Smiles 1876), Harvie-Brown & Buckley (1895), Sim (1903) and Harvie-Brown (1906). There were then two *Birds of Scotland* reviews (Baxter & Rintoul 1953; Thom 1986), two UK bird atlases (of breeding birds - Sharrock 1976; and of wintering birds - Lack 1986) and a large growth in published papers in journals such as *Scottish Birds*, before the appearance of Buckland *et al.* (1990). A modern avifauna covering Moray and Nairn was published shortly afterwards (Cook 1992) and rare species in Aberdeen and Aberdeenshire were documented by Phillips (1997). Since 1990, a second UK Breeding Bird Atlas has been published (Gibbons *et al.* 1993) and, very recently, a third *Birds of Scotland* (Forrester *et al.* 2007). The birds of the Cairngorms National Park, which covers around one-quarter of our area, have been covered principally by Nethersole-Thompson & Watson (1974, 1981), Dennis (2002) and Shaw *et al.* (2006).

In Scotland, other breeding bird atlases have been published for South-east Scotland (Murray *et al.* 1998) and Fife (Elkins *et al.* 2003), with fieldwork completed in Ayrshire, Clackmannanshire and Clyde (some data are available for these unpublished atlases on the National Biodiversity Network - www.searchnbn.net). Currently, fieldwork is underway for the third UK and Ireland national breeding and wintering bird atlas (2007–2011) at a 10-km square resolution, though with some 'tetrads' (see Chapter 1) surveyed in detail within each 10-km square. Some local areas in Scotland are using the opportunity to carry out their own tetrad-based projects - either initial or repeat atlases.

Our atlas covers an area of around 8,686 square kilometres (approximately 3.6% of the UK's and 11% of the Scottish land areas, with 2,340 component tetrads). As such we believe it is the largest tetrad atlas ever undertaken. Indeed, the area surveyed is larger than some 31 nation states in the world! A project of such scale presents considerable challenges, and these are considered further under *Survey Methods* (Chapter 1). However, we believe that the 348 participating local birdwatchers rose successfully to these challenges and produced high quality results. We are also proud to have undertaken what is the first 'repeat' breeding bird atlas in Scotland and amongst the few so far completed in the UK. We hope the results are of interest and of use to a wide range of people and organisations, and will stand as a tribute to the hard work and enthusiasm of so many.

Ian Francis and Martin Cook

March 2011

Chapter 1. *Survey methods and data analysis*

The aims of the atlas

The main aim of this atlas was to find the highest level of proof of breeding for every species in every defined recording area ('tetrad' - see below), thereby building composite distribution maps of all breeding birds in the area during the period of the atlas (2002–2006). A secondary aim was to collect, using maps, information on the precise locations of some nesting birds and their habitats, together with some counts of birds within tetrads. We also aimed to compare our results with a previous atlas from 1981–1984 (*NES 1st Atlas*).

Bird abundance and habitat quantification

From the outset, this was designed to be a distribution atlas of breeding birds and we did not aim to record bird abundance in any quantified way, nor carry out any kind of detailed measurements of habitat or land cover within tetrads. Some local breeding bird atlases have recorded bird abundance, and increasingly, national atlases are doing so (see Gibbons *et al.* 2007), including the 2007–2011 UK bird atlas. We considered this issue carefully, but the consensus at the outset was that because the scale of the survey was so large, and the uncertainty of successful completion sufficiently real, we did not wish to add complexity to the methods and risk deterring observers. Although we have made attempts to assess local populations (see below), these were often not based on quantitative survey. However, we would argue that the enormous geographic scale of the atlas, and the successful achievement of the task, offsets the lack of bird abundance measures to a substantial degree. We also decided that asking observers to record habitat variables was not realistic, and judged that this sort of information would be readily available from other sources.

Survey area and recording units

This breeding bird atlas ran for a period of five years from 2002 to 2006 and covered the geographic areas of Moray, Aberdeenshire and the City of Aberdeen, as described in more detail in Chapter 2. The recording unit was the tetrad, a now-familiar grouping of four 1-km squares of the national grid. Twenty-five tetrads make up one 10-km square and each tetrad is given a reference letter as shown in Figure 1.1. Thus every tetrad in the area can be referenced uniquely by the 10-km square reference and the tetrad letter (e.g. NJ62F) as shown below.

Within our survey area of 8,686 square kilometres, there are 2,340 whole or part tetrads, and every one was visited to record breeding birds during the five year atlas period, though coverage levels varied very widely (see Figure 1.4).

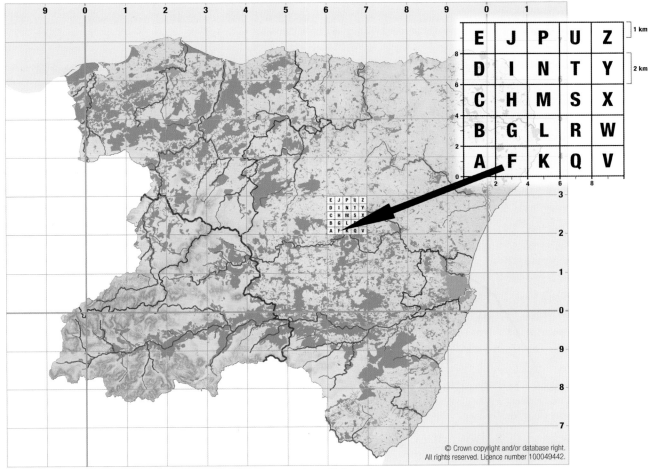

Figure 1.1. Tetrad reference diagram showing 10-km square in context and tetrad letter codes.

Figure 1.2. Illustration of the extent of land coverage of a tetrad. Cairn Toul area, 2004. © *Jill Matthews*

Recording methods and instructions

Simple recording cards were developed for the project, using best practice from elsewhere. Examples of these are given in Annex 3. Cards were of two types - for tetrad survey visits and for supplementary records. In addition, it was possible to enter records using a data entry page maintained by Paul Doyle at his Wildlife Web site, accessed through the project website www.nescotlandbirdatlas.org.uk. However, this facility attracted only a small fraction of record submissions and it was eventually discontinued. Detailed instructions were produced and the recording cards included basic summaries of the main points. One distinctive feature of our tetrad recording cards was that each held an extract of the relevant Ordnance Survey map covering the tetrad (see Annex 3). Observers were encouraged to annotate this map with any birds or habitat features of interest, as well as to write any comments and note any counts or population estimates for any species within the tetrad. This information was extracted separately from the main atlas records and transferred to a spreadsheet that could be analysed for conservation purposes (*e.g.* Barn Owl sites, heronries, wetlands with waders). Entering such information was optional, but it did yield 1,750 detailed location records or species counts.

Recording breeding activity

Breeding records were categorised using the now standard European Bird Census Council (EBCC) Atlas Breeding Codes, as used with small variations in most national and local breeding bird atlases and as shown in Table 1.1.

Table 1.1. Atlas breeding categories used in the North-East Scotland Breeding Bird Atlas 2002–2006.

Presence

    O   OBSERVED using tetrad during breeding season but not thought to be breeding (excludes flying over)

Breeding categories

(Possible breeding)
    H   Bird(s) in possible breeding HABITAT
    S   SINGING bird present

(Probable breeding)
    P   PAIR in breeding habitat
    T   TERRITORY (repeated territorial behaviour)
    D   DISPLAY and courtship
    N   Visiting probable NEST site
    A   AGITATED behaviour /ANXIETY calls
    I   Brood patch indicating INCUBATION
    B   BUILDING nest or excavating nest hole

(Confirmed breeding)
    DD   DISTRACTION DISPLAY/injury feigning
    UN   USED NEST or egg shells from period of atlas
    ON   OCCUPIED NEST (adults sitting/entering)
    FL   FLEDGED YOUNG (recent; fledged or downy young)
    FY   FOOD for YOUNG, or adult carrying faecal sacs
    NE   NEST containing EGGS
    NY   NEST containing YOUNG

The only variation we adopted from standard previous categories was the extension of the 'T' (permanent territory) category, which most commonly relies on repeated visits, to include also multiple singing birds on one survey visit. This change was made to accommodate the likelihood of there being only one survey visit to many of our most remote tetrads. We also added one category: the inclusion of 'O' - a bird observed in the tetrad during the breeding season but not thought to be breeding there. This typically covers foraging species such as gulls, herons and Rook. We considered this to be a useful way of capturing the breeding season range of species that forage widely but nest in only a few places. Similar modifications were made in the South-east Scotland Atlas (Murray *et al.* 1998) amongst others and have since been adopted for the 2007–11 BTO/SOC UK atlas.

Fieldwork organisation, coverage and observer effort

The objective was to cover the area within the five-year period and we aimed to ensure that coverage kept pace with this need. A small steering group was established at the outset to co-ordinate the project (see Annex 1). Local observers were allocated tetrads on demand but this became increasingly targeted as the project proceeded. Certain parts of the area received low levels of coverage until later in the atlas period; these were largely the same parts that were covered less well in 1981–84. All fieldwork was undertaken by volunteers except for some input from staff in RSPB Scotland, Forestry Commission Scotland and Scottish Natural Heritage, as well as some information provided by consultant ornithological surveyors carrying out other projects, usually wind farm surveys. Survey coverage was coordinated for Moray by Martin Cook and for other areas by Ian Francis.

From the outset, we were concerned that we might not be able to achieve the task we had set ourselves. The scale of the survey was enormous, with a risk we would not attract enough observers to visit all tetrads. In the end, this was not the case, but it did require a considerable amount of effort to ensure that coverage levels were maintained.

Participation

In total, 348 people took part in the survey - 258 in Aberdeenshire, 67 in Moray and 23 from outwith the area. Most participants covered one or two tetrads or contributed supplementary records. However, as is often the case with participatory surveys, a small number of observers did much more, and gathered the bulk of the records - in fact, excluding organisational datasets, 33% of the records were collected by the top 10 recorders and 47% by the top 20; 90% of the records were collected by 193 people. The level of participation compares favourably with other breeding bird atlases.

Measures of observer effort

The 1981–84 atlas did not record any measures of observer effort. In 2002–06 we requested that observers note how many hours they spent in each tetrad and this was done for 1,904 tetrads (81% of the total). The average time spent recording per tetrad was 7.7 hours, but this ranged from less than half an hour for marginal tetrads with only thin slivers of eligible land to over 90 hours for tetrads in which the observer lived - so this average is not a very meaningful measure. In fact, any effort measure cannot easily take account of habitat variation and observer ability, and a simple time measure is not greatly revealing.

However, in total, 14,586 hours of observer effort were actually recorded on cards during the atlas period and if one extends this, using average figures for the remaining tetrads where effort was not recorded, the total estimated recording time spent on the project was almost 17,000 hours. Such figures cannot easily be compared with other atlases, as similar information is usually not presented (though in Hertfordshire, the mean number of hours per tetrad was higher at 15.5 (439 tetrads), giving over 7,600 hours of total fieldwork (Smith *et al.* 1993). But in short, our atlas effort represents a phenomenal amount of work and stands as a testament to the enthusiasm of local birdwatchers. Further information on this is given in Annexes 2 and 3.

The impacts of differing observer coverage and effort between the two atlases

As stated above, we do not know what level of survey effort was expended in the 1981–84 atlas. It was also an 'all year round' project, hence there was no focus purely on breeding records. Even for the 2002–06 atlas our information is partial. Nevertheless, our impression is that a greater level of effort was undertaken during 2002–06. Evidence for this comes principally from the fact that the majority of species (74%) show a clear increase in range (the number of occupied recording units) between the two atlases. For reasons considered elsewhere, we do not consider that this was always a true picture and in some cases, the apparent range expansion contradicts other lines of evidence. This issue is considered further in Chapter 5.

Coverage of the area

Dedicated atlas recording took place in all of the 2,340 tetrads during the survey period. However, as noted above, there were great variations in intensity of coverage, and the degree of under- or over-recording that this may have led to depends mainly on habitat complexity. Ideally the best way of assessing coverage would be to derive a measure for each tetrad of what proportion of species were found compared with a theoretical list of expected species. In practical terms, such a measure was very difficult to derive, although it was attempted for Moray from *a priori* assessments of tetrads. The reality, however, was that covering the sheer number of tetrads in this survey meant that there was little available resource to tackle any relatively under-recorded tetrads without extending the survey period, which we felt was inappropriate. Therefore, variation in survey coverage

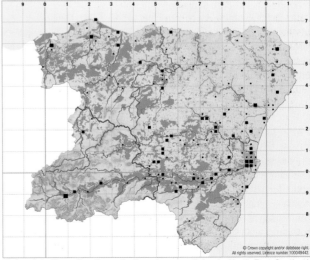

Figure 1.3. Home locations of atlas observers living in North-East Scotland, where known (dot sizes = 1, 2–4, 5–10 and >10 observers per tetrad).

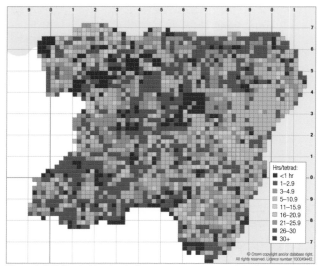

Figure 1.4. Estimated levels of atlas survey coverage per tetrad.

remains an issue in interpreting the maps, though we consider this is not serious for many species because most tetrads received a basic level of coverage. Figure 1.3 shows the pattern of home locations of observers, indicating that certain parts of the area lie a considerable distance from active birdwatchers, and this is certainly one factor that influenced coverage intensity, though several other factors affected the eventual species totals per tetrad.

Figure 1.4 illustrates the estimated survey coverage in each tetrad, in terms of hours. As noted above, effort was recorded for 1,904 tetrads (81% of the total) and the average time spent recording per tetrad was 7.7 hours. This average has been used for the remaining 19% of tetrads in producing the map above, and can only be regarded as an approximate indication of survey efficiency. The effort map bears a close resemblance to the species richness map in Chapter 4, but it is by no means a clear cut relationship. The issue of observer effort and its impacts is considered further in Chapter 5.

Treatment of marginal and coastal tetrads
For those 129 tetrads that overlapped with adjacent regions, only the land area within the North-East Scotland boundary was surveyed. On the coast, any tetrad containing land on which a bird could theoretically nest was included. This meant that a very few coastal, wave-washed rocks were not covered. In total, 135 coastal tetrads were included in the survey.

Progress of the survey
The tetrad allocations and coverage matched well the ideal division of effort into five equal blocks. There was a slight drop in coverage levels by years 3 and 4, but the final year brought the coverage back on target and ensured that all tetrads were visited. The target per annum was 468 tetrads and this was largely achieved (a range of 402 to 521 tetrads *per annum*).

Progress maps
Figure 1.5 shows the coverage patterns as they developed during the first four years of the survey (2002–2005; by the end of 2006 all tetrads had been covered). The least 'popular' areas for visits were similar to those in the 1981–84 atlas - the north-western part of Aberdeenshire (Turriff down to Huntly), the uplands between Donside and south Moray and in southern mid Deeside, and the Howe of the Mearns in the south. These maps show only tetrads visited for surveys and not supplementary records. Only 128 out of the 2,340 tetrads had no records at all by the end of year 4 (2005).

Data processing and map production
Tetrad recording cards were collected at the end of each season and records were combined with the small number of online submissions. Some retrospective information was uncovered year on year, but all data were entered into a Microsoft Excel 2007 spreadsheet and periodic multiple backup copies taken. In total, 116,878 records were submitted to the atlas. Errors were corrected regularly and this was especially true as distribution maps were generated and as species authors reviewed the data when writing accounts. Undoubtedly, errors remain in the data given the large size of the dataset, but we hope these are few in number.

Distribution maps were created using DMAP, written by Alan Morton (www.dmap.co.uk), using text files generated from sorted Excel spreadsheets. The atlas base map was compiled using GIS layers based (under licence) on Ordnance Survey outline information with the addition of topographic data supplied with permission by Intermap and woodland outlines supplied with permission by Scottish Natural Heritage. DMAP distribution maps were overlain on this base map as a final layer. The atlas 'base' map was constructed by Harry Scott, combining 13 separate layers of information from different sources (including NESBReC) which were supplied as editable EPS files. Within Adobe Illustrator, using the 'OS Contours' layer as the base, the 12 remaining layers were overlaid before being re-scaled and positioned using registration marks consistently positioned on them all. Line strengths and colours were then adjusted accordingly until the desired appearance was achieved. At this point the individual species distribution dot overlays (supplied as EPS files from DMAP) were imported and scaled using the same registration points, before saving the completed EPS 'base' map file. Since each of these EPS files was now 45.5MB in size, their file size was reduced by opening them in Photoshop as a 'flat image' and cropping to the area required, before saving them as high resolution JPG files of 4.5MB ready to be imported in to the final page-layout document.

Confidential species
From the beginning of the survey, records of rare breeding species were kept in a separate Excel spreadsheet and a separate DMAP file group. The records were not made available except for urgent conservation-related purposes (for example, wind farm developments) and always in conjunction with any relevant local ornithologist, such as species co-ordinators within the North-East Scotland Raptor Study Group or Grampian Ringing Group. After the survey period, it became clearer which species remained potentially vulnerable from detailed disclosure of actual or potential breeding locations, and a reduced set of 21 sensitive species continued to be kept separate and secure. Records for these species were not submitted to the NBN or local Biological Records Centre (see below) but remain available by request for conservation purposes. Many of them were also submitted to the Rare Breeding Birds Panel or Scottish Raptor Monitoring Scheme by local recorders or the Raptor Study Group.

Comparison with the 1981–84 atlas
The first atlas for Aberdeen City and Aberdeenshire used 395 unique recording units (Buckland *et al.* 1990) - see Figure 1.6. These were almost all bounded by 10 km grid lines of the national grid, within which their margins and areas were dictated by local geographical features, intended to map precisely onto meaningful features on the ground (rather than the superimposition of a regular

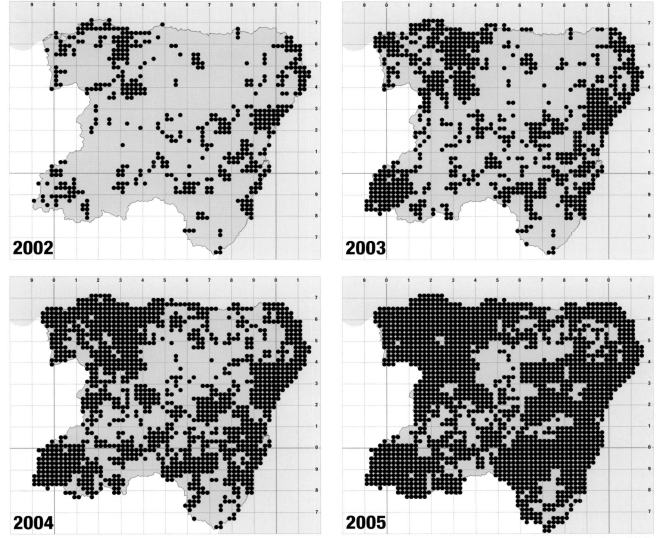

Figure 1.5. Survey progress in terms of the cumulative pattern of tetrads surveyed during the first four years of the project: coverage was complete by the final year (2006).

grid, often dividing sites of bird importance). This meant that the recording units varied greatly in size and shape. We chose a tetrad-based system, in common with most atlases, and this led to lack of correspondence between the recording units of the two atlases.

We chose to address this by ascribing every tetrad to a previous 1981–84 recording unit, using the detailed unit boundary maps from 1981–84 which are held at the Queen Mother Library at the University of Aberdeen. Each tetrad was allocated to the old recording unit that held the largest proportion of the tetrad. This meant that most old units were covered by more than one tetrad and some by many tetrads. When comparing the old breeding records with the new, the maximum level of breeding evidence in any of the overlapping tetrads was used to compare with the breeding level in the old unit, and was then mapped using the old unit boundaries. It was not possible to do this the other way round - that is, convert the old unit data to tetrad distributions. The comparison maps shown in each species account therefore reduce the data from a maximum of 2,340 dots to a maximum of 395 dots. This method means that in detail there will be some technical misallocations of modern breeding records into old units, but in most cases the general picture is clear. It does mean though that a record from a defined habitat type, such as within a coastal tetrad, is often mapped centrally in the old unit, and not always exactly where that habitat lies. A good example of

this is when the dots for cliff nesting seabirds are mapped a little way inland - centrally in the old recording unit.

A tally of old and new records allows some comparison of change, but for species with large changes in range between the two atlases, the simple visual comparison of the two distributions is often very revealing. It is obvious for example that no matter how one compares the previous and current distribution of Corn Bunting, there has been a substantial decline in range, and this sort of clear change applies to many species. The issue of how variation in observer coverage is likely to have influenced these apparent range changes is considered in Chapter 5.

Archiving and availability of the atlas data
The main Excel spreadsheets are held by the editors and on file at the RSPB Regional Office in Aberdeen. However, it was agreed from the outset that records would be made available to the North East Scotland Biological Records Centre (NESBReC - www.nesbrec.org.uk) and also lodged with the National Biodiversity Network (see www.searchnbn.net) through the SOC's *Bird Recording in Scotland* Project (http://www.the-soc.org.uk/soc-recorders.htm) co-ordinated by Clive McKay. In 2008, all cleaned and error-checked records (80,783 unique or maximum breeding level records excluding sensitive species) were made available to both these data-holding centres. We hope that these atlas data will be used for a wide range of purposes through these websites, and we invite any requests

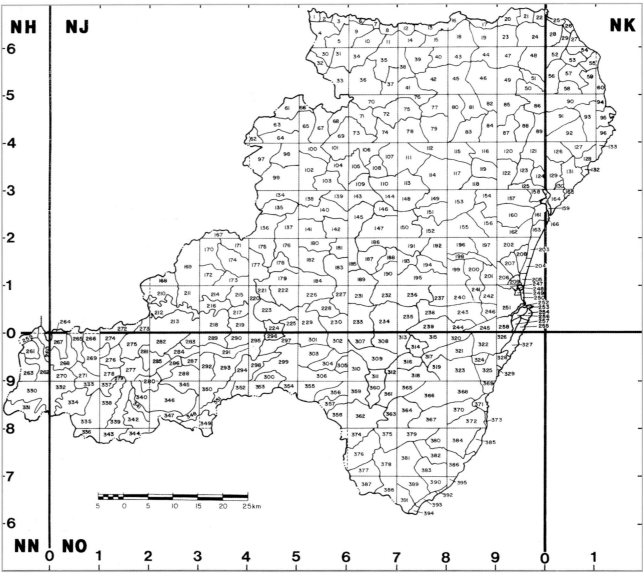

Figure 1.6. Recording Units used in the first North-East Scotland bird atlas 1981–84 (Buckland *et al*. 1990).

for collaborative data analysis so that the information resulting from the survey can be utilised fully. The hard copies of the atlas recording cards and maps have been archived at the University of Aberdeen (North-East Scotland Breeding Bird Atlas. Archive collection MS 3835: Special Libraries & Archives, University of Aberdeen).

Species richness and distribution patterns for selected species groups

Simple coincidence mapping using DMAP allowed richness maps to be produced for all species or for selected combinations of species. This issue is explored further in Chapter 4. This was also the best method of assessing the progress of the survey each year, as shown in Figure 1.5.

Population estimates

Although the atlas project did not set out to count or estimate breeding populations, the population figures in **bold** given in species accounts are based on what we consider to be good information. These estimates are thought to be quite accurate since they are based on recent dedicated surveys or monitoring schemes that cover all or most breeding localities for the relevant species. Estimates are most accurate for some raptors, most seabirds and

some very rare species and we consider that we can confidently state a very or reasonably accurate breeding population for 62 species, (*c*. 33% of the total).

Other population estimates (for the remaining 127 species) are calculated or derived from more indirect sources and are less accurate, but are still the best available for the area. These are given in *italics* and relate mainly to the bulk of common and widespread species, plus some birds such as rails or owls where breeding numbers are very difficult to survey for various reasons. Such estimates have usually been produced either from proportions of estimated numbers in a wider area such as Scotland or the UK, or using indirect measures such as the results of the BTO's Breeding Bird Survey (BBS) or other projects. However, it is important to note that the number of BBS plots surveyed in North-East Scotland is typically around 40 *per annum*, insufficient to allow any statistically valid analysis of breeding densities for our area. More details are given in Annex 4.

The process of writing species accounts

Once near-final datasets had been assembled (by early 2008), volunteers were requested from among local ornithologists who had taken part in the atlas to write species accounts. In some cases there were clear candidates, based on a long history of local study or involvement, but many species were adopted *de novo* by volunteers who had the skills and knowledge to contribute. We are very grateful to the 60 people who drafted accounts for the atlas, as we believe that this gives the book a much wider grounding in local knowledge than would have been the case otherwise. Although there were inevitably variations in style and content, we hope that we have been able to standardise without creating repetition. All species went through several iterations in the draft stage, and almost all were commented on by other local ornithologists. It is important to stress that the opinions and analysis contained within each species account are those of the individual authors and do not necessarily reflect the opinions or policy of the Scottish Ornithologists' Club or any of the organisations supporting the atlas financially. Nevertheless, the editors take final responsibility for any factual errors or omissions in species accounts, and all other chapters were written by us. The whole process of drafting the atlas to the final version took around two and a half years.

Taxonomic issues

The sequence and scientific nomenclature of the species list follows Sangster *et al.* (2010). The English names used are those in common use in the area, as adopted by both the annual North-east Scotland and Moray & Nairn Bird Reports.

Photographs used in the atlas

A distinctive feature of this atlas is the widespread use of many colour photographs depicting habitats and breeding activity of the species concerned. We believe that in recent years many aspects of breeding ecology, in particular habitats, nests, eggs and young, have been neglected in birding books and journals. Yet these aspects of a bird's annual cycle are critical to its survival and conservation. We aimed to compile as wide a selection as possible of such photographs, ideally taken by local photographers in or close to North-East Scotland. In the end, around 73% of the breeding bird photographs in the atlas came from North-East Scotland, with a further 17% taken by local photographers elsewhere, mainly in Scotland, the UK or northern Europe. Around 10% of images came from other photographers. We thank Harry Scott for co-ordinating this very effectively, particularly since he had been through a similar exercise for the SOC's '*Birds of Scotland*'.

The production and funding of the atlas

The search for suitable photographs began shortly after information was distributed to writers of species accounts and as drafts began to be submitted, a page count estimate was produced. This allowed quotations to be obtained from potential printers (we took the decision early on that we would not use a publishing company). Any necessary permissions or licences for maps were organised and as a rough cost estimate appeared, we were then able to seek funding from various sources. Further details of these are given in the Acknowledgements.

Recommendations for future atlas surveys

The progress of this atlas was similar to many comparable projects, judging from the methods chapters in other published atlases. In many ways, the work develops a plan and logic that follows from the basic objectives and the examples of many predecessors. However, there are some actions that we would suggest are well worth pursuing in future atlases, especially in similar parts of the UK with low to moderate human population densities.

1. *Definitely count birds.* This was recommended by Gibbons *et al.* (2007) and we endorse this. When the initial meetings to discuss the atlas were held, we were concerned that the scale of the project was so large that even basic coverage might not be achieved. Therefore we chose not to ask observers to count birds in any standardised way. However, the response by local birdwatchers even in an area without major population centres was very good and given the very great levels of input made by some observers, we think that counting birds even in a large tetrad atlas is feasible. In some remote areas, this may mean seeking funding to employ contract workers, but it would be worthwhile. The coverage levels realised and methods used in the 2007–2011 UK-wide BTO/SOC atlas also indicate that observers are becoming more willing to accept the need for counting. The key issue is to make sure that the counting does not detract from the fundamental task of gaining good breeding records for tetrads. A decision then has to be made which balances the advantages of a count measure (which in any case is only effective for a proportion of species) against the extra time needed and the possibility of deterring observers. Possibly the best way of resolving this is to adopt the method used in Cumbria (Stott *et al.* 2002) where a dedicated team of counters supplemented the overall atlas effort.

2. *Record observer survey time and recording effort.* Although any measures of these factors have deficiencies, they do provide some approximate idea of effort levels, which can be compared with other surveys, and this would aid interpretation of apparent changes.

3. *Use efficient online methods of data entry and storage.* The success of this in the 2007–11 BTO/SOC atlas demonstrates that nowadays this approach is well worthwhile. It would save many, many hours of data entry by the atlas organisers!

4. *Capture records from sectors of society not usually involved in surveys such as this.* The involvement of land managers such as farmers, foresters, gamekeepers and hunters would add some extra records for remote areas. Although this may lead to a need for the verification of some records, the advantages of doing this seem clear to us. We did ask some farmers and gamekeepers, but only a few participated. This could be improved upon.

5. *Use OS map-based recording cards* and ask observers to annotate with bird locations and bird habitats of interest (see Annex 3). This yielded some very useful records of conservation interest that would not have been gained in other ways.

6. *Do not feel obliged to ask observers to record habitat data.* This kind of information is now so widespread and covered by other survey sources that a simple method of habitat recording adds little to the sophistications that can be achieved with satellite and aerial-photograph based data sources. Collaboration with an academic institution may be necessary to realise this, but the level of data analysis needed to extract the full value from atlas datasets probably requires this anyway.

7. *Place all data in a publicly available place as soon as possible.* The National Biodiversity Network and the North East Scotland Biological Records Centre hold most of our data. This can be accessed by anyone for agreed purposes without reference to us, and therefore allows maximum value to be extracted from the atlas data. Observers' agreement to do this should be built in to the project at the outset.

Figure 2.1. Map of North-East Scotland.

Chapter 2. *The bird habitats, landscape and land use of North-East Scotland*

North-East Scotland - a portrait

North-East Scotland is extraordinarily rich in birds and bird habitats - a fact that is often overlooked in the ornithological literature. This richness is reflected in both the number of breeding species (173 since 1968 and 153 during this atlas period) and the national and international importance of some of the breeding populations. We have, for example, 10% or more of the UK national population of 22 species (Annex 4), and this in part reflects the high habitat diversity within the area. The satellite image within the end covers of the book illustrates this wide variety of land cover - from some of the UK's highest mountains to a spectacular and very diverse coastline. In terms of plant communities, North-East Scotland lies in the Boreal zone of Europe (Polunin & Walters 1985) and in this it differs from much of the rest of Scotland and the UK. It holds nationally important concentrations of the UK's native pinewoods, managed coniferous plantations, arctic-alpine land, lowland raised bogs, coastal sand dunes and dune heath. Heather moorland, arable farmland and coastal shingle are also disproportionately well-represented in a Scottish context. Many renowned bird localities are found here: the Cairngorms, Mar Lodge, Lochnagar, Glen Tanar, the Moray Firth, Findhorn Bay, Loch Spynie, Loch of Strathbeg, the Ythan estuary, Fowlsheugh. The ornithological richness of North-East Scotland is also illustrated by the fact that the area is often second in the UK only to Norfolk in the annual spring national bird race competition, with 156 species, a Scottish record, found by a local birding team in one day on 14th May 2004.

The geography and bird habitats of Scotland were described recently by Benn & Douse (*BS3*) but the only comprehensive general description of the physical and human geography of North-East Scotland was published by the British Association in 1963. Much has changed since then, but the chapters on geology, geomorphology, climate and soils remain largely relevant, as are many aspects of the remaining subjects dealt with there. Moray is also included within it. Further general introductions to different parts of the area were published by Scottish Natural Heritage (2002, 2009) in their *Natural Heritage Futures* series. This chapter considers land cover and habitats in some detail. The implications for birds of habitat and land use change are dealt with in Chapter 6.

Physical geography and geology

North-East Scotland as defined in this atlas covers an area of 8,686 km^2, approximately 3.6% of the UK land area and 11% of Scotland, and lies centred around 57°N, 2°W (Figure 2.2). It comprises the local authority areas of Moray (2,247 km^2), Aberdeenshire (6,320 km^2) and Aberdeen City (188 km^2). The physical landscape of the whole area was considered by the British Association (1963) and by Merritt & Leslie (2009), while that of the 'North-east Scotland' recording area (Aberdeen City and Aberdeenshire) was described by John Smith in Buckland *et al.* (1990), so the detail will not be repeated here. Further information on landscape and environmental history can be found in RCAHMS (2008). Bird habitats in Moray were described by Cook (1992) but there is no recent conveniently summarised account of the physical geography of Moray alone.

Habitat: in this atlas, the term 'habitat' is used to describe the different vegetation and land cover types of North-East Scotland, as well as the strict definition of "the local environment inhabited by an organism" (*Cambridge Illustrated Dictionary of Natural History*, CUP, 1987). We have followed popular usage (for example the UK Biodiversity Action Plan) in adopting a single term for these purposes. However, 'land cover' has been retained when reporting on the Land Cover surveys below. We have also used the term 'alpine' to refer to the high tops, their vegetation and birds, though 'montane' is often used elsewhere; see Nethersole-Thompson & Watson (1974) for further details.

In general, much of North-East Scotland is underlain by old, hard rocks, either metamorphic schists or igneous intrusions, especially granite, though there are also substantial outcrops of more base-rich rocks. Long-continuing erosion has led to the development of a succession of stepped relief regions increasing in elevation away from the sea. This has resulted in some large, relatively level areas dissected by river valleys, leading to land of an open, rolling character with relatively few sharp topographic rises. This has formed a characteristic open and frequently Heather-dominated landscape quite different from the central and western Highlands. At lower levels, a series of plains or low plateaux is now dominated by agricultural land.

Moray stretches from Ben Macdui in the Cairngorms (Scotland's second highest mountain at 1,309 m) to the Moray Firth coast, which is mostly low-lying with extensive afforested sand dunes and long shingle bars. The River Spey flows to the sea through its centre and the River Findhorn enters the sea at Findhorn Bay. Moray contains some large extents of upland moorland and alpine habitat, forest plantations cover over one-quarter of its area and a large zone of rich agricultural land stretches along the Laich of Moray in the north.

Figure 2.2. The location and extent of North-East Scotland.

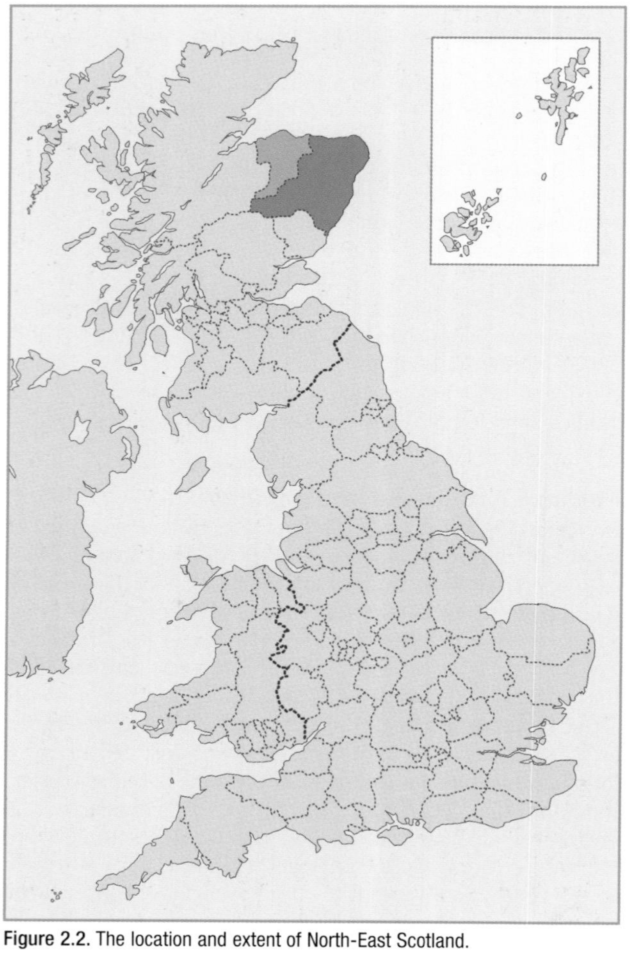

The south-western and southern fringes of Aberdeenshire are formed by the Cairngorms, Lochnagar and the Mounth, where extensive alpine habitat grades down into moorland and peatland. There are some large and important native pinewoods, mainly in Deeside, as well as a high cover of plantation forestry, dominated by Scots Pine. Central and south-eastern Aberdeenshire is a mosaic of improved agricultural land, forestry, woodland and moorland, with particularly productive land in the south-eastern Howe of the Mearns. In north-eastern Aberdeenshire, Buchan, a low-lying agricultural area (topographically a 'platform', sometimes termed 'the Buchan plain' in this atlas), has few plantations and little semi-natural habitat, apart from remnants of raised bogs (mosses). The Aberdeenshire coast is very varied, composed mainly of hard rock cliffs, but with some extensive sand dune complexes and coastal heath. The rivers North Esk, Dee, Don, Ythan and Deveron are the main watercourses, but there are rather few bodies of standing water. Where the Dee and Don meet the North Sea lies the City of Aberdeen, which has much countryside within its boundary and scattered remnants of semi-natural habitat within the built-up area.

The Cairngorms National Park covers an area of 3,800 km^2, almost half of which lies in North-East Scotland (see Figure 2.3), though the Park boundaries were extended in 2010 to include Highland Perthshire, which reduces this proportion. The Park is dominated in its centre by the Cairngorms, the highest and most extensive alpine habitat in the UK, dropping in all directions to lower moorland and woodland. A full description of the geology, topography and land cover in the Cairngorms area is given in Nethersole-Thompson & Watson (1974, 1981), Watson (1992), Gimingham (2002) and Shaw & Thompson (2006); see also Scottish Natural Heritage/British Geological Survey (1994).

Climate

The climate of the North-East was described within the British Association (1963) publication and in general much of that analysis still applies; further information is given by the Meteorological Office (1989) for the period 1951–1980. Some climatic parameters were also mapped for the 'North-east Scotland' recording area by Buckland *et*

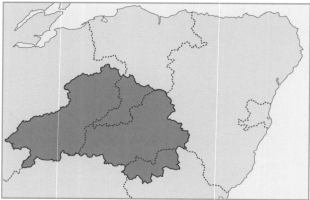

Figure 2.3. The Cairngorms National Park boundary 2003–2010, and North-East Scotland.

al. (1990). Several features characterise the climate. Much of the eastern and northern lowlands lie in the lee of the Cairngorms, partly sheltered from the prevailing south-westerly wind, and quite dry compared with western Scotland. Rainfall varies from between 1,520 mm and 2,250 mm over the Cairngorms to around 650 mm in coastal areas, which are very dry. In winter, precipitation often falls as snow, and the North-East is on average the snowiest part of the UK; even now, in mid-altitude areas one can expect over 30 days of lying snow each winter, with around 60 days at Braemar and even more on the mountains, where a few snow patches persist in the Cairngorms through most summers (e.g. Watson et al. 2008). Temperature inversions can lead to very low temperatures in upland glens, with late frosts well into June. Braemar has reported some of the coldest overnight temperatures in Britain (e.g. -27.2°C in January 1982). Average annual maximum daily temperatures are cool, at just over 10°C at both Braemar and Craibstone near Aberdeen, though these have probably increased by up to one degree since 1980. Average annual minimum daily temperatures are 4.5°C at Craibstone and 2.5°C at Braemar. In winter, the Moray coast can be relatively mild due to warming dry winds descending from the Cairngorms (having shed moisture there) and Kinloss and Lossiemouth at times record the warmest winter temperatures in the UK. In summer, inland parts of Aberdeenshire and Strathspey can record high temperatures, though coastal areas tend to be cooler and breezier, sometimes with sea fog or 'haar', due to cool temperatures in the North Sea all year round.

For birds, key features of the climate include the topography created by cold, exposed conditions on the mountain tops, which provides areas suitable for alpine species to breed. The dryness of the east and along the Moray Firth coast, coupled with land drainage, has resulted in soils that are generally dry with few large wetlands remaining. However, relatively low evapo-transpiration rates allow soils in places to remain moist, benefiting waders. The cool sea temperatures also create productive foraging grounds for seabirds from coastal colonies.

The climate of the area is projected to change in the coming decades, in line with global trends. There is some evidence of gradually increasing temperatures, particularly in summer, changes to the phenology of spring warming, fewer and less severe snowy periods particularly at mid-altitudes (Harrison et al. 2001, Barnett et al. 2006) and

increasingly erratic rainfall events (including spring and summer floods). Although average summer precipitation showed no trend from 1961–2004, winter precipitation increased slightly and decreased summer rainfall is anticipated (Barnett et al. 2006). The possible responses of the area's breeding birds to such changes are considered further in Chapter 6.

Human geography

The population of the area is 525,930 (National Census). Approximately 16,000 people live in the Cairngorms National Park (Cairngorms National Park Authority 2007 - mostly in Strathspey, outwith our area). The population density in North-East Scotland is approximately 10% below the average for Scotland (Mackey et al. 1998), but settlements are well scattered and large areas with few habitations are found only in the high ground of the west and south. Aberdeen City is by far the most populous settlement (214,000), and is Scotland's third largest city. There is much new development and growth around the urban fringe. Other large towns include Elgin, Forres, Peterhead, Fraserburgh and Inverurie. Much of the coast is undeveloped and unpopulated, with many relatively inaccessible and undisturbed areas. Oil, gas and related industries dominate the traditionally buoyant economy, with considerable development taking place and a growing population, mainly around Aberdeen and Elgin and along major transport corridors. The Aberdeen City region is the most prosperous in Scotland and one of the wealthiest in the UK (Scottish Enterprise 2008).

Land cover and changes over time

There have been several summaries of land cover and natural habitats relevant to North-East Scotland. All differ in their categorisation, sources and presentation methods. For this reason, and also because of lack of survey information for some habitats, all figures below should be viewed as approximate; there are few habitats for which accurate extents or precise definitions can be given. Alexander et al. (1998) summarised habitat information from various sources for the whole of the North-East and Leaper (1999) did the same for the Cairngorms area, as audits of UK Biodiversity Action Plan species and habitats. Prior to that, natural habitats in the former Grampian Region were surveyed and summarised by Grampian Regional Council (1988) - many of these are mapped in Buckland et al. (1990), along with agricultural census data for that time.

A major analysis of land cover classes in Scotland during the 1980s was undertaken as part of the National Countryside Monitoring Scheme - NCMS (Mackey et al. 1998). This remains the most detailed regional analysis, and though it is now dated, some clear patterns and trends relevant to today are shown. For example, some 87% of the land surface of North-East Scotland is made up of just four major habitat types - grassland, arable farmland, Heather moorland and coniferous plantation. Compared with Scotland as a whole, all of these are present in higher proportions than the national figures. Conversely, the North-East holds relatively small extents of blanket mire (though lowland raised mires are well-represented) and less of the land area is occupied by water bodies. Indeed, the area is well-drained and often dry in character, with many former wetlands long gone. A more recent national analysis (LC2000 - see below) provides regional land cover totals and the same four major land uses occupied 85.1% of North-East Scotland in 2000 - very similar to the NCMS total. Further details of land cover and habitat types are given in Tables 2.1, 2.2 and 2.3.

Table 2.1. General land cover table for North-East Scotland (Grampian) in the 1980s (Mackey *et al.* 1998). *n.b.* - only terrestrial habitats were considered in the survey; coastal and marine areas were excluded.

Land cover/habitat type *Listed in descending order of cover*	Area (km²)	% of N-E Scotland land area *% Scottish land area in brackets*		% change in N-E Scotland from 1940s to 1980s *See Fig 2.4 for illustration of changes*	% change in Scotland, 1940s to 1980s
Grassland	2,650	31%	(28%)	Variable: see note *	(variable)
Arable	2,036	23%	(11%)	+28%	(+11%)
Heather moorland	1,647	19%	(15%)	-35%	(-23%)
Coniferous plantation	1,228	14%	(12%)	+276% to +334%	(+462% to +969%)
Mire (upland & lowland)	357	4%	(23%)	-13% / -77%	(-11% / -44%)
Built-up areas/bare ground	343	4%	(4%)	+43%	(+46%)
Bracken and scrub	171	2%	(3%)	-12% to -51%	(+1% to +79%)
Broad-leaved woodland	205	2%	(1%)	-37%	(-23%)
Lochs and rivers (including wet ground)	50	1%	(3%)	No significant change	(-12% / NS)
Length (km)					
Hedgerows	2,812			-66%	(-54%)
Ditches	8,463			+231%	(+101%)
Tracks	6,532			+81%	(+29%)

*Smooth grassland -41%, 'Intermediate' grassland +170%, Rough grassland +13%

Land cover and habitats not explicitly accounted for above

These figures do not explicitly account for many of the commonly-recognised habitats within the area. Alexander *et al.* (1998) addressed the UK Biodiversity Action Plan habitats and additional information is given in Table 2.2. More recent information from the Forestry Commission's National Inventory of Woodland and Trees (1997–2003), updated by the Forestry Commission (2008) is also included, along with updated wetland extents as assessed by Biggins & Francis (2007). The terrestrial habitats listed are all included by implication within one of the categories above, so are not additional. The extent of the Scottish and UK resource found within the area is also given.

Land cover changes from the 1940s to the 1980s

Mackey *et al.* (1998) summarised changes in land cover classes between the 1940s and 1980s (see Table 2.1). They showed that the coniferous woodland area expanded greatly in that period, as did the areas of arable farming, urban and developed land. These expansions were largely at the expense of 'smooth' grassland (change from improved grassland to arable crops), Heather moorland (losses to grassland and forestry) and broad-leaved woodland. Hedgerow length declined greatly while tracks and ditches lengthened. Arable gains were greater than in Scotland as a whole and losses of Heather moorland, broad-leaved woodland and hedgerows were also higher. The rate of afforestation was less than the Scottish average, probably

Table 2.2. Some specific land cover and habitats in North-East Scotland.

Land cover/habitat type	Area (km²) [or km length where relevant]	% of Scottish resource if known	% of UK resource if known	Comments on extent/source [Alexander *et al.*1998; FCS data for forest types; Biggins & Francis 2007 for wetlands; Barne *et al.* 1996 for coastal]
Terrestrial				
Total forest & woodland 2008	1,550	12%	5.5%	Significant representation: *c.*18% of N-E Scotland land area
Native Caledonian pinewoods	36.7	23%	23%	Significant representation
Coniferous plantation	1,228	15%	8%	Significant representation
Birch woodland	112			Significant representation
Upland oak woodland	6.59			Insignificant nationally
Beech woodland	12.9	-		Insignificant nationally
Wet and riparian woodland	14.9			Unknown significance
Heather moorland	1,647	8%	4%	Good representation
"Montane" = alpine (definitions vary)	215	9%	8%?	Significant representation
Lowland raised bog (incl. damaged/former bogs)	53.6	19%	8%	Significant representation
Lowland fen (incl. probable unclassified sites)	16.3			Unknown significance
Reedbed	1.53	13%	2%	Significant representation
Standing water (excluding rivers)	24.4	1.6%		Insignificant nationally
Coastal				
Estuaries	14.27		0.3%	Insignificant nationally
Saltmarsh	3.1	4%	0.6%	Insignificant nationally
Coastal vegetated shingle	1.54	19%	2.5%	Significant representation
Sand dunes	70.2	22%	14%	Significant representation
Sand dune heath	3.12	15%	12%	Significant representation
Coastal cliffs	[108 km]	6%	3%	Good representation
Coastal heathland (not dune)	3.55			Insignificant nationally

The Breeding Birds of North-East Scotland

because parts of North-East Scotland were already well-wooded; the 1980s forest cover was proportionally higher than nationally. Some of the changes from the 1940s to 1980s are shown in Figure 2.4 below, together with an indication, if known, of likely changes since the 1980s.

Recent land cover and changes since the 1980s

To what extent have these changes continued to the present day? A wide range of surveys and data sources is now available, but none deals specifically with the North-East and differing land classification systems have been used, making comparison with the NCMS (Mackey *et al.* 1998) difficult. For example, there has been a focus on UK Biodiversity Action Plan 'Broad and Key' (Priority) habitats (see www.ukbap.org.uk/NewPriorityList.aspx), which differ in detail from the categories used by the NCMS. The Countryside Survey 2000 (CS2000, www.countrysidesurvey.org.uk) produced complete land cover maps for the UK for 1990 and 2000 using 'Broad Habitats' and presented some detailed analyses of trends. A satellite-based land cover survey (LC2000) has also been undertaken by the Centre for Ecology and Hydrology (see http://www.ceh.ac.uk/sci_programmes/BioGeoChem/LandCoverMap2000.html) and data at the regional level for North-East Scotland have been extracted by A. Gimona (Macaulay Institute). LC2000 also used a different land

cover classification to the NCMS above. It is not possible directly to relate the two for all habitats, though some are similar. However, data from LC2000 include all terrestrial land cover types. The summary tables are presented below.

The total area for North-East Scotland differs slightly from the NCMS total, and some other cover types show different figures to those tabulated in Table 2.1 above. This is in part due to definitions and in some cases due to the time elapsed since the two surveys; the grassland/arable balance changed substantially over that period for example (more arable, less grassland) and that is probably a real change despite definition differences.

For those land cover types that occupy more than 1% of the land surface, the overall land use balance is shown in Figure 2.5; the four largest land covers (arable, grassland, moorland and plantation) occupy 85.1% of the land surface, very similar to the 87% found by the NCMS (see above). Thus, the general picture is shared between all land cover survey data sources, but the details differ, and an analysis of this is beyond the scope of this chapter.

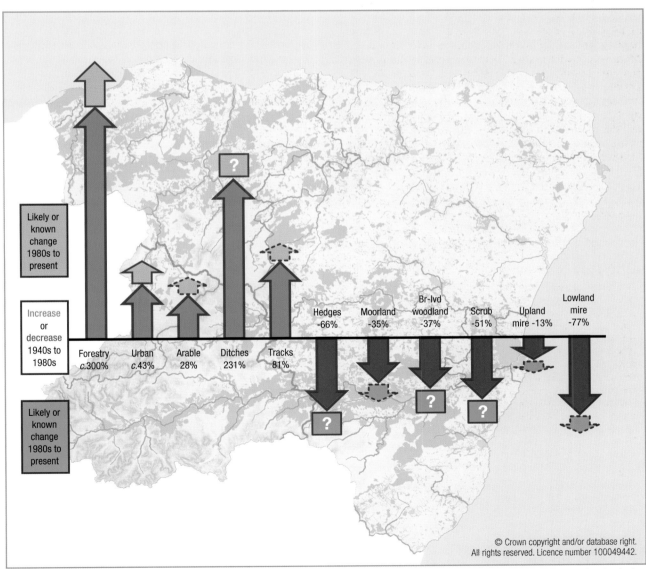

Figure 2.4. Changes in land cover in North-East Scotland from 1940s to 1980s (Mackey *et al.* 1998), with likely changes from 1980s to present shown in paler shades.

Chapter 2. Bird habitats, landscape and land use of North-East Scotland

Table 2.3. Land Cover in North-East Scotland, 2000 (LC2000 data).

LC2000 Land Cover type	Land cover (km^2)	% of North-East Scotland land area
Water (inland)	19.8	0.2
Littoral rock	5.5	0.1
Littoral sediment	11.8	0.1
Saltmarsh	2.7	0.0
Supra-littoral rock	0.4	0.0
Supra-littoral sediment	13.9	0.2
Bog (deep peat)	110.8	1.3
Dense dwarf shrub heath (Heather moorland)	1159.1	13.3
Open dwarf shrub heath (Heather moorland)	611.5	7.0
"Montane" habitats	514.2	5.8
Broad-leaved / mixed woodland	395.7	4.5
Coniferous woodland	1163.1	13.3
Improved grassland	1493.3	17.1
Neutral grass	282.4	3.2
Set-aside grass	0.0	0.0
Bracken	2.0	0.0
Calcareous grass	50.2	0.6
Acid grassland	369.8	4.2
Fen, marsh, swamp	0.1	0.0
Arable cereals	75.4	0.9
Arable horticulture	2022.3	23.1
Arable non-rotational	234.5	2.7
Suburban / rural development	137.6	1.6
Continuous urban	26.0	0.3
Inland bare ground	41.6	0.5
TOTAL North-East Scotland	**8,744**	**100**

In terms of likely habitat *change* for North-East Scotland since the 1980s, NCMS and LC2000 cannot be compared easily for the period from the 1980s to 2000. For Scotland as a whole, an analysis of broad habitat types from CS2000 was undertaken by McGowan *et al.* (2002). A further survey was undertaken in the UK Countryside Survey 2007 and the summary report (Carey *et al.* 2008) presents some useful recent trends in land cover, habitats and certain ecological characteristics relevant to the entire country, and many of these will be applicable to North-East Scotland. No further updated information on regional land cover is available from this sample survey until the land cover map for 2007 is finalised.

General trends for the period since 1990 emerged from both these reports for Scotland and the UK. Some are listed below, with local comments added where possible. For almost all habitats, there is little information for North-East Scotland that might allow any quantification of these changes, though some information on environmental trends is available from two sites in or very close to our area that are monitored under the long-term UK Environmental Change Network (ECN) - the Allt a' Mharcaidh in the Cairngorms and Glen Saugh - see http://www.ecn.ac.uk/Database/index.html.

■ The area of fen, marsh and swamp in Scotland increased between 1990 and 1998, which may be due to a decline in land management in some areas (this appears to be less evident in North-East Scotland).

■ The area of broad-leaved woodland increased, mostly in the lowlands and in part due to new planting; in the UK the area increased by 6.9% (a trend apparent in North-East Scotland).

■ There was no significant change in the area of coniferous woodland in the UK between 1998 and 2007 (in North-East Scotland there was some coniferous planting, especially in the North-east lowlands under the Grampian Challenge Fund/Locational Premium, which produced 5,100 ha of new planting of which 3,000 ha were coniferous, but most new planting generally in the area was of broad-leaves). In the North-East then, there has probably been a slight further increase in woodland cover since the late 1990s.

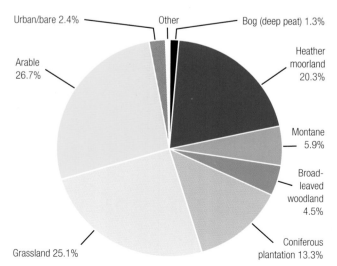

Urban/bare 2.4%
Other
Bog (deep peat) 1.3%
Arable 26.7%
Heather moorland 20.3%
Montane 5.9%
Broad-leaved woodland 4.5%
Grassland 25.1%
Coniferous plantation 13.3%

Figure 2.5. The main land cover of North-East Scotland in 2000 (LC2000).

The Breeding Birds of North-East Scotland

Plate 2.1. Curlew, Glen Clunie, May 2004. © *Ed Duthie* Curlews are vulnerable to wetland loss, changes in farming practice and predation, but creation of habitat can provide suitable conditions for breeding birds.

- The area of arable land in the uplands increased in Scotland, but in the UK as a whole it decreased by 9.1%, mainly through conversion to grassland (the area of which increased by 5.4% in the lowlands). There is some evidence for an increase in arable area in North-East Scotland.

- Large-scale declines in moorland appeared to have ceased between 1990 and 1998 in Scotland. In the UK, the area of Bracken decreased and acid grassland increased between 1998 and 2007. However, the amount of acid grassland decreased in the lowlands in Scotland.

- There were signs of nutrient enrichment in bogs and waterside vegetation in Scotland, but the water quality of most headwater streams improved in the UK; at the two local ECN sites, surface water and precipitation became slightly less acid from 1999 to 2008, though there was evidence of a slight increase in surface water nitrate at Glen Saugh.

- The number of ponds in the UK increased by 11% between 1996 and 2007 but their biological condition deteriorated (likely to be the case in North-East Scotland - many hundreds of new ponds have been constructed recently, often in areas prone to eutrophication).

- The lengths of fences increased and walls declined in Scotland; in the UK, the length of managed hedges declined by 6% between 1998 and 2007 after a period of stability since 1990.

Main land cover, habitat changes and key bird species

The vegetation of some of the main habitats was described by Peter Marren in Buckland *et al.* (1990) for their smaller 'North-east Scotland' recording area. In addition, some analyses of bird distributions in relation to habitat and physical parameters for 1983–85 were presented there. Scottish Natural Heritage (2002) also published more recent descriptions of different sub-divisions of the area, and the plant communities of north Aberdeenshire were described by Welch (1993). The section that follows here illustrates the specific habitats of the North-East 20 years on from the first atlas. The structure broadly follows UK BAP terminology, with much of the information taken (although unattributed) from Alexander *et al.* (1998). The boxes summarise some of the characteristic and more localised or rare bird species breeding in each. These have been selected using the available atlas data and other information, rather than through any formal analysis, and are usually not complete lists. Nonetheless, they give a flavour of the birds likely to be encountered and also indicate some rarer species that might utilise each habitat.

Alpine habitats

A summary description of the 'high tops', their alpine habitats and birds was given by Sandy Payne and Adam Watson in Buckland *et al.* (1990). More information is available in Nethersole-Thompson & Watson (1974, 1981), Watson (1992), Gimingham (2002) and Shaw & Thompson (2006). North-East Scotland has some of the most extensive and diverse high altitude habitats in the UK, with extensive alpine plateaux, steep mountain sides, large corries, boulder fields and large areas of summit heath and grassland. Snow lies in many areas for two-thirds of the year with a few snow patches lasting through most summers. Although recreation levels are locally high, most parts are less disturbed. There is little evidence of significant large-scale change in habitat extent or quality in recent decades, but some local factors such as the development of ski areas have caused changes in areas nearby. High-level deer grazing and atmospheric pollution may also have influenced vegetation and bird communities (Scottish Natural Heritage 2002).

Plate 2.2. Braeriach and Cairn Toul from the north, 2005. © *J. Matthews*

Plate 2.3. Beinn Mheadhoin from Cairn Gorm, 2008. © *I. Francis*

Plate 2.4. An Socach, 2005. © *I. Francis*

Breeding birds of alpine habitats in North-East Scotland.

Typical: Wheatear, Meadow Pipit, Golden Plover, Ptarmigan.

Localised or rare: Dotterel, Snow Bunting, Golden Eagle, Dunlin.

Plate 2.5. **Snow Bunting**, Cairn Lochan, June 2005. © *Derek McGinn*

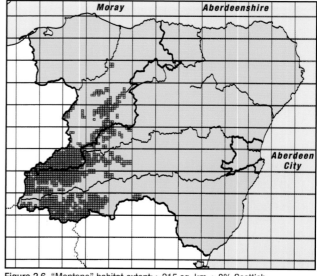

Figure 2.6. "Montane" habitat extent: >215 sq. km, >8% Scottish.

The Breeding Birds of North-East Scotland

Plate 2.6. Blanket bog pools, Carn Liath, Lecht, 2007. © I. Francis

Blanket bog

Most blanket bog in North-East Scotland is relatively dry and has been affected by centuries of burning, grazing, drainage and peat cutting. Nevertheless, there are scattered areas of bog pools and active peat-forming plant communities. The vegetation is dominated largely by Heather, Hare's-tail Cottongrass and Deer-grass with various mosses depending on site conditions. Some parts are eroded, with large extents of peat hags. Bog pools are often the most rewarding areas for breeding birds, which tend to be distributed at low densities elsewhere.

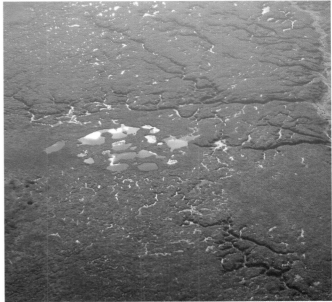

Plate 2.7. Bog pool systems, Scors Burn, Blackwater Forest, 1999. © I. Francis

---

Breeding birds of blanket bog in North-East Scotland.

Typical: Meadow Pipit, Golden Plover, Red Grouse.

Localised or rare: Dunlin, Teal.

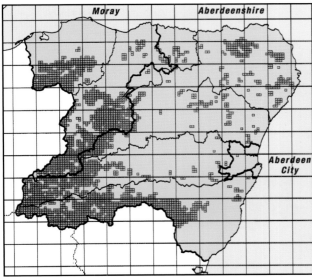

Figure 2.7. Blanket peat and lowland peat (357 sq. km).

Plate 2.8. Dry, upland blanket bog with former peat cutting faces at 720 m, Scraulac, Donside, 2006. © I. Francis

Plate 2.9. Glen Feardar, Invercauld, 2004. © *I. Francis*

Plate 2.10. Unmanaged Heather moorland with scrub, Breda, 2008. © *I. Francis*

Plate 2.11. Strip burning of Heather moorland, Candacraig, 2008. © *I. Francis*

Plate 2.12. Upland acid grassland, Coleburn, Rothes Glen, 2001. There are no figures for the extent of upland grasslands of all types within the area. © *I. Francis*

Moorland and upland grasslands

North-East Scotland has very large areas of Heather moorland, a high proportion of which is managed through burning to improve Red Grouse stocks for shooting. It is often mixed with, or lies adjacent to, upland acid grassland. Many moorlands and grasslands are grazed by sheep (increasingly on Heather moors to act as a method of controlling ticks), or by cattle too, usually on in-bye grasslands. Where moorland is not managed, scrub and trees often regenerate, particularly in Donside and parts of Moray. On most moorlands, though, management is intensive with very frequent burning, short Heather and, increasingly, new tracks created to facilitate shooting and management. Heather moorland decreased by 35% between 1940s and 1980s, principally due to the expansion of afforestation and conversion to grassland; this has largely ceased now.

Breeding birds of Heather moorland and upland grassland in North-East Scotland.

Typical: Red Grouse, Meadow Pipit, Skylark, Snipe, Wheatear, Curlew.

Localised or rare: Twite, Merlin, Hen Harrier, Black Grouse, Ring Ouzel, Short-eared Owl, Common Gull.

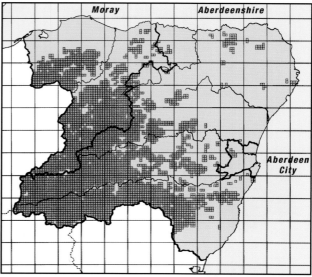
Figure 2.8. Heather moorland (1,647 sq. km; 8% Scottish and 4% UK resource).

Caledonian pinewoods

North-East Scotland (mainly Deeside) holds an important proportion of the remaining Scottish Caledonian pinewoods, and they are of very high nature conservation interest. A detailed account of pinewood habitats and their birds was given by Alan Knox in Buckland *et al.* (1990). While Scots Pine is dominant, the woodlands contain varying amounts of broad-leaved trees (principally birch) and Juniper scrub. There are eleven officially listed native pinewood remnants (Forestry Commission, Caledonian Pinewood Inventory) but also numerous other areas of self-sown pine of native origin, some of which are quite large. The list includes the well-known woods in Glen Tanar, Ballochbuie and the Forest of Mar but all the pinewoods of North-East Scotland are widely viewed as some of the 'jewels in the crown' of natural habitats in our area. They are very important for some nationally rare breeding birds. Historically, there have been some large losses in extent and quality of native pinewoods in Scotland, but this trend has probably now reversed. However, all sites have been managed to some extent, affecting the woodland structure and most may contain some trees of non-local origin. Several areas of 'New Native Pinewoods' were planted on moorland in the 1990s, especially in Moray; these are only now becoming established due to slow growth rates.

Breeding birds of Caledonian pinewoods in North-East Scotland.

Typical: Chaffinch, Coal Tit, Goldcrest, Siskin, Willow Warbler, Redstart, Wren, Mistle Thrush, Tree Pipit, Tawny Owl.

Localised or rare: Scottish Crossbill, Parrot Crossbill, Golden Eagle, Capercaillie.

Plate 2.13. Native pinewood, Glen Tanar, 2006. © *I. Francis*

Plate 2.14. Glen Derry, 2007. © *I. Francis*

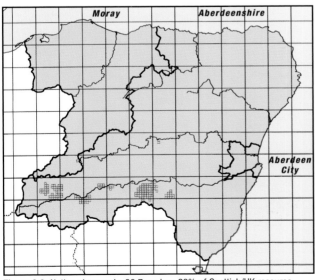
Figure 2.9. Native pinewoods: 36.7 sq. km; 23% of Scottish/UK resource.

Plate 2.15. Coilacriech Wood - long-established, self-sown and planted pine woodland near Ballater, 2007. © *I. Francis*

Plate 2.16. Birch woodland at Torphantrick, Ballater, 2005. © *I. Francis*

Upland broad-leaved woodlands

There are approximately 130 km^2 of upland broad-leaved woodland in North-East Scotland, of which some 85% is birch dominated. Ash woods are very rare (169 ha in total; though Ash trees in hedges are widespread). Oak woodlands also are few in number; most of them are SSSIs. Beech woodland is found as small planted patches, as shelterbelts and as fringes to larger woods. Birch forms large extents of national significance and in many ways this species, along with Scots Pine, characterises the 'Scandinavian' feel of parts of Deeside and upper Speyside in particular. Some birch woodlands are mature with Juniper scrub (though generally the shrub layer in birch woods is sparse) and many are also used as shelter for grazing sheep and cattle, keeping ground vegetation short. In other areas, birch colonisation of moorland fringes has occurred, forming quite extensive regenerating young woodland. The birds of one such area at Muir of Dinnet were studied by Gillings *et al.* (1998), where Willow Warbler and Chaffinch were the dominant breeding species. Patches of Aspen woodland are also found, in greatest quantity around Crathie and Dinnet in Deeside, but though these are important for fungi and invertebrates their bird interest has not been studied. In marginal upland farmland there has been much recent planting of small woodlands, especially along watercourses. Further aspects of the ecology and management of woodland birds in Deeside were examined by French *et al.* (1986).

Breeding birds of upland broad-leaved woodlands in North-East Scotland.

Typical: Willow Warbler, Great Spotted Woodpecker, Wren, Chaffinch, Great Tit, Redstart, Tree Pipit, Treecreeper, Spotted Flycatcher, Cuckoo, Woodcock, Lesser Redpoll, Blue Tit.

Localised or rare: Wood Warbler, Green Woodpecker.

Plate 2.17. Upland oak woodland, Mossat, Donside, 2009. There are *c.*6.6 km^2 in the area. © *I. Francis*

Plate 2.18. Beech (not native here) occurs largely on coniferous plantation fringes and in shelterbelts in both uplands and lowlands: Tillyfourie, 2005. There are *c.* 13 km^2 of this woodland type in the area. © *I. Francis*

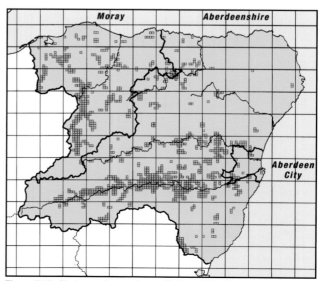

Figure 2.10. Birch woodland extent in North-East Scotland: 112 sq. km - a nationally important concentration.

Coniferous plantations

Edlin (1963) gives the early history of plantations in the area, together with information on wildlife, and though dated this remains the only published general account of all forests in North-East Scotland. Conifer plantations now cover around 14% of North-East Scotland and their area has increased over three-fold since the 1940s. The plantation area is dominated by Scots Pine on drier soils and Sitka Spruce on wetter sites, each covering similar extents, plus rather less Norway Spruce, Lodgepole Pine, European and Japanese Larch, Douglas Fir and smaller stands of other species (especially Corsican Pine in the coastal plantations of Moray). Many of the older Scots Pine plantations are widely spaced with well-developed ground vegetation and these can be important habitats for birds, though common bird densities tend to be higher in younger plantations of both pine and spruce. Clear-felling is the most common system of management, but increasingly alternative systems are being used in a move towards 'continuous cover' forestry. As plantations are harvested and replanted, they are increasing in diversity, with more mixtures of species, a higher proportion of broad-leaves and more open space.

Plate 2.19. Selectively felled Scots Pine with regeneration (Continuous Cover Forestry), near Dinnet, 2009. © *I. Francis*

Breeding birds of coniferous plantations in North-East Scotland.

Typical: Chaffinch, Coal Tit, Goldcrest, Wren, Robin, Woodpigeon, Siskin, Song Thrush, Sparrowhawk, Common Crossbill, Bullfinch, Jay, Grasshopper Warbler, Buzzard.

Localised or rare: Goshawk, Long-eared Owl, Scottish Crossbill, Capercaillie, Crested Tit (*Moray only*).

Plate 2.20. Pine plantation landscape near Aboyne, 2009. © *I. Francis*

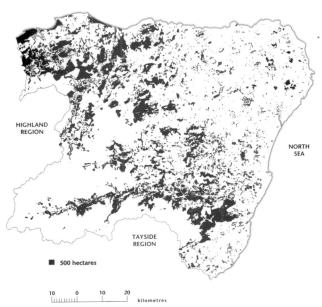

Figure 2.11. Plantations in North-East Scotland: 1,228 sq. km (15% of Scottish, 8% of UK resource). Source: Forestry Commission (1997).

Plate 2.21. Sitka Spruce dominated plantation and large clear-felled area, North Drumtochty, Fetteresso Forest, 2009. © *I. Francis*

Plate 2.22. Juniper scrub, Green Hill of Strathdon, 2000. © *I. Francis*

Plate 2.23. Gorse and Broom scrub near Rhynie, 1994. © *I. Francis*

Plate 2.24. Bracken with gradual woodland spread, Rafford, 2005. © *I. Francis*

Scrub and Bracken

North-East Scotland holds many areas of dense scrub, composed primarily of Gorse (Whin) and Broom, and ranging in cover from small patches and hedge lines to whole hillsides. There are also nationally important concentrations of Juniper scrub, some of which lie within designated sites. Willow scrub, however, is rare and localised. Up to 2% of the land area of North-East Scotland is covered in scrub of all kinds - a distinctive bird habitat. Bracken is less widespread compared with further west in Scotland. Scrub often acts as nurse cover for young trees and forms early stages of woodland colonisation. It is also found within woodland, sometimes mixed with Bracken. There has been little work on birds in Gorse and Broom communities in our area, but Gillings & Fuller (1998) recorded 18 breeding bird species in Juniper scrub at sites in North-East Scotland. In addition, regenerating birch woodland forms a scrub community when young, and the study by Gillings *et al.* (1998) described the bird communities of such an area at the Muir of Dinnet in Deeside.

Breeding birds of scrub and Bracken communities in North-East Scotland.

Typical: Yellowhammer, Linnet, Whitethroat, Song Thrush, Willow Warbler, Chaffinch, Dunnock.

Localised or rare: Whinchat, Black Grouse.

The Breeding Birds of North-East Scotland

Lochs, reservoirs and ponds

Lochs cover less than 1% of North-East Scotland and there are very few reservoirs of any size. The total extent of standing water (not including rivers) was estimated by the NCMS as 2,440 ha, or just 1.6% of the Scottish total. There is no comprehensive inventory, but from OS maps there are probably fewer than 150 water bodies of more than c.2–3 ha in size, with around 14 of these higher than c.500 m altitude in the Cairngorms. There is no available breakdown into the different ecological types of loch. The bulk of the standing water is held in a few large upland oligotrophic lochs such as Loch Muick. Some of these are among the highest in the UK, including Loch Etchachan at 900 m. Lower-level, moderately nutrient rich or mesotrophic lochs are scattered in the lowlands, including the Dinnet lochs. Richer, eutrophic lochs include Loch of Strathbeg and Loch Spynie. These lochs within farmed areas are almost all very important for large numbers of breeding and wintering birds. In the lowlands there has been an enormous increase in the number of new ponds created in recent years, frequently under agri-environment schemes, with probably many thousands now in existence across the area. Some of the new ponds are stocked with fish and there has been an increase in pay fisheries, which has benefited Ospreys.

Breeding birds of lochs and ponds in North-East Scotland.

Typical: Mute Swan, Mallard, Tufted Duck, Little Grebe, Moorhen, Coot.

Localised or rare: Black-throated Diver, Red-throated Diver, Goldeneye, Greylag Goose, Black-headed Gull.

Plate 2.26. Well-established pond near Laithers, Turriff, 2006. © I. Francis

Plate 2.27. Nutrient-rich, eutrophic lowland loch, Loch Spynie, Moray, 1999. © I. Francis

Plate 2.28. Mesotrophic lowland loch, Corby Loch near Aberdeen, 2009. © I. Francis

Plate 2.25. Mallard, Aboyne Loch, May 2009. © Harry Scott

Plate 2.29. Nutrient-poor upland oligotrophic loch, Loch Avon, Cairngorms (Moray), 2008. © I. Francis

Plate 2.30. River Don upper reaches near Corgarff, 2008. © *I. Francis*

Plate 2.31. River Clunie, upland oligotrophic tributary of the Dee, 2005. © *I. Francis*

Plate 2.32. River Deveron, Forglen, Turriff, 1994. © *I. Francis*

Rivers

The flowing waters of North-East Scotland range from the smallest upland and coastal burns to large rivers. The main rivers that have their entire catchments within the area are the Dee (141 km), Don (134 km), Deveron (98 km), Ythan (63 km) and Lossie (58 km). The Spey has the lower third of its 166 km within Moray; along with the Dee it is one of the largest rivers in Scotland and both rise at around 1,310 m, higher than any other British rivers. The Dee has a catchment of 2,100 km^2. Most rivers in the North-East have good water quality and the Dee is oligotrophic from source to mouth. The Ythan, by contrast, has poorer water quality, rising entirely in a fertilised, farm landscape. Both the Dee and Spey are designated as being of European importance for nature conservation. Detailed information about the Dee can be found in Jenkins (1985), the Spey in Jenkins (1988) and the Ythan in Gorman (1997). The smaller rivers and burns vary enormously in their characteristics but all form important bird habitats within the wider environment.

Breeding birds of rivers and burns in North-East Scotland.

Typical: Dipper, Mallard, Grey Wagtail, Pied Wagtail, Common Sandpiper, Goosander.

Localised or rare: Common Tern, Red-breasted Merganser, Kingfisher.

Plate 2.34. River North Esk, lowland mesotrophic river near Marykirk, 2005. © *I. Francis*

Plate 2.35. Typical burn running through farmed landscape near Muir of Fowlis, Alford, 2009. © *I. Francis*

Plate 2.33. River Spey, north of Fochabers, 1999. © *I. Francis*

The Breeding Birds of North-East Scotland

Farmland and boundary features - hedges, dykes, ditches and tracks

The state of agriculture in part of the region in 2007 was reviewed by Cook *et al.* (2008). Aberdeenshire has 9% of Scotland's agricultural land but most agricultural activity is disproportionately higher than this: cereals (27% of Scottish area); Oil-seed Rape (35%); potatoes (16%); beef breeding herd (15%); feeding cattle (26%); pigs (57%); poultry (14%); full time labour (15%). Only sheep (6%) and dairy cattle (5%) are under-represented by proportion and declining. Around one-third of the cereals grown are fed to cattle. There has been a steady shift towards winter cereals (32% of the total) but Aberdeenshire is still dominated by spring Barley, a growing proportion of which is sold for malting. The areas of fruit and vegetable crops have increased sharply recently. Farmland (arable and grassland) accounts for over half the land surface of North-East Scotland.

Plate 2.36. Spring Barley field near Elgin, 2006. © *I. Francis*

Aberdeenshire is the lead area for 'finishing' Scottish cattle, carrying a quarter of the country's total. Despite declining cattle numbers in Scotland as a whole, numbers feeding in Aberdeenshire increased between 2003 and 2007. Aberdeenshire is intensively farmed by Scottish standards. Almost half the grass is mowed and overall stocking rates are double the national average. Formartine and Kincardine and the Mearns are the most heavily cropped parts (60–63% of the arable area), which almost certainly creates large 'gaps' in range for several species in these areas. However, comparing Aberdeenshire with some other parts of the UK, the mixed farming, pockets of unimproved land, spring cropping and many small and part-time farms operating at lower intensity can favour certain aspects of biodiversity. There are also small but important areas managed under agri-environment schemes, producing good bird habitats such as field margins, hedges and wild bird cover.

Plate 2.37. Improved Rye-grass dominated grassland near Dufftown, 2005. © *I. Francis*

Across the North-East, there are around 4,500 farm occupiers with 7,122 holdings. Of these 2,900 receive state Single Farm Payments as indicative of the true numbers of farming businesses, implying an average active farm size of 180 ha. Numbers of both very small holdings and large commercial units are growing (Cook *et al.* 2008). These figures illustrate the importance of farming in North-East Scotland, and farmland provides vital habitats for some birds, particularly seed-eaters and waders.

North-East Scotland is not rich in hedges, but dry stone dykes are common, often associated with a line of Broom or Gorse. There are many tracks and ditches created for drainage. Track verges can provide some nesting cover, but hedges, dykes and ditches are often important features in farmland, providing nest sites, feeding areas and song posts. Hedges and dykes decreased in the latter half of the 20th century, but some hedges are now being created under agri-environment schemes. Ditch and track lengths have increased with drainage and increased vehicular access onto farms.

Plate 2.38. Weedy Turnip field near Alford, 2001. © *I. Francis*

Breeding birds of farmed habitats (including boundary features) in North-East Scotland.

Typical: Yellowhammer, Linnet, Sedge Warbler, Tree Sparrow, Lapwing, Oystercatcher, Pheasant, Skylark, Swallow, Pied Wagtail, Magpie, Kestrel, Rook, Jackdaw, Carrion Crow.

Localised or rare: Corn Bunting, Quail, Redshank, Grey Partridge, Lesser Whitethroat.

Plate 2.39. Oil-seed Rape field near Dunecht, 2009. © *I. Francis*

Plate 2.40. Cattle-grazed farmland, Glenlivet, 2007. © I. Francis

Plate 2.44. Wild bird cover crop near New Byth, 2007. © I. Francis

Plate 2.41. Field margin and unsprayed conservation headland near Fraserburgh, 2007. © A. Perkins

Plate 2.45. Farm drainage ditch near Whitehouse, 2006 - ditch lengths have increased since the 1940s with c.8,463 km in the area. © I. Francis

Plate 2.42. Blackthorn hedge planted on a farm near Tarland, 2006. There are 2,812 km of hedges in North-East Scotland (a loss of 66% since 1940s). © I. Francis

Plate 2.46. New track created along field margin for wind farm, St John's Wells, 2009. © I. Francis

Plate 2.43. Dry stone dyke and field margin near Ythanwells, 2005. © I. Francis

Plate 2.47. Outdoor pigs near Hopeman, 2008. © I. Francis

Lowland grasslands

There are no available combined figures for the extent of all lowland grasslands in the North-East. They form part of the farmland area but also extend into other, more semi-natural habitats. The photographs illustrate the diversity of grassland types, and clearly they form important habitats for waders and open country birds such as Skylarks. The management regime is critical, with some grassland left rough and lightly or seasonally grazed; other fields are more commonly cut for silage or grazed intensively. Such areas can be good feeding areas for birds but breeding species can lose many nests through trampling, disturbance and predation. Grassland management can be very intensive, with rolling carried out and large quantities of fertiliser routinely used, but some species-rich areas are sown under agri-environment schemes.

Breeding birds of lowland grasslands in North-East Scotland.

Typical: Skylark, Meadow Pipit, Lapwing, Curlew, Reed Bunting.

Localised or rare: Redshank, Snipe.

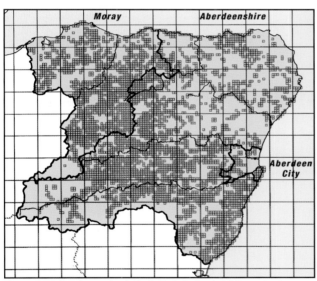

Figure 2.12. Rough grassland, North-East Scotland (total grassland area = 2,650 sq. km).

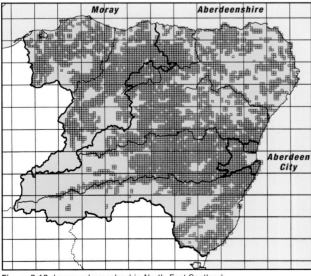

Figure 2.13. Improved grassland in North-East Scotland.

Plate 2.48. Seasonally wet floodplain grassland near Coull, 2008. © *I. Francis*

Plate 2.49. Improved grassland near Keith, 2005. © *I. Francis*

Plate 2.50. Lowland semi-improved acid grassland near Rosehearty, 2005. © *I. Francis*

Plate 2.51. Artificially created species-rich grassland, Corsekelly farm, St. Combs. © *Hywel Maggs*

Lowland raised bogs and heathland

Figure 2.14 shows the distribution and extent of lowland raised bogs; there is no accurate map for lowland heaths, but there are few sites and their extent is not large. Lowland heathlands occur on shallow acid soils, often linked with acid grassland or cliff-top heathland areas. They also overlap in nature with Heather moorland extending down from higher altitudes. Raised bogs are formed from deep peat and when intact their only water source is rainfall, so plant communities are those of acid, nutrient-poor conditions. However, most sites in North-East Scotland have been damaged through drainage, cutting and burning, and now grade into more disturbed, cut-over peatlands. Nevertheless, they are an important resource in a national context, covering 54 km² (depending on definitions), and forming 19% and 8% of

Plate 2.52. Reidside and Blackhills Moss, Aberchirder, 1994. © *I. Francis*

Plate 2.53. Lowland heath near Loch of Park, Banchory, 2009. © *I. Francis*

Plate 2.54. Lowland raised mire near Gardenstown, 2005. © *I. Francis*

Plate 2.55. St Fergus and Rora Mosses, now mostly cut-over for peat extraction, 1994. © *I. Francis*

Plate 2.56. Grasshopper Warbler, Uig, May 2009. © *Ian Hay*

The Breeding Birds of North-East Scotland

the Scottish and UK total. There are also intergrades between raised and blanket bogs in the North-East ("intermediate bogs") but this is beyond the scope of this chapter. Within Scotland, the central lowlands, Dumfries & Galloway and the North-East are the main centres of raised bog development. About half of our raised bog area is sufficiently undamaged to be considered of conservation interest (Scottish Wildlife Trust data). Most of the extant sites are in Aberdeenshire, where there are several hundred remnants of various sizes; 45 of these have some primary (uncut) open bog surface. Many raised bogs have been lost through conversion to agriculture and forestry, with several industrial peat-cutting sites still active. The raised bogs of the North-East are valuable semi-natural, wildlife-rich habitats within a generally farmed landscape.

Table 2.4. Lowland wetland habitats in North-East Scotland (from Biggins & Francis 2007).

Wetland habitat type	Area (km^2)	% of Scottish (UK) resource if known	National context
Wet and riparian woodland	14.9		Unknown significance
Lowland raised bog (incl. damaged/former bogs)	53.6	19% (8%)	Significant representation
Lowland fen (incl. probable unclassified sites)	16.3		Unknown significance
Reedbed	1.53	13% (2%)	Significant representation

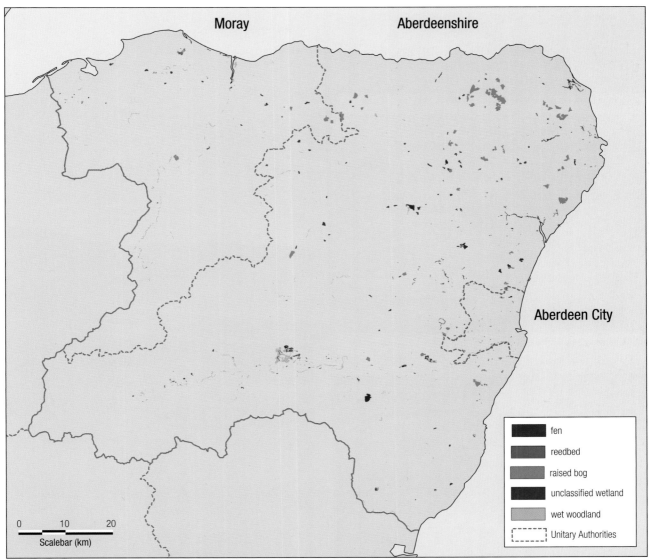

Figure 2.14. Distribution and extent of lowland wetland habitats in North-East Scotland. This composite map shows the extent of raised bog, fen, reedbed and wet woodland habitats in North-East Scotland (Biggins & Francis 2007).

Plate 2.57. Fen at Loch Spynie, 2008. © *I. Francis*

Fens and reedbeds

The distribution and extent of these two habitat types is shown in Figure 2.14. Both are scarce, especially reedbeds, with only about 150 ha spread between *c.* 33 sites, most very small indeed. The largest three (Loch Spynie, Loch of Strathbeg and the Dinnet lochs) between them hold over half of the reedbed area. Common Reed dominates at all these sites, with willow scrub encroachment. Fens are more widespread but are less well known and there are problems of ecological definition and inter-gradation, especially at the margins of raised bogs and with reed swamps and wet grassland. Typically, fens contain high levels of sedge and rush cover, with tall herb communities dominated by Meadowsweet and Yellow Flag Iris. Willow scrub is often frequent and water tables are high all year. Many sites are completely unmanaged and undergoing gradual vegetation succession to wet woodland or drier marshy grassland. They often form areas of rank habitat within wider farmed landscapes and are an important part of the bird habitat matrix in the North-East.

Plate 2.58. Swamp and fen by the River Don at Keig, Alford, 2005. © *I. Francis*

Breeding birds of fens and reedbeds in North-East Scotland.

Typical: Sedge Warbler, Reed Bunting, Grasshopper Warbler, Snipe, Willow Warbler, Teal, Mallard, Water Rail, Curlew.

Localised or rare: Bearded Tit, Marsh Harrier, Spotted Crake.

Plate 2.59. Reedbed at Loch of Strathbeg, 2006. © *I. Francis*

Plate 2.61. Reedbed at Loch Kinord, Dinnet, 2007. © *I. Francis*

Plate 2.60. North-East Scotland's largest reedbed, Loch Spynie, 2005. © *I. Francis*

The Breeding Birds of North-East Scotland

Plate 2.62. Wet Alder woodland near Midmar, 2007. © *I. Francis*

Wet and riparian woodlands

The distribution and extent of these habitats is shown in Figure 2.14. Riparian woodland can be difficult to measure and ecological definitions vary. It is woodland growing in a fairly thin strip along rivers and burns, usually where land is either wet and inundated or on steep river banks which are difficult to cultivate, and influenced by the humidity of the river. In some areas, such as the lower Spey, it may occupy open floodplains and braided shingle, which can be frequently flooded. Wet woodlands can grade into fen and raised bog, as well as marshy grassland. Their humidity and wet ground leads to abundant invertebrates, and they also provide nest holes for birds in such species as Alder. Since it is difficult to use this land for other purposes (except for grazing), these woods are often relatively unmanaged and may form a network of wooded bird habitat within more intensively managed farmland. Their total extent is small compared with other woodland types.

Plate 2.63. Wet willow woodland at Loch Spynie, 2008. © *I. Francis*

Breeding birds of wet or riparian woodland in North-East Scotland.

Typical: Blackcap, Garden Warbler, Willow Warbler, Sedge Warbler, Long-tailed Tit, Wren, Starling, Stock Dove, Woodpigeon, Goosander.

Localised or rare: Goldeneye.

Plate 2.64. Riparian woodland by the River Spey at Craigellachie, 2005. © *I. Francis*

Plate 2.65. Lowland woodland at Tore of Troup, 1997. © *I. Francis*

Plate 2.66. Lowland woodland and parkland trees, Forglen, 1993. © *I. Francis*

Plate 2.67. Parkland trees at Gight, Methlick, 2000. © *I. Francis*

Plate 2.68. Lowland Beech wood by River North Esk, Fettercairn, 2005. © *I. Francis*

Plate 2.69. Stock Dove, Fife, February 2007. © *John Anderson*

Lowland broad-leaved woodland and parkland

Lowland woodlands are very varied, and grade into woodlands of a more upland character; a clear definition is not possible. There are many areas of long-established broad-leaved woodland, often on 'ancient woodland' sites though these are individually usually small in extent. More common are planted broad-leaved woodlands, often containing Sycamore or Beech; some of these are well-established, and can be found in urban areas, but there has also been much recent planting on farmland. In North-East Scotland, coniferous plantations are also frequent in the lowlands, as shelterbelts and as more extensive plantings. The area recorded as 'parkland' by the NCMS in the late 1980s was 2,200 ha, but within this grazed wood pasture is likely to be rare. There are some fine veteran trees within parkland and country house policy woodlands in North-East Scotland. Some of these are now within arable farmland, but the main characteristic of this habitat is the presence of large trees suitable for a wide range of hole-nesting birds. The surrounding grassland or farmland can also provide good hunting or feeding habitat.

> **Breeding birds of lowland woodland and parkland in North-East Scotland.**
>
> **Typical:** Starling, Jackdaw, Stock Dove, Tawny Owl, Tree Sparrow, Treecreeper, Spotted Flycatcher, Kestrel.
>
> **Localised or rare:** Green Woodpecker, Hawfinch, Barn Owl.

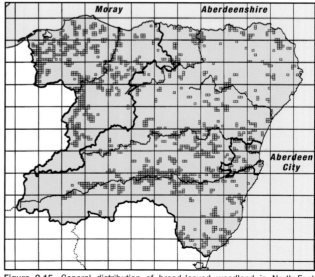
Figure 2.15. General distribution of broad-leaved woodland in North-East Scotland: 205 sq. km.

The Breeding Birds of North-East Scotland

Urban, gardens, industry, quarries and recreation areas

The wildlife and habitats within Aberdeen City were summarised by Marren (1982). In North-East Scotland, there were 343 km² of built up and related bare land in the 1980s, 4% of the land area; this will have risen considerably since then. The mix of buildings, gardens, open spaces and urban woodlands is probably typical of settlements elsewhere in the country and they provide habitat for many common birds and a few scarce ones.

There are no available figures for the extent of quarried land, but there are numerous granite quarries across the area, both active and disused, and a wide range of other small quarries and borrow pits, often used as excavation sites for track construction and building material. Some of these are very old. In north Moray and the Howe of the Mearns, there are active sand and gravel quarries, where the dynamic habitat provides suitable nest sites for some ground and bank-nesting species. In 2005, there were 28 active mineral working sites in North-East Scotland - 15 for crushed/hard rock and 13 for sand and gravel (Scottish Aggregates Survey 2005). Production was 2.25 million tonnes, 60% of which was rock and 40% sand and gravel. Most of the latter is concentrated in the lower Don and Ythan valleys and in Moray, where in 2003/04 there were 17 active quarries supplying mostly sand and gravel with some hard rock for crushing (Moray Structure Plan Report of Survey). Quarry numbers, production levels and the proportion of sand and gravel all appear to have fallen since 1988 (140 workings in the former Grampian Region - Grampian Regional Council [1991]).

Within and around the urban areas, and also well out in the countryside, are open recreation areas, typified by golf courses. There are already 70 of these in North-East Scotland, with more planned. There is no accurate figure for the total land area occupied, but the 53 18-hole courses (at *c.* 50 ha each) and 17 9–12 hole courses (at *c.* 25 ha each) equate to at least 3,075 ha or *c.* 0.35% of the land area (see Visit Scotland 2005 for numbers and SAC area data).

Breeding birds of urban areas in North-East Scotland.

Typical: Oystercatcher, Herring Gull, Feral Pigeon, House Sparrow, Starling, Swift, House Martin.

Localised or rare: Peregrine, Common Gull, Common Tern.

Plate 2.71. Elgin from the air, 1999. © *I. Francis*

Plate 2.72. Craigenlow granite quarry, Dunecht, 2010. © *I. Francis*

Plate 2.73. Cloddach sand and gravel quarry, Elgin, 2007. © *J. Matthews*

Plate 2.70. Oystercatcher, Donside, April 1986. © *John Edelsten*

Plate 2.74. Murcar Golf Course, Aberdeen, 2007. © *I. Francis*

Plate 2.75. Herring Gull, Crawton, June 2009. © *Ed Duthie*

Plate 2.76. Coastal heath and cliffs at Findon Ness, Portlethen, 1994. © *I. Francis*

Plate 2.77. High seabird cliffs at Troup Head, 2004. © *I. Francis*

Plate 2.78. Coastal heath at Longhaven cliffs, 2007. © *I. Francis*

Plate 2.79. Strahangles Point. © *D. Goulder*

Coastal cliffs and maritime heaths

Descriptions of coastal habitats and their seabirds were given by Bill Bourne and Mark Tasker in Buckland *et al.* (1990). Hard rock cliffs extend to around 108 km of North-East Scotland's coast (Barne *et al.* 1996), which is some 6% of the Scottish and 3% of the UK total. Much of this has only a narrow fringe of cliff-top vegetation, usually grassland, but there are small patches of coastal/maritime heath, amounting to around 3.5 km², a figure that is insignificant nationally. Most of the coastal cliffs hold nesting seabirds (often just Fulmars and Herring Gulls), but North-East Scotland also holds some of the largest cliff seabird colonies in mainland Britain, including three major Special Protection Areas with many tens of thousands of seabirds. Our cliffs are among the most natural of the habitats we have, but their seabirds are dependent on the rapidly changing marine environment, and we cannot be sure that the large colonies will continue to survive in their current numbers.

Breeding birds of coastal cliffs and clifftop heaths in North-East Scotland.

Typical: Herring Gull, Kittiwake, Fulmar, Guillemot, Razorbill, Puffin, Shag, Feral Pigeon, Jackdaw, Rock Pipit, Eider, Stonechat, Linnet, Wren.

Localised or rare: Peregrine, Raven, Black Guillemot, Gannet.

The Breeding Birds of North-East Scotland

Rocky shores and coastal shingle

No figures are available for the extent of rocky shore in North-East Scotland, but it is quite extensive with some large areas on the Moray coast between Burghead and Lossiemouth, between Rosehearty and Fraserburgh and between Gourdon and Inverbervie. Parts are tidally inundated but above this, there is substantial bird nesting habitat. Moray has impressive extents of bare shingle, and although vegetated shingle accounts for only 1.5 km^2, we have some of the best examples in Britain at Culbin and Kingston, with 19% of the Scottish and 2.5% of the UK total. Nesting birds are limited due to the unstable or wave-washed substrate, but these coastal habitats are still a valuable resource for species breeding nearby and are also used heavily by birds in winter.

Breeding birds of rocky shores and coastal shingle in North-East Scotland.

Typical: Rock Pipit, Oystercatcher, Eider, Ringed Plover, Common Gull.

Localised or rare: Arctic Tern, Little Tern.

Plate 2.81. Extensive rocky intertidal shore near Rosehearty, 2007. © *I. Francis*

Plate 2.82. Rocky intertidal shore at Logie Head, Cullen, 1994. © *I. Francis*

Plate 2.83. Shingle bar near Kingston, 2006. © *I. Francis*

Plate 2.80. Nairn and Culbin bars are shingle and sand dune dominated, and are some of the most outstanding examples of their type in Britain. 1999. © *I. Francis*

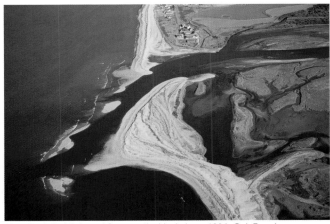

Plate 2.84. Aerial view of Speymouth shingle bars, 1994. © *I. Francis*

Plate 2.85. Extensive sand dune complex at Sands of Forvie, 2005. © *I. Francis*

Sand dunes

The North-East holds a substantial concentration of sand dunes, amounting to around 70 km², with some of the largest extents and best examples in the country. Most ecological types are present, from mobile fore dunes to more stable vegetated dunes with their associated dune slack wetlands. On stable acid sand, dune heath may develop (a habitat also present in nationally important concentrations), and dune scrub and woodland are also found. Apart from at St. Cyrus in the very south, most sand dunes are found along the central and northern east coast, with scattered sites in Moray, including Culbin Sands, once the largest mobile sand system in Britain, but now stabilised by decades of conifer afforestation. Although sand dunes can be amongst the least modified of all terrestrial habitats, there has been loss or degradation due to a variety of human activities.

Breeding birds of sand dunes in North-East Scotland.

Typical: Skylark, Shelduck, Meadow Pipit, Ringed Plover, Oystercatcher.

Localised or rare: Sandwich Tern, Arctic Tern, Little Tern, Black-headed Gull, Eider.

Plate 2.88. Skylark, Cairnbulg, August 2008. © *Ed Duthie*

Plate 2.86. Lossiemouth beach and sand dunes, 2009. © *I. Francis*

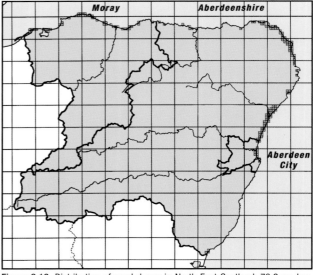

Plate 2.87. Sand dunes and flooded dune slacks, Menie Estate, 2006 - scheduled to be lost to golf development. © *I. Francis*

Figure 2.16. Distribution of sand dunes in North-East Scotland: 70.2 sq. km. (22% of Scottish and 14% of UK resource).

Plate 2.89. **Shelduck**, St. Cyrus, May 2003. © *Harry Scott*

Estuaries and saltmarsh

There are few estuaries in North-East Scotland and little saltmarsh. Estuaries cover *c.* 14 km^2, around 0.3% of the UK total, divided between nine main sites. Findhorn Bay is by far the largest, with the Ythan estuary and St. Cyrus next in size. They provide immensely rich bird feeding and hold distinctive breeding bird communities around them, though there are many intergrades into sand dunes and other coastal habitats. The small total area of saltmarsh in North-East Scotland is found mainly at Culbin Sands, Findhorn Bay, Spey Bay, the Loch of Strathbeg and within the Ythan estuary. Saltmarshes hold breeding open country passerines and nesting Redshanks, but tidal inundation is a constant threat during the breeding season.

Breeding birds of estuaries and saltmarsh in North-East Scotland.

Typical: Ringed Plover, Shelduck, Redshank, Oystercatcher, Meadow Pipit, Skylark.

Localised or rare: Eider, Common Tern.

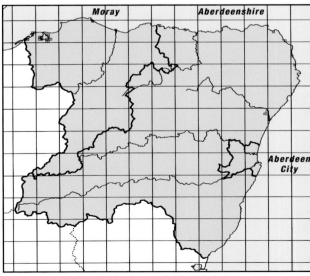

Figure 2.17. Distribution of saltmarsh in North-East Scotland: 3.1 sq. km. (insignificant nationally).

Plate 2.90. The Ythan estuary, 1994. © *I. Francis*

Plate 2.91. The Lossie estuary, 2008. © *I. Francis*

Plate 2.92. The largest area of saltmarsh in North-East Scotland is in Findhorn Bay, 1999. © *I. Francis*

The sea

Although the sea is clearly not a nesting habitat, its nature and condition are crucial to the survival of many of our coastal breeding species. Most of the open coast of the North-East is classed as 'exposed' or 'moderately exposed', with sheltered shores confined to the estuaries. Sand is the commonest intertidal sediment and most of the inshore area has a coarse sandy seabed, with gravel or sandy gravel from extending from Spey Bay to Rattray Head. Our seas include part of the Moray Firth and part of the open North Sea, which is influenced both by oceanic water from the North Atlantic and by freshwater from several major rivers. Offshore, water becomes thermally stratified in summer but closer to the coast, the water remains well-mixed throughout the year. The stratification extends into the Moray Firth but off the Aberdeenshire coast there is a tidal front (the Buchan front), in the transition zone between stratified and well-mixed water masses. This area is rich in plankton and of great importance to feeding seabirds (Doody *et al.* 1993; see also Barne *et al.* 1996).

Plate 2.93. Razorbill, Crawton, June 2009. © *Ed Duthie*

Plate 2.94. Gannet, Troup Head, September 2009. © *Ian Francis*

The Breeding Birds of North-East Scotland

Chapter 3. *The breeding birds of North-East Scotland: species accounts*

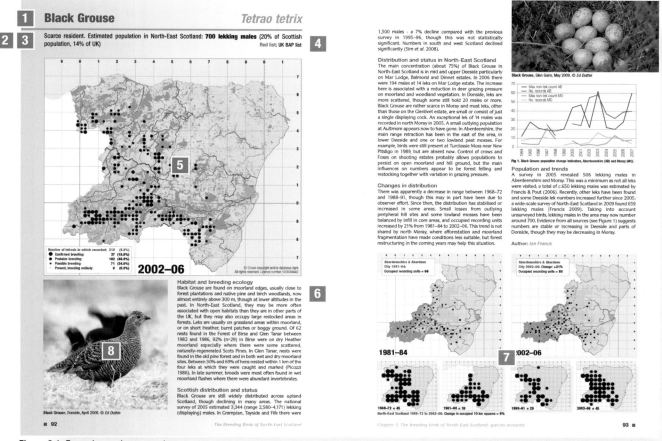

Figure 3.1. Example species account.

Introduction to the species accounts

The main accounts cover all native species which were considered to have at least 'possibly' bred during the atlas period 2002–06 (see Chapter 1). In addition, some 'feral' or 'escaped' species are covered, and at the end, a few other species are listed which met the same 'possible breeding' criteria at other times since the first UK atlas in 1968–72, but which did not breed during any atlas period. Species known to have occurred but not bred during the breeding season are also listed. Further explanation of the species accounts is set out below, in relation to the numbered points on the example illustration.

In all accounts, the term 'North-East Scotland' means the whole of the area covered by this atlas, including Moray. The term 'North-east Scotland' relates to the Aberdeenshire and Aberdeen City SOC recording area - as covered by the first 1981–84 atlas (Buckland *et al.* 1990) and the annual North-east Scotland Bird Reports.

1 Species order and taxonomic issues

The taxonomic sequence of species follows Sangster *et al.* (2010). In relation to sub-species, reference is made to the three breeding in our area which are endemic to Scotland (Ptarmigan, Crested Tit and Linnet - see Forrester *et al.* 2007). Other sub-species are mentioned where authors

have considered there is distinctive information to include. The English names are those in common use in North-East Scotland, such as in the North-east Scotland and Moray & Nairn Bird Reports.

2 Status line and population estimate

The status summary gives an outline of the breeding occurrence in the area, including the year-round status (see Annex 4 for details of the method). The population estimate that follows is exactly that - an *estimate*, based on considered evaluation of all possible sources. No counts of breeding populations were undertaken during fieldwork for this atlas, as explained in Chapter 1, and our estimates can be divided into two categories. Estimates in **bold** are based on detailed surveys or monitoring, or good knowledge, and are considered to be very or fairly accurate; those in *italics* are based on an evaluation of wider survey and population estimates, leading to an approximate population figure for our area. In general, such estimates were derived from figures published elsewhere, often involving a proportional breakdown of national estimates, taking into account habitat suitability. We stress that all estimates in italics should be viewed with some caution; they are presented as a rough guide to the likely breeding numbers in the area, to set each species in context. We offer these estimates as a challenge to local ornithologists - to confirm, refine or improve them!

3 Proportions of national populations in North-East Scotland

The estimated percentages of Scottish and UK breeding populations in North-East Scotland are given (in Chapter 6 and in Annex 4, some figures for Europe are also provided). These were taken in most cases from Forrester *et al.* (2007) or Baker *et al.* (2006), but occasionally more up to date figures have been used. Again, these should be considered as very rough guides, since not only are there uncertainties about population levels in our area, but this can also apply nationally. In some cases, published estimates differ, due to varying dates of assessment, and this can lead to paradoxical situations such as a Scottish estimate being larger than the published UK estimate. We have attempted to deal with this as sensibly as possible; for example, for a bird breeding only in Scotland, we have used the 'Birds of Scotland' estimate for the UK if this differs from that in Baker *et al.* (2006). In a few other cases, another adjustment has been made, described in the text.

4 Species conservation status

The presence of a species on any of several conservation priority lists is noted. These include, if relevant: Red and Amber status on the 'Birds of Conservation Concern' list (Eaton *et al.* 2009), Annex 1 of the EU 'Birds' Directive, Schedule 1 of the Wildlife & Countryside Act 1981 (as amended), UK Biodiversity Action Plan Priority Species and the Scottish Biodiversity List. For the Red and Amber lists, we have noted each 'species' that qualifies, regardless of the complexities of qualifying sub-species or seasonal populations, and since qualification criteria are also reviewed regularly, we recommend that the original publication is consulted for full details. Chapters 4 and 6 also provide further information relevant to all these conservation listings.

5 The main atlas map

This shows the composite breeding distribution in North-East Scotland for the five year period 2002–06. The species mapped are all those showing at least 'possible breeding' during the atlas. The mapping units are tetrads (2x2 km squares) in most cases, though for a few sensitive species 10-km square resolution has been used, and in a very few cases no map at all is provided, due to the sensitivity of the species even at this mapping resolution. The key to the symbols is given on the maps and explained further in Chapter 1. It is important to stress that the symbol sizes relate to levels of proof of breeding, and not abundance. The map background is used under license from the Ordnance Survey. Figures for the number of occupied tetrads, and the proportion in each breeding category, are also provided. These figures relate to the number of tetrads during the 2002–06 period, and are included even if a 10-km map is shown, or no map is present. Grid lines are shown at 10 km intervals and Local Authority and Cairngorms National Park boundaries are shown. For orientation, reference should be made to the main geographical map of the area in Chapter 2, and to the map in the end sheets.

6 Species texts

For most species, the text is divided into five sections, though for some minor breeding species these have been combined.

■ *Habitat and breeding biology.* This section gives a general outline of habitat used and aspects of the breeding biology; these may apply generally to Scotland, drawing heavily on species accounts in Forrester *et al.* (2007), but where possible, more specific reference to information from North-East Scotland has been made.

■ *Scottish distribution and status.* To provide context for breeding status in North-East Scotland, a summary for Scotland as a whole is given, using information mainly from Forrester *et al.* (2007). In some cases, reference is made to the status outwith the breeding season, and occasionally to the UK as a whole.

■ *Distribution and status in North-East Scotland.* This is the first of three sections dealing solely with our area. It is an attempt to summarise the distribution pattern during the atlas period (including important areas or concentrations) and give an overall impression of factors that might have influenced this. For some species, updated information from 2007–2009 has been used, if available. Grid references of places mentioned can be found in the gazetteer in Annex 7.

■ *Changes in distribution.* This section describes how the breeding distribution may have changed since the first North-east atlas period for Aberdeenshire and Aberdeen City, conducted during 1981–84 (Buckland *et al.* 1990) and over the longer term for the whole area at a coarser scale, using information from the two previous national breeding bird atlases which covered the periods 1968–72 (Sharrock 1976) and 1988–91 (Gibbons *et al.* 1993).

■ *Population and trends.* The final section presents a breeding population estimate for our area, using a variety of sources and methods described in the text. Any evidence for population change is also summarised. For some species, updated information from 2007–2009 has been used.

7 Distribution change maps

Maps from previous atlases are presented for most species to illustrate these changes, together with the numbers of occupied recording units and the percentage changes in these and in occupied 10-km squares over specified time periods. For direct comparison, the figures exclude the 'present but not breeding' category used in the 2002–06 atlas (the yellow dots shown on many main atlas maps).

These maps fall into two categories:

■ *Comparison with the 1981–84 atlas*: This pair of maps relates solely to the Aberdeenshire and City of Aberdeen area, as Moray was not surveyed during this period. It compares the distribution in the earlier atlas with 2002–06, using the recording units adopted by the first atlas. Tetrad records from 2002–06 were each allocated to an original recording unit to allow this (see Chapter 1). On these maps, some coastal seabirds may be plotted slightly inland (centrally in the old recording unit). For some species, maps are not available or have not been used. These are primarily rare breeding birds, where either they were not mapped using these units in the first atlas, or we have judged that such a map for 2002–06 would be too revealing. In a very few cases, we have added records available from 1981–84 that were not mapped in Buckland *et al.* (1990).

■ *Comparison with all earlier breeding atlases*: This sequence of four maps shows changes in breeding distributions at a 10-km square scale, beginning with the first UK atlas in 1968–72. We thank the BTO for allowing us to use this information. For some species, maps are not available or have not been used. These are mostly rare breeding birds in 1981–84 which were not mapped using these units in that atlas. We have not included in the national atlas maps any extra records for the mapped periods which have become known to us since the publication of the atlases; the maps show only the data held by the BTO. However, any such records are referred to in the text.

Please note that the BTO mapping data for both national atlases include only two breeding categories, as used in the *BTO 2nd Atlas*. Hence these maps use only two dot sizes and the largest could indicate either probable or confirmed breeding. The local atlas maps both use three breeding categories and three dot sizes.

8 Photographs
We have included, where possible, a wide selection of photographs showing breeding activity for each species. In around 73% of cases, these have been taken by local photographers in North-East Scotland and we are very grateful to them for the provision of these images.

Site accounts
Throughout this chapter, we have included a series of portraits of selected sites and bird areas across North-East Scotland. These give an impression of the habitats and breeding birds that can be found in different parts of the region. We have tried to ensure that the position of these sites within the species accounts bears some resemblance to the habitats used by the adjacent species, but sometimes there is no such link. For this reason, in all site accounts, we do not intend to imply that the species with an account immediately next to it necessarily breeds in the area illustrated. The sites chosen complement areas illustrated in other chapters, and are not intended to form a comprehensive inventory of all breeding bird sites.

Table 3.1. Site accounts within Chapter 3. (See map on pages 8–9, Chapter 2, for locations)

Site		Page
01	St. Cyrus	63
02	Glen Tanar	97
03	Dava moor	109
04	Forest of Birse	131
05	Ythan estuary and Sands of Forvie	171
06	Culbin Bar and Sands	183
07	Lochnagar and the Mounth	187
08	Speymouth	191
09	Loch of Skene	224
10	Loch Spynie	225
11	Ballochbuie Forest	254
12	Forest of Mar	255
13	Portknockie cliffs	287
14	Ladder Hills	305
15	River Findhorn	334
16	Cloddach Quarry	335
17	Loch of Strathbeg	386
18	Fowlsheugh	387
19	Cairn Lochan to Ben Macdui	406
20	Muir of Dinnet	407

Plate 3.1. Black Grouse, Donside, April 2008. © *Ed Duthie*

Mute Swan
Cygnus olor

Scarce resident. Estimated population in North-East Scotland: **100 pairs** (8% of Scottish population, 2% of UK)

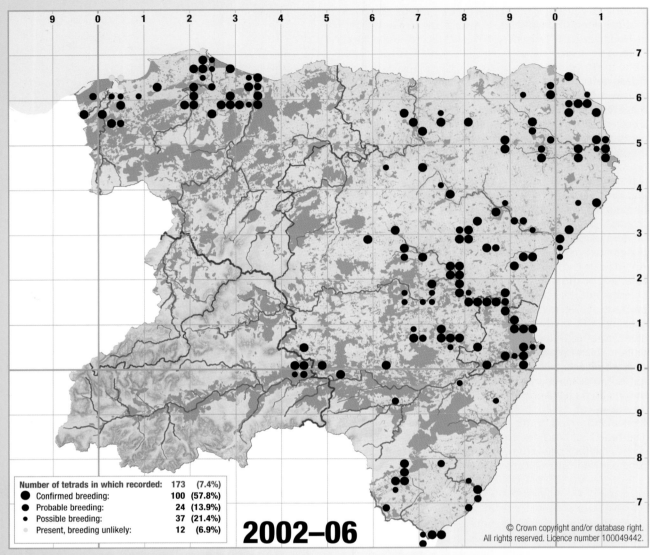

Number of tetrads in which recorded:	173	(7.4%)
● Confirmed breeding:	100	(57.8%)
● Probable breeding:	24	(13.9%)
● Possible breeding:	37	(21.4%)
● Present, breeding unlikely:	12	(6.9%)

2002–06

Mute Swan, Aboyne Loch, July 2006. © *Harry Scott*

Habitat and breeding biology

Mute Swans breed beside eutrophic lochs, large ponds and the slow-flowing lower reaches of rivers; in fact any body of freshwater that contains sufficient submerged or floating vegetation to feed adults and cygnets. They also nest beside estuaries and on higher ground in salt marshes. Although most waters only hold single pairs, there may be several pairs nesting quite close together especially when reeds obscure incubating birds from each other. At Loch Spynie in 1999 there were four active nests within 700 m in the reeds fringing the loch. Most pairs remain on their territory all year, leaving only in freezing conditions. They usually pair for life. The clutch of 3–9 eggs is generally laid in April and incubated for five weeks. The young fledge at about 12 weeks old but often remain with their parents until chased from the territory during autumn.

Scottish distribution and status

The Scottish breeding population is mostly to be found in low-lying areas of north-east, east, south-west and central Scotland. There are also concentrations in the southern islands of the Outer Hebrides, in Orkney and on Islay. The national census in 2002 revealed 1,375 territorial pairs of which 1,012 were breeding. Over the last 25 years the

Scottish population has increased substantially, by 70% between 1983–90 and by a further 41% between 1990–2002 (Brown & Brown 2005).

Distribution and status in North-East Scotland

In North-East Scotland, Mute Swans breed in low-lying areas, mostly below 50 m above sea level but occasionally higher as at Hopewell near Tarland at 180 m. Many of the region's rivers are too fast-flowing and oligotrophic, so few breed along the River Dee in contrast to the more gentle, nutrient-rich River Don which is well populated as far upstream as Inverurie. Similar contrast is apparent between the rapid middle reaches of the River Spey and its slower flow to the sea below Fochabers, where several pairs breed in riverside backwaters. The majority of pairs, however, breed in still, eutrophic and well-vegetated freshwaters ranging in size from pools of little more than 100 m diameter to the expanses of Loch of Strathbeg where up to 31 pairs have been known to nest (Thom 1986). Especially favoured areas for Mute Swans are lowland Moray, Donside and east Buchan.

Changes in distribution

Examination of the comparative maps for Aberdeenshire/ Aberdeen City reveal an increase of 38% in occupied recording units between 1981–84 and 2002–06, although breeding did not take place in all of these. For conspicuous birds such as Mute Swans this increase in range is likely to be genuine. In 10-km squares bordering the coast there has been little change (26 v. 28 occupied recording units) but occupied units in inland squares have increased from 40 to 63. This perhaps reflects the fact that prime sites in low-lying areas are fully occupied and the expanding population is now making use of less optimal inland waters.

Population and trends

The breeding population of North-East Scotland in 1983 was 76 pairs with a further 34 territorial pairs that were not proved to have bred (Brown & Brown 1985). In the 2002

Mute Swan, Kintore, May 2008. © *Ann Burns*

census, only 55 breeding pairs were found and there were 52 non-breeding territorial birds (Brown & Brown 2005). Much of this decline can be attributed to changes at Loch of Strathbeg where 31 pairs in 1978 had reduced to 17 pairs in 1983 and only three by 2002 - probably caused by a decline in water quality due to eutrophication (Thom 1986, *NES 1st Atlas*, I. Francis pers. comm.). During 2002–06, breeding was confirmed in 101 tetrads and probably took place in a further 24. The total of 125 occupied tetrads is, however, a composite picture over a five-year period. If we assume that 75% of occupied tetrads held a breeding or territorial pair in any one year (roughly the case in Moray at least) and that 90% of tetrads held only one pair while 10% held two, then the population would comprise around 100 breeding or territorial pairs. This compares with 81 such pairs located in the 2002 census. It is likely that some additional breeding sites were found during the five-year Atlas period that were not located during the one-year 2002 census. Despite the expansion of range there appears to have been little change in numbers since the 1983 census when 110 breeding and territorial pairs were counted (Brown & Brown 1985).

Author: *Martin Cook*

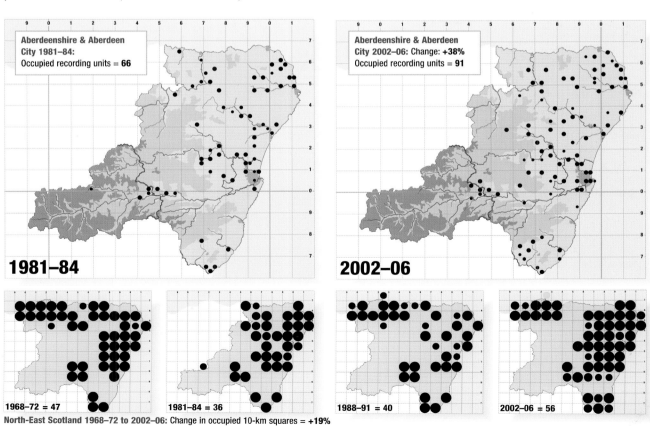

Aberdeenshire & Aberdeen City 1981–84: Occupied recording units = **66**

1981–84

Aberdeenshire & Aberdeen City 2002–06: Change: **+38%** Occupied recording units = **91**

2002–06

1968–72 = 47

1981–84 = 36

1988–91 = 40

2002–06 = 56

North-East Scotland 1968–72 to 2002–06: Change in occupied 10-km squares = **+19%**

Whooper Swan

Cygnus cygnus

Occasional probable breeder; a few present in summer. Winter visitor and passage migrant. Estimated population in North-East Scotland: usually **0 pairs**

Amber list; Schedule 1; Annex 1; Scottish BAP list

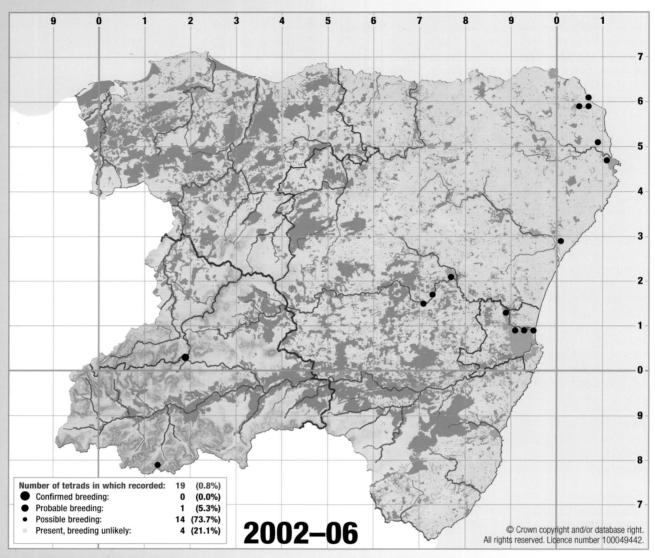

Number of tetrads in which recorded: 19 (0.8%)
- ● Confirmed breeding: 0 (0.0%)
- ● Probable breeding: 1 (5.3%)
- ● Possible breeding: 14 (73.7%)
- · Present, breeding unlikely: 4 (21.1%)

2002–06

Habitat and breeding biology
In Scotland, most summering or nesting birds are found on lowland freshwater lochs, though marshes and upland pools may be used (Spray in *BS3*). In North-East Scotland, upland lochs surrounded by moorland have held birds, but most summer records have come from lowland ponds and rivers.

Scottish distribution and status
A rare breeding bird in Scotland with 3–7 pairs annually, mainly in north-west Scotland and Shetland. Also 10–30 summering individuals present, some of which may be injured birds unable to return to Iceland. However, Whooper Swans are common winter visitors, with a Scottish total of 4,142 in 2005. Almost all wintering birds are from the Icelandic breeding population. Scottish breeding birds are presumably also derived from this population, though feral birds breed in some areas (Spray in *BS3*).

Distribution and status in North-East Scotland
Most summering birds during 2002–06 were present in north-east Buchan and along the lower parts of the River Don. Very few individual birds were involved (probably injured individuals) and the mapped records may show some duplication. There were only three upland records - a

bird at Loch Vrotachan, Deeside on 14th May 2005 (probably a migrant), one on Dava Moor in Moray in 2006 (this bird summered at Lochindorb in Badenoch & Strathspey) but more intriguingly, a bird showing anxiety and behaviour indicative of a possible nest at Loch Builg in 2006. There were other records from here that summer,

Whooper Swan, Sweden, May 1993. © *John Massie*

including a pair, but no confirmation of nesting. Traditionally favoured sites for summering birds in Moray have been Findhorn Bay and Speymouth (Cook 1992), though they were less frequent there during 2002–06.

Changes in distribution

The extent of summering in North-East Scotland has always been very variable and no clear distributional trend is apparent. More birds appear to be summering in localities previously favoured in the east of the area, such as the Don and around the Loch of Strathbeg, when compared with the situation during 1981–84 (*NES 1st Atlas*).

Population and trends

Scottish and UK wintering numbers have increased since 1986 (Spray in *BS3*). Breeding numbers also appear to have increased nationally since the account of Thom (1986). In North-East Scotland, there appears to have been a small increase in the number of birds summering since 1981–84 (*NES 1st Atlas*). This may reflect more wintering birds and therefore a greater likelihood of injured birds remaining, but in fact winter trends at principal sites in the North-East have been very variable and this may not be the driving factor.

Author: *Ian Francis*

Whooper Swan, Cruden Bay, October 2008. © *Ed Duthie*

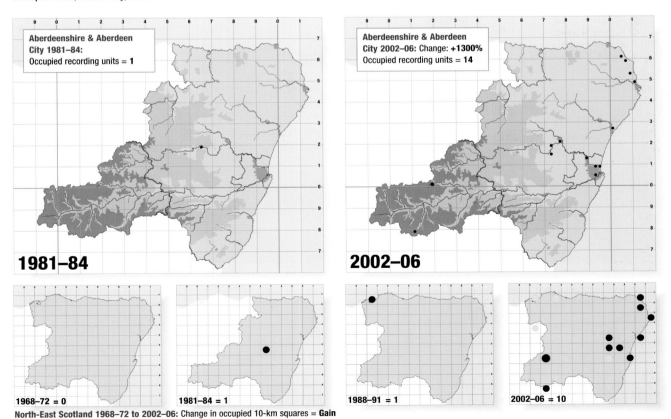

Aberdeenshire & Aberdeen City 1981–84:
Occupied recording units = **1**

1981–84

Aberdeenshire & Aberdeen City 2002–06: Change: **+1300%**
Occupied recording units = **14**

2002–06

1968–72 = 0

1981–84 = 1

1988–91 = 1

2002–06 = 10

North-East Scotland 1968–72 to 2002–06: Change in occupied 10-km squares = **Gain**

Greylag Goose

Anser anser

Rare resident feral breeder. Winter visitor and passage migrant. Estimated population in North-East Scotland: *50–100 pairs* (10% of Scottish feral population, probably <1% of UK)

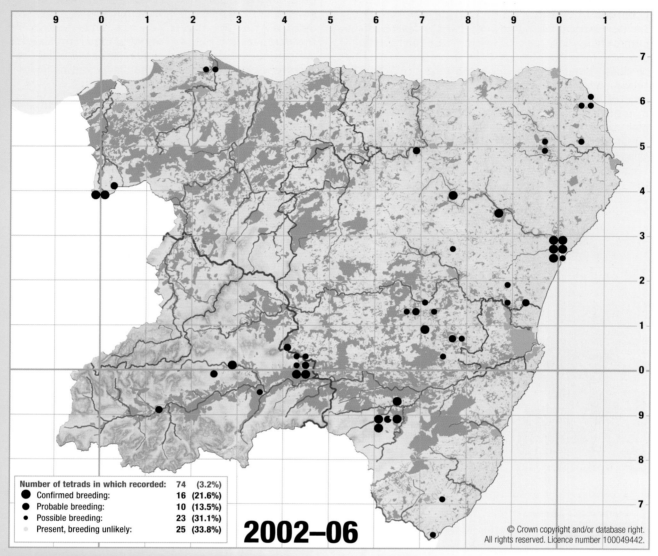

Number of tetrads in which recorded:	74	(3.2%)
● Confirmed breeding:	16	(21.6%)
● Probable breeding:	10	(13.5%)
● Possible breeding:	23	(31.1%)
○ Present, breeding unlikely:	25	(33.8%)

2002–06

Greylag Goose, Loch Kinord, May 2008. © *Harry Scott*

Habitat and breeding biology

In Scotland, naturalised populations are associated with water bodies surrounded by parkland or agricultural land; native birds breed in more upland, Heather and peat-dominated landscapes with lochans (Swann in *BS3*). In North-East Scotland, both such general habitats are used. There have been no local studies of breeding Greylags and there is little information on breeding biology in this area. Scottish Greylags in western and southern Scotland lay eggs in April (mean clutch size 5.9 in one study), which hatch in late April or early May. There is some indication from timing of moult aggregations that birds in North-East Scotland may nest a little later than this. Local Greylags have hybridised with Canada Geese (at the Ythan estuary) and produced young, as is the case nationally. Breeding birds with young aggregate with non-breeders to form moulting flocks in several areas, such as the Dinnet lochs (over 70 birds counted in 2006 and 2007), near Strachan, or in favoured riverside areas such as near Gairnshiel, Deeside (42 in 2008 - H. Scott pers. comm.). There is also a large, well-established moulting flock (196 including 92 young in 2003) just outside the current Moray boundary at Lochindorb.

Scottish distribution and status

At least 700 pairs of re-established, naturalised Greylags breed in Scotland, in addition to the larger native population (with post-breeding numbers of some 20,000 birds) found in north-west Scotland. Although the feral population is widespread, it is concentrated more in southern and central areas, where many of the original introductions took place early last century (Swann in *BS3*).

Distribution and status in North-East Scotland

Greylag Geese have established themselves as a regular, resident breeding species over the last 20 years. The atlas map shows a wide scattering of breeding records with four main concentrations, around Dava Moor in Moray (an outlier of the nearby Lochindorb population), mid Deeside around Dinnet, Deeside around Strachan and Glen Dye, and around the Ythan estuary. Our breeding birds may include those from the expanding Scottish population derived from released or escaped stock further south. However, there were several local introductions, for example in Deeside in the 1960s (*e.g.* at Strachan - D. Jenkins pers. comm.) and at Balmoral Estate in the 1970s (A. Watson *in litt.*) with occasional breeding records up to the early 1980s (Bourne 1982, *NES 1st Atlas*). Some birds also escaped from a collection at Culterty Field

Greylag Goose, Loch Kinord, May 2006. © *Harry Scott*

Station on the Ythan estuary in the late 1960s and formed a small breeding population; at least one gander also paired with a Canada Goose and produced hybrid young. The Culterty and Strachan birds came from eggs moved from Galloway by D. Jenkins and G. Dunnet, which in turn had been sourced from Hebridean stock; the Culterty collection was initiated by Dr. H. Edgar Smith prior to its purchase by Aberdeen University (I. Patterson, D. Jenkins, S. Anderson pers. comm.). Local breeding Greylags appear to be fairly sedentary with no evidence of movement out of the area during the year. In winter, many thousands of Icelandic Greylag Geese are found in North-East Scotland but most of these have departed by mid April.

Changes in distribution

Comparison with the 1981–84 atlas map shows a clear increase from three to 34 occupied recording units by 2002–06. In Moray, breeding was first recorded in 2002 at Loch Allan, Dava Moor, within the current administrative boundary, though they did breed in 1998 at Lochindorb, now outside Moray, and between 1992–99 some birds summered at Loch Spynie (M. Cook pers. comm.). There is some evidence of a slow colonisation of upland areas, especially in Deeside and south-west Moray.

Population and trends

All evidence suggests a large increase in the numbers and distribution of feral and re-established birds over the past 20 years, both nationally and in our area. The population in North-East Scotland is now probably around 50–100 pairs, with the single largest concentration around Dinnet (perhaps 30 pairs), and now some seven or eight pairs further west in Deeside around the Gairn (R. Duncan pers. comm.). Wintering numbers of Icelandic birds in North-East Scotland increased until the late 1990s but since then have dropped substantially.

Author: *Ian Francis*

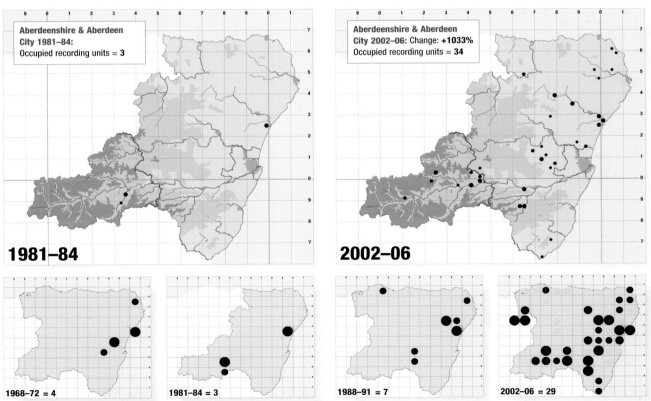

Aberdeenshire & Aberdeen
City 1981–84:
Occupied recording units = 3

1981–84

Aberdeenshire & Aberdeen
City 2002–06: Change: +1033%
Occupied recording units = 34

2002–06

1968–72 = 4

1981–84 = 3

1988–91 = 7

2002–06 = 29

North-East Scotland 1968–72 to 2002–06: Change in occupied 10-km squares = +625%

Canada Goose

Branta canadensis

Very rare feral breeder. Passage migrant. Estimated population in North-East Scotland: **2–4 pairs** (<1% of Scottish and UK population)

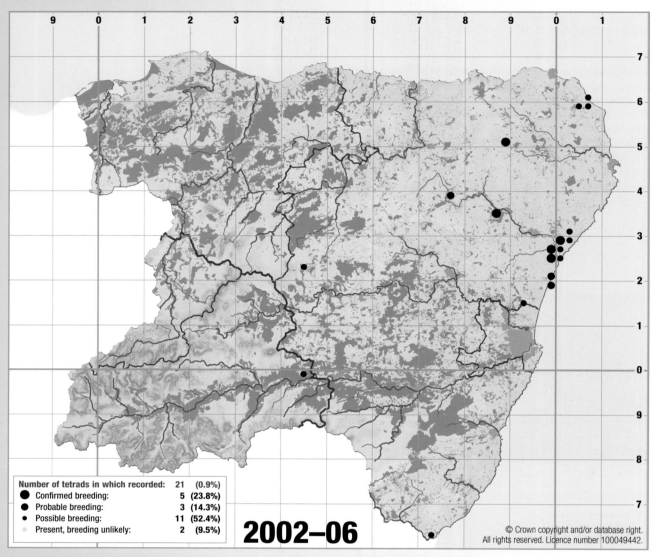

Number of tetrads in which recorded: 21 (0.9%)
- ● Confirmed breeding: 5 (23.8%)
- ● Probable breeding: 3 (14.3%)
- • Possible breeding: 11 (52.4%)
- ○ Present, breeding unlikely: 2 (9.5%)

2002–06

Habitat and breeding biology
There have been no studies of the breeding biology in Scotland and there is no information about the small population in North-East Scotland. Evidence from elsewhere in the UK suggests that nests are usually found in rank vegetation, often sheltered by bushes, usually near water and often on small islands in ponds, features shared with Scottish breeding birds (Ogilvie in *BS3*). This is also likely to be true for North-East Scotland.

Scottish distribution and status
The Canada Goose is a relatively scarce and localised introduced breeder in Scotland (Ogilvie in *BS3*). It is thought that most birds are of the nominate sub-species *B. c. canadensis*, but there is no clear evidence of how true this is for birds in our area. Most of the Scottish breeding population is found in southern and central Scotland. Hybridisation with feral Greylag Geese is widespread, and this has been recorded in North-East Scotland too. Most feral breeders are sedentary, but Canada Geese from England pass through Scotland to form moulting flocks, chiefly in the Beauly Firth. The Scottish breeding population is estimated at 300–800 pairs, itself only around 3% of the UK population (Ogilvie in *BS3*).

Distribution and status in North-East Scotland
During 2002–06, there were confirmed breeding records in five tetrads, all but one within the Ythan catchment and most near the estuary or at Haddo House. Some of these records involve mixed pairs of Canada and Greylag Geese. All breeding birds in our area probably originate from the slowly spreading Scottish feral population, originally derived from releases and escapes from collections. It is also probable that some escaped birds from the former wildfowl collection at Culterty Field Station on the Ythan estuary have formed some of our local breeding birds (S. Anderson pers. comm.). Canada Geese have not yet bred in Moray, with very few potential breeding records. Birds from further south in the UK passing to and from the moulting area in the Beauly Firth are often seen in North-East Scotland, mainly in May and June, and very occasionally birds have moulted in our area (*NES 1st Atlas*, Cook 1992).

Changes in distribution
Comparison with the 1981–84 atlas map shows a clear increase from one to 14 occupied recording units by 2002–06. There was only one instance of probable breeding during the 1981–84 atlas period (the record was not shown in *NES 1st Atlas*), and, effectively, this species

has only recently begun breeding in North-East Scotland. Although there was suspected breeding from the mid 1990s, the first known probable breeding involved two juveniles on the Ythan estuary in 1998 with confirmed breeding in 2000 when a Canada/Greylag pair nested. In 2002, a pair of Canada Geese nested and reared six young, with two other hybrid pairs reported.

Population and trends

In Scotland, the feral breeding population is increasing (Ogilvie in *BS3*), a trend shared by North-East Scotland. Three pairs and one hybrid pair were reported in 2005; this remains the highest single year total. In addition to this slow spread of breeding and hybrid birds, there appear to be more records of Canada Geese throughout the year, not just linked to moult migration periods. It is likely that this species will continue to increase and become more widespread in North-East Scotland as it has done in most other parts of Britain.

Author: *Ian Francis*

Canada Goose, Manitoba, Canada, June 2000. © *Ed Duthie*

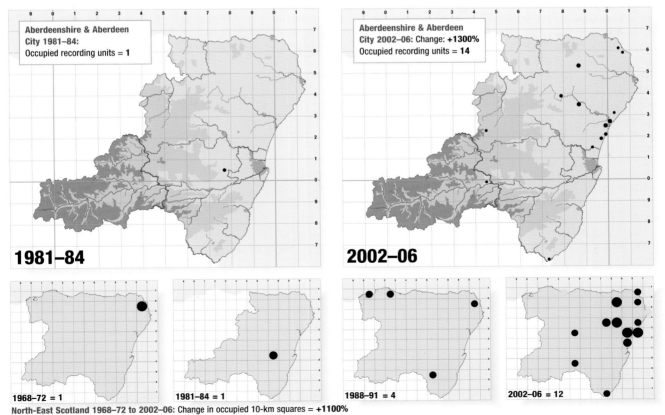

Aberdeenshire & Aberdeen City 1981–84: Occupied recording units = 1

1981–84

Aberdeenshire & Aberdeen City 2002–06: Change: +1300% Occupied recording units = 14

2002–06

1968–72 = 1

1981–84 = 1

1988–91 = 4

2002–06 = 12

North-East Scotland 1968–72 to 2002–06: Change in occupied 10-km squares = +1100%

Barnacle Goose

Branta leucopsis

Very rare feral breeder. Passage migrant and winter visitor. Estimated population in North-East Scotland:
1 pair (10% of Scottish feral population, <1% of UK)

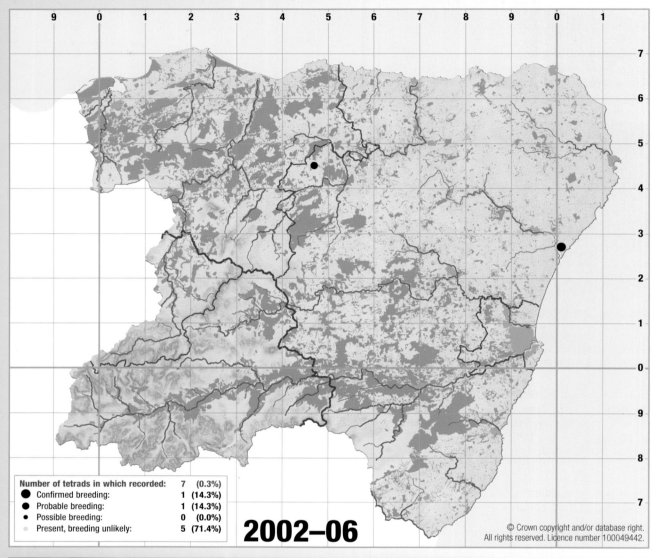

Number of tetrads in which recorded:	7	(0.3%)
● Confirmed breeding:	1	(14.3%)
● Probable breeding:	1	(14.3%)
● Possible breeding:	0	(0.0%)
Present, breeding unlikely:	5	(71.4%)

2002–06

Barnacle Goose, Skene, October 2005. © *John Young*

Barnacle Goose habitat around Culterty Field Station, Newburgh, 1994. © *Ian Francis*

Habitat and breeding biology

All summering or breeding birds in North-East Scotland probably originate from collections (with a slight possibility of injured wintering birds), so their nesting or summer habitat probably reflects this influence and few meaningful conclusions can be drawn. Areas with persistent summering or breeding (mainly near the Ythan estuary) are estuarine and riverside habitats, with some scrub and woodland amidst a mixed agricultural landscape.

Scottish distribution and status

There are several hundred feral Barnacle Geese in the UK and small numbers of free-winged feral birds are found in Scotland, some of which nest, with breeding recorded in at least eight different areas of the country (Ogilvie in *BS3*). There is no recent estimate of this population. In 2005, at least 120 breeding pairs were recorded in the UK with five in Scotland (Holling *et al.* 2007). Wintering wild birds are found mostly in north-west Scotland (Greenland population) and on the Solway Firth (Svalbard population).

Distribution and status in North-East Scotland

There were seven records during 2002–06. In Moray, one was at Tugnet (Speymouth) on 2nd June 2002, and there was an unusual record of a pair at an inland location near Keith in 2006. In Aberdeenshire, one was inland near Cullerlie in 2002, but the remaining records came from the Loch of Strathbeg (one bird summered in 2006) and from the Ythan estuary, where a pair bred successfully in 2003 and up to five birds were present during summer 2004. The source of these birds is not known, but escapees from a former wildfowl collection at Culterty Field Station on the Ythan estuary are considered unlikely (I. Patterson pers. comm.). In 2007, a pair was present in May near Ballater (Deeside), again an unusual record. Wild Barnacle Geese of Svalbard origin occur commonly as passage migrants near the coast in autumn and again in spring (as late as early June), with several hundreds regularly wintering at Loch of Strathbeg.

Changes in distribution

Occasional summering or feral birds have been noted in the area previously, such as in 1979, 1982, 1991, in 1999 at Loch of Strathbeg, the Ythan estuary and Haddo House, and in 2001 around the Ythan estuary - similar areas to those found in 2002–06. However, prior to these dates they appear to have been absent.

Population and trends

Numbers of feral Barnacle Geese in North-East Scotland are very low, with only around one pair proved to be breeding and a very small number of additional summering birds. However, this represents a change to their status 20 years ago, when they did not occur as a summering bird in Aberdeenshire in 1981–84 (*NES 1st Atlas*). There have been only three records in Moray prior to 2002, mostly thought to have been birds that originated in captivity (Cook 1992). In Scotland, numbers of breeding feral birds are probably increasing (Ogilvie in *BS3*) and in the UK there has certainly been an increase (Holling *et al.* 2007). Wintering Svalbard birds have increased in numbers at Loch of Strathbeg since the late 1990s, reflecting a general increase in this population and a greater proportion of Solway-wintering birds stopping short in North-East Scotland.

Author: *Ian Francis*

Shelduck

Tadorna tadorna

Scarce resident and migrant breeder. Estimated population in North-East Scotland: *125 pairs* (7% of Scottish population, 1% of UK)

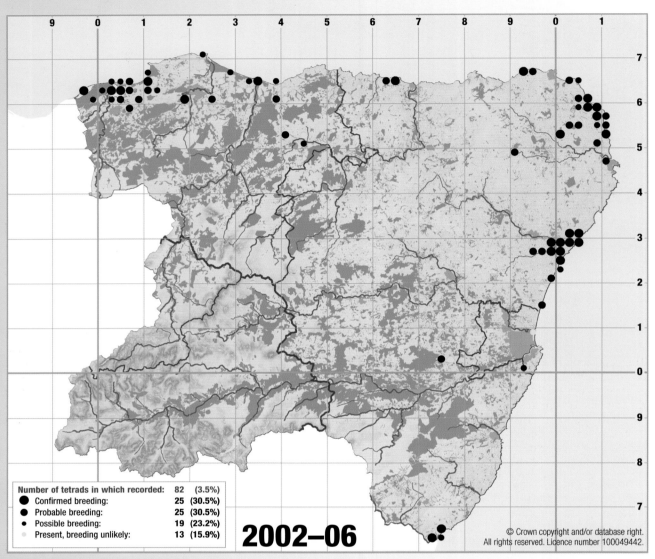

Number of tetrads in which recorded:	82	(3.5%)
● Confirmed breeding:	25	(30.5%)
● Probable breeding:	25	(30.5%)
• Possible breeding:	19	(23.2%)
Present, breeding unlikely:	13	(15.9%)

2002–06

Habitat and breeding biology
Shelducks are found primarily on estuaries and muddy shores, with some on freshwater bodies, mainly near the coast but occasionally up to 20 km inland. They commonly nest in sand dunes near feeding areas, with nests usually in disused Rabbit burrows. Inland breeders nest in banks and other uncultivated areas in farmland, usually in holes and cavities, sometimes in bale stacks and farm buildings. First eggs are laid in mid to late April, with ducklings emerging from mid May and fledging in late July.

Scottish distribution and status
Shelducks are common and widespread throughout Scotland, wherever there are estuaries and muddy shores, but the species is absent from rocky and cliff-bound coastlines. The Scottish population is estimated to be 1,750 breeding pairs (Patterson in *BS3*). Most of these birds leave on moult migration to the Helgoland Bight on the north-west German coast in July, leaving behind those rearing ducklings and those using a major moulting area in the Firth of Forth. During the return migration in autumn and winter, there are large concentrations in the Forth and Solway, with smaller numbers in the Montrose Basin and Eden estuary, before the birds disperse to their breeding areas.

Distribution and status in North-East Scotland
Although Shelducks can be found in North-East Scotland throughout the year, the species is best regarded as a migrant, since most of the population leaves on moult migration in July. There are very few in the region between September and November, with the birds returning gradually to breeding areas between December and March. The whole population is present only from April to June, with a peak usually in May (Patterson 1982). In the breeding season, Shelducks in the North-East are concentrated where there are muddy shores and sand dune systems, notably around the Ythan estuary, the Loch of Strathbeg and the western part of the Moray coast. There are smaller groupings at St Cyrus, near Banff and around Findhorn, with scattered occurrences inland, chiefly near the main coastal concentrations. The species is absent from the rocky and cliff coastlines in the region; south of Aberdeen, south of Peterhead and parts of the north coast.

Changes in distribution
The distribution of Shelducks in the North-East has changed very little in the last 25 years, probably because it is constrained by the availability of suitable habitats. There was some limited extension of range between 1981–84 and

Shelduck, Balcomie, June 2008. © *John Anderson*

2002–06, mainly by expansion outwards from the main concentrations and more inland occurrences.

Population and trends

The population of Shelducks in North-East Scotland in the breeding season (April to June) was estimated by taking, for each year from 1999 to 2006, the highest monthly total for the combined main sites in Moray (*MNBR*s) and for the Loch of Strathbeg and Ythan estuary combined (*NESBR*s), including in both cases any birds recorded elsewhere in the county during the same months. The overall mean total over the eight years was 129 birds for the Moray sites and 235 for the Loch of Strathbeg and Ythan estuary, giving a combined total of 364 birds at the main sites. This is likely to be an underestimate, since incubating females and scattered pairs breeding away from the main sites would be less likely to be counted. It is difficult to gauge the degree of underestimation, but the total spring population is likely to be around 500 birds. The total population has remained fairly stable, with the combined total at the main sites fluctuating between 328 (1999) and 400 (2003–05). If it is assumed that around half of the birds are territorial breeding adults (Patterson in *BS3*), then the breeding population in North-East Scotland can be estimated as 125 pairs.

Author: *Ian Patterson*

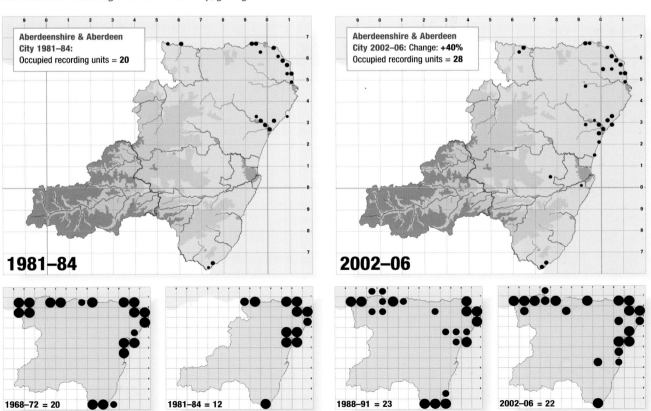

North-East Scotland 1968–72 to 2002–06: Change in occupied 10-km squares = **+10%**

Mandarin Duck *Aix galericulata*

Very rare feral resident. Estimated population in North-East Scotland: Up to **5 pairs** (10% of Scottish population, <1% of UK)

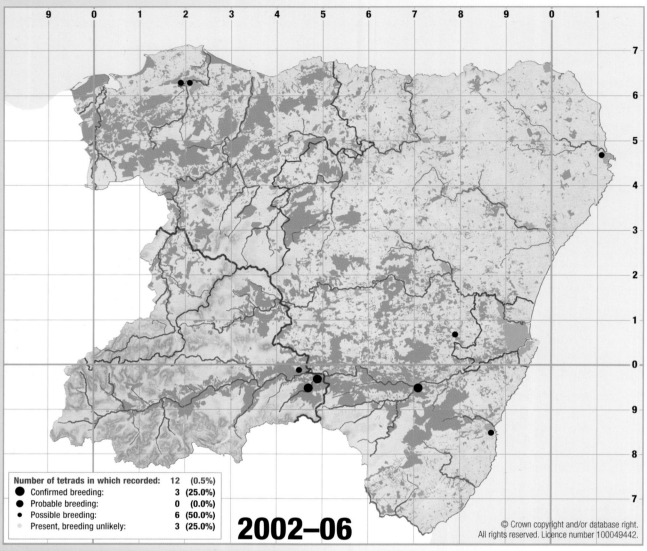

Number of tetrads in which recorded: 12 (0.5%)
- ● Confirmed breeding: 3 (25.0%)
- ● Probable breeding: 0 (0.0%)
- • Possible breeding: 6 (50.0%)
- Present, breeding unlikely: 3 (25.0%)

2002–06

Mandarin Duck, Glen Tanar, May 2006. © *Harry Scott*

Habitat and breeding biology

Mandarins are hole-nesting ducks that favour slow-flowing inland rivers and open fresh water in the vicinity of deciduous woodland, where they readily take to nest boxes. Eggs are laid during mid April. In a study around Loch Eck (Argyll), it was found that clutches in 12 nests ranged from 7–22 eggs (average 11.5) and larger clutches were accounted for by a second female 'dumping' eggs in the nests of other pairs (Anderson & Petty 1996). Duckling survival is difficult to monitor due to their very elusive nature once they leave the nest.

Scottish distribution and status

The Mandarin is a scarce but widespread alien introduced species that has colonised various regions of Scotland since the early 1960s. It is likely that the whole Scottish population has originated from captive sources. Scotland's first breeding population established itself around Perth from locally released birds. Having built up to an estimated 20 pairs it declined rapidly in the late 1980s. During the 1990s, three more populations developed, at Loch Eck (Argyll), Strathnairn (Inverness) and Eye Water (Borders) with 20, 15 and 10 pairs respectively (Jardine in *BS3*). A further five regions have recently recorded breeding pairs

The Breeding Birds of North-East Scotland

and the current breeding population in Scotland is now estimated to be around 50 pairs.

Distribution and status in North-East Scotland

The first record of a Mandarin in North-East Scotland was of a single male on the estuary of the River Don in April 1976 (*NESBR* 1976). Subsequent sightings have involved small numbers of one to three individuals, predominantly in spring, from a selection of regular sites until 2000. Since then, records have been increasing, with the region's highest count being a group of up to nine drakes on the River Lossie (Elgin) in November 2005. In April 1989, the region's first Mandarin nest was found in a Goosander nest box adjacent to a River Dee tributary near Ballater (M. Marquiss pers. comm.). Breeding was not confirmed again in North-East Scotland until 2002, and in 2003 a female was seen with five fledged young in Glen Tanar. The only other suspected nest site may be near the Feugh mouth, on the River Dee near Banchory. A local ghillie reported seeing a brood here in 2005 and again in 2006, when five ducklings with a female were seen on 30th June. No nest has been located in this area, suggesting that the brood may have travelled down river from the natal area. The local population appears to be resident but some birds disperse throughout North-East Scotland, only returning to breeding grounds in early March (pers. obs.).

Changes in distribution

Following the first record in 1976, in addition to the 1989 breeding attempt, there were only three further records by 1990 - a male at Banchory-Devenick in November–December 1981, a pair near Kintore in April 1984 and an eclipse male at Davan in June 1988 (*NES 1st Atlas*). Subsequently, since 1990, sightings of one to two individuals have become almost annual from a wide variety of inland rivers and lochs. The most regular source of records between 1990–95 was from around the River Deveron, from Bridge of Alvah north to the coast at Banff.

Since then, records from early spring and summer have predominantly originated from areas adjacent to the River Don near Inverurie and the River Dee from Girdle Ness west to Dinnet, where small numbers have bred.

Populations and trends

A small breeding colony, involving a minimum of seven adults (three males and four females), could be accounted for in 2005 when three females bred in Glen Tanar. During 2006, four nests were found in the area and there were five in 2007. However, three of the 2007 nests appeared to have been predated and only one of the remaining clutches hatched successfully. Another poor season followed; just one female was seen in mid Deeside during 2008, incubating a clutch which subsequently proved to be infertile. During this period, 2005–08, six breeding females were ringed but only three have been re-sighted; one was shot at Birse four months after ringing, the other two were re-caught on nests close to their ringing sites during the following year.

Author: *Harry Scott*

Mandarin Duck, Glen Tanar, May 2006. © *Harry Scott*

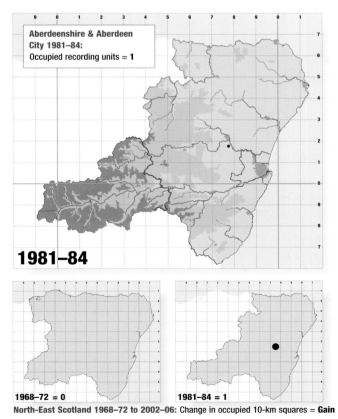

Aberdeenshire & Aberdeen City 1981–84:
Occupied recording units = 1

1981–84

1968–72 = 0

1981–84 = 1

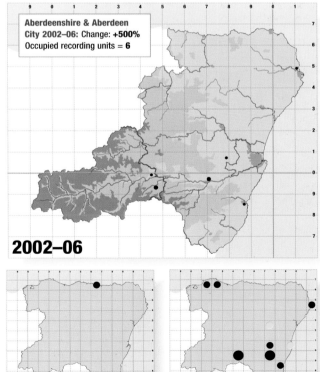

Aberdeenshire & Aberdeen City 2002–06: Change: **+500%**
Occupied recording units = **6**

2002–06

1988–91 = 1

2002–06 = 7

North-East Scotland 1968–72 to 2002–06: Change in occupied 10-km squares = **Gain**

Wigeon
Anas penelope

Rare breeder. Winter visitor and passage migrant. Estimated population in North-East Scotland: *25–50 pairs* (12% of Scottish population, 10% of UK)

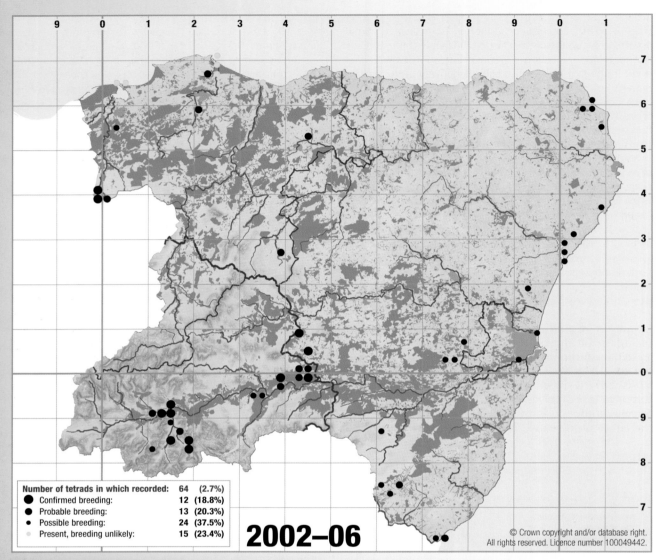

Number of tetrads in which recorded:	64	(2.7%)
● Confirmed breeding:	12	(18.8%)
● Probable breeding:	13	(20.3%)
• Possible breeding:	24	(37.5%)
○ Present, breeding unlikely:	15	(23.4%)

2002–06

Wigeon, Glen Clunie, June 1991. © *Stuart Rae*

Habitat and breeding biology

Wigeon are chiefly upland breeders in North-East Scotland. They nest on the ground, often close to water such as along the shores of lochs and pools, on islands and in marsh land. Nesting habitat around the Dinnet lochs consists of scattered birch wood and Heather moorland while in Glen Clunie they nest in Heather near to ditches and the river. Nests are usually well hidden and are lined with down and some vegetation. At Glen Clunie, birds arrive from mid March into April; adult females and ducklings were found to return to breed at the same site in subsequent summers (pers. obs.). First egg-laying takes place around the end of April and, after hatching, the female leads her brood to a safe area of water. They fledge after 40–45 days (Mitchell in *BS3*). Males leave the breeding area in June, followed by females and fledged young in August.

Scottish distribution and status

Wigeon were first recorded breeding in Scotland, in Sutherland, in 1834 and there followed a period of expansion up to the mid 20th century. They now breed in scattered localities in many upland parts of the mainland as well as in the Uists and the Northern Isles, with concentrations in Perth & Kinross, Caithness and Orkney. The

The Breeding Birds of North-East Scotland

Scottish population was recently estimated at 240–400 pairs (Mitchell in *BS3*).

Distribution and status in North-East Scotland

Since colonisation, Wigeon have always been scarce and localised breeders. In 2002–06 the distribution was focussed on three areas, mid Deeside, upper Deeside and Dava. In mid Deeside, the population is centred around the Dinnet lochs - Davan and Kinord. In upper Deeside, breeding Wigeon were found in the Dee valley close to Braemar and in the nearby glens - Clunie and Callater. At Dava, a few pairs breed around small lochans scattered over 5 km^2 of moorland.

Changes in distribution

Wigeon were breeding in Moray prior to 1900 (Baxter & Rintoul 1922) but breeding had still not been recorded in Aberdeenshire by 1940 (Mitchell in *BS3*). In 1968–72, Wigeon were confirmed to be breeding in 14 10-km squares in the North-East, including Deeside and Dava, but also in coastal areas such as Loch of Strathbeg, Forvie, Loch Spynie and Culbin (*BTO 1st Atlas*). In 1981–84, breeding was proved only in Deeside and at nearby Tillypronie, although it was considered probable in seven other recording units in Aberdeenshire including Loch of Strathbeg (*NES 1st Atlas*). In 1988–91, proof of breeding was obtained in Dava (where the small area of occupied breeding habitat is situated at the intersection of four 10-km squares) and Deeside, but also in south Kincardine and, on the coast, at Forvie. Although the distribution of occupied recording units where breeding was proved in Aberdeenshire/Aberdeen City between 1981–84 and 2002–06 is similar, the number of such units has risen substantially. There are also many more occupied recording units near to the east coast, but breeding was no more than possible in most of these areas, and in some cases late migrant birds may have been involved.

Wigeon, Dava, June 2008. © *Martin Cook*

Population and trends

Wigeon is a difficult species to census accurately and no detailed count of breeding pairs has been attempted in the North-East. We can do little more than propose that 1–2 pairs bred in each of the 25 tetrads where breeding was confirmed or probable in 2002–06 - suggesting a total population of 25–50 pairs. This is likely to be a smaller population than in the 1980s and early 1990s, when estimates included 15–30 pairs centred on the Dinnet lochs in 1981–84 (*NES 1st Atlas*), 25 pairs in the Braemar/Glen Callater/Glen Clunie area of upper Deeside in 1989–94 (pers. obs.) and *c.*10 pairs in Moray in the 1980s (M. Cook pers. comm.).

Author: *Judy Duncan*

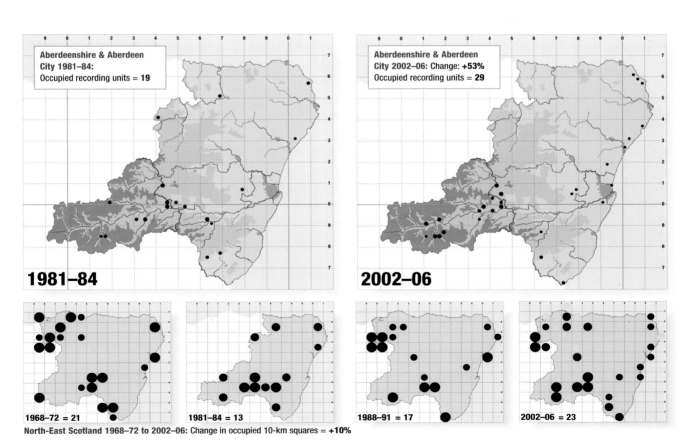

Aberdeenshire & Aberdeen City 1981–84: Occupied recording units = **19**

1981–84

Aberdeenshire & Aberdeen City 2002–06: Change: **+53%** Occupied recording units = **29**

2002–06

1968–72 = 21   1981–84 = 13   1988–91 = 17   2002–06 = 23

North-East Scotland 1968–72 to 2002–06: Change in occupied 10-km squares = +10%

Gadwall

Anas strepera

Very rare breeder. Visitor at all seasons. Estimated population in North-East Scotland: **0–5 pairs** (2% of Scottish population, <1% of UK)

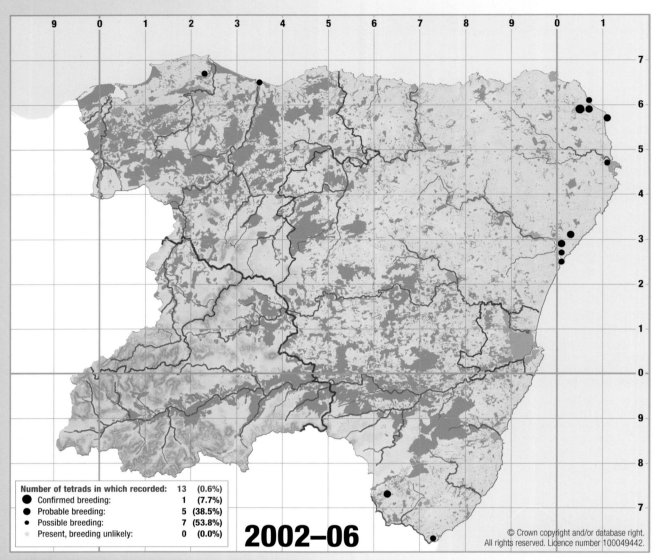

Number of tetrads in which recorded:	13	(0.6%)
● Confirmed breeding:	1	(7.7%)
● Probable breeding:	5	(38.5%)
● Possible breeding:	7	(53.8%)
● Present, breeding unlikely:	0	(0.0%)

2002–06

Gadwall, Morton Loch, Fife, February 2008. © *John Anderson*

Habitat and breeding biology

Gadwall are secretive breeders occupying lowland, nutrient-rich wetlands with an abundance of aquatic vegetation. In North-East Scotland, most breeding season records are from regularly occupied sites close to the coast, and especially from two large wetland complexes in the east of the region. Both these sites hold spring passage birds from which breeding pairs are likely to be derived. The only broods seen during 2002–06 were in an area containing a mosaic of shallow freshwater pools and marshy grassland.

Scottish distribution and status

The first confirmed breeding record of Gadwall in Scotland was at Loch Leven (Perth & Kinross) in 1909, possibly originating from escapes from captivity (Fox in *BS3*). Since then the species has colonised many parts of mainland Scotland and the islands though it remains rather localised. Core breeding areas are Fife, south-east Perth & Kinross, south Angus and Orkney. The Scottish breeding population is estimated at 100–150 pairs with the largest number being on Loch Leven (Fox in *BS3*).

Gadwall, Suffolk, January 2011. © *Bryan Wright*

Distribution in North-East Scotland

Gadwall are most numerous in North-East Scotland during spring passage when peak numbers are generally noted in early or mid May. Only a small number of birds appear to remain during the summer although the secretive nature of the species during the breeding season may mean that some are overlooked. Fewer birds are recorded on autumn passage than in spring, though over a more protracted period, and small numbers appear to overwinter. Three sites account for the majority of records. The highest count during the atlas period was of 14 birds at Loch of Strathbeg on 8th May 2005 (*NESBR* 2005). Regular records also come from around the Ythan estuary and from Loch Spynie. Most summer records also come from Loch of Strathbeg and the Ythan estuary; the only confirmed instances of breeding in North-East Scotland were at these sites. Gadwall have never bred in Moray (or in Nairn) (*contra* Fox in *BS3*).

Changes in distribution

Breeding records are always hard to confirm and usually rely on young being seen. Differentiating spring passage birds from breeding birds is a matter of judgement with many records of probable breeding being likely to refer to migrants in apparently suitable breeding locations.

Nonetheless the embryonic breeding population appears to mirror closely the distribution of favoured passage locations, although there are as yet no confirmed breeding records from Loch Spynie. However, a record of probable breeding at an inland site in the south of the region hints at the possibility of there being undiscovered pairs at other less well-watched locations.

Population and trends

The Gadwall is a recent addition to the breeding birds of North-East Scotland. Whilst there had been a number of breeding season records, including a pair displaying in mid June 1999 at Loch Spynie (*MNBR* 1999), the first confirmed breeding record did not come until 2001 when two adults were seen with three young on the Ythan estuary (*NESBR* 2001). The only confirmed breeding during 2002–06 was in the final year when three separate broods were noted at Loch of Strathbeg. Although it is thought that some ducklings were predated by an Otter, a minimum of six young fledged (D. Funnell pers. comm.). Whilst some breeding attempts may go undiscovered the breeding population is unlikely to have exceeded five pairs during 2002–06.

Author: *Nick Littlewood*

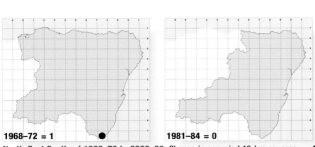
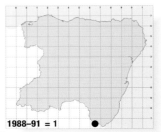
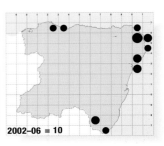

North-East Scotland 1968–72 to 2002–06: Change in occupied 10-km squares = **+900%**

Teal

Anas crecca

Scarce breeder. Winter visitor and passage migrant. Estimated population in North-East Scotland: *150–200 pairs* (7% of Scottish population, 4% of UK)

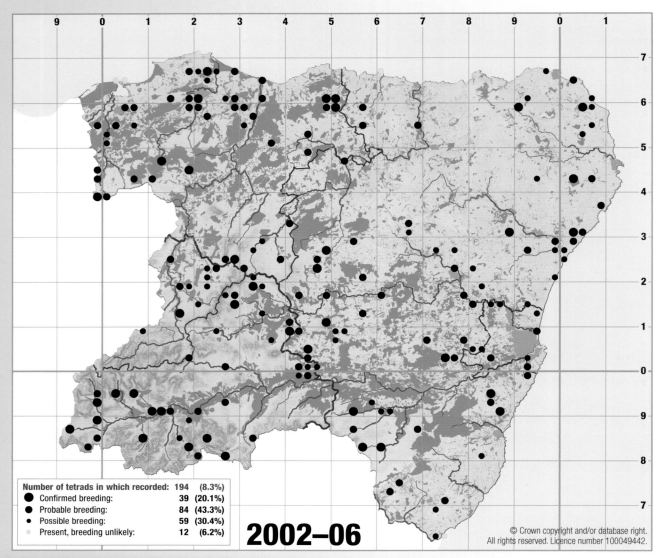

Number of tetrads in which recorded:	194	(8.3%)
● Confirmed breeding:	39	(20.1%)
● Probable breeding:	84	(43.3%)
● Possible breeding:	59	(30.4%)
Present, breeding unlikely:	12	(6.2%)

2002–06

Teal, Baads Moss, 1975. © *Graham Rebecca*

Habitat and breeding biology

Teal breed in a variety of freshwater habitats wherever there is suitable cover, including freshwater marshes, small pools, river margins and large water bodies. In Scotland, oligotrophic lochs are favoured and so peatlands in upland Scotland are the breeding stronghold. In lowland areas, eutrophic waters are used, but these areas are less favoured, with lower densities than in upland areas. They usually nest within 5–10 m of the water's edge, but can occasionally be over 100 m from open water, often in wet flushes. Nesting is usually solitary, typically in dense vegetation. The clutch of 8–11 eggs takes approximately three weeks to incubate and the first broods hatch from early June, with fledging taking place after about a month.

Scottish distribution and status

Teal are thinly but widely distributed across much of the Scottish mainland where suitable habitat exists. They also breed on the Outer Hebrides, some of the Inner Hebridean islands and in the Northern Isles. Birds are limited to wetland areas, with peak densities in Orkney, the Flow Country margins, the fens of Strathspey, Islay and the Uists - all areas characterised by peat based mires with well vegetated pool networks. Teal typically arrive on breeding territories throughout March and April, and males normally depart by mid July to congregate in moulting areas, with females and juveniles following after. The Scottish population is estimated at 1,950–3,450 pairs (Lauder in *BS3*).

Distribution and status in North-East Scotland

Teal are thinly but widely spread across North-East Scotland, breeding beside lowland lochs and ponds as well as upland pools in moorland areas. Breeding was confirmed over a wide range of altitudes from near sea level to about 800 m near Lochnagar. As might be expected, few Teal are to be found on the highly agricultural Buchan plain, with most records around Loch of Strathbeg and the Ythan/Forvie area. The marshes, pools and gravel workings of lowland Moray appear better populated although confirmation of breeding was not often obtained and it is likely that birds at some of these sites were summering non-breeders.

Changes in distribution

There is little evidence of any change in distribution since 1968–72, with the apparent retraction of range in 1988–91 more likely to be due to reduced observer coverage than to a genuine scarcity. This is supported by the Aberdeenshire/Aberdeen City maps where little change in the number of occupied recording units is evident. It would appear, however, that since 1981–84 Teal have become more widespread in lowland northern Aberdeenshire, where 42 recording units were occupied to the north of the River Don in 2002–06, compared with only 27 during 1981–84, a 56% increase.

Population and trends

During 2002–06, Teal were thought to be at least possibly breeding in 182 tetrads, and were probably or certainly doing so in 123 of these. If we assume one breeding pair in half of the tetrads in the 'possible' category, one pair in each of the 'probable' category tetrads, and 1–2 pairs where breeding was confirmed, then a total of 153–192 breeding

pairs of Teal in North-East Scotland can be estimated. Clearly, however, no claim of great accuracy can be attached to this estimate. Few breeding records are submitted to annual bird reports and the increased number during 2002–06 can be attributed to fieldworkers recording in areas which are not usually visited. This variable level of coverage makes it impossible to detect changes in population size over the short to medium term.

Author: *Andy Jensen*

Teal, Tillypronie, May 2005. © *Harry Scott*

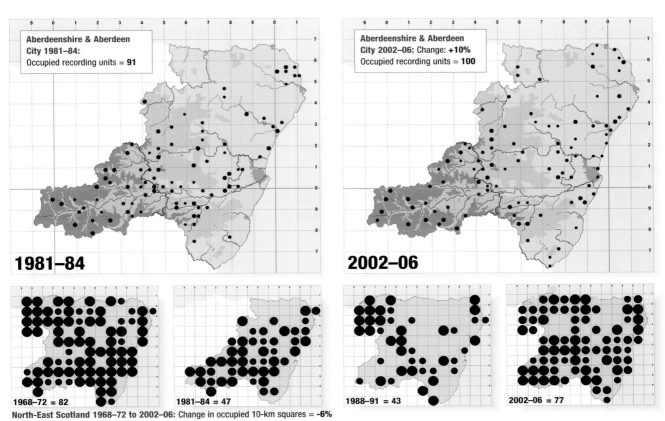

Aberdeenshire & Aberdeen City 1981–84:
Occupied recording units = **91**

1981–84

Aberdeenshire & Aberdeen City 2002–06: Change: **+10%**
Occupied recording units = **100**

2002–06

1968–72 = 82   1981–84 = 47   1988–91 = 43   2002–06 = 77

North-East Scotland 1968–72 to 2002–06: Change in occupied 10-km squares = -6%

Green-winged Teal

Anas carolinensis

Occasional in breeding habitat. Rare visitor, mostly in winter. Estimated population in North-East Scotland: usually *0 pairs*

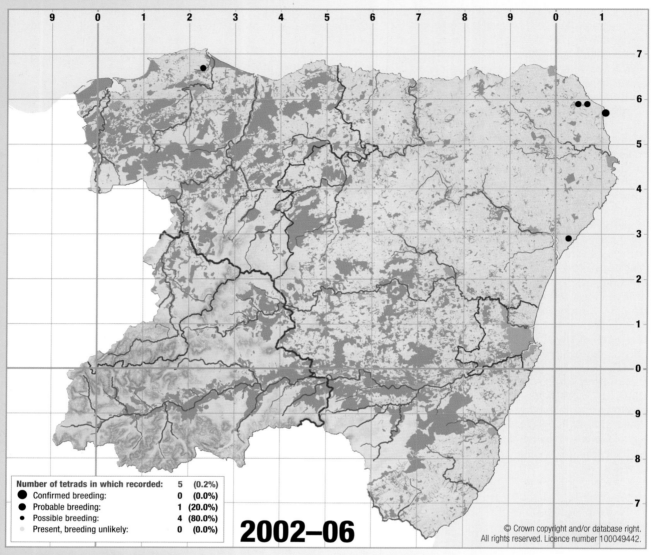

Number of tetrads in which recorded: 5 (0.2%)
- ● Confirmed breeding: 0 (0.0%)
- ● Probable breeding: 1 (20.0%)
- • Possible breeding: 4 (80.0%)
- Present, breeding unlikely: 0 (0.0%)

2002–06

Habitat and breeding biology

The Green-winged Teal is the North American counterpart of our familiar Eurasian Teal. It occupies a similar range of freshwater habitats and may visit coastal marshes and estuaries (Pennington in *BS3*).

Scottish distribution and status

Formerly a very rare winter visitor to Scotland, with only five records during 1950–1965, the Green-winged Teal has occurred much more frequently since the late 1980s and there were over 200 records by 2004. They are seen most frequently in the Western and Northern Isles, with over 30 records each, but also occur widely on the mainland where eight SOC recording areas have 10–19 records. All records, until 2004 at least, were of adult males - females and immatures being almost inseparable from Eurasian Teal. There have been a few sightings of hybrid Green-winged x Eurasian males, mostly in North-East Scotland (Pennington in *BS3*).

Distribution and status in North-East Scotland

The first Green-winged Teal in the North-East was found at Forvie in 1957, and there were around a further 40 records up to the end of 2008 (Phillips 1997, *NESBRs*, *MNBRs*). The

exact number of birds is difficult to determine, due to moving and returning individuals. The majority of birds are seen between October and April but there have been six May records and four in June. During the 2002–06 Atlas period there were five early summer records. Four of these were of single males; at Loch Spynie on 1st–2nd June 2002 (*MNBR* 2002), at Loch of Strathbeg on 10th May 2003 and 18th June 2006, and at Cotehill Loch on 25th–27th May 2006 (presumably this bird moved to Loch of Strathbeg) (*NESBR* 2003, 2006). Of greater significance, perhaps, was a male paired to a female teal at Rattray on 12th May 2002 (*NESBR* 2002). It was not possible to assign the female bird to species level and a mixed pairing between Green-winged and Eurasian Teals is possible. Indeed, suspected hybrids have been seen at Loch of Strathbeg in February 1994, March and December 1995, May 1996 (and at Donmouth in January 1996), January 1997 and February 2000 (*NESBRs*), although there is no indication that these were reared locally.

Author: *Martin Cook*

See photograph on page 123.

St. Cyrus

St. Cyrus National Nature Reserve holds a range of coastal, grassland and cliff habitats and is a northern outlier for many southern species of plant and invertebrate. Once holding a large colony of Little Terns, now almost entirely gone, the area still holds a diverse breeding bird community including Mute Swan, Shelduck, Grey Partridge, Buzzard, Oystercatcher, Herring Gull, Cuckoo, Kingfisher, Stonechat, Sedge Warbler, Whitethroat and Reed Bunting. Peregrines nest close by and can often be seen here. August 2003.
© *Harry Scott*

Mallard   *Anas platyrhynchos*

Common resident. Winter visitor. Estimated population in North-East Scotland: **2,350–2,850 pairs** (9% of Scottish population, 3% of UK)

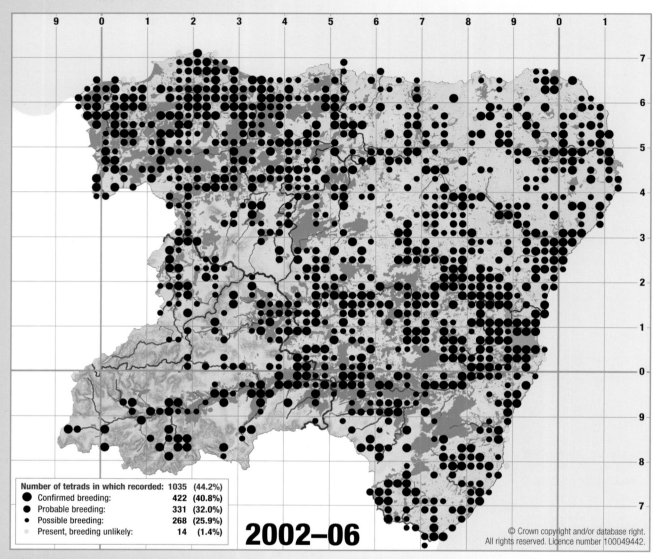

Number of tetrads in which recorded:	1035	(44.2%)
● Confirmed breeding:	422	(40.8%)
● Probable breeding:	331	(32.0%)
● Possible breeding:	268	(25.9%)
● Present, breeding unlikely:	14	(1.4%)

2002–06

Habitat and breeding biology

The Mallard is the most widespread breeding duck species in North-East Scotland. Freshwater bodies of any size are utilised including lochs, ponds, rivers and even very small burns. Most breeding records are from the lowlands although some pairs nest on Heather moorland (*NES 1st Atlas*) and the species has been recorded at over 800 m altitude in the breeding season (Lauder & Ogilvie in *BS3*). Nests are typically situated on the ground in tall vegetation close to water; April and early May see the peak number of incubating females (Lauder & Ogilvie in *BS3*). While nests are often not difficult to find, most confirmed breeding records come from sightings of small ducklings.

Mallard, Loch Kinord, May 2006. © *Harry Scott*

Scottish distribution and status

Breeding Mallards can be found almost anywhere in Scotland. Only in the most mountainous areas of northern Scotland is the species scarce or absent. Mallards are most abundant in southern and central mainland Scotland with high densities also in parts of the Hebrides and Orkney. The Scottish population is estimated at between 17,000 and 43,000 pairs (Lauder & Ogilvie in *BS3*).

Distribution in North-East Scotland

Wetlands throughout most of North-East Scotland support breeding Mallards. The most continuously occupied areas include the middle and lower parts of the rivers Dee, Don and Ythan as well as the lower Findhorn and Spey and their tributaries. However there are gaps in the distribution. The species is absent from much of the mountainous area in the south-west of the region, though it has been recorded breeding here up to 500 m altitude, and is also sparsely distributed across the intense arable areas of the Buchan plain and in densely forested regions such as Fetteresso and Clashindarroch. The population is augmented by releases of captive-raised birds for shooting which can mingle with local breeding birds. Some of these releases can be very substantial in number, *e.g.* 5,000 birds on Auchmacoy

Estate in the east of the region in 2007 (A. Drysdale pers. comm.), and have the potential to distort significantly the distribution picture of this species.

Changes in distribution

There is some evidence of a recent increase in areas occupied by Mallards. In Aberdeenshire/Aberdeen City, 263 occupied recording units in 1981–84 (*NES 1st Atlas*) increased to 313 occupied recording units in 2002–06, with much of this increase being in the Buchan plain. During 1988–91 there were seven, scattered, 10-km squares wholly or largely within the region covered by this atlas for which there were no breeding-related records (*BTO 2nd Atlas*). Breeding was confirmed in all of these during 2002–06.

Population and trends

This abundant species is difficult to census accurately due to its use of a wide variety of sites including very small burns and drainage ditches. This is evidenced by the very wide numeric range given for the Scottish population estimate. However, using estimated densities given by Lauder & Ogilvie (in *BS3*) of 40–50 pairs/10-km square in lowland areas, and 10 pairs/10-km square in upland areas, a North-East Scotland population estimate would be 2,350–2,850 pairs. There is no evidence of any recent change in breeding numbers although large releases of captive-bred birds may cause at least localised fluctuations.

Author: *Nick Littlewood*

Mallard, Ballater, June 2008. © *Harry Scott*

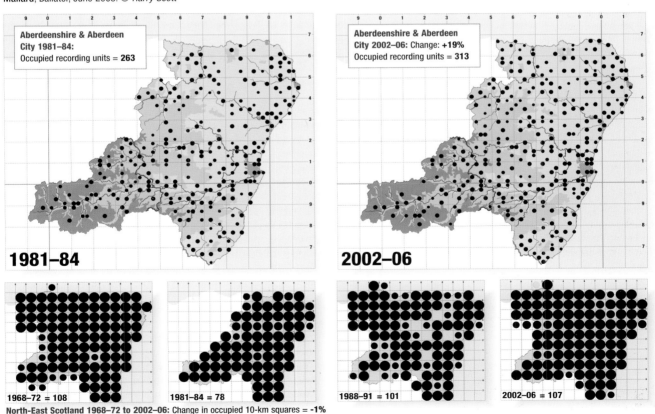

1981–84

Aberdeenshire & Aberdeen City 1981–84: Occupied recording units = **263**

2002–06

Aberdeenshire & Aberdeen City 2002–06: Change: **+19%** Occupied recording units = **313**

1968–72 = 108

1981–84 = 78

1988–91 = 101

2002–06 = 107

North-East Scotland 1968–72 to 2002–06: Change in occupied 10-km squares = **-1%**

Pintail

Anas acuta

Occasional breeder. Winter visitor and passage migrant. Estimated population in North-East Scotland: usually **0 pairs**

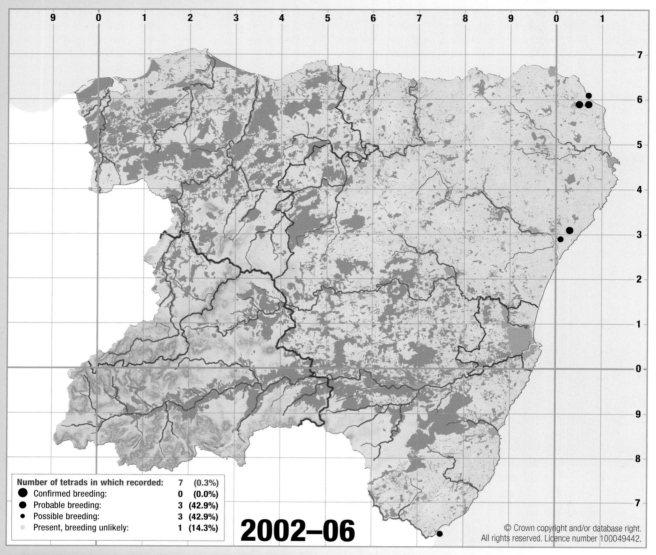

Number of tetrads in which recorded:	7	(0.3%)
● Confirmed breeding:	0	(0.0%)
● Probable breeding:	3	(42.9%)
• Possible breeding:	3	(42.9%)
○ Present, breeding unlikely:	1	(14.3%)

2002–06

Pintail, Finnmark, June 2005. © Ian Francis

Habitat and breeding biology

Lowland nutrient-rich freshwater lochs are favoured in the breeding season. One key site for this species in North-East Scotland, Loch of Strathbeg, contains a complex of shallow pools set within a mosaic of marshy grassland. The other main area, around the Ythan estuary, has a small number of more isolated ponds and small lochs within a lowland area of mixed land-uses.

Scottish distribution and status

The Pintail is a relatively recent colonist with breeding in Scotland first proved at Loch Knockie (Inverness) in 1869 (Meek in *BS3*). Since then, breeding has occurred sporadically in many parts of mainland Scotland and the islands but by the start of the 21st century the majority of nesting pairs were on Orkney. The Scottish breeding population is estimated to be 20–25 pairs (Meek in *BS3*).

Distribution in North-East Scotland

Two main areas hold most breeding season records of this species in North-East Scotland. Loch of Strathbeg regularly hosts the most significant wintering numbers of continental and Icelandic-breeding Pintail and breeding has occurred here in the past (*BTO 1st Atlas*) but, although pairs were

Pintail, Fife, February 2007. © *John Anderson*

Changes in distribution

Breeding evidence has been recorded at just a handful of sites in North-East Scotland. Loch Spynie held breeding birds before 1914 and possibly later. The species bred at an inland site in southern Aberdeenshire in the 1930s and a female with ducklings was seen on a Dava lochan in 1970 (Berry 1939, Cook 1992). In 1968–72 breeding was confirmed in two 10-km squares in the vicinities of Loch of Strathbeg and the Ythan estuary (*BTO 1st Atlas*) but there was no recorded presence during 1988–91 (*BTO 2nd Atlas*). Although there are no recent confirmed breeding records these last two core areas still account for most breeding season records.

Population and trends

The Pintail has never been other than a very rare breeding bird in North-East Scotland. However it is evident that this tiny breeding population may have dwindled to extinction. Birds were noted copulating at Loch of Strathbeg in 2000 (D. Funnell pers. comm.) but no breeding-related activity has been noted since then although failed nesting attempts may easily go unnoticed due to the secretive nature of the species at this time of year. However, as the core sites are relatively well watched, successful breeding is less likely to be missed. Taken together with the virtual absence of summering birds elsewhere it must be assumed that this species has now effectively disappeared as a breeding bird in the region.

Author: *Nick Littlewood*

seen, there was no confirmed breeding during 2002–06. Records in the Ythan estuary area may refer to passage birds, although a number of apparently suitable lochs and pools are frequented by other breeding dabbling ducks and could conceivably support breeding attempts by Pintail. With the exception of presumed late spring passage birds, the species is very rarely recorded elsewhere in the region during the breeding season.

Pintail, Fife, September 2007. © *John Anderson*

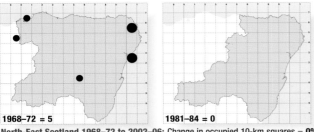

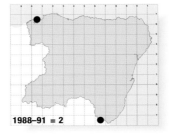

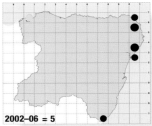

1968–72 = 5   **1981–84 = 0**   **1988–91 = 2**   **2002–06 = 5**

North-East Scotland 1968–72 to 2002–06: Change in occupied 10-km squares = 0%

Garganey

Anas querquedula

Occasional summer migrant breeder. Passage migrant. Estimated population in North-East Scotland: usually **0–2 pairs** (0–50% of Scottish population, 0–2% of UK)   Schedule 1; Scottish BAP list

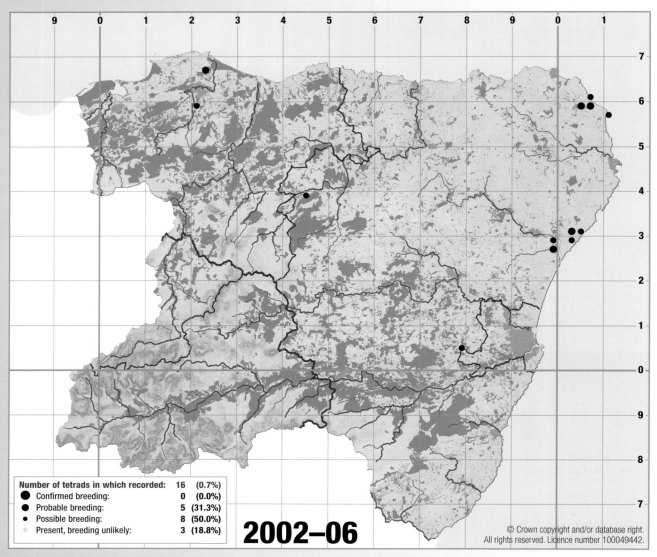

Number of tetrads in which recorded: 16   (0.7%)
● Confirmed breeding: 0   (0.0%)
● Probable breeding: 5   (31.3%)
● Possible breeding: 8   (50.0%)
  Present, breeding unlikely: 3   (18.8%)

2002–06

Habitat and breeding biology

Garganey are freshwater ducks, preferring discrete, well-vegetated pools often near the coast. They are early spring visitors to Scotland; a few arrive in the last few days in March, although the main passage is in April and May. Breeding attempts have been suspected several times in Scotland and this was first proved in North-East Scotland in 1990 when a nest was found at the Loch of Strathbeg RSPB reserve. The nest was in a patch of Soft Rush fairly well concealed in Yorkshire Fog and was 750 m from the pools where the female fed and preened in the early morning. Unfortunately the attempt was unsuccessful (Christer 1991).

Scottish distribution and status

In Scotland, Garganey are widespread but scarce spring passage migrants. Most favoured areas are Clyde, Lothian, North-East Scotland, the Northern Isles and the Outer Hebrides (Andrews in *BS3*). A few are recorded annually in the autumn. Some stay through the summer but breeding was only proved twice prior to 1990. Since then, however, breeding has been almost annual in locations widespread through Scotland, but the population in any one year is unlikely to exceed 1–2 pairs (Andrews in *BS3*).

Distribution and status in North-East Scotland

Garganey are predominantly scarce spring migrants, appearing annually in North-East Scotland. During 2002–06 most records came from Loch of Strathbeg, Slains, Meikle Loch, the Ythan estuary and Loch Spynie. Annual spring totals during this period ranged between four in 2005 and 15 in 2002. Breeding was not confirmed during 2002–06 although in 2005 six birds were seen at Loch of Strathbeg on 21st August, and a juvenile on 29th August, suggesting that breeding may have taken place (*NESBR* 2005). Garganey were also seen at Loch of Strathbeg in July in 2004 and 2006, well beyond the normal spring passage period. More recently, in 2008, a nest and two broods of young were seen there (*NESBR* 2008, D. Funnell pers. comm.).

Changes in distribution

The spring passage of Garganey has increased in Scotland in recent years. Furthermore, there has been an increased tendency for birds to stay longer and in larger groups. The first confirmed breeding in Scotland was as long ago as 1928 but recently there has been an increase in possible, probable and confirmed breeding attempts throughout Scotland. During 1968–72 there were no records of Garganey in North-East Scotland (*BTO 1st Atlas*) but by

The Breeding Birds of North-East Scotland

1975–84 they were almost annual (*NES 1st Atlas*) and, as today, most records came from the Strathbeg and Slains areas. The sole breeding records remain those at Loch of Strathbeg in 1990 (Christer 1991) and 2008 (*NESBR* 2008).

Population and trends
During 2002–06, Garganey were recorded as probable breeders at five sites and as possible breeders at eight. The probable breeding records related to pairs of birds in suitable habitat. Garganey are best considered as increasing

scarce migrants to North-East Scotland and rare, less than annual, breeders with a usual population of 0–2 pairs. At Loch of Strathbeg, 2008 proved to be an exceptional year with three pairs proved to breed, and four other pairs present of which two probably bred and two possibly did so (*NESBR* 2008, D. Funnell pers. comm.).

Author: *Ken Shaw*

Garganey, River Ugie, March 2008. © *Chris Gibbins*

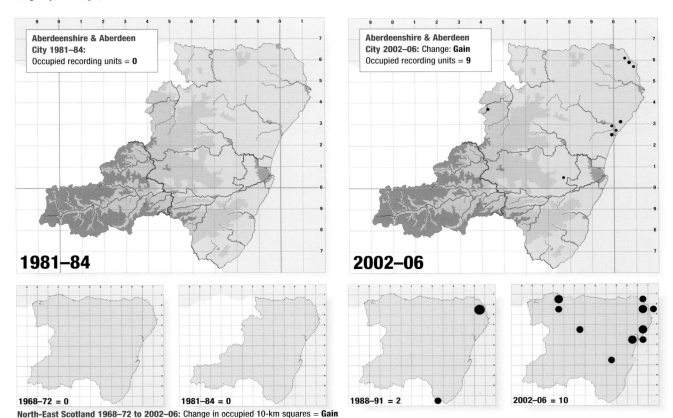

Aberdeenshire & Aberdeen City 1981–84:
Occupied recording units = **0**

1981–84

Aberdeenshire & Aberdeen City 2002–06: Change: **Gain**
Occupied recording units = **9**

2002–06

1968–72 = 0

1981–84 = 0

1988–91 = 2

2002–06 = 10

North-East Scotland 1968–72 to 2002–06: Change in occupied 10-km squares = Gain

Shoveler

Anas clypeata

Very rare breeder. Winter visitor and passage migrant. Estimated population in North-East Scotland:
2–5 pairs (<1% of Scottish and UK population)

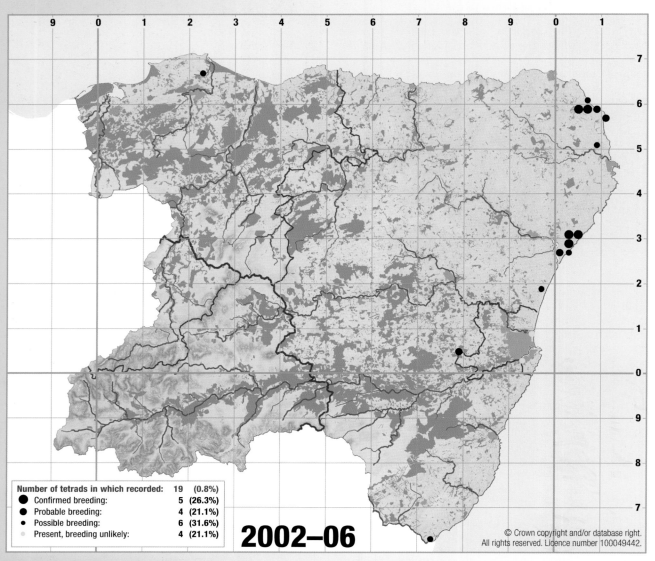

Number of tetrads in which recorded:	19	(0.8%)
● Confirmed breeding:	5	(26.3%)
● Probable breeding:	4	(21.1%)
• Possible breeding:	6	(31.6%)
○ Present, breeding unlikely:	4	(21.1%)

2002–06

Habitat and breeding biology

Shovelers feed by filtering plankton and are therefore dependent on shallow nutrient-rich freshwater sites. All but one of the confirmed and probable breeding records during 2002–06 came from two large wetland complexes in the north-east of the region. Within these sites, breeding birds favour water bodies with ample shoreline vegetation. Little is known about the breeding ecology of birds in our area and confirmed breeding records generally relate to sightings of unfledged young. Large gulls have been seen to predate chicks in North-East Scotland and it is also suspected that Otters may do this (D. Funnell pers. comm.). Scottish breeding sites are often occupied from April onwards when the return of breeding birds may coincide with the presence of wintering birds from further north (Fox in Wernham *et al.* 2002).

Scottish distribution and status

Breeding sites are distributed throughout much of Scotland with the largest populations in Angus & Dundee, Dumfries & Galloway, Orkney and the Outer Hebrides. In the mid 19th century the species was a rare breeder in Scotland. However, the population increased steadily in range and number, and by 2000 was estimated to comprise 260–390 pairs. The

Scottish breeding population is thought to winter in southern England and southwards as far as Spain (Mitchell in *BS3*).

Distribution in North-East Scotland

Breeding records in North-East Scotland are concentrated in two areas. At Loch of Strathbeg, broods are usually observed on small, shallow pools bordered by marshy grassland, although breeding might also occur in some years in dune slack pools. In the Slains lochs area, breeding records come from freshwater sites to the north of the Ythan estuary with abundant shoreline vegetation. Most of the remaining scatter of records could equally refer to migrant or wintering birds as to breeding birds. Loch Spynie regularly hosts the species, including records in May, June and July, but with no clear breeding evidence during 2002–06. Breeding has only occasionally occurred in Moray in recent times, most recently on a pool south of RAF Lossiemouth in 1995 (*MNBR* 1995).

Changes in distribution

There is evidence of a contraction in the distribution of breeding birds. Breeding has been noted in the Slains lochs and Ythan estuary area since early in the 20th century (Sim 1903, cited in *NES 1st Atlas*) whilst in 1968–72 two 10-km

Shoveler, location unknown, June 2008. © *John Chapman*

squares in the Loch of Strathbeg area were occupied (*BTO 1st Atlas*). These sites remain the core areas. However, at Loch Spynie, where breeding occurred periodically until at least 1989 (Cook 1992), there was no confirmed or suspected breeding during 2002–06. In addition to these three areas, confirmed or probable breeding was noted in six 10-km squares during 1968–72, in one of which breeding may also have taken place during 1988–91 (*BTO 1st Atlas, BTO 2nd Atlas*). None of these was occupied in 2002–06. Although the number of 10-km squares with records was higher in 2002–06 than in either 1981–84 or 1988–91, there was no confirmed breeding away from Loch of Strathbeg or the Ythan estuary area and it is possible that all other records refer to passage birds.

Population and trends

In line with some former Scottish strongholds for breeding Shovelers, there has been a decline in the population of this species in North-East Scotland. In 1978, which may have been an exceptional year, there were four breeding pairs at Loch of Strathbeg and up to five at Slains lochs. However, in 1981–84 breeding was confirmed in just a single 10-km square (*NES 1st Atlas*). In 2002–06 there were no more than two pairs in any one year in the Slains lochs area and only one at Loch of Strathbeg. Whilst nesting attempts that fail before the chick stage may go unnoticed, it is unlikely that the North-East Scotland breeding population currently exceeds five pairs in any one year.

Author: *Nick Littlewood*

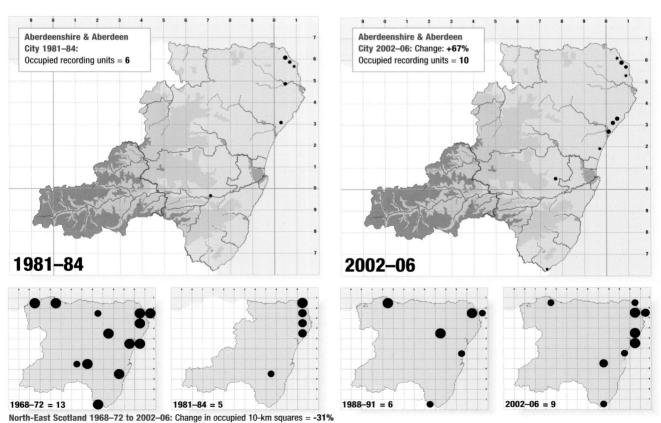

Aberdeenshire & Aberdeen City 1981–84:
Occupied recording units = **6**

1981–84

Aberdeenshire & Aberdeen City 2002–06: Change: **+67%**
Occupied recording units = **10**

2002–06

1968–72 = 13

1981–84 = 5

1988–91 = 6

2002–06 = 9

North-East Scotland 1968–72 to 2002–06: Change in occupied 10-km squares = **-31%**

Pochard

Aythya ferina

Very rare breeder. Winter visitor and passage migrant. Estimated population in North-East Scotland: **1–2 pairs** (5% of Scottish population, <1% of UK)

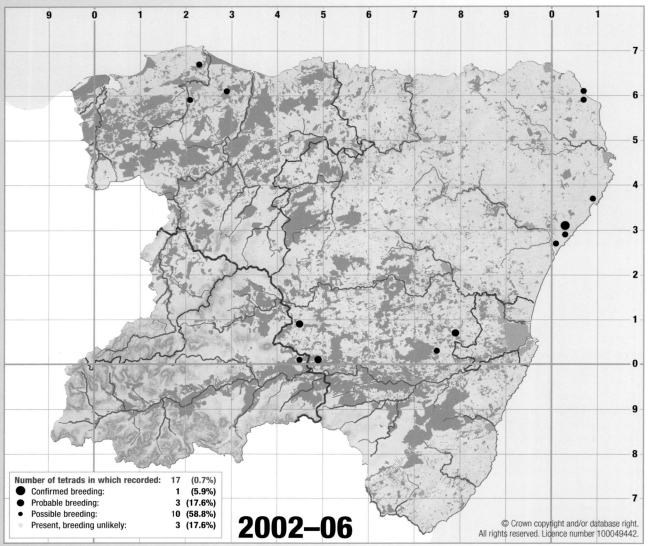

Number of tetrads in which recorded:	17	(0.7%)
● Confirmed breeding:	1	(5.9%)
● Probable breeding:	3	(17.6%)
● Possible breeding:	10	(58.8%)
○ Present, breeding unlikely:	3	(17.6%)

2002–06

Pochard, Clyde, January 2010. © *Gavin Chambers*

Habitat and breeding ecology

In the breeding season, Pochards occupy shallow eutrophic lochs with extensive open water and prolific submerged vegetation. Well-vegetated margins are required to conceal the nest which, in other parts of the UK at least, is often a mound of aquatic vegetation in a water-logged reedbed (*BTO 1st Atlas*). There is little information on the breeding biology of Scottish Pochards, but elsewhere a typical clutch contains 8–10 eggs and laying begins in May, followed by an incubation period of 24–28 days (*BWP*).

Scottish distribution and status

The Pochard is a very scarce breeder in Scotland, predominantly at sites in Perth & Kinross, Fife, Borders, Angus & Dundee, Lothian, Dumfries & Galloway and Orkney. During 1995–2004, Pochards only bred regularly in Perth & Kinross, Fife and Orkney (Fox in *BS3*). Loch Leven is the prime breeding site in Scotland, holding up to 14 pairs in 2004. Following the first documented breeding in Scotland, in Argyll in 1871, the range expanded over many areas of Scotland until in 1938 they nested in 17 counties. By 1964, however, only six counties continued to support a breeding population. The most recent Scottish population estimate is 25–50 pairs (Fox in *BS3*).

Pochard, Clyde, January 2010. © *Gavin Chambers*

Distribution and status in North-East Scotland

Pochards are now very uncommon in summer, appearing irregularly on only a small number of lochs. During 2002–06, breeding was confirmed only at Meikle Loch, where a brood of ducklings was seen in 2002. In addition, breeding was considered to have probably taken place at Lazy Well (upper Donside), Braeroddach Loch (Deeside) and Loch of Skene. Hybrids of Pochard x Tufted Duck, resembling either Redhead or Lesser Scaup have both been recorded in the region but there is no evidence that they arose from local breeding activity.

Changes in distribution

The Pochard has always been a scarce breeder in North-East Scotland, but numbers have declined since the 1960s–early 1970s and breeding is now only sporadic. It took place in eight 10-km squares during 1968–72 (*BTO 1st Atlas*), three 10-km squares in 1988–91 (*BTO 2nd Atlas*) and only one 10-km square in 2002–06. Although the species appears more widely distributed in Aberdeenshire in 2002–06 than in 1981–84, the incidence of proved breeding is little changed.

Population and trends

There were 10–12 pairs in Moray in 1920, but numbers subsequently declined until the last breeding took place in 1979 (Cook 1992). In Aberdeenshire there is no evidence that more than a very few pairs have ever bred in one year since nesting was first recorded in 1937 (Baxter & Rintoul 1953). Although birds were present in 14 tetrads during 2002–06 there was only one instance of confirmed breeding. It is therefore likely that only 1–2 pairs breed sporadically in North-East Scotland at present. Autumn flocks have also declined greatly since the 1950s–early 1980s when peak annual numbers at Loch of Strathbeg often exceeded 500 (*NES 1st Atlas*); counts there now seldom approach 100.

Author: *John Wills*

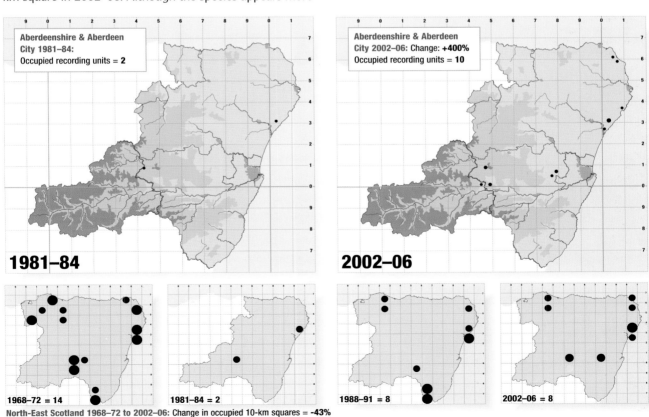

Aberdeenshire & Aberdeen City 1981–84:
Occupied recording units = 2

1981–84

Aberdeenshire & Aberdeen City 2002–06: Change: **+400%**
Occupied recording units = **10**

2002–06

1968–72 = 14

1981–84 = 2

1988–91 = 8

2002–06 = 8

North-East Scotland 1968–72 to 2002–06: Change in occupied 10-km squares = -43%

Tufted Duck
Aythya fuligula

Scarce resident. Winter visitor and passage migrant. Estimated population in North-East Scotland: **150–200 pairs** (7% of Scottish population, 2% of UK)

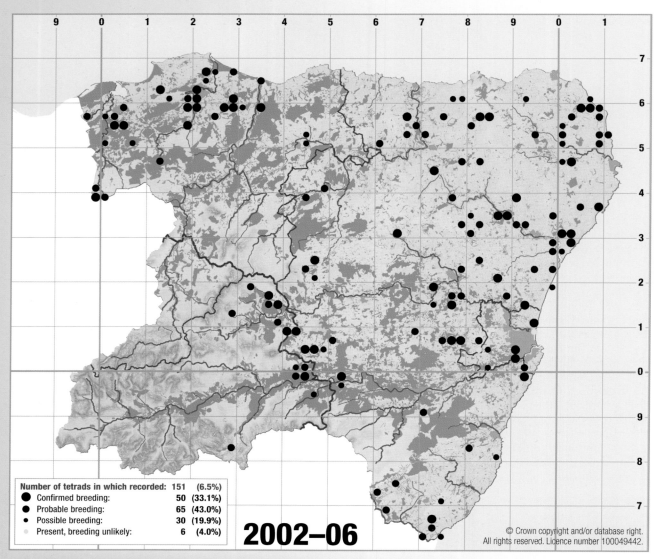

Number of tetrads in which recorded:	151	(6.5%)
● Confirmed breeding:	50	(33.1%)
● Probable breeding:	65	(43.0%)
● Possible breeding:	30	(19.9%)
Present, breeding unlikely:	6	(4.0%)

2002–06

Tufted Duck, Baads Moss, Peterculter, 1978. © *Graham Rebecca*

Habitat and breeding biology

Tufted Ducks breed beside shallow, lowland, eutrophic water bodies, with thickly vegetated margins, submerged vegetation and invertebrate-rich benthic sediments. Slow-flowing rivers and deeper upland oligotrophic lochs may also be used. Nesting occurs in tall, rank, tussocky vegetation, usually within 100 m of the water's edge and often on islands. Birds arrive on their breeding sites in April, nesting later and in a more concentrated breeding period (May–early July) than most other duck species in Scotland. Broods typically contain five or six ducklings, but fledging success is diminished significantly by predation losses. Dispersal occurs after fledging in August when most juveniles join sizeable flocks of moulting adults on favoured large, open, shallow lochs such as Loch of Skene and Loch of Strathbeg.

Scottish distribution and status

The Tufted Duck became a well-established Scottish breeder by the 1880s in the central lowlands and was common across eastern Scotland by the turn of the century. By 1955 most mainland recording areas had been colonised as well as the Northern Isles and Outer Hebrides. The total Scottish population is estimated at 2,250–2,700 pairs (Lauder in *BS3*). Loch Leven is the most important site in

Scotland with a breeding population of 200–550 pairs during 1993–2004 and upwards of 3,000 birds in the post-breeding moulting flock. Although the BBS UK trend has shown a 67% increase between 1994–2007 (Risely *et al.* 2008), the Scottish population has not increased to the same degree (Lauder in *BS3*, Austin *et al.* 2008).

Distribution and status in North-East Scotland

Tufted Ducks are widespread breeders in both Aberdeenshire and Moray. They are also common winter visitors and migrants in both areas. Breeding sites are found on many lowland water bodies throughout the region, the most numerous being in Buchan, Moray, mid Deeside and upper Donside, at altitudes up to 400 m. They are generally absent from the uplands except on a few lochs such as Loch Muick on Deeside and the Dava lochans in Moray. The most favoured sites are, in Aberdeenshire, Lochs Davan and Kinord, Loch of Strathbeg, Loch of Skene, Meikle Loch, Haddo Country Park and Cruden Bay brickworks, and in Moray, Loch Spynie, Loch na Bo, Loch Oire and Cloddach gravel pit. Hybrids of Tufted Duck x Pochard and Tufted Duck x Ring-necked Duck have both been recorded in the region, but there is no evidence of local breeding by these species pairs.

Changes in distribution

There has been a substantial range extension over the past 40 years. In 1968–72 Tufted Ducks were found in 47 10-km squares (*BTO 1st Atlas*) and this number has increased to 59 10-km squares by 2002–06. An apparent decline in 1988–91 (*BTO 2nd Atlas*) is likely to be due to reduced observer coverage. In terms of occupied recording units in Aberdeenshire/Aberdeen City there was a 94% increase from 46 in 1981–84 (*NES 1st Atlas*) to 89 in 2002–06. This spread is largely the result of infilling between former sites, but is perhaps most evident in north-east Aberdeenshire.

Tufted Duck, Finnmark, June 2006. © *Harry Scott*

Population and trends

In Aberdeenshire the prime site in the early 1970s–1980s was Loch of Skene where as many as 50 pairs attempted to breed (*NES 1st Atlas*) but numbers have declined significantly since, due, probably, to a deterioration in water quality. The maximum number of broods recorded in any year between 1993 and 2006 was 28 in Moray in 1995 and 30 in Aberdeenshire/Aberdeen City in 1996 (*MNBRs, NESBRs*). If this is taken to represent a conservative 30% of the total breeding population (Lauder in *BS3*) then there may be close to 200 breeding pairs throughout the region. During 2002–06 breeding was possible, probable or confirmed in 145 tetrads with several pairs in some tetrads. This would support an estimated breeding population in the range of 150–200 pairs in the region.

Author: *John Wills*

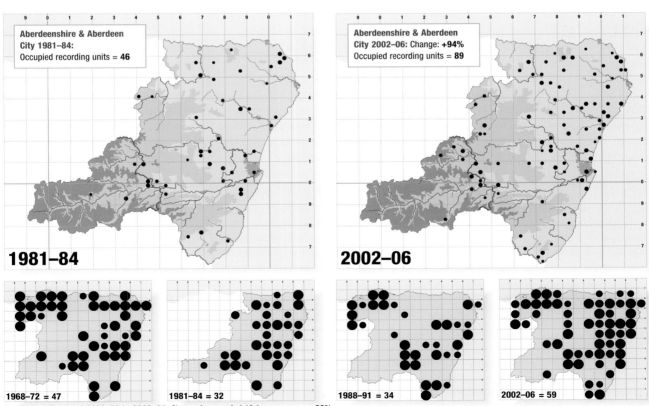

Aberdeenshire & Aberdeen City 1981–84:
Occupied recording units = 46

1981–84

Aberdeenshire & Aberdeen City 2002–06: Change: +94%
Occupied recording units = 89

2002–06

1968–72 = 47

1981–84 = 32

1988–91 = 34

2002–06 = 59

North-East Scotland 1968–72 to 2002–06: Change in occupied 10-km squares = +26%

Scaup

Aythya marila

Occasional in breeding habitat. Winter visitor and passage migrant. Estimated population in North-East Scotland: **0 pairs**

Red list; Schedule 1; UK and Scottish BAP lists

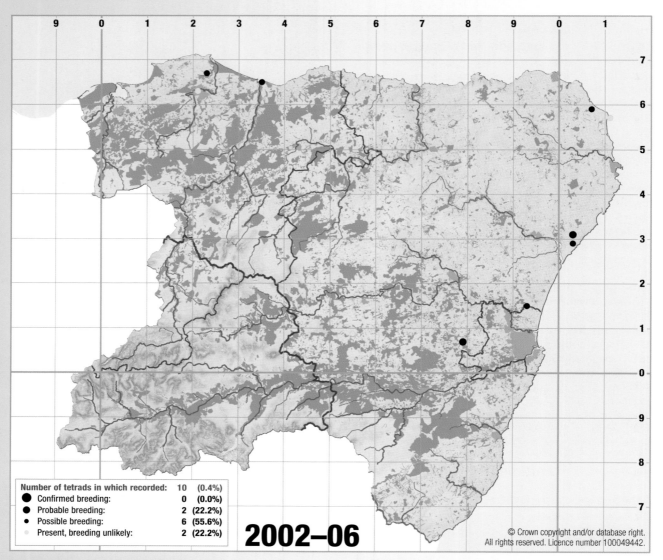

Number of tetrads in which recorded: 10 (0.4%)
● Confirmed breeding: 0 (0.0%)
● Probable breeding: 2 (22.2%)
● Possible breeding: 6 (55.6%)
○ Present, breeding unlikely: 2 (22.2%)

2002–06

© Crown copyright and/or database right. All rights reserved. Licence number 100049442.

Habitat and breeding biology
In their arctic and subarctic breeding range, Scaup occupy tundra, open coniferous forest and upland birch woods, breeding beside well-vegetated lakes and pools with marginal cover. The nest is placed close to water, concealed among tussocks or reeds, or under overhanging scrub (*BWP*).

Scottish distribution and status
In Scotland, the Scaup is primarily a fairly common but localised winter visitor and passage migrant on coasts and estuaries, although the presence of a few birds on freshwater in summer is not unusual (Fox & Ogilvie in *BS3*). Since 1897, breeding has been confirmed in 22 years, but only once since 1979. Most breeding has taken place in the Outer Hebrides (on the Uists) and in Orkney. Mainland records have been in Caithness, Sutherland and Ross & Cromarty (Fox & Ogilvie in *BS3*).

Distribution and status in North-East Scotland
Scaup are uncommon winter visitors in North-East Scotland. Numbers were formerly much higher, with up to 600 off the Moray coast in the 1970s, but since then the Ythan estuary has been the most favoured site. Even here, numbers are now small, seldom exceeding 5–10 in recent

years. Scaup have never been known to breed in the North-East but there are a few inland records in May–July in most years. During 2002–06, sites involved were Loch of Strathbeg, Meikle Loch, Cotehill Loch, Loch of Skene and Cooper Park (Elgin). At Meikle Loch, a pair was seen on 1st May 2004 and 28th–30th April 2005, with up to five birds in early May 2006. At Loch of Skene, there were five on 1st May 2004, seven on 5th May 2005 and a male in June–July 2007, with a female on 26th June. In 2008, two males and a female spent the summer at Loch of Strathbeg but, as with all previous summer records in the North-East, no stronger evidence of breeding activity was noted (*NESBR*s).

Author: *Martin Cook*

The Breeding Birds of North-East Scotland

Scaup, Newburgh, March 2008. © *Ed Duthie*

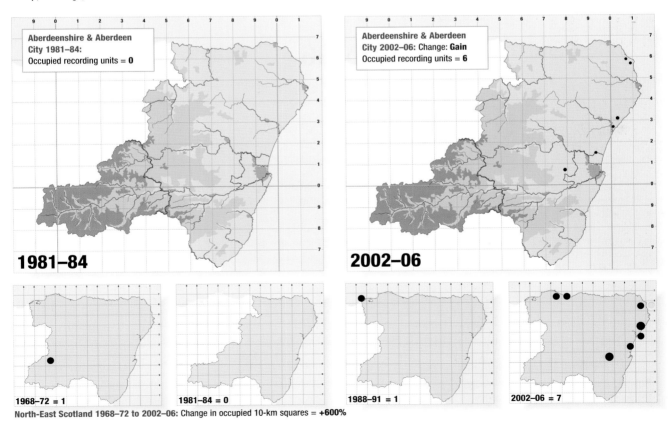

Aberdeenshire & Aberdeen City 1981–84:
Occupied recording units = **0**

1981–84

Aberdeenshire & Aberdeen City 2002–06: Change: Gain
Occupied recording units = **6**

2002–06

1968–72 = 1

1981–84 = 0

1988–91 = 1

2002–06 = 7

North-East Scotland 1968–72 to 2002–06: Change in occupied 10-km squares = +600%

Eider

Somateria mollissima

Common resident and migrant. Estimated population in North-East Scotland: *1,500–2,000 breeding females* (9% of Scottish population, 6% of UK)

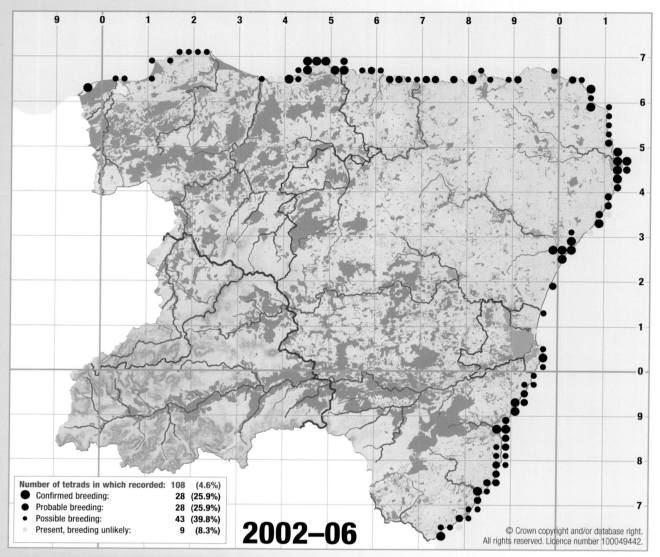

Number of tetrads in which recorded:	108	(4.6%)
● Confirmed breeding:	28	(25.9%)
● Probable breeding:	28	(25.9%)
● Possible breeding:	43	(39.8%)
· Present, breeding unlikely:	9	(8.3%)

2002–06

Eider, Ythan estuary, May 2005. © *Harry Scott*

Habitat and breeding biology

Eiders have a coastal distribution and are widely distributed on rocky shores, with concentrations in shallow areas and estuaries with extensive mussel beds. They are occasionally recorded on freshwater bodies close to the coast. Nests are usually in short vegetation close to the shoreline on rocky coasts, but the birds spread more widely in sand dune systems. The first eggs are laid in mid to late April, with ducklings emerging from mid May and fledging in late July.

Scottish distribution and status

Eiders are widely distributed around the whole of the Scottish coastline, apart from the Solway coast. Main breeding concentrations are on the east coast at the Ythan estuary and around the Firth of Forth, and on the west coast in the Firth of Clyde. Smaller concentrations are found at Montrose, Cromarty, in Orkney and the in Western Isles (Waltho in *BS3*).

Distribution and status in North-East Scotland

Breeding Eiders are distributed in small numbers around almost the whole coastline of North-East Scotland, although with lower densities on some sandy shores, such as the coast immediately north of Aberdeen and parts of the Moray coast. Most of the birds in the region are found in the Ythan estuary, which supports the highest concentration of breeding Eiders in Britain, with a mean peak number of 4,466 (peak 6,224 birds in 1981–84 when counts were unusually high). Around a quarter of the Ythan birds spend the winter in the estuary while the remainder move (via the large post-breeding concentration at Murcar, north of Aberdeen) to the Abertay Sands (Waltho in *BS3*), returning to the Ythan in late March and early April. Numbers reach a peak during May before declining rapidly as females begin to incubate and many of the males depart.

Changes in distribution

The distribution of breeding Eiders in North-east Scotland remained very similar between 1981–84 and 2002–06, with only minor changes, most of which were additional records of probable and possible breeding. It is likely that the distribution has remained the same since North-East Scotland was colonised by Eiders in the period between 1900 and 1950 (Waltho in *BS3*).

Population and trends

The population of Eiders breeding at the Ythan estuary was assessed during 1999–2006 by targeted high tide counts, commissioned by Scottish Natural Heritage. These were carried out at weekly intervals for six weeks from late April, to maximise the likelihood of detecting the brief seasonal peak in numbers. The counts included the coastline from Collieston to the Ythan mouth, since the birds there are part of the same breeding population. The mean peak population in 1999–2006 was 4,466 - close to the long-term average of 4,595 between 1961 and 2006 (which has not shown any obvious upward or downward trend). The number of adult females in 1999–2006 varied from 1,271 in 2001 to 2,025 in 2005, with a mean of 1,565. There is little information on the numbers of breeding Eiders elsewhere in North-East Scotland, where many of the records in the breeding season refer to counts of large flocks. For example, 237 birds at Girdleness (Aberdeen) in May 2001 was a

Eider, Iceland, June 2006. © *Sam Alexander*

number far in excess of those likely to be nesting locally and presumably included mostly non-breeding or passage birds. The number of Eider broods recorded on the Moray coast averaged seven per year in 1999–2006 which, allowing for nest failures and some post-hatching mortality, suggests no more than about 20 breeding females. From similar small numbers at the Loch of Strathbeg, and scattered records elsewhere, it is estimated that there were about 100 breeding females in coastal areas of North-East Scotland away from the Ythan estuary in 1999–2006.

Numbers since 2006

A decrease of over 1,000 in the peak number of Eiders on the Ythan between 2005 (5,364 birds) and 2006 (4,297) continued in the two following years, with peaks of 3,262 in 2007 and 2,739 in 2008. There was a similar decrease in the peak number of adult females, with 2,025 in 2005, 1,533 in 2006, 1,151 in 2007 and 1,066 in 2008. The number of Eiders spending the winter on the Ythan also decreased, to less than half of the numbers counted in earlier years. This decline in both breeding and wintering numbers may be associated with a noticeable increase over the same period in the amount of green algae growing on the mussel beds in the estuary, probably reducing the birds' main food supply. There was a small increase in total numbers in 2009, with a peak of 3,447 birds, although there was no increase in the number of adult females, with a peak of 1,050.

Author: *Ian Patterson*

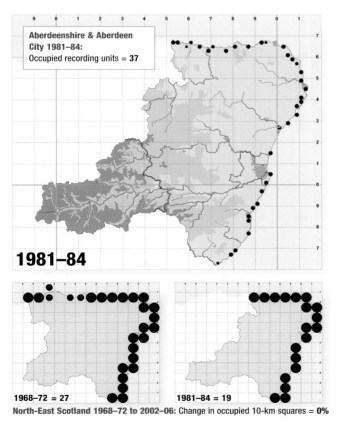

Aberdeenshire & Aberdeen City 1981–84:
Occupied recording units = 37

1981–84

1968–72 = 27   1981–84 = 19

North-East Scotland 1968–72 to 2002–06: Change in occupied 10-km squares = 0%

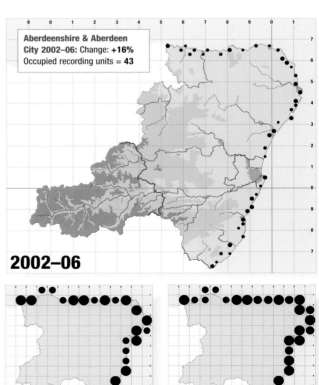

Aberdeenshire & Aberdeen City 2002–06: Change: +16%
Occupied recording units = 43

2002–06

1988–91 = 24   2002–06 = 27

Goldeneye   *Bucephala clangula*

Rare breeder. Winter visitor and passage migrant. Estimated population in North-East Scotland:
30 breeding females (20% of Scottish and UK population)

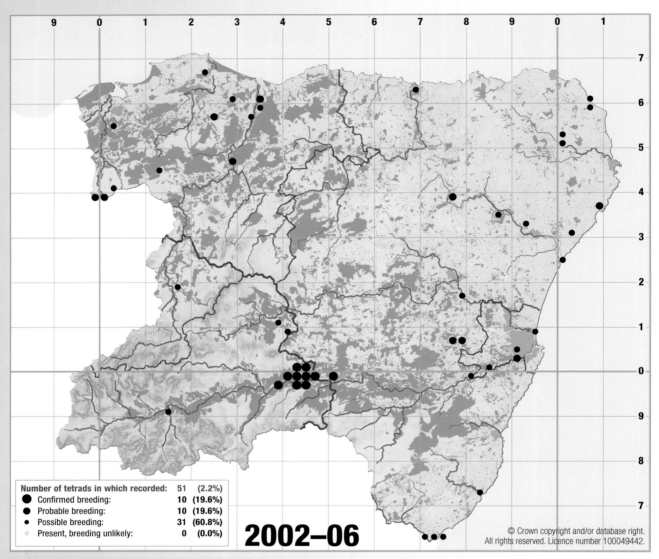

Number of tetrads in which recorded:	51	(2.2%)
● Confirmed breeding:	10	(19.6%)
● Probable breeding:	10	(19.6%)
• Possible breeding:	31	(60.8%)
○ Present, breeding unlikely:	0	(0.0%)

2002–06

Goldeneye, Deeside, May 2009. © *Harry Scott*

Habitat and breeding biology

In mid Deeside, breeding females have readily taken to nest boxes provided in the vicinity of the lochs and the River Dee. They now only occasionally use natural tree holes in this area. The local breeding population is thought to return to the area during January and immediately starts nest prospecting and displaying. Eggs are laid between mid March and the end of April, after which all clutches generally hatch by early June. Most ducklings are led to Loch Kinord where they remain until fledging in late July. The remaining females, with many of their young, then leave the area, heading towards Loch of Skene and the coast.

Scottish distribution and status

Goldeneye are uncommon and localised breeders which first nested in Badenoch & Strathspey in 1970. Although nest boxes were subsequently provided throughout much of northern Scotland, the population during the 1990s was almost exclusively located in Badenoch & Strathspey until 2000, when the colonisation of Deeside took place (Buxton in *BS3*). Currently, the Scottish breeding population is estimated at around 150 breeding females, of which over 100 are in Strathspey. However, this number should be treated with caution as an unknown number of nests in natural sites remain undetected and it is well known that some breeding females lay eggs in the nests of other individuals.

Distribution and status in North-East Scotland

Goldeneye numbers have increased steadily in mid Deeside during recent years, reflecting the establishment of a breeding population there in 2000; there were 184 birds on the Dinnet Lochs in March 2006. Elsewhere, during recent winters, counts at the region's principal sites have also increased; Loch of Skene and Loch of Strathbeg, both peaked at 334 birds during 2006 and there were 66 at Loch Spynie in April 2000. There were 89 Goldeneye on the Ythan Estuary in January 2004, but generally coastal areas hold fewer than 20

The Breeding Birds of North-East Scotland

Goldeneye, Deeside, May 2005. © *Harry Scott*

birds. During the summer months, after the peak northerly passage of birds in March, numbers across the region decline rapidly until only the key sites such as Loch of Skene and Loch of Strathbeg hold small numbers of non-breeders.

Changes in distribution

During the 1960s and 1970s, Goldeneye were predominantly winter visitors, occasionally recorded in large numbers on inland waters during milder weather but more regularly observed on the sea, feeding at inshore effluent discharges. There has been a considerable change in Goldeneye distribution since the 1980s and early 1990s, when very few birds summered but the first breeding was recorded in the region. This involved a female with nine small ducklings on the River Dee, near Cults, in June 1982 (E. Duthie pers. comm.). This was followed in 1986 by the first breeding record in Moray when a female with a brood of four young was seen on the Dava lochans. Subsequently, breeding was recorded there in 1987, 1990, 1998 and 1999. As there is now a larger breeding population in the North-East, winters are usually milder and

there are no inshore effluents, birds are more often found frequenting the freshwater lochs and rivers where, in mid Deeside specifically, numbers early in the season have steadily increased year-round since 2000. The increase in numbers passing through mid Deeside in late spring is reflected in the seven-fold increase to 29 occupied recording units in Aberdeenshire/Aberdeen City over the period 1981–84 to 2002–06.

Populations and trends

Table 1. The Goldeneye breeding population in mid Deeside since 2000.

	Occupied boxes	Occupied natural holes	Total nest attempts
2000	-	1	1
2001	-	-	-
2002	1	2	3
2003	1	3	4
2004	6	3	9
2005	9	3	12
2006	16	2	18
2007	27	1	28
2008	25	1	26
2009	30	1	31

During 2005–09, a total of 34 breeding females has been caught and ringed as part of an intensive study of their colonisation. This area now contains around a quarter of the current UK breeding population, with around 30 nesting attempts each year. The speed of the mid Deeside colonisation (Table 1) is illustrated by the fact that after just eight seasons of nesting attempts, the region now holds similar numbers to those recorded in Badenoch & Strathspey after the first eleven seasons. Since the early records from 1986–99, no further confirmed breeding has been recorded in Moray. Across North-East Scotland, many stretches of river and inland open water often hold a few birds during the summer months and among these is perhaps the potential for further colonisation.

Author: *Harry Scott*

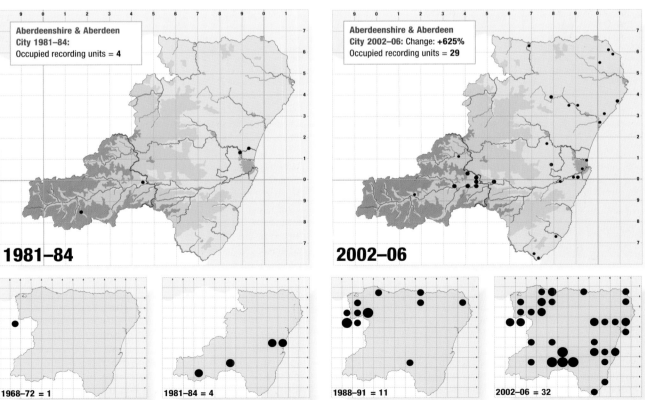

Red-breasted Merganser   *Mergus serrator*

Rare breeder. Present on the coast all year. Estimated population in North-East Scotland: **25–50 pairs** (2% of Scottish population, <2% of UK)

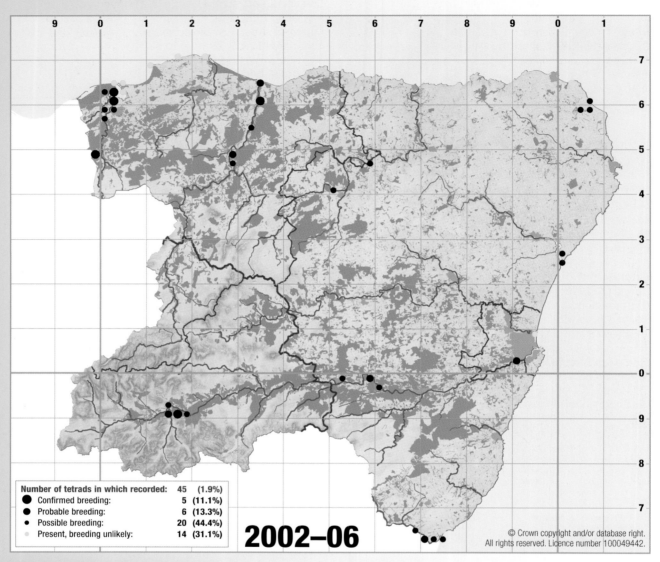

Number of tetrads in which recorded: 45   (1.9%)
● Confirmed breeding: 5   (11.1%)
● Probable breeding: 6   (13.3%)
• Possible breeding: 20   (44.4%)
∙ Present, breeding unlikely: 14   (31.1%)

2002–06

Habitat and breeding biology

Red-breasted Mergansers are fish-eating ducks of shallow marine and brackish waters, some using rivers and large mesotrophic lochs during the breeding season. They feed on small fishes and large invertebrates, and breed late so enabling their ducklings to exploit the summer abundance of tiny shoaling fish (Marquiss *et al.* 1998). They arrive in the breeding areas in April and May and lay eggs in May and June; the drakes leaving for their offshore moulting areas as ducks incubate (Marquiss & Duncan 1993). Nests are concealed in thick riparian vegetation, often on islets and occasionally concentrated in association with gull or tern colonies. Ducklings hatch in June and July and are led to nearby backwaters, later moving to congregate on wider river sections and open expanses of lochs or estuaries. Breeding production is low at between 1–3 young/spring female (reviewed in Marquiss & Duncan 1993). Juveniles fledge in August as adult ducks move to moult in estuaries or sandy coastal bays.

Scottish distribution and status

Red-breasted Mergansers are long-established breeding birds in Scotland. Formerly restricted to the west coast and Northern Isles, there was an increase in the mid 19th century as they expanded their range to encompass the recent distribution. They are relatively abundant, with the highest numbers on the coastal areas of the north and west and on the Isles, far fewer on the east and scarce in most of the south. They winter on the coast where they are joined by immigrants from Iceland and parts of Fennoscandia. The breeding population is thought to be of the order of 2,000 pairs, but this is largely guesswork as there has been no effective census of coastal breeders (Marquiss in *BS3*).

Distribution and status in North-East Scotland

The map demonstrates well the disjunct breeding distribution in the North-East. Confirmed breeding is mainly on the lower parts of the Rivers Findhorn, Spey and North Esk. The discontinuous occurrence on the Dee shows that breeders favour wide, shallow sections with shingle islands, at the mouth, near Aboyne and by Braemar. Birds were recorded in tetrads elsewhere in the region, but without observations of broods there is little evidence of breeding. The only two places with persistently good breeding numbers are on the lower reaches of the Rivers Findhorn and North Esk.

The Breeding Birds of North-East Scotland

Changes in distribution

For most of the 19th century, Red-breasted Mergansers were apparently only winter visitors to North-East Scotland. From 1885 to 1890 breeders apparently increased in Moray (Harvie-Brown & Buckley 1895) and subsequent spread led to breeding populations on most rivers by 1939 (Berry 1939). Numbers then decreased substantially to produce the present distribution illustrated by the first BTO breeding Atlas. The distribution of records in 2002–06 was similar to the distribution in 1981–84 (*NES 1st Atlas*) but with a reduction in records for the River Dee, probably because there are now fewer breeding pairs.

Population and trends

It is difficult to estimate the breeding population because densities vary so much from place to place, and between years. Numbers in most parts of the North-East are low, so census work is labour intensive. Even where there are more pairs, the numbers change annually; the total on the River North Esk varied twofold over a seven year study, 1987–93 (Marquiss & Duncan 1993). There are long series of regular counts of moulting birds in July and August offshore at St. Cyrus, but these are also highly variable and, in any case, cannot relate to local population change because their numbers so exceeded the local breeding population that the majority of moulters must originate outwith the North-East. With incomplete survey and little idea of trends we can only guess that the 2002–06 population of North-East Scotland was between 25 and 50 breeding pairs.

Author: *Mick Marquiss*

Red-breasted Merganser, Newburgh, May 2010. © *John Chapman*

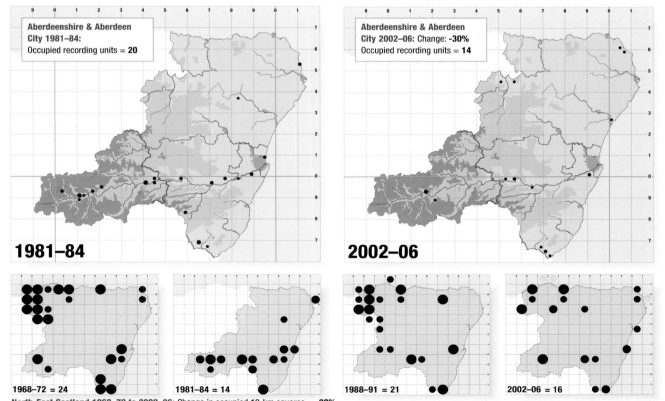

Aberdeenshire & Aberdeen City 1981–84: Occupied recording units = **20**

1981–84

Aberdeenshire & Aberdeen City 2002–06: Change: **-30%** Occupied recording units = **14**

2002–06

1968–72 = 24

1981–84 = 14

1988–91 = 21

2002–06 = 16

North-East Scotland 1968–72 to 2002–06: Change in occupied 10-km squares = **-33%**

Goosander

Mergus merganser

Scarce resident and migrant breeder. Estimated population in North-East Scotland: **100 pairs** (4% of Scottish population, <4% of UK)

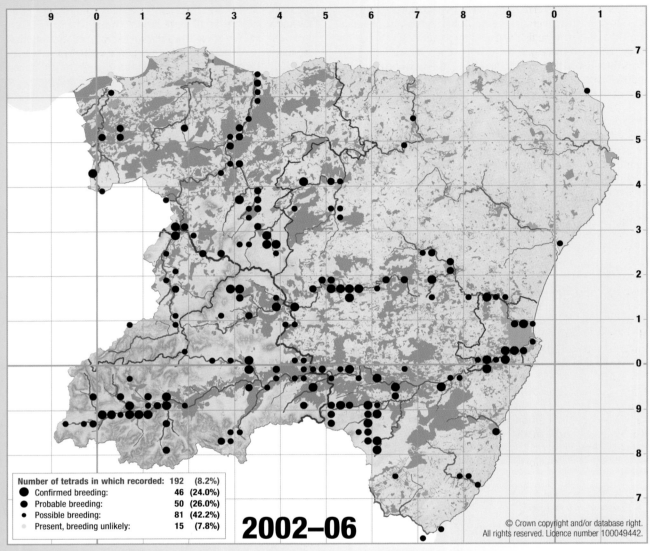

Number of tetrads in which recorded:	192	(8.2%)
● Confirmed breeding:	46	(24.0%)
● Probable breeding:	50	(26.0%)
● Possible breeding:	81	(42.2%)
Present, breeding unlikely:	15	(7.8%)

2002–06

Goosander, Ballater, May 2008. © *Harry Scott*

Habitat and breeding biology

Goosanders are fish-eating ducks of freshwater lochs, rivers and shallow inshore firths. Most breed by rivers, nesting in cavities in trees and rocky cairns, often high up the tributaries. During February they forage on still waters, but occasional pairs visit tributaries to prospect nest sites (Marquiss & Duncan 1994a). In March and April they switch to foraging on the main stems of rivers, and eggs are laid from April onwards. Drakes abandon the breeding areas by June, gathering on still waters and estuaries to fatten prior to their moult migration to north Norway. Goosanders do not usually breed until their second year. Yearling ducks spend May and June prospecting nest sites before leaving in July, along with failed adult female breeders, to moult on Scottish estuaries and inner firths. From successful nests, ducklings hatch in late May and June and are brought by the female to brood rearing areas up to 15 km downstream. By August, adult females that have produced fledged young have left to moult and flying juveniles use the lower reaches of rivers, gathering in September to roost communally on still waters, prior to dispersal to winter quarters (Marquiss & Duncan 1994b).

The Breeding Birds of North-East Scotland

Scottish distribution and status

The Goosander is a relatively recent colonist with first proven breeding in 1871, the numbers soon increasing and spreading rapidly across Scotland. Most of the current population is concentrated on the largest river systems of southern and eastern Scotland, with particularly high densities on the Rivers Tweed and Annan, associated with their rich and diverse fish communities. Numbers are low on short river systems, *e.g.* in the north and west, and only a few pairs breed on the islands. In 2006, there were probably 2,000–3,000 breeding pairs in Scotland. It was thought that numbers increased during the 1980s, decreased in the 1990s and perhaps increased subsequently (Marquiss in *BS3*).

Distribution and status in North-East Scotland

Observations in tetrads recorded pairs in nesting areas and broods on their rearing areas, well distributed along the three largest rivers, Spey, Don and Dee. There were also records along the Fiddich and upper Deveron, but few for the lower Deveron and almost none for the Ythan and Ugie. Goosanders are highly mobile ducks commuting many kilometres between nesting, foraging and brood areas. Also, non-breeding first year birds are especially mobile using both the tributaries and the main stem of the river in May prior to their exodus to the moulting grounds. Consequently there were probably far fewer breeding pairs than records of occupied tetrads. From a national survey (1987) and other counts, it is known that compared with elsewhere in Scotland, Goosanders in the North-East live at intermediate densities, averaging 1–2 breeding pairs/10 km of river (Marquiss *et al.* 1998).

Changes in distribution

The distribution of records in 2002–06 was remarkably similar to the distribution in 1981–84 (*NES 1st Atlas*). There were more records in the recent atlas, particularly in mid Donside, but this is difficult to evaluate considering there was less recording effort in previous atlases. In the absence of systematic counting of breeding birds, it is impossible to know whether there has been a change in abundance. One notable change is in the increase around Aberdeen City. This is in part because Goosanders now breed closer to Aberdeen and rear broods on the lower Dee. Another change has been in the numbers of female Goosanders moulting on North-East river estuaries. In the early 1980s there were moulting birds at Speymouth but since then, new groups have been detected at Lossiemouth, Findhorn, Dee and Donmouth.

Population and trends

Estimates of Goosander populations are best derived from the numbers of adult drakes counted along 10 km sections of river in April (Marquiss & Duncan 1994). Such counts are time-consuming so there have been relatively few rivers systematically surveyed and none monitored for more than a few years. It is thus difficult to assess population and trends. Annual numbers are not stable - on the River Dee for example, the total for the whole watershed fell from 67 pairs to 29 over seven years of intensive studies from 1988–1994. Breeding success varied even more; annual counts on the Rivers Dee and North Esk found brood densities varying between 0 and 0.4 broods/km and overall production between 0 and 3.6 fledged ducklings per spring female. There were no systematic counts during the Atlas period (2002–06) so we can only guess conservatively at a North-East Scotland population of perhaps 100 pairs.

There have been regular counts of moulting females. The flock at Speymouth has doubled from 50 in 1985 to 74–128 in the Atlas years and new moulting groups have established at other sites. However, such increase does not necessarily indicate an increased breeding population. Some of these moulters are known to be local breeding females but most are probably from further south (Hatton & Marquiss 2004).

Author: *Mick Marquiss*

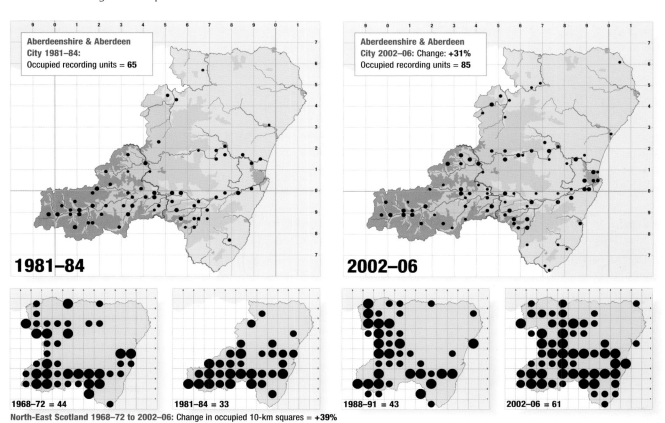

Aberdeenshire & Aberdeen City 1981–84:
Occupied recording units = **65**

1981–84

Aberdeenshire & Aberdeen City 2002–06: Change: **+31%**
Occupied recording units = **85**

2002–06

1968–72 = 44

1981–84 = 33

1988–91 = 43

2002–06 = 61

North-East Scotland 1968–72 to 2002–06: Change in occupied 10-km squares = +39%

Ruddy Duck

Oxyura jamaicensis

Occasional feral breeder. Summer visitor. Estimated population in North-East Scotland: usually **0 pairs**

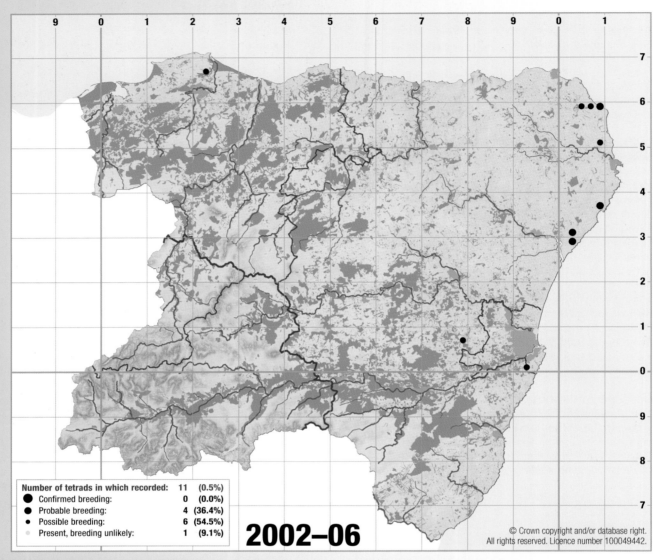

Number of tetrads in which recorded: 11 (0.5%)
- ● Confirmed breeding: 0 (0.0%)
- ● Probable breeding: 4 (36.4%)
- ● Possible breeding: 6 (54.5%)
- Present, breeding unlikely: 1 (9.1%)

2002–06

Ruddy Duck, Clyde, October 2005. © *John Anderson*

Habitat and breeding biology

Ruddy Ducks are found on shallow freshwater lochs with plentiful emergent vegetation. They rarely occur on the coast, on rivers or in estuaries, which contrasts with their behaviour in their native North America. Pairs return to potential breeding sites from early April to early June, one of Scotland's latest breeding ducks. The breeding season is quite extended, with broods recorded as late as September, although Ruddy Ducks are rarely double brooded in Scotland. Only two nests have ever been found in Scotland (Andrews in *BS3*). Productivity is high, but so too are losses to predation. Birds emigrate south in late autumn/early winter, mostly to southern Scotland and England.

Scottish distribution and status

Most Ruddy Ducks are concentrated in the Borders and in central Scotland, extending to southern Perthshire, Fife and Angus & Dundee. The first record was in Perth & Kinross in 1954, with the first breeding record in Angus & Dundee in 1979. Numbers rapidly increased and may have reached an estimated 100 pairs by 1999. Since the first organised cull in 1999–2001, numbers have declined in most areas. The total Scottish population was estimated at about 50 pairs in 2003 (Andrews in *BS3*).

Ruddy Duck, Clyde, October 2005. © *John Anderson*

Distribution and status in North-East Scotland

Ruddy Ducks favour only a few lochs in North-East Scotland: Loch Spynie in Moray, and, in Aberdeenshire, Loch of Strathbeg, Meikle Loch, Cotehill and Sand Lochs, and Loch of Skene. There are only occasional sightings elsewhere. The species was first recorded in Aberdeenshire in 1981 and in Moray in 1984. Breeding has been confirmed only at Loch of Strathbeg, Cotehill Loch and Pitscow (Mintlaw), the last record being in 1996 (*NES 1st Atlas*, *NESBRs*, Andrews in *BS3*). One or two pairs are regularly observed in May and June at Loch of Strathbeg and Meikle Loch indicating probable breeding in most years. Autumn juveniles have been observed at both sites and at Mintlaw in 1996 (*NESBRs*). There has been no evidence of any breeding in Moray. Birds are normally observed through the autumn to late September, with the occasional individual overwintering. Maximum numbers in most years are 7–10 in Aberdeenshire and 1–4 in Moray.

Changes in distribution

Ruddy Ducks were first recorded in North-East Scotland in 1981 when there were ten on Meikle Loch in May. The next records were in 1984 at Loch Spynie (the first for Moray) and, more notably, at Loch of Strathbeg where three broods of ducklings were seen (*NES 1st Atlas*, Cook 1992). Since

that time, Ruddy Ducks have become regular but scarce summer visitors, with records at seven sites in 2002–06 compared to the two sites in 1981–84.

Population and trends

The organised culls in England and southern Scotland have had an immediate effect on the UK population with around 45% decline since 2001 to levels akin to the late 1980s (Austin *et al.* 2008). Numbers have declined in their Central Lowlands core areas and only Ross & Cromarty has experienced an apparent population increase in recent years. During 2002–06 the culls appeared to have no significant impact on the few annual sightings in the North-East, with ten or more birds recorded each year. Since then however there has been a decline in numbers with only two records in 2007 and one in 2008. The estimated breeding population in North-East Scotland in 2002–06 was probably no more than one or two pairs annually despite the fact that breeding was never proved during that period, with passage migrants contributing the remaining records (*NESBRs*, *MNBRs*). The decline since 2006 makes it unlikely that breeding will take place again in the near future.

Author: *John Wills*

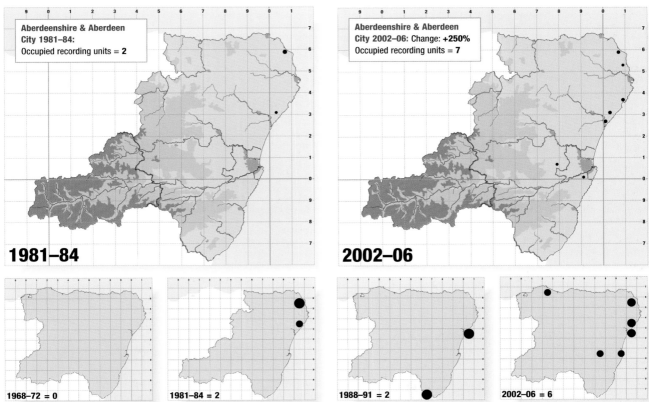

North-East Scotland 1968–72 to 2002–06: Change in occupied 10-km squares = **Gain**

Red Grouse

Lagopus lagopus

Very common resident. Estimated population in North-East Scotland: at least *40,000 birds* in spring (16% of Scottish population, 13% of UK)

Amber list; UK BAP list

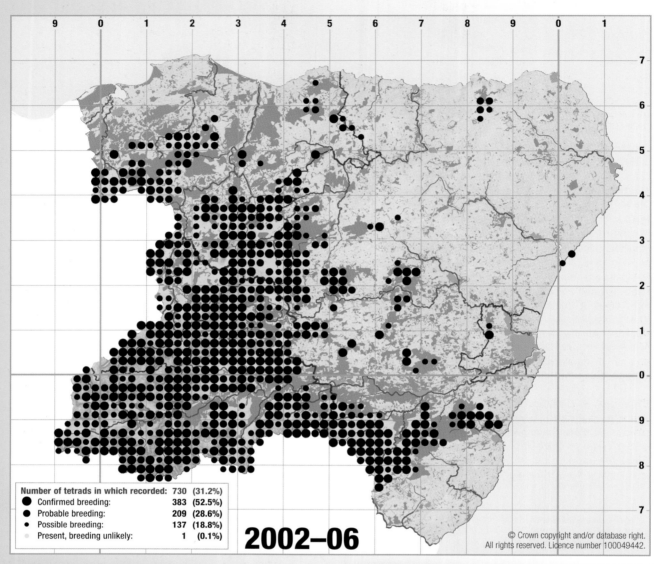

Number of tetrads in which recorded: 730 (31.2%)
- ● Confirmed breeding: 383 (52.5%)
- ● Probable breeding: 209 (28.6%)
- • Possible breeding: 137 (18.8%)
- ○ Present, breeding unlikely: 1 (0.1%)

2002–06

Habitat and breeding biology

Red Grouse breed on Heather moorland. Most of this was originally forest, but was deforested in prehistoric times to make way for grazing farm animals and, locally, cultivation. It has been kept treeless since by muirburn, and also by farm stock (and recently Red Deer) eating tree seedlings. It reverts to natural woodland if burning and grazing stop, as can be seen well at Muir of Dinnet. Heather dominates the moorland vegetation, forms the main food of adult birds, and provides physical cover from predators. Above 600 m altitude, the Heather's annual growth largely balances annual die-back caused by weather, so the plants do not grow increasingly tall. At lower altitudes it becomes rank unless burned or heavily grazed. Tall Heather supports few birds, and short over-grazed Heather supports no breeders. Densities are high on a mixture of nutritious short heath for food, beside taller heath for cover. They are highest where this occurs on relatively fertile soils above base-rich bedrock. Red Grouse live from coastal moors up to the foot of the alpine zone. The hen nests in her cock's territory - in a scrape lined with plant litter, in Heather tall enough to hide her. She takes her newly hatched chicks to flushes and bogs, where the chicks eat insects as well as plant material. After 2–3 weeks they switch to a plant diet similar to that of the adults and move back to Heather areas.

Red Grouse, Corgarff, June 2006. © *Chris Jones*

The Breeding Birds of North-East Scotland

Scottish distribution and status

Red Grouse, a UK endemic sub-species *L. l. scoticus* of the circumpolar Willow Ptarmigan or Willow Grouse, are widely distributed on Scottish moorland, including on many islands. They have declined greatly in abundance on almost all moorland, coinciding with poorer standards of muirburn involving under-burning (not enough young Heather made available as nutritious food) or over-burning (not enough old Heather left for physical cover). Overgrazing by sheep, and in some areas by Red Deer, has reduced the Heather's abundance and height on much moorland, removing food and cover. Large tracts have been lost by subsidised conversion of Heather to agricultural grassland and coniferous plantations. Because of insufficient counts, accurate estimates of numbers cannot be made. A tentative estimate is over 200,000 birds in spring (Watson & Moss 2008).

Distribution and status in North-East Scotland

The birds are still locally common and were present in 730 tetrads in 2002–06, though they are generally scarcer than previously. The adverse factors for Scotland (described above) apply also to the North-East. Here are some of Scotland's best known grouse moors, where the primary land use is the shooting of Red Grouse and the income that this generates; sheep grazing or Red Deer are secondary interests. Most moors run from the south side of the Mounth in Kincardineshire, into Deeside and Donside, continuing by upper Deveron and Fiddich to Speyside, and across to the Moray moors. Birds still breed on some lowland peat-mosses and isolated low hills such as Ben Aigan and Hill of Fare, though less commonly than in past decades.

Changes in distribution

Large tracts of moorland have been converted to coniferous plantations, as at Fetteresso and Clashindarroch, and smaller ones to native woodland by natural tree regeneration, as at Glen Tanar. Many small areas of moorland have been transformed to agricultural grassland. These changes also fragmented the habitat, leading to fewer birds. Red Grouse have apparently gone from many lowland peat-mosses, associated with less burning and grazing; indeed in the 2002–06 atlas birds were recorded in the lowlands only at Sands of Forvie and near Tore of Troup. However, they were still present, and bred, within the Aberdeen City boundary, on Brimmond and Elrick Hills. Sheep Ticks have increased on much moorland (along with more sheep, Roe Deer and Red Deer as tick hosts) and on some tick-infested moors the louping ill virus has greatly reduced the stocks of Red Grouse. The habitat losses described above have operated mainly at the margins of the range towards the lowlands, and the overall distribution in North-East Scotland has changed little between 1981–84 and 2002–06. The retraction from the lowland and coastal areas towards Fraserburgh and Peterhead is apparent in the different atlases.

Population and trends

Numbers fluctuate much from year to year. Cycles (fluctuations more regular than random) of 10-year period have been recorded in the Cairngorms and near the Kincardineshire coast, about seven-years on two Deeside moors, and no cycles on two other Deeside moors (Moss & Watson 2001). Some of the highest population densities recorded for this species were found in Deeside during the 1970s (Watson & Moss 2008), with up to over 300 birds/km^2 in spring. However, densities have been lower since 1990. Numbers have fallen very low on many moors since 2000, associated with over-burning. Shooting bags and counts show evidence of long-term decline. The area of Heather moorland in Grampian Region (= North-East Scotland) fell by 35% between the 1940s and 1980s (Mackey *et al.* 1998) and large losses have occurred since, though it still accounts for about one fifth of the total Heather moorland in Scotland. Given this, and assuming 5–10 Red Grouse territories/km^2 across their North-East distribution, a rough estimate would be 40,000 birds in spring.

Author: *Adam Watson*

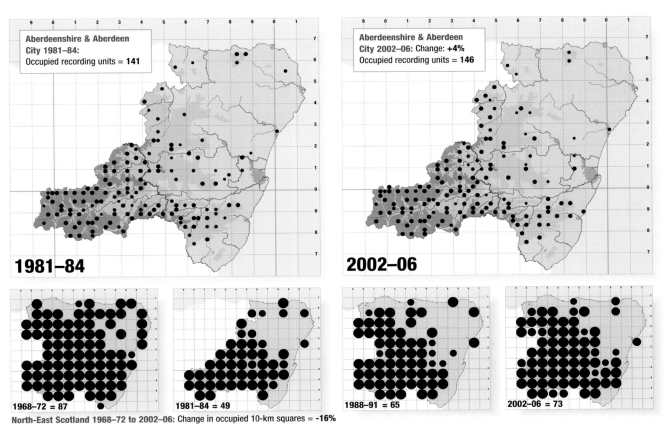

North-East Scotland 1968–72 to 2002–06: Change in occupied 10-km squares = **-16%**

Ptarmigan

Lagopus muta

Common resident. Estimated population in North-East Scotland: up to *10,000 birds* in spring (30% of Scottish and UK population)

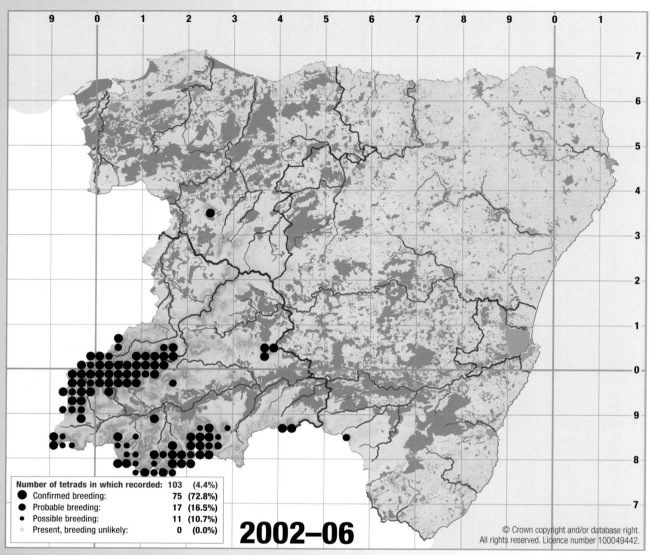

Number of tetrads in which recorded: 103   (4.4%)

●	Confirmed breeding:	75	(72.8%)
●	Probable breeding:	17	(16.5%)
•	Possible breeding:	11	(10.7%)
	Present, breeding unlikely:	0	(0.0%)

2002–06

Habitat and breeding biology
Breeding Ptarmigan are confined to the alpine zone, where plants remain short and prostrate in the windy climate. The zone starts at its highest altitude on the relatively continental Lochnagar, on average at 825 m there. It begins on average at 760 m in the slightly less continental Cairngorms massif (Watson 1965a) and the outlying Ben Rinnes, and at 600 m or lower in the windier oceanic western Highlands. The lowest record for breeding birds is at 180 m near Cape Wrath. Ptarmigan only rarely nest on the highest summits above 1,250 m, where most ground is bare. In the nesting season they overlap for up to 300 m in altitude with Red Grouse, but the two separate according to habitat, the lowest Ptarmigan on patches of short heath with rocks, the highest Red Grouse on patches of tall Heather. Adult Ptarmigan at all seasons feed mainly on shoots of heath plants such as Crowberry, Blaeberry and Heather. They avoid continuous grassland, which offers little food. Only when snow and rime cover the alpine zone completely do they descend to the upper moorland, to eat Heather projecting above the snow. Alpine vegetation is too short to hide summering birds, so they use boulders as physical cover from predators. The hen nests in her cock's territory, a scrape lined with plant litter. She takes her chicks to flushes

and small patches of grassy vegetation among boulders, where the chicks eat insects, plant shoots and flowers. After they are 2–3 weeks old they switch to a vegetable diet as the family moves to grassy heath among boulders.

Scottish distribution and status
Ptarmigan, the endemic Scottish sub-species *L. m. millaisi* of the circumpolar Rock Ptarmigan, are widely distributed across the Scottish alpine zone, and have summered on many islands. Local extinctions occur from time to time on small areas of suitable habitat, especially on islands or small hilltops that lie far from the main area of distribution. Since 1800 the distribution has contracted in southern and western Scotland including the islands, in association with less heath due to overgrazing by sheep, but has not changed materially on high infertile hills such as the Cairngorms. Few counts have been done on different hills and years, so an accurate estimate of Scottish numbers cannot be made, though a range of 2,000–15,000 pairs has been suggested (Rae in *BS3*).

Distribution and status in North-East Scotland
Most birds are in the Cairngorms massif, but many are on the Mount from Carn Ealar east to Mount Keen, and a

Ptarmigan, Creag an Leth-choin, June 2009. © *Paul Bingham*

few (at least in some years) on Morven, Ben Rinnes and Mount Battock. In winter, there are records from lower hills where Ptarmigan do not breed and, exceptionally, one was on a coastal cliff-top south of Cove Bay in November 1953 (Rae in *BS3*).

Changes in distribution

There is no evidence of any material changes in distribution on the main areas occupied within this region, as the atlases illustrate. Both local atlases showed a similar number of occupied recording units in Aberdeenshire in 1981–84 and 2002–06.

Population and trends

Average population density exceeds that in studies abroad including the Arctic, in association with greater abundance of the main food-plants, with maximum densities sometimes exceeding 100 birds/km^2 in spring (Watson & Moss 2008). Numbers fluctuate greatly from year to year. On the Cairngorms massif they show cycles (fluctuations more

regular than random) peaking about every ten years, while fluctuations on the Cairnwell hills are shorter and irregular (Watson *et al.* 1998). Density on the Cairnwell hills tends to exceed that on the Cairngorms, in association with food-plants on the relatively fertile soils and base-rich bedrock there being more nutritious than on the acidic granite bedrock of the Cairngorms. Because numbers fluctuate so greatly and few hills have been studied, there is no published evidence of any long-term change, either locally or in Scotland as a whole, during the last few decades. An estimate for the Cairngorms massif, based on many counts, was 5,000 birds in a peak spring and 1,300 in a low spring (Watson 1965b), and numbers on the main study area later rose 1.6-fold, which would give a peak of 8,000. This included much ground in Inverness-shire, but omitted the larger area on the Mounth. Hence a rough estimate would be 10,000 birds in a peak spring for North-East Scotland.

Author: *Adam Watson*

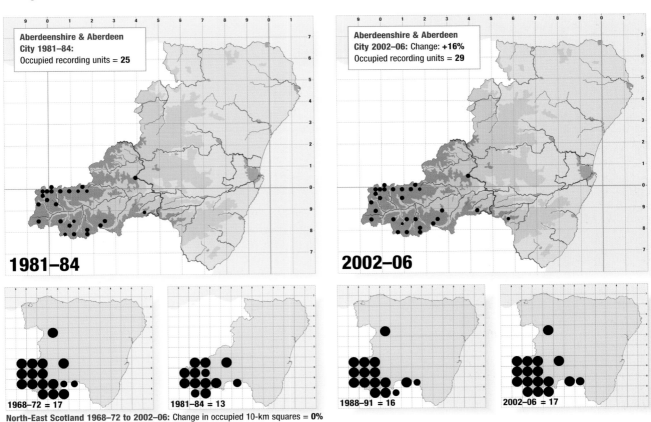

Aberdeenshire & Aberdeen City 1981–84:
Occupied recording units = **25**

1981–84

Aberdeenshire & Aberdeen City 2002–06: Change: **+16%**
Occupied recording units = **29**

2002–06

1968–72 = 17

1981–84 = 13

1988–91 = 16

2002–06 = 17

North-East Scotland 1968–72 to 2002–06: Change in occupied 10-km squares = **0%**

Chapter 3. The breeding birds of North-East Scotland: species accounts

Black Grouse

Tetrao tetrix

Scarce resident. Estimated population in North-East Scotland: **700 lekking males** (20% of Scottish population, 14% of UK)

Red list; UK BAP list

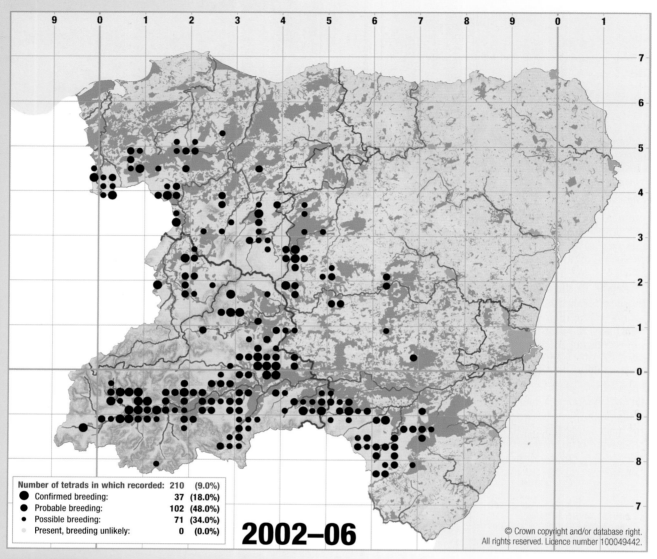

Number of tetrads in which recorded: 210   (9.0%)
- ● Confirmed breeding: 37   (18.0%)
- ● Probable breeding: 102   (48.0%)
- ● Possible breeding: 71   (34.0%)
- Present, breeding unlikely: 0   (0.0%)

2002–06

Black Grouse, Donside, April 2008. © *Ed Duthie*

Habitat and breeding ecology

Black Grouse are found on moorland edges, usually close to forest plantations and native pine and birch woodlands, now almost entirely above 300 m, though at lower altitudes in the past. In North-East Scotland, they may be more often associated with open habitats than they are in other parts of the UK, but they may also occupy large restocked areas in forests. Leks are usually on grassland areas within moorland, or on short Heather, burnt patches or boggy ground. Of 62 nests found in the Forest of Birse and Glen Tanar between 1982 and 1986, 92% (n=29) in Birse were on dry Heather moorland especially where there were some scattered, naturally-regenerated Scots Pines. In Glen Tanar, nests were found in the old pine forest and in both wet and dry moorland sites. Between 30% and 69% of hens nested within 1 km of the four leks at which they were caught and marked (Picozzi 1986). In late summer, broods were most often found in wet moorland flushes where there were abundant invertebrates.

Scottish distribution and status

Black Grouse are still widely distributed across upland Scotland, though declining in many areas. The national survey of 2005 estimated 3,344 (range 2,580–4,171) lekking (displaying) males. In Grampian, Tayside and Fife there were

1,500 males - a 7% decline compared with the previous survey in 1995–96, though this was not statistically significant. Numbers in south and west Scotland declined significantly (Sim *et al.* 2008).

Distribution and status in North-East Scotland

The main concentration (about 75%) of Black Grouse in North-East Scotland is in mid and upper Deeside particularly on Mar Lodge, Balmoral and Dinnet estates. In 2006 there were 194 males at 14 leks on Mar Lodge estate. The increase here is associated with a reduction in deer grazing pressure on moorland and woodland vegetation. In Donside, leks are more scattered, though some still hold 20 males or more. Black Grouse are rather scarce in Moray and most leks, other than those on the Glenlivet estate, are small or consist of just a single displaying cock. An exceptional lek of 14 males was recorded in north Moray in 2005. A small outlying population at Aultmore appears now to have gone. In Aberdeenshire, the main range retraction has been in the east of the area, in lower Deeside and one or two lowland peat mosses. For example, birds were still present at Turclossie Moss near New Pitsligo in 1989, but are absent now. Control of crows and Foxes on shooting estates probably allows populations to persist on open moorland and hill ground, but the main influences on numbers appear to be forest felling and restocking together with variation in grazing pressure.

Changes in distribution

There was apparently a decrease in range between 1968–72 and 1988–91, though this may in part have been due to observer effort. Since then, the distribution has stabilised or increased in some areas. Small losses from outlying peripheral hill sites and some lowland mosses have been balanced by infill in core areas, and occupied recording units increased by 21% from 1981–84 to 2002–06. This trend is not shared by north Moray, where afforestation and moorland fragmentation have made conditions less suitable, but forest restructuring in the coming years may help this situation.

Black Grouse, Glen Gairn, May 2009. © *Ed Duthie*

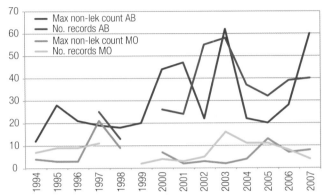
Fig 1. Black Grouse population change indicators, Aberdeenshire (AB) and Moray (MO).

Population and trends

A survey in 2005 revealed 506 lekking males in Aberdeenshire and Moray. This was a minimum as not all leks were visited; a total of *c.*650 lekking males was estimated by Francis & Pout (2006). Recently, other leks have been found and some Deeside lek numbers increased further since 2005; a wide-scale survey of North-East Scotland in 2009 found 659 lekking males (Francis 2009). Taking into account unsurveyed birds, lekking males in the area may now number around 700. Evidence from all sources (see Figure 1) suggests numbers are stable or increasing in Deeside and parts of Donside, though they may be decreasing in Moray.

Author: *Ian Francis*

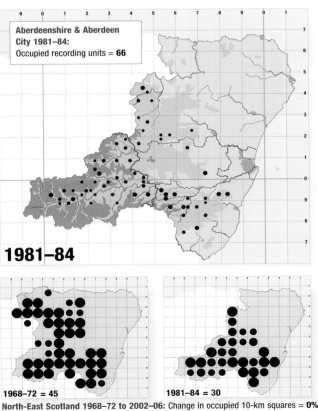

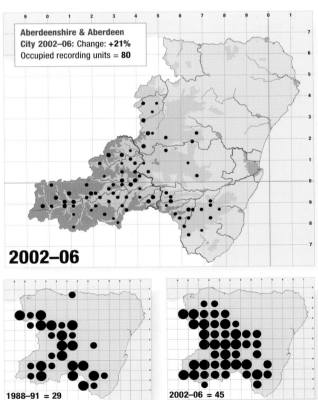

North-East Scotland 1968–72 to 2002–06: Change in occupied 10-km squares = 0%

Capercaillie

Tetrao urogallus

Rare resident. Estimated breeding population in North-East Scotland: **220 adults** (11% of Scottish and UK populations)

Red list; Schedule 1; Annex 1; UK and Scottish BAP lists

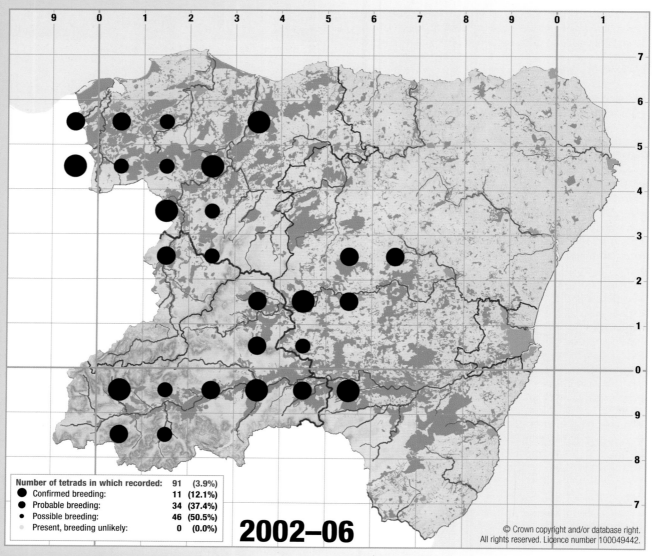

Number of tetrads in which recorded: 91 (3.9%)
- ● Confirmed breeding: 11 (12.1%)
- ● Probable breeding: 34 (37.4%)
- ● Possible breeding: 46 (50.5%)
- ○ Present, breeding unlikely: 0 (0.0%)

2002–06

© Crown copyright and/or database right.
All rights reserved. Licence number 100049442.

Habitat and breeding ecology

Capercaillie are found mainly in coniferous forests, particularly mature Scots Pine woods, and usually nest and rear young where there is abundant Blaeberry. In North-East Scotland, hens also nest in birch woods with Blaeberry and in commercial woods comprising mainly Sitka Spruce and Lodgepole Pine. Forest bogs and wet flushes with Cottongrass are used by hens in spring and by hens with broods in summer. Old Caledonian pinewood remnants, such as at Glen Tanar and Ballochbuie, used to support very high densities of birds and much of the North-East Scotland population. However, over the last 15 or so years, this has changed because of reduced productivity within these Caledonian pinewoods, and most Capercaillie are now found in conifer plantations, where some densities are now much higher than in Glen Tanar and Ballochbuie.

Scottish distribution and status

The current Capercaillie range in Scotland extends from a remnant, and very isolated, southern population at Loch Lomond, northwards to the shores of the Dornoch Firth. The tiny Glen Affric population is also isolated and effectively extinct but a small population is still found in upper Tayside. In Moray, lower Deeside and Strathdon, small and generally

declining populations persist. However, the bulk of the population is now within the Cairngorms National Park boundary, particularly in Strathspey. The most recent national census, during the winter of 2003–04 (Eaton *et al.* 2007) estimated a population of 1,980 birds (95% confidence limits 1,284–2,785). This estimate was 84% bigger than that of the previous survey in 1998–99, but the confidence limits of both surveys were wide. Other counts in the intervening period between the two national surveys confirmed the increase, at least in some parts of the range.

Distribution and status in North-East Scotland

Two sub-populations of Capercaillie occur in North-East Scotland, with a total of 31 known leks active in at least one year in 2002–06; 17 of these leks had displaying cocks in every year in 2002–06. Only three leks had an average of more than 4 cocks during this period. The smaller sub-population, in Moray, is found at low density in woods along the rivers Findhorn and Spey, with 11 known active leks in this area in at least one year in 2002–06. In 2006, based on extrapolations from lek counts, this sub-population is likely to have contained at least 60 birds. The larger sub-population is located in Deeside and Strathdon, with most birds between Ballater and Strachan. In total, there were 20 known leks in this area that were active in at least one year in 2002–06 and in 2006, based on extrapolations from lek counts, this sub-population is likely to have contained at least 160 birds. In both sub-populations it is likely that the number of leks known in 2002–06 represents the bulk of the extant population, as extensive survey work was carried out during this period. A genetic analysis (Piertney *et al.* 2007) found that the Moray and Deeside/Strathdon sub-populations were genetically distinct, suggesting that dispersal between the two sub-populations is infrequent.

Changes in distribution

Since 1981, Capercaillie have disappeared almost completely from areas east of a line from Banchory to Keith. The remaining few birds east of this line, near Bennachie, have a precarious hold. Throughout Moray, between 1999 and 2006, the population continued to shrink and in 2006 appeared to be confined to a small number of core woods, with very few birds reported elsewhere. A similar pattern was observed in Strathdon, with only three active leks on two sites remaining in 2006. In Deeside, the situation has been more positive, although there has been a shift in the distribution, such that plantations replaced the designated Caledonian pinewoods as the most important habitat. In 2002, about half of all known lekking cocks were in designated Caledonian pinewoods (Special Protection Areas). By 2006, this had dropped to 25% of all known lekking cocks. Table 1 illustrates the changes in the number of cocks across North-East Scotland in 2002–06.

Table 1. Comparison between the numbers of cocks counted on 27 leks in 2002 with number counted in 2006, with consistent effort.

Region	2002	2006
Moray	19 (8 active leks)	11 (5 active leks)
Deeside	23 (13 active leks)	31 (12 active leks)
Strathdon	16 (6 active leks)	7 (3 active leks)

Table 2. Number of cocks counted on 27 leks with consistent effort from 2002 to 2006.

Sub-population and no. of leks	2002	2003	2004	2005	2006
Moray (n=8 leks)	19	17	15	11	11
Deeside/Strathdon (n=19 leks)	39	32	35	46	38

Population and trends

In North-East Scotland, there were probably around 220 adults (110 breeding hens) in 2006. This is based on a 1:1 sex ratio, which was found in the last national survey (Eaton *et al.* 2007), having multiplied the number of cocks counted at leks by two, based on the fact that cocks on leks are thought to be underestimated by 50% (Watson & Moss 2008), due to young cocks (less than 3 years old) not displaying regularly or displaying away from leks. It is very unlikely that the population was much larger than this. Between 2002–06, 27 leks in North-East Scotland were counted with relatively consistent effort in each year. These counts revealed a decline in Moray, and a more stable population in Deeside and Strathdon (see Table 2). It is not possible to obtain reliable counts of hens at leks. However, hen densities were estimated during brood counts carried out at five sites in Deeside. These revealed a worrying decline in hens between 2002–06 (see Table 3). Productivity in Deeside and Strathdon was comparable with national productivity estimates, and was extremely low in 2003 and 2004. It should also be borne in mind, that these counts are made at what are thought to be the best sites.

Much conservation work has been carried out for Capercaillie, particularly in Deeside, with many deer fences removed and marked. Collisions with such fences, as well as the indiscriminate use of snares, are implicated in the decline of the species in North-East Scotland (Watson & Moss 2008). In addition, most Capercaillie woods in Deeside are surrounded by heavily keepered grouse moors, so predation pressure is probably lower than in Moray, where the landscape surrounding Capercaillie woods tends to be agricultural, with high densities of generalist predators such as crows and Foxes. Therefore, it is not surprising that the Capercaillie population in Deeside appear to be faring better than the Moray population, which appears to be in terminal decline. If the fortunes of Capercaillie in designated pinewoods in Deeside could be improved, the long-term viability of the species in the area would be enhanced. However, habitat for Capercaillie in all areas covered by this Atlas is limited in terms of extent and quality, so all of the sub-populations remain vulnerable.

Author: *Kenny Kortland*

Table 3. Brood counts in Deeside and Strathdon from 2002 to 2006. Counts carried out by Game and Wildlife Conservation Trust and Robert Moss.

Year	Area searched (km^2)	Cocks	Hens	Hens per km^2	Broods	Chicks	Chicks per hen	Chicks per hen Scotland
2002	9.1	9	14	1.51	7	10	1.13	1.1
2003	13.4	24	19	1.42	5	8	0.42	0.86
2004	15.2	13	18	1.18	4	9	0.50	0.31
2005	15.2	14	11	0.72	3	9	0.82	0.72
2006	15.2	10	12	0.8	5	13	1.1	1.4

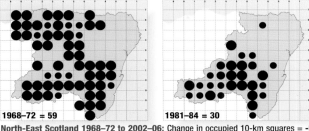

1968–72 = 59

1981–84 = 30

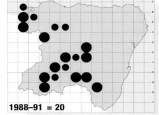

1988–91 = 20

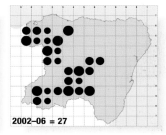

2002–06 = 27

North-East Scotland 1968–72 to 2002–06: Change in occupied 10-km squares = -54%

Capercaillie, Mar Forest, April 1992. © *Stuart Rae*

Capercaillie, Mar Forest, May 1975. © *Rab Rae*

Glen Tanar

Including one of Scotland's largest and best known native Caledonian pinewoods, Glen Tanar encompasses large areas of open moorland, and also contains broad-leaved woodland, rivers, burns and ponds. Breeding birds of the estate include Mandarin, Goosander and Goldeneye, Red Grouse and Black Grouse with Ptarmigan on the high southern edge at Mount Keen. As with all of Deeside, Capercaillie are now very rarely seen in the native pinewoods. Several birds of prey nest, along with seven species of wader. Whinchat and Ring Ouzel are present in open ground areas and Cuckoo, Green Woodpecker, Tree Pipit, Wood Warbler and Spotted Flycatcher breed in woodlands. All three species of crossbill are known from here. April 2011 © *Adam Francis*

Red-legged Partridge

Alectoris rufa

Rare resident breeder. Commonly released on shooting estates. Estimated population in North-East Scotland: up to *100 pairs* (20% of Scottish population, <1% of UK)

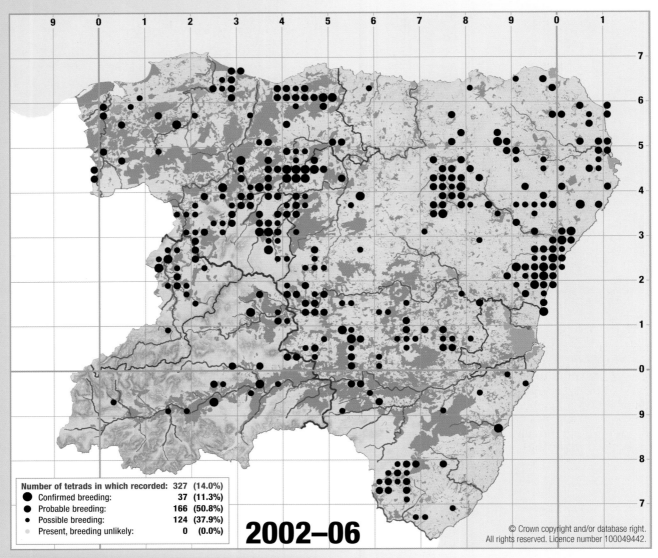

Number of tetrads in which recorded:	327	(14.0%)
● Confirmed breeding:	37	(11.3%)
● Probable breeding:	166	(50.8%)
● Possible breeding:	124	(37.9%)
○ Present, breeding unlikely:	0	(0.0%)

2002–06

Red-legged Partridge, near Alford, August 2008. © *Bill Burns*

Habitat and breeding biology

The favoured habitat of Red-legged Partridges is thought to be open, farmed areas with dry, sandy soils and warm summer temperatures (Parish in *BS3*). In North-East Scotland, however, the release of birds for recreational shooting means that they occur in a wide range of habitats including rough grassland and moorland edges. They nest in long vegetation, often along the edge of agricultural fields. Females may lay two almost simultaneous clutches, with one being incubated by her and the other by her mate (Jenkins 1957, Green 1984). Eggs hatch in June or July but successful breeding is rare in Scotland (Parish in *BS3*).

Scottish distribution and status

Ritchie (1920) contrasted the success of establishing Red-legged Partridges in England with the lack of success in Scotland although he noted that "in recent years it has become established in Fifeshire." By 1953 many attempts had been made to introduce them into Scotland without success (Baxter & Rintoul 1953). Parslow (1973) gave no breeding records for Scotland. By 1968, releases had taken place and breeding had been noted in Aberdeenshire and Moray but it is uncertain whether self-supporting feral populations became established (Thom 1986). The current distribution in Scotland is patchy, covering the low ground areas of eastern and southern Scotland, with isolated populations on a few islands off the west coast including Islay, Colonsay, Arran and Bute. The Scottish population was estimated at 1,300–3,500 pairs in 2000; this number being dependent on continuing releases. The self-sustaining population may be less than 500 pairs (Parish in *BS3*).

Distribution and status in North-East Scotland

Red-legged Partridges occupy a patchy range with concentrations in some areas, separated by much unoccupied countryside. Areas of high density are explained by repeated large releases of captive-reared stock on shooting estates. In Moray this is evident to the east of Elgin, inland from Buckie, in the Keith-Dufftown area, up Strath Avon and in Glenlivet. The occupied range in Aberdeenshire is centred on the Fyvie-Turriff area, the Mearns around Fettercairn, mid Donside and the coastal lowlands between Newburgh, Newmachar and Balmedie. Releases on a smaller scale also take place more widely. Although they do breed occasionally and with limited success (D. Jenkins pers. comm.), in the absence of these releases the distribution would undoubtedly be far more restricted; indeed it is uncertain whether the species would survive at all in the North-East.

Changes in distribution

The Red-legged Partridge has shown considerable range expansion due to large scale releases of birds for recreational game shooting. In 1968–1972 birds were present in five 10-km squares with breeding confirmed in four of these (*BTO 1st Atlas*) but by 1988–91 there were 25 occupied 10-km squares, although breeding was proved in only five (*BTO 2nd Atlas*). A huge increase occurred by 2002–06 when confirmed breeding was recorded in 22 10-km squares and birds were present in a further 56 10-km squares. However, breeding was only confirmed in a small number of squares which suggests (for a species for which breeding is relatively easy to prove) that birds are being

released into areas where habitat and climate do not favour the establishment of a self-sustaining breeding population. In 1981–84, Red-legged Partridges were located in Aberdeenshire in only 20 recording units (*NES 1st Atlas*) but by 2002–06 this number had increased to 131. Over this period they have spread onto low ground on the Buchan plain, into the Mearns, up the Dee valley (aided by further releases) and westwards to the Moray border. The large increase in the distribution reflects a change in recreational game shooting interests, with Red-legged Partridges being released on an annual basis to supplement the small naturalised breeding population.

Population and trends

The population of Red-legged Partridges in North-East Scotland has shown a spectacular rise in numbers and distribution between 1988–91 and 2002–06 due to the increase in popularity of releasing them for sport shooting. Some very large releases have taken place in recent years, notably 10,000 on Invercauld Estate in 2005 (*NESBR 2005*). Although birds were recorded in 327 tetrads during 2002–06, and a minimum of 37 apparently breeding pairs was found, it is not clear if a self-sustaining population could exist in North-East Scotland if large-scale releases ceased. Given that the estimated self-sustaining population in Scotland is less than 500 pairs (Parish in *BS3*) the maximum number in North-East Scotland is unlikely to exceed 100 pairs. This would make the population vulnerable, in the absence of continued releases, to extinction from a run of cool, wet summers or severe winters.

Author: *Alister Clunas*

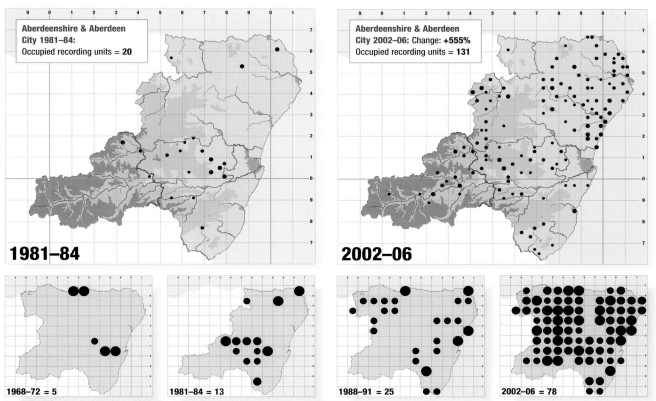

Aberdeenshire & Aberdeen City 1981–84:
Occupied recording units = **20**

1981–84

Aberdeenshire & Aberdeen City 2002–06: Change: **+555%**
Occupied recording units = **131**

2002–06

1968–72 = 5

1981–84 = 13

1988–91 = 25

2002–06 = 78

North-East Scotland 1968–72 to 2002–06: Change in occupied 10-km squares = **+1460%**

Grey Partridge

Perdix perdix

Common resident. Released on some shooting estates. Estimated population in North-East Scotland: *3,400–3,650 pairs* (28% of Scottish population, 5% of UK)

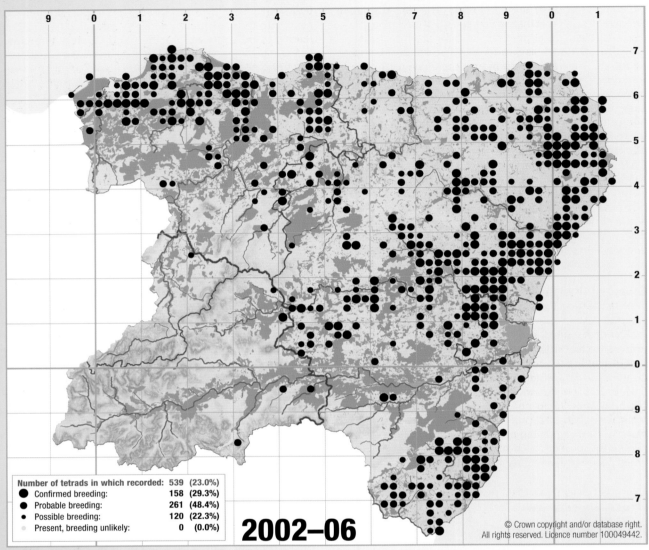

Number of tetrads in which recorded:	539	(23.0%)
Confirmed breeding:	158	(29.3%)
Probable breeding:	261	(48.4%)
Possible breeding:	120	(22.3%)
Present, breeding unlikely:	0	(0.0%)

2002–06

Grey Partridge, Skene, June 1985. © *John Young*

Habitat and breeding biology

Grey Partridges are widely distributed in most lowland parts of North-East Scotland, with highest densities in areas which contain a combination of arable farmland and suitable cover for nesting. They nest on the ground in areas of dense cover. Hedge bases and other field boundaries are probably the most common nest sites, but other uncultivated areas adjacent to farmland, such as coastal grassland and heath and even young conifer plantations, also provide nesting habitats. Winter coveys are usually not recorded after February, and egg laying starts in April or May with the first chicks usually being recorded in North-East Scotland in early June.

Scottish distribution and status

The species is widespread across most parts of lowland Scotland, usually below 300 m, and is most abundant in arable areas in the south and east. The Scottish population is estimated to lie within the range 10,500–14,600 pairs (Parish in *BS3*). In common with the rest of the UK, the Scottish population of the Grey Partridge has declined greatly since World War I.

Distribution and status in North-East Scotland

Grey Partridges breed widely across lowland arable areas of North-East Scotland with the majority of the population on farmland within 20 km of the coast. They are most frequent in lowland parts of Moray and the eastern lowland parts of Aberdeenshire, such as the Howe of the Mearns, lower Donside, the lower Ythan valley and in Buchan. There still seems to be a good presence in certain areas of central Aberdeenshire such as Strathbogie, Garioch and the Howe of Alford. They appear to be markedly scarcer in north-western Aberdeenshire, even in arable areas close to the coast. There are few records from ground above 300 m, although in 2004 a pair was recorded in moorland next to Loch Muick at an altitude of more than 400 m. Large areas of woodland are generally avoided, although young conifer plantations are occasionally used as nesting sites. Grey Partridges also breed in well-vegetated coastal sand dunes, such as Culbin Bar in Moray.

Changes in distribution

Some decline in the range of the Grey Partridge in North-East Scotland was noted between 1968–72 (*BTO 1st Atlas*) and 1981–84 (*NES 1st Atlas*) with this being most marked in upland areas such as upper Deeside. This contraction was confirmed in 1988–91 (*BTO 2nd Atlas*). The current distribution suggests that this decline in range is continuing, with a 9% decrease in the number of occupied recording units in Aberdeenshire/Aberdeen City between 1981–84 and 2002–06. The greatest loss of range has continued to be in upland areas, with birds no longer recorded around Braemar, only a few records in the Ballater/Aboyne area and none in upper Donside. This decline may be due to more frequent cold, wet periods in early summer when broods are highly vulnerable to chilling, and to 'cleaner' and more intensive agricultural practice with fewer weedy fields and less marginal vegetation providing cover from predation.

Grey Partridge, Echt, June 1977. © *Ed Duthie*

Population and trends

The Scottish population is around 10,500–14,600 pairs (Parish in *BS3*) and based on the area of suitable habitat in the North-East as a proportion of the area of such habitat across Scotland as a whole (approximately 25%), a North-East Scotland population of 3,400–3,650 pairs can be estimated. The Grey Partridge population continues to decline, with the BBS recording a 39% decrease in the UK between 1994 and 2007 (Risely *et al.* 2008) and a steady decline in abundance in North-East Scotland between 1994 and 2006. This reduction in the size of the population is probably due to a number of factors such as predation and a shortage of insect food for chicks.

Author: *David Law*

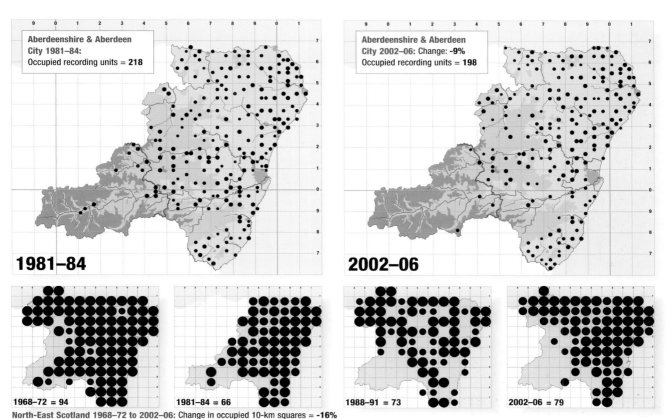

Aberdeenshire & Aberdeen City 1981–84:
Occupied recording units = 218

1981–84

Aberdeenshire & Aberdeen City 2002–06: Change: -9%
Occupied recording units = 198

2002–06

1968–72 = 94   1981–84 = 66   1988–91 = 73   2002–06 = 79

North-East Scotland 1968–72 to 2002–06: Change in occupied 10-km squares = -16%

Quail

Coturnix coturnix

Rare summer visitor and breeder. Passage migrant. Estimated population in North-East Scotland:
20–30 singing males (46% of Scottish population, 16% of UK)

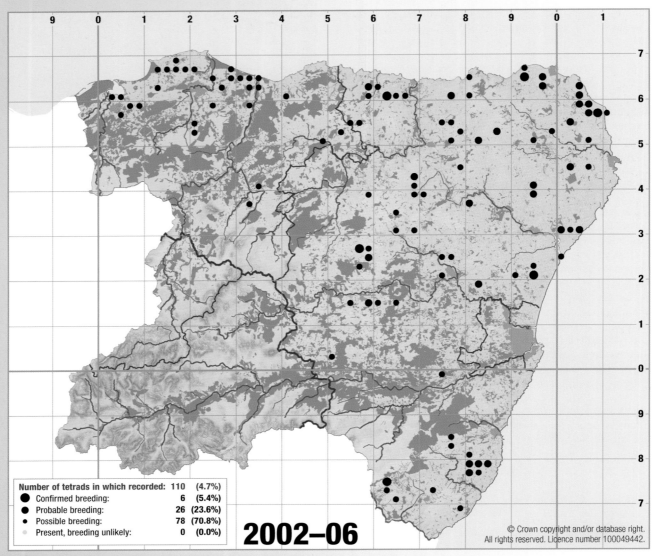

Number of tetrads in which recorded:	110	(4.7%)
● Confirmed breeding:	6	(5.4%)
● Probable breeding:	26	(23.6%)
● Possible breeding:	78	(70.8%)
○ Present, breeding unlikely:	0	(0.0%)

2002–06

Quail, Morayscairn, June 1997. © *Martin Cook*

Habitat and breeding biology

Quail occur predominantly on lowland farms. Males may be polygynous and are usually heard singing from cropped land, particularly spring sown Barley (Gill 1992, Watson 2001), from late May until August. They nest on the ground within crops or grassy fields, feeding on seeds and insects. Quail have developed a unique breeding strategy: birds in north Africa or Mediterranean areas may nest early in the year and their young are capable of northerly migration two months after hatching. It is believed that males which are heard singing in North-East Scotland later in the summer could be young birds raised further south the same year, or adults that have already bred elsewhere (Harvey in *BS3*).

Scottish distribution and status

In Scotland, Quail are mainly found in the eastern lowlands but also in the central lowlands, the south-west and the Northern Isles. The breeding population is estimated at 10-100 calling males (Harvey in *BS3*); however, numbers may depend on the strength of spring passage, which varies annually. The largest recent influx occurred during 1989 when 750 singing males were recorded (Murray 1991).

The Breeding Birds of North-East Scotland

Distribution and status in North-East Scotland

Quail arrive in the region from mid May but most are not recorded until early June, after which, singing birds may be heard until late August. Nests and broods of chicks are very difficult to find among standing cereal crops, which explains the low incidence (4.5%) of occupied tetrads where breeding was confirmed. The distribution map is a composite for five years and therefore exaggerates the distribution in any one year. Nonetheless it indicates the extent of the range which Quail might occupy in a year of high population. Clearly the arable lowlands are favoured, especially in Moray, Buchan, Garioch and south of Stonehaven. Despite variations from year to year, surveys on Aberdeenshire farmland have revealed the presence of birds annually at some sites such as near Rosehearty and also at Barras in southern Aberdeenshire (where up to eight singing birds were present annually).

Changes in distribution

Since the early 1970s, Quail have been described as rare or uncommon summer visitors to the region. Between 1975 and 1988, 13 birds were recorded in Aberdeenshire, with four in 1976 being the highest annual total (*NES 1st Atlas*). During 1981–84, records came from just six sites. The increase in distribution during 2002–06 could be due to the erratic nature of Quail occurrence and increased observer coverage during fieldwork for the present Atlas, although evidence from Scotland as a whole suggests that a genuine sustained increase may have taken place in recent decades (Harvey in *BS3*). Similarly, in Moray, there were few records in the 1970s and 1980s although, in common with Aberdeenshire, a widespread influx occurred in 1989 across north Moray (Cook 1992). Since 1992, they have been recorded in every year.

Populations and trends

Estimating the breeding population by the number of singing males may be misleading - males sing on migration and are known to move around within summers, in

Quail, Fair Isle, April 2007. © *Paul Baxter*

response to the availability of mates (Harvey in *BS3*). Once mated, males may stop singing, thus becoming difficult to detect. However, the number of singing males reported during each year of Atlas fieldwork, together with the numbers during 1989 when the largest influx recorded in the region took place, is shown in Table 1.

Table 1. Singing male Quail in North-East Scotland.

	1989	2002	2003	2004	2005	2006
Moray	86	13	4	2	6	8
Aberdeenshire	60	20	17	34	33	16

Based on these data, and bearing in mind the possibility of some double-counting of shifting birds, the recent population could be estimated at 20–30 singing males, but with substantial variation from year to year.

Author: *Hywel Maggs*

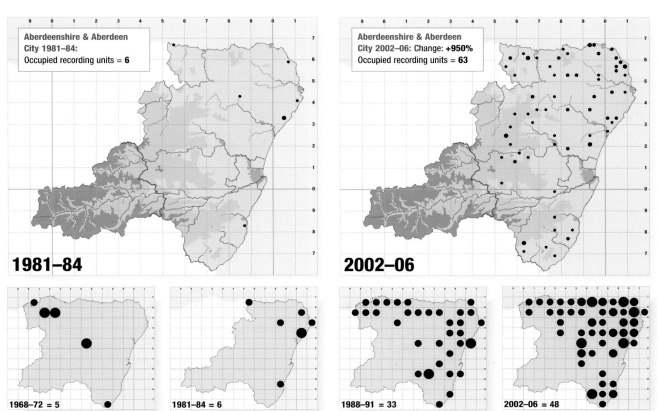

Aberdeenshire & Aberdeen City 1981–84: Occupied recording units = **6**

1981–84

Aberdeenshire & Aberdeen City 2002–06: Change: **+950%** Occupied recording units = **63**

2002–06

1968–72 = 5

1981–84 = 6

1988–91 = 33

2002–06 = 48

North-East Scotland 1968–72 to 2002–06: Change in occupied 10-km squares = **+860%**

Pheasant

Phasianus colchicus

Very common resident. Commonly released on shooting estates. Estimated population in North-East Scotland: *40,000 'pairs'* (11% of Scottish population, 2% of UK)

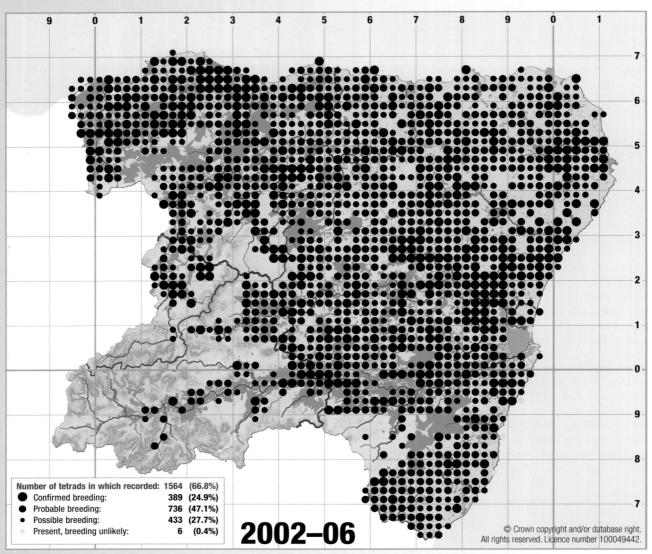

Number of tetrads in which recorded:	1564	(66.8%)
● Confirmed breeding:	389	(24.9%)
● Probable breeding:	736	(47.1%)
● Possible breeding:	433	(27.7%)
· Present, breeding unlikely:	6	(0.4%)

2002–06

Habitat and breeding biology

Self-sustaining populations of wild Pheasants are found primarily in arable areas which provide a mixture of woodland for shelter and night time roosting, along with open fields for feeding. Smaller numbers occupy a range of habitats from coastal scrub to suburban areas and the moorland edge. In parts of Buchan, the only cover may be rank vegetation along ditches and hedgerows or in Turnip fields. Cover crops such as Kale and other brassicas, which are sown specifically for game birds, can harbour large concentrations of (predominantly released) Pheasants, and cover is especially important in late winter when other vegetation has died down (D. Jenkins pers. comm.). The nest is made on the ground wherever there is dense vegetation or scrub to offer shelter and concealment. Egg laying begins in late April and chicks hatch from late May onwards; small juveniles from replacement clutches can be seen as late as early September. In autumn, large numbers often congregate on stubbles, and in many places they are fed to maintain high densities and to keep them on the desired areas for shooting.

Scottish distribution and status

The main populations of Pheasants are to be found in the south and east of Scotland as far north as Orkney. Optimum areas stretch up the east coast from Borders to Aberdeenshire. They are absent from the western Highlands, Outer Hebrides and Shetland. The most recent estimate, in 2007, suggested a naturalised breeding population of 348,000–367,000 pairs in Scotland (Parish in *BS3*).

Distribution and status in North-East Scotland

Pheasants are widespread breeders in the arable lowlands of North-East Scotland and, as males are conspicuous visually and through their distinctive calls, the map is likely to be fairly complete. What is more difficult to determine is the extent of the natural population within North-East Scotland, as it is difficult to decide with certainty whether birds which are reported as possible breeders are wild or of captive origin. They are found throughout the lowland areas and as far up Deeside as Inverey, which is the highest cultivated farmland in the survey area. They overlap with Grey Partridge over much of the range; both species are encouraged on sporting estates and farms where shooting takes place. They also live alongside Red Grouse and Black Grouse on some moorland fringes, where release pens are nearby. Close examination reveals absence from many of the larger moorland and forest blocks, the uplands above around 400 m and from the city of Aberdeen. There is also a rather

The Breeding Birds of North-East Scotland

lower density within Buchan, perhaps due to the limited presence of suitable woodland cover. They do, however, inhabit the mature plantations of the Moray coast where block felling within the forests offers feeding opportunities. Birds were found on the sparsely vegetated coastal bars off Culbin Forest, although breeding was not proved there.

Changes in distribution

At the 10-km square level there has been no change in the number of occupied squares since 1968–72 (*BTO 1st Atlas*). Comparison of the Aberdeenshire/Aberdeen City maps for 1981–84 and 2002–06 also reveals very little change in general distribution. There has, however, been a substantial 30% increase in occupied recording units in the Buchan area, north-east of a line from the mouth of the River Deveron to the mouth of the River Ythan. Factors such as favourable habitat change, release localities and improved observer coverage may all play a part in this apparent spread.

Population and trends

Pheasants were probably introduced into Britain by the Romans prior to 400 AD and were well established over much of England by the late 16th century, when they were first brought into Scotland (Parish in *BS3*). Large numbers, often several hundreds up to many thousands, are released on estates for shooting purposes and to supplement the wild population. *The Economic and Environmental Impact of Sporting Shooting* (PACEC report 2006) estimated that as many as 22 million birds were being released in the UK each autumn and 89% of surveyed lowland shooting estates provided supplementary feed to game birds through the winter. Many of these released birds are shot or do not survive, and released birds do not breed well (D. Jenkins pers. comm.). Attempts to estimate the breeding population of Pheasants in North-East Scotland are complicated by the lack of local data, the impact of releases on shooting estates and the polygynous breeding strategy of the species. In 1993 the average British breeding density

Pheasant, Glen Muick, June 2009. © *Rab Rae*

was given as 3.9 territorial males/km^2 and 7.3 females/km^2 (*BTO 2nd Atlas*). Assuming that this figure remains true, and is relevant to North-East Scotland, it might be reasonable to adopt a density of 30 breeding females per tetrad where breeding was confirmed or probable, and 15 where breeding was only possible. This translates into a population of around 40,000 'pairs', though this term is not very appropriate for this species.

Author: *Rob Fuchs*

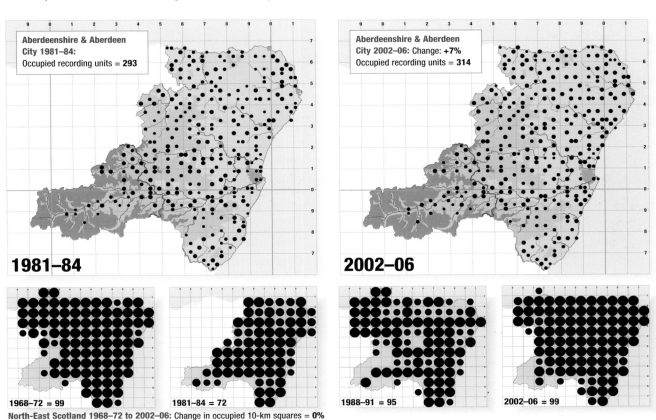

Aberdeenshire & Aberdeen City 1981–84: Occupied recording units = **293**

1981–84

Aberdeenshire & Aberdeen City 2002–06: Change: **+7%** Occupied recording units = **314**

2002–06

1968–72 = 99   1981–84 = 72   1988–91 = 95   2002–06 = 99

North-East Scotland 1968–72 to 2002–06: Change in occupied 10-km squares = 0%

Red-throated Diver
Gavia stellata

Very rare breeder. Present on the coast all year. Estimated population in North-East Scotland: Up to 3 pairs (<1% of Scottish and UK population)

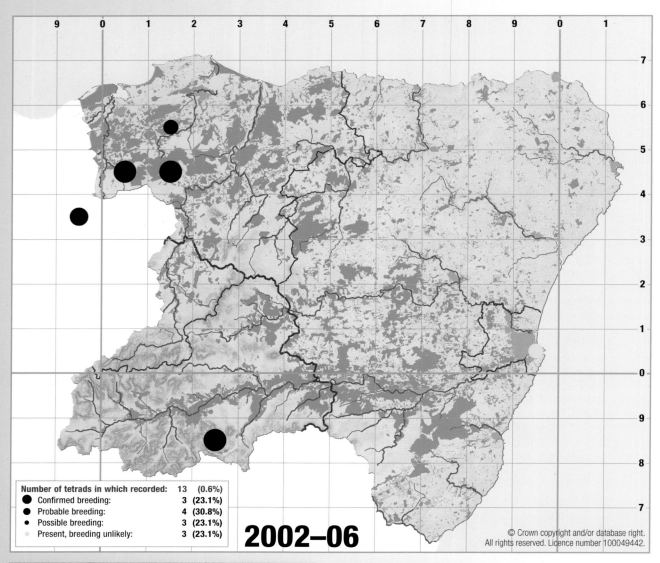

Number of tetrads in which recorded:	13	(0.6%)
● Confirmed breeding:	3	(23.1%)
● Probable breeding:	4	(30.8%)
• Possible breeding:	3	(23.1%)
○ Present, breeding unlikely:	3	(23.1%)

2002–06

Red-throated Diver, Iceland, June 2004. © *Sam Alexander*

Habitat and breeding biology
Red-throated Divers typically nest on small lochans on blanket bogs and moorland. During 2002–06, breeding was proved on only three such lochans whose areas were 0.5, 1.0 and 2.0 ha respectively. Two were at an altitude of 380–390 m above sea level while the third was at 730 m. The divers usually arrive on the breeding lochs in April and the clutch of two eggs is laid in May. Some birds remain inland until at least mid August, even if breeding is unsuccessful.

Scottish distribution and status
The Scottish breeding distribution shows a marked northerly and westerly bias, corresponding to areas of bog and moorland with small lochans. The range extends as far south as the Mull of Kintyre but main concentrations are in the Outer Hebrides, Orkney and Shetland with good numbers in the coastal areas of the extreme north-west of the mainland. There is a scattering of inland pairs throughout the Highlands (*BTO 2nd Atlas*). The Scottish population was estimated at 1,255 breeding pairs in 2006 (Holling *et al.* 2009) which represents an apparent 34% increase since 1994.

The Breeding Birds of North-East Scotland

Red-throated Diver, Canada, June 2000. © *John Chapman*

Distribution and status in North-East Scotland

During the five years 2002–06, Red-throated Divers were found inland only in Moray and upper Deeside. Nesting was confirmed on three lochans and there were four other sites where breeding was considered probable. During the breeding season, birds regularly leave the nesting lochans, which typically contain inadequate food for a pair and brood, to fish on larger lochs. Such behaviour may therefore account for some of the instances of 'probable breeding'.

Changes in distribution

There is no suggestion that Red-throated Divers have ever been anything but rare breeders in North-East Scotland. A pair bred in Aberdeenshire on at least one occasion in the early 1980s (*NES 1st Atlas*) and breeding first took place in Moray in 1986 (Cook 1992). Since that time the population has failed to spread, despite the presence of other apparently suitable breeding lochans. The majority of Scottish Red-throated Divers commute from the breeding lochans to the sea or larger lochs to fish, and the distance from the former and general scarcity of the latter may be one reason why they have remained rare in North-East Scotland.

Population and trends

The known breeding population has never exceeded three pairs in one year. Even if the 'probable breeding' records for the Atlas years did relate to nesting attempts they show a composite picture for the five years and overstate the position in any one year. It is possible that the occasional pair may nest undetected on a remote lochan but it is probably safe to say that the annual breeding population never exceeds five pairs and may be as few as one or two. This has remained the case since the early 1980s.

Author: *Martin Cook*

Red-throated Diver, Clyde, June 2006. © *John Anderson*

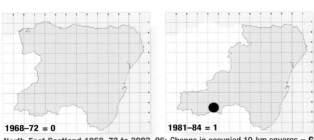

1968–72 = 0

1981–84 = 1

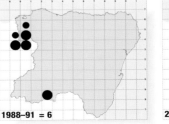

1988–91 = 6

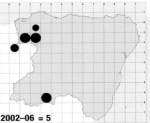

2002–06 = 5

North-East Scotland 1968–72 to 2002–06: Change in occupied 10-km squares = **Gain**

Black-throated Diver

Gavia arctica

Occasional breeder. Winter visitor and passage migrant. Estimated population in North-East Scotland: **0–1 pair** (<1% of Scottish and UK population)

Amber list; Schedule 1; Annex 1; UK and Scottish BAP lists

Number of tetrads in which recorded:	5	(0.2%)
● Confirmed breeding:	0	(0.0%)
● Probable breeding:	2	(40.0%)
• Possible breeding:	3	(60.0%)
○ Present, breeding unlikely:	0	(0.0%)

Black-throated Diver, North-East Scotland, June 2007. © *Martin Cook*

Habitat and breeding biology

Black-throated Divers breed beside nutrient-poor lochs on peaty moorlands. Nesting has been reported on lochs as small as 0.05 km^2 but larger lochs are preferred. Pairs catch fish either on the breeding loch or on larger lochs nearby. The nest is usually an open scrape lined with a little vegetation and situated very close to the water's edge. If the loch contains a small island then this is often used. Floating rafts are readily adopted where these have been provided as part of a conservation programme, though a raft placed on a large loch in North-East Scotland for five years was not occupied. Lochs are reoccupied in March or early April and the clutch, usually of two eggs, is generally laid in May - the third week in May being the peak time. If the eggs are lost, perhaps due to predation or changes in water level, a replacement clutch is often laid. Chicks fledge at about nine weeks old and soon leave the breeding lochs for the sea.

Scottish distribution and status

The breeding range extends over the northern and western Highlands of mainland Scotland together with the Outer Hebrides. About three-quarters of breeding pairs are to be found on lochs in the extensive wet peatlands of Caithness, Sutherland, west Ross & Cromarty and the Outer Hebrides. The national survey of the Scottish breeding population in 2006 found 217 pairs (Eaton *et al.* 2007).

Distribution and status in North-East Scotland

During the five-year period of this atlas, a pair was present in spring on one upland loch in 2005 and 2006. They investigated the artificial nesting raft on the loch but did not nest. In different areas in 2006 three adults were on a large loch in June and a single bird was elsewhere in July. In neither case was there any further evidence of breeding.

Black-throated Diver, North-East Scotland, July 2007. © *Ian Francis*

Changes in distribution

There is no historical record of breeding in Aberdeenshire, or in Moray as presently constituted. Nineteenth century records from Morayshire (Baxter & Rintoul 1953) relate to Lochindorb which is no longer a part of modern Moray. There have been occasional inland records in more recent years, such as 1989, 1990 and a pair briefly in 1997. However, breeding was finally proved in 2007 when one pair laid eggs but failed to raise young at an inland loch. Eggs were also laid at the same site, but failed to hatch, in 2008 and 2009.

Population and trends

In many years no Black-throated Divers are seen on inland lochs and no breeding takes place. Once breeding is established, however, occupancy of a favoured loch may become traditional and it is to be hoped that a pattern of regular breeding begins on the loch that was used by one pair in 2007–2009.

Author: *Martin Cook*

Dava moor

This moorland landscape contains many, mostly small, lochans where Red-throated Diver, Little Grebe, Greylag Goose, Goldeneye, Wigeon, Teal, Mallard and Tufted Duck breed. Waders in the adjacent moors and bogs include Golden Plover, Lapwing, Curlew, Common Sandpiper and Snipe. There are small Scots Pinewoods in which Siskin, Lesser Redpoll and a few pairs of Crested Tits can be found. Tree Pipit, Spotted Flycatcher and Redstart nest in the birchwoods. Moorland breeding species include Red Grouse, Meadow Pipit, Skylark, Stonechat and Wheatear. June 2008 © *Martin Cook*

Fulmar
Fulmarus glacialis

Very common resident and migrant breeder. Passage migrant. Estimated population in North-East Scotland: **10,000 AOS** (2% of Scottish population, <2% of UK)

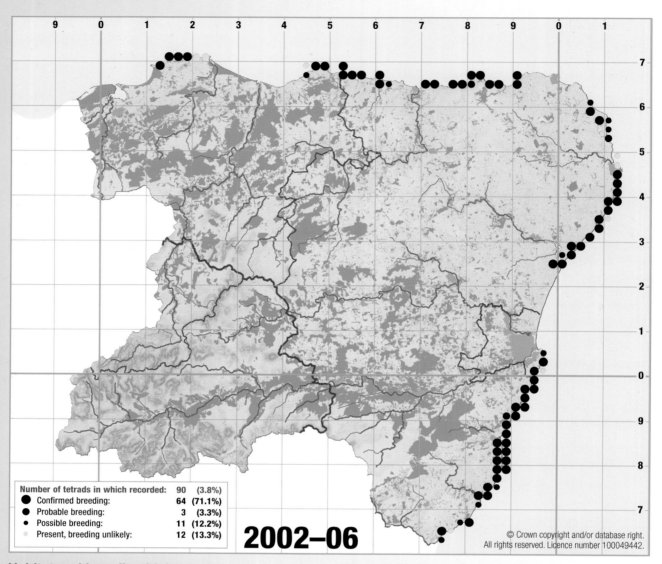

Number of tetrads in which recorded: 90 (3.8%)
- **Confirmed breeding:** 64 (71.1%)
- **Probable breeding:** 3 (3.3%)
- Possible breeding: 11 (12.2%)
- Present, breeding unlikely: 12 (13.3%)

2002–06

© Crown copyright and/or database right.
All rights reserved. Licence number 100049442.

Habitat and breeding biology

Whilst the vast majority of Fulmars breed on sea cliffs, a few also nest in dunes and man-made structures such as quarries and buildings. These are usually situated within 15 km of the coast. Birds may appear at the colonies at any time of year with most breeding birds occupying nest sites by January. A single egg, laid in May, hatches in June and the young depart in August or September. Few return to breed before they are ten years old, either at the natal colony or, not uncommonly, a distant one. Outside the breeding season, Fulmars have an oceanic distribution.

Scottish distribution and status

Fulmars are common around much of the Scottish coast, with large colonies on the Northern Isles and Outer Hebrides. They were restricted to St. Kilda (Outer Hebrides) prior to 1878 when Foula (Shetland) was colonised. There followed a rapid spread around the coast during the 20th century when numbers increased dramatically until 1990, since when a slight decline has been detected. The Scottish population was most recently counted in 1998–2002 when 486,000 apparently occupied breeding sites (AOS) were found (Seabird 2000).

Distribution and status in North-East Scotland

Fulmars' preferred breeding sites are on ledges of both vegetated and bare cliffs, which offer best protection from mammalian predators such as Brown Rat and Mink. It is unsurprising therefore that Fulmar distribution in our area closely mirrors coastline with cliffs of 30 m or more. Thus, none are found between Aberdeen and the Ythan estuary or around Fraserburgh where the coast is comprised of sand dunes. The tallest sea-cliffs such as those around the Bullers of Buchan and Fowlsheugh support the greatest number of breeding pairs. Smaller colonies are found on the coast of north Aberdeenshire and Moray where the cliffs tend to be smaller. A few apparently anomalous occupied tetrads such as at Newburgh and Rattray Head can be explained by the Fulmar's habit of occasionally using buildings or sand dunes. In such areas the numbers of birds nesting tends to be very small and they are generally less successful.

Changes in distribution

Fulmars first colonised Pennan Head in 1916 and breeding was confirmed at Fowlsheugh in 1920. By the early 1980s Fulmars had occupied most of our sea cliffs and were found breeding in dunes around Rattray and Forvie as well as on buildings in Banff, Stonehaven and Johnshaven. Fetteresso

Fulmar, Crawton, April 2008. © *Ed Duthie*

Castle (3.5 km inland from Stonehaven) and Ternemny Quarry near Aberchirder (14 km inland) held several breeding pairs (*NES 1st Atlas*). Although these last two sites are no longer occupied, Fulmar distribution in our area today is otherwise very similar; 39 recording units in Aberdeenshire/Aberdeen City were occupied in 2002–06 compared with 40 in 1981–84.

Population and trends

Between Operation Seafarer (1969–1970) and the Seabird Colony Register (1985–87), Fulmars in our area increased from 4,480 AOS to 8,775 - an increase of 96%. This increase was not uniform however. In Banff & Buchan the increase was from 2,176 to 3,192 (up 47 %) whilst in Kincardine numbers rose from 1,173 to 4,273 (up 264 %) (Lloyd *et al*.1991). Since

the time of the Seabird Colony Register, numbers have risen slightly, compared with a slight decline nationally. The population on our coasts was around 10,000 AOS in 1998–2002 (Seabird 2000), an increase of 14 % compared with 1985–87. The increase and spread of Fulmars is generally attributed to the rise in the fishing industry although it is debated whether it was an increase in offal and discards from this industry or the increase in prey species following the removal of marine predators which has benefited them most. There is evidence that these discards have recently decreased and this, together with an increased mortality from long-line fishing, may account for the recent Scottish decrease in Fulmar numbers (Tasker in *BS3*).

Author: *Richard Schofield*

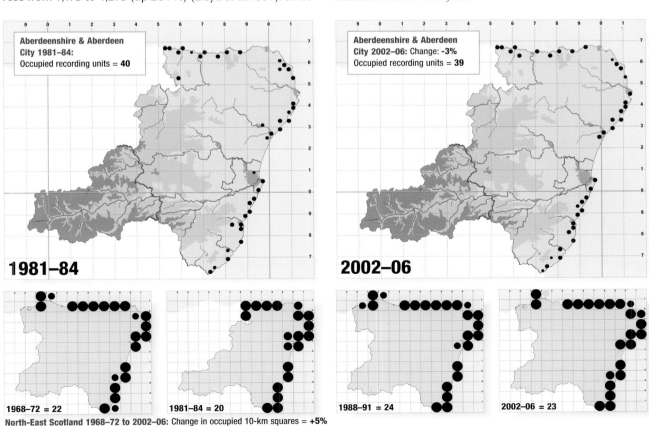

Gannet

Morus bassanus

Common breeder, in one colony. Present offshore all year. Estimated population in North-East Scotland: **1,800 pairs** (<1% of Scottish and UK population)

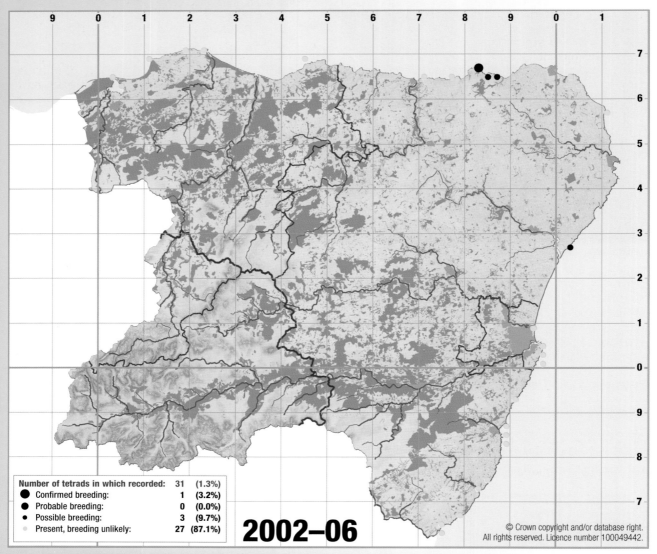

Number of tetrads in which recorded:	31	(1.3%)
● Confirmed breeding:	1	(3.2%)
● Probable breeding:	0	(0.0%)
● Possible breeding:	3	(9.7%)
● Present, breeding unlikely:	27	(87.1%)

2002–06

Gannet, Troup Head, April 2009. © *Martin Cook*

Habitat and breeding biology

The sole breeding site in North-East Scotland is at Troup Head, near Gardenstown, where the Gannets occupy broad sea cliff ledges on a largely north-facing headland. Birds are present for nine to ten months of the year. They generally arrive at the nest sites in January (earliest was 6th January 2005) although arrival can be as late as mid February. Most Scottish breeders usually lay one egg, commencing in the first week of April. At Troup Head, laying dates have varied considerably with first eggs not laid until late April/early May in the early 1990s, then becoming earlier as the colony increased (late March in late 1990s) before becoming later again in line with other colonies (S. Wanless pers. comm.). Eggs hatch after 43 days and the nestling period lasts around 91 days (Zonfrillo in *BS3*). At Troup Head, breeding is usually completed by the end of October, by which time most birds have departed, leaving some unfledged chicks and a few injured immatures behind (pers. obs.).

Scottish distribution and status

In Scotland, there are 14 breeding colonies, with around 182,500 apparently occupied nest sites, which amounts to about 43% of the global population of this species (Zonfrillo in *BS3*) - the British population is 218,000 nests (Wanless *et al.* 2005). The colony at Troup Head is the only Scottish mainland site, and one of only two mainland colonies in the UK (along with Bempton in Yorkshire). The origins of the Troup Head Gannets are unknown. In winter, there are still a few thousand Gannets in Scottish waters, but most move well out to sea and further south-west in Europe.

Distribution and status in North-East Scotland

Gannets are present offshore during much of the year around all the coast of North-East Scotland but are scarce in mid winter. The breeding site at Troup Head is very limited in its extent, though there is some possibility of further breeding on nearby ledges. The only other area where birds have come ashore on cliffs suitable for nesting is near Collieston on the east coast. However there is no evidence of any breeding activity away from Troup Head; indeed, the cliff face at Troup appears to be one of the few areas which provides any quantity of larger ledges suitable for nesting.

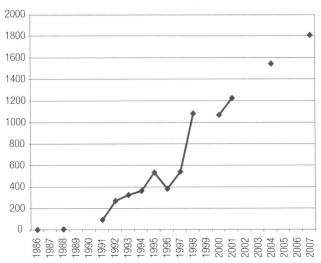

Figure 1. Occupied nests at Troup Head 1986-2007 (JNCC data).

Changes in distribution

Since 1985, the colony has increased greatly in size within a limited area, leading to the consolidation and expansion of the nesting area on the Troup Head cliffs over twenty years, but the distribution has not expanded significantly when viewed at a regional scale. Twenty-four years on, there is still only one breeding site on the coast of our area.

Population and trends

Gannets colonised North-East Scotland in 1985, with eight adults present on the cliffs at Troup Head (pers. obs.) and the first nest in 1986. By 1988, the first chicks were recorded fledging from the site (Matthews & North 1989, Wanless *et al.* 1996). Figure 1 shows the subsequent increase in size of the breeding colony until 2007 when 1,810 apparently occupied nests were counted (Mavor & Addlesee 2007). During the early period of the colony's formation, high annual rates of increase were recorded *e.g.* +177.6% between 1989–1992, +25.2% between 1992–95 and +25.8% between 1995–98. Clearly, numbers have continued to increase at this site since breeding was first recorded, although in recent years the rate of increase has been slower, averaging 4.2%, 5.4% and 8.0% per annum in the periods 1998–2001, 2001–04 and 2004–07 respectively (Mavor & Addlesee 2007, Lewis *et al.* 2001). Breeding success at Troup Head has been broadly similar to other Scottish colonies (S. Wanless pers. comm.). However, not all birds present at the colony are actually breeding - there have been expansions onto adjacent ledges by 'club' birds (congregating immatures and young adults) and numbers of these may fluctuate according to weather conditions (W. R. P. Bourne pers. comm.).

Author: *Stuart Cutts*

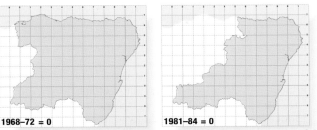

Extent of Gannet colony, Troup Head, 1990. © *Sam Alexander*

1968–72 = 0

1981–84 = 0

North-East Scotland 1968–72 to 2002–06: Change in occupied 10-km squares = Gain

Expanded Gannet colony, Troup Head, June 2010. © *Ian Francis*

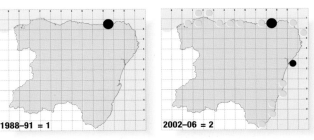

1988–91 = 1

2002–06 = 2

Cormorant
Phalacrocorax carbo

Scarce resident and migrant breeder. Estimated population in North-East Scotland: **300 pairs** (8% of Scottish population, 3% of UK)

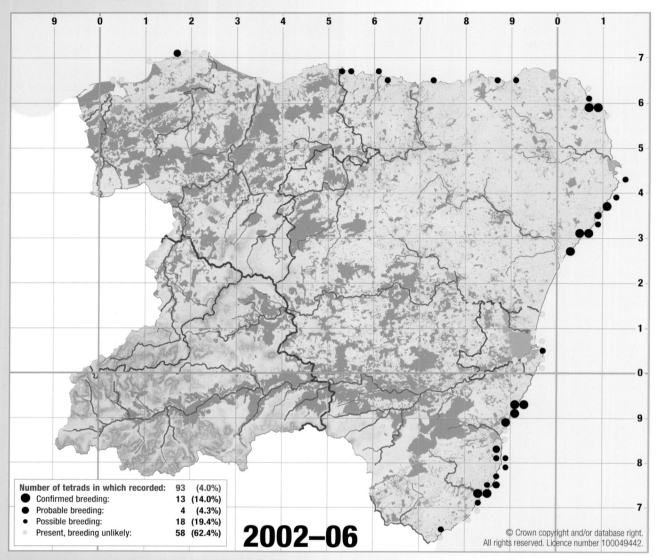

Number of tetrads in which recorded:	93	(4.0%)
● Confirmed breeding:	13	(14.0%)
● Probable breeding:	4	(4.3%)
● Possible breeding:	18	(19.4%)
● Present, breeding unlikely:	58	(62.4%)

2002–06

Cormorant, near Newburgh, July 2010. © *John Chapman*

Habitat and breeding biology
Cormorants are colonial coastal breeders in North-East Scotland, favouring offshore stacks and islands but also using other sites such as cliff headlands and one of the islands at Loch of Strathbeg. Birds start returning to the colonies in late February and egg-laying usually begins around mid April with the last chicks fledging by August. The clutch usually consists of 3–5 eggs and is incubated for around 30 days (Carss & Murray in *BS3*). Nesting failures caused, for example, by spring storms can result in the laying of repeat clutches and consequent late fledging.

Scottish distribution and status
During 1999–2002, a total of 3,626 apparently occupied nests was found around the coasts of Scotland (Seabird 2000). Declines in some areas from previous censuses were offset by increases in others. There are 12 major colonies that are well scattered around the coast from Dumfries & Galloway to Shetland, with largest numbers in the south and west. Although there are historical records of inland breeding in Scotland, none was observed in any of the three national seabird censuses carried out since 1969; any recent breeding on freshwater has been within 5 km of the coast (Carss & Murray in *BS3*).

Distribution and status in North-East Scotland

All Cormorant colonies in the North-East during 2002–06 were on the east coast of Aberdeenshire although breeding has subsequently begun on the north coast near Strahangles Point. East coast colonies are to be found on cliffs between Bullers of Buchan and Hackley Head, and between Newtonhill and Inverbervie. A very different breeding site is used at Loch of Strathbeg where a small colony nests on an island in the loch, more than 1 km from the sea.

Changes in distribution

Breeding records of Cormorant in North-East Scotland during the 20th century were sporadic and isolated, and involved very small numbers. One pair bred at Covesea (Moray) in 1962 (Cook 1992), several pairs bred at Troup Head in 1963 (*NES 1st Atlas*), and breeding was confirmed between Stonehaven and Inverbervie during 1968–72 (*BTO 1st Atlas*). Another claimed record at Covesea during this period is no longer acceptable (Cook 1992). In 1977, a nest was found at Whinnyfold (*NES 1st Atlas*) and in 1995 a small colony became established at Loch of Strathbeg (*NESBR 1995*), where breeding has continued ever since. Other occupied nests were recorded in 1995 between Buchan Ness and Collieston (*NESBR 1995*). No breeding was reported from elsewhere until 2001 when a new colony of 30+ nests was reported at Hackley Head, Forvie (J. Massie pers. comm.) and a previously existing colony was reported from near Inverbervie (J. Hardey pers. comm.). In 2003, there was a colony at Perthumie Bay, Stonehaven and two nests were partially built at Covesea, although they were subsequently abandoned. Other colonies have become established at Coldwells, south of Peterhead (*NESBR 2006*), Dunbuy, Cruden Bay (*NESBR 2008*) and Strahangles Point. It is not clear what has driven this colonisation. The breeding habitat of coastal stacks and islands has always been available so other factors such as changes in fish availability may have contributed. Ringing has shown that the initial colonisation involved considerable immigration from other Scottish colonies and even from the continent. Chicks ringed in Orkney, Moray Firth (2), Firth of Forth (2), Firth of Clyde and Denmark have been recorded breeding in these recently established colonies in North-East Scotland. The Danish bird is of special interest as it is likely to been of the Continental race *P. c. sinensis*, although it is suspected that some *P. c. carbo* do breed in some Danish colonies (T. Bregnballe pers. comm.).

Population and trends

Cormorants were not confirmed as breeding in North-East Scotland during 1981–84 (*NES 1st Atlas*) but the population increased from 13 apparently occupied nests in 1985–88 (SCR Census) to 146 nests in 1999–2002 (*Seabird 2000*) - the Inverbervie colony rising from one nest to 88 over this period. During 2002–06, Cormorants bred in 12 tetrads, with a total population of nearly 300 pairs. The largest colonies in recent years have been at Hackley Head (81 nests in 2005), Inverbervie (c. 80 nests in 2008) and Dunbuy (50 nests in 2008) (*NESBRs*). This represents a remarkable recent colonisation of North-East Scotland by this species. These numbers need to be treated with slight caution, however, as Cormorants may shift breeding colonies, and even fail to breed, from one season to the next. Hence, the number and distribution of colonies, and the population of Cormorants within them, varies from year to year. An annual search of the entire coastline and several visits to every colony would be required to determine more accurate breeding numbers. High breeding success and subsequent recruitment into colonies has helped maintain the success of this recent colonisation. Numbers at inland roosts (*e.g.* at the Dinnet lochs) have also increased, and inland breeding at such sites could be a real possibility in the future if the birds here are not disturbed (H. Scott , I. Francis pers. comm.).

Author: *Raymond Duncan*

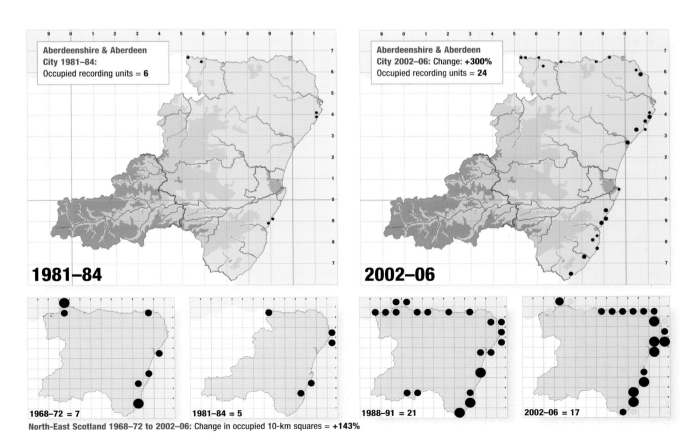

1981–84

Aberdeenshire & Aberdeen City 1981–84:
Occupied recording units = **6**

2002–06

Aberdeenshire & Aberdeen City 2002–06: Change: **+300%**
Occupied recording units = **24**

1968–72 = 7   1981–84 = 5   1988–91 = 21   2002–06 = 17

North-East Scotland 1968–72 to 2002–06: Change in occupied 10-km squares = **+143%**

Shag
Phalacrocorax aristotelis

Scarce resident. Winter visitor. Estimated population in North-East Scotland: **730–1,000 pairs** (3% of Scottish population, <3% of UK)

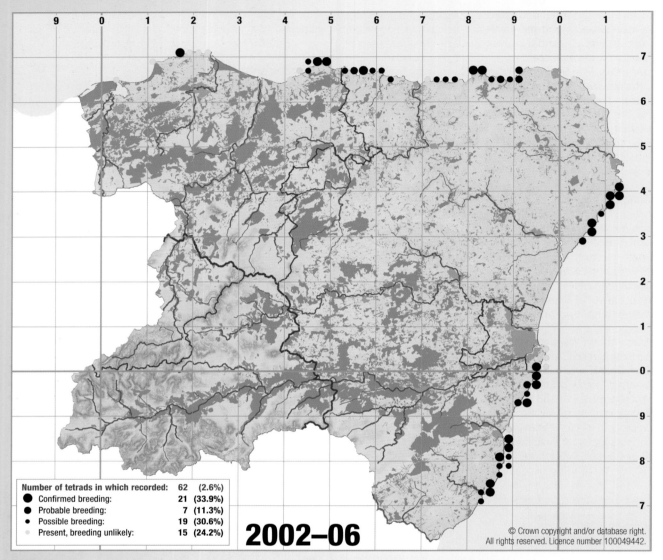

Number of tetrads in which recorded:	62	(2.6%)
● Confirmed breeding:	21	(33.9%)
● Probable breeding:	7	(11.3%)
● Possible breeding:	19	(30.6%)
● Present, breeding unlikely:	15	(24.2%)

2002–06

Shag, Bullers of Buchan, June 2009. © *Chris Jones*

Habitat and breeding biology

The Shag is an exclusively marine species, frequenting coastal cliffs, especially those with sheltered inlets or caves, during the breeding season. Shags' nests, which are often bulky, are constructed near the base of such cliffs, often at the entrance to a cave or under an overhang. Typical colonies in North-East Scotland are small, ranging up to 50 pairs, with the exception of the Bullers of Buchan which may hold 300+ pairs. This compares with colonies containing 500 or more pairs elsewhere in Scotland. The breeding season is variable but often prolonged. In some years birds gather nesting material from mid February while in others fledglings have been noted in September. It is assumed that this variation is linked to food supply (M. L. Tasker pers. comm.). Most of the foraging during the breeding season takes place in the sea close to the breeding colonies, but some birds travel up to 16 km along the coast.

Scottish distribution and status

Shags are widely distributed around the Scottish coast, with the greatest concentrations to be found in the north and west. The largest colonies are located in Shetland, Argyll, Outer Hebrides and Orkney. During 1998–2002, *c.* 21,500 occupied nests were counted in Scotland (Seabird

2000) but due to the variable breeding strategy of the Shag this estimate may be too low, possibly by as much as one third (Wanless & Harris in *BS3*).

Distribution and status in North-East Scotland

In North-East Scotland, suitable breeding habitat for Shags is to be found along the north coast, mainly between the Portknockie cliffs and those just to the west of Rosehearty, and along the east coast from Boddam to Forvie and again from Aberdeen to Gourdon. Greatest numbers frequent the cliffs between Boddam and Cruden Bay. Although they are common residents, there is ample suitable breeding habitat for the population to increase. In addition, the carrying capacity of the marine environment for Shags in the North-East does not appear to have been reached, as the numbers which over-winter here far outnumber the breeding population (pers. obs.).

Changes in distribution

Low numbers of Shags bred along the north and east coasts of Aberdeenshire in the 19th century, only becoming fully established from the middle of the 20th century. The Moray coast was not colonised until 1986, when two pairs nested at Portknockie; breeding first took place at Covesea in 1998. The comparative maps of Aberdeenshire/Aberdeen City indicate a 35% increase in occupied recording units between 1981–84 and 2002–06.

Population and trends

The most recent estimate of the Shag population in North-East Scotland is derived from a single count of apparently occupied nests during Seabird 2000, with totals of 697 in Aberdeenshire and 33 in Moray. Since that time, numbers in Moray have gradually increased until in 2009 there were 119 apparently occupied nests (M. Cook pers. comm.). Numbers in Aberdeenshire have increased from 293 pairs in 1968–70 (Operation Seafarer) to 697 pairs in 1998–2002 (Seabird 2000). The population in fact peaked in 1992 (P. I. Mitchell

Shag, Bullers of Buchan, July 1982. © *Martin Cook*

pers. comm.), but a large winter die-off in 1993/94 significantly affected the east coast colonies. The overall increase has led to an expansion in all colonies, but most notably in those between Aberdeen and Gourdon. As described above, single counts could underestimate the population by as much as one third (Wanless & Harris in *BS3*) which would place the North-East Shag population within a range of 730–1,000 pairs. It is probable therefore that the population has more than doubled since the late 1960s - it seems likely that a combination of factors has caused this increase, including a plentiful supply of food and an availability of nest sites.

Author: *Mike Innes*

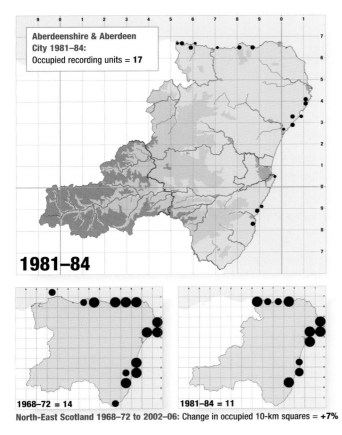

Aberdeenshire & Aberdeen City 1981–84:
Occupied recording units = 17

1981–84

1968–72 = 14   1981–84 = 11

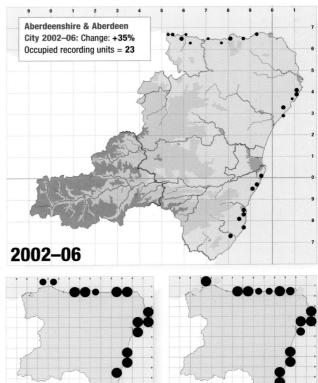

Aberdeenshire & Aberdeen City 2002–06: Change: +35%
Occupied recording units = 23

2002–06

1988–91 = 14   2002–06 = 15

North-East Scotland 1968–72 to 2002–06: Change in occupied 10-km squares = +7%

Bittern

Botaurus stellaris

Occasional visitor in summer. More records in winter. Estimated population in North-East Scotland: **0 pairs**

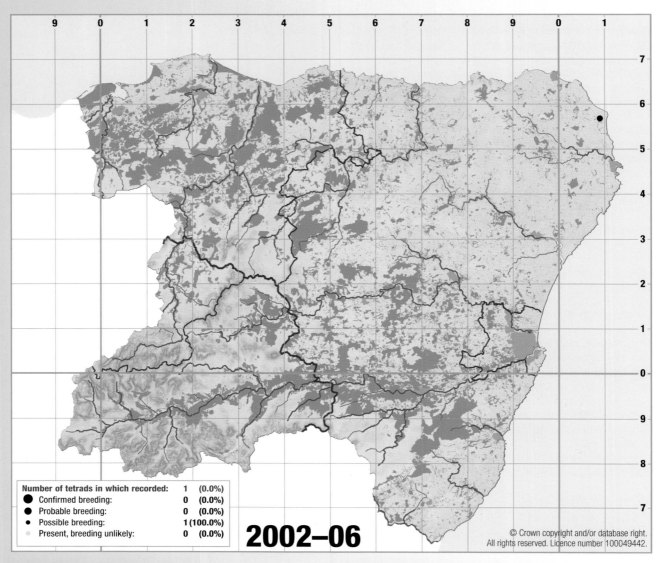

Number of tetrads in which recorded:	1	(0.0%)
● Confirmed breeding:	0	(0.0%)
● Probable breeding:	0	(0.0%)
• Possible breeding:	1	(100.0%)
Present, breeding unlikely:	0	(0.0%)

2002–06

Habitat and breeding biology
Breeding Bitterns favour densely vegetated wetlands with extensive shallow standing water. In England, they occupy large reedbeds with pools of open water which provide margins along which they hunt for fish and amphibian prey. In the 19th century, during the period when they bred in Scotland, their breeding habitat included rivers and wetlands fringed by Common Reed as well as fens with Yellow Flag Iris, rushes and sedges (Gilbert in *BS3*).

Scottish distribution and status
Historically, Bitterns appear to have been fairly common resident breeders in southern Scotland as far north as the Great Glen although there are no records relating to North-East Scotland. The population dwindled as wetland drainage proceeded and breeding ceased around 1830. In more recent times, Bitterns have been scarce winter visitors and passage migrants, with the great majority of records in the south and east of the country and very few north of Aberdeenshire (Gilbert in *BS3*).

Distribution and status in North-East Scotland
There were 25 records in North-East Scotland during 1970–2006, mostly in autumn and winter. There were two at Loch of Strathbeg in 2002 and again in 2003; otherwise all records were of single birds. During 2002–06 there were annual autumn/winter records at Loch of Strathbeg but none elsewhere (Cook 1992, Phillips 1997, *NESBRs*, *MNBRs*). More significantly perhaps, there were two records at Strathbeg in April and May 2004 (*NESBR* 2004). Following a serious decline to as few as 11 booming males in 1997 the English population is now increasing and expanding its range, with 82 booming males at 43 sites in 2009 (RSPB). If this trend continues, there is hope for recolonisation of Scotland and the reedbeds at Loch of Strathbeg may prove attractive.

Author: *Dominic Funnell*

See photograph on page 123.

Little Egret
Egretta garzetta

Occasional visitor, mostly in spring and summer. Estimated population in North-East Scotland: **0 pairs**

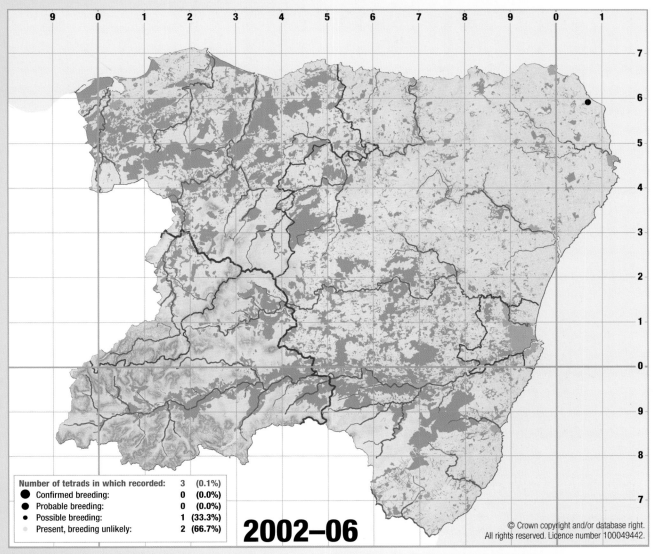

Number of tetrads in which recorded: 3 (0.1%)
- ● Confirmed breeding: 0 (0.0%)
- ● Probable breeding: 0 (0.0%)
- • Possible breeding: 1 (33.3%)
- Present, breeding unlikely: 2 (66.7%)

2002–06

Habitat and breeding biology
In their European, including English, breeding range, Little Egrets are found along the shallow margins of inland and coastal waters. They breed colonially in reedbeds, bushes and trees, often in association with other heron species. In England, they nest in existing colonies of Grey Herons. They lay a clutch of 3–6 eggs which are incubated for around three weeks, followed by a 40–45 day fledging period (*BWP*).

Scottish distribution and status
Little Egrets are uncommon visitors to Scotland, most frequently recorded in spring and early summer. The first records were in 1954 and they remained rare visitors until the mid 1980s. Since 1986, the Little Egret has become an annual visitor to Scotland reflecting the rapid expansion of the population in England. It has now occurred in nearly all recording areas in Scotland and the total number of records exceeds 150 (Hogg in *BS3*). The most favoured areas, with more than 20 records each, are North-east Scotland, Dumfries & Galloway and Argyll.

See photograph on page 123.

Distribution and status in North-East Scotland
The first Little Egret in North-East Scotland was seen at Loch of Strathbeg in May 1974 (Phillips 1997). The next two records were in June 1983, at Haddo House lake and in Findhorn Bay, the first for Moray (Cook 1992). There was a marked increase in records during the 1990s, and since 1995 they have become annual visitors. There have now been around 30 records although there is likely to have been some duplication as birds move between sites. Most records have been of single birds, at Loch of Strathbeg and the Ythan estuary, and all but two arrived in May or June. In 2002, two birds were at Loch of Strathbeg from 16th May–8th June (*NESBR* 2002).

The English breeding population has increased dramatically from two pairs in 1996 (Brown & Grice 2005) to 425–478 pairs at 60 sites in 2006 (Holling *et al.* 2009). Assuming that the range continues to spread northwards it seems inevitable that the species will become an increasingly frequent visitor to North-East Scotland and its establishment as a breeder is a real possibility, especially if winters are mild.

Author: *Dominic Funnell*

Grey Heron
Ardea cinerea

Scarce resident. Winter visitor. Estimated population in North-East Scotland: *340–500 pairs* (10% of Scottish population, 3% of UK)

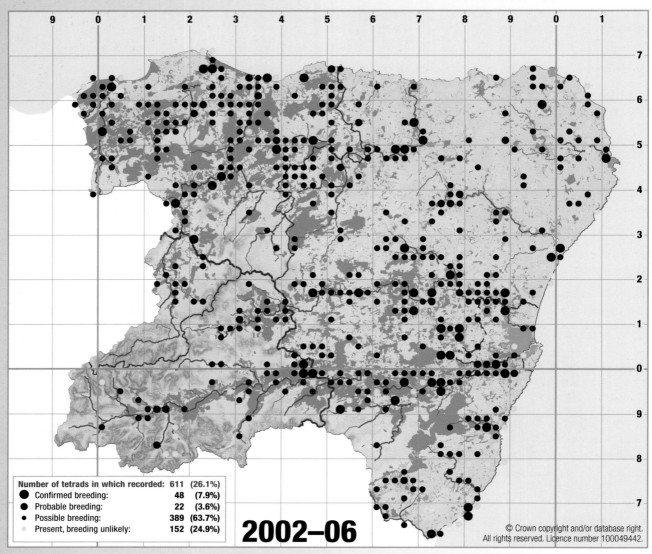

Number of tetrads in which recorded:	611	(26.1%)
● Confirmed breeding:	48	(7.9%)
● Probable breeding:	22	(3.6%)
• Possible breeding:	389	(63.7%)
○ Present, breeding unlikely:	152	(24.9%)

2002–06

Grey Heron, Ythan estuary, May 2011. © *Ewan Weston*

Habitat and breeding biology

Grey Herons forage in shallow water, using rivers, streams and burns, loch margins, marshes, upland bogs, tidal creeks on estuaries and algae-covered rocky seashores. They mostly eat fish but seasonally exploit other foods such as small mammals in autumn and winter, frogs in early spring, and ducklings in summer (Marquiss & Leitch 1990). They breed colonially, nesting in trees and commuting up to 20 km to feed. Eggs are laid from early March, coincident with the first seasonal food abundance as frogs congregate to spawn. In initial breeding attempts, young hatch in late March and April, and fledge in June. Breeding often fails, in which case there is usually a second attempt and occasionally a third. Foraging can be poor in spring when water levels are high but gets progressively easier as fish are concentrated by falling water levels in summer (Marquiss 1993). Nest failure is more frequent during persistent rainfall, and in such years the last attempts do not fledge young until August. The earliest fledged juveniles are by then independent and well practiced at fishing.

Scottish distribution and status

Grey Herons are common and widely distributed across Scotland with the highest breeding densities at estuaries

The Breeding Birds of North-East Scotland

with coastal marshes (Marquiss 1989). They are relatively scarce in the peat dominated wetlands of the north-west and virtually absent from the hills above 650 m. Birds breeding in upland areas tend to move towards the coast during harsh weather and Scandinavian birds winter on our north and east coasts. The breeding population has gradually increased since the mid 1970s and was estimated at 4,200 nests in 2004 (Marchant, cited in Marquiss in *BS3*).

Distribution and status in North-East Scotland

Grey Herons are relatively easy to detect and the scatter of occupied tetrads probably closely reflects the distribution of foraging birds, with most along the main rivers, clustered around a few lowland standing waters, and on coastal marshes. There are fewest records across the Buchan plain and above 500 m in the Cairngorms. Heronries can be quite difficult to detect particularly where there are only one or two nests, but again the pattern of tetrads with probable and confirmed breeding follows the known foraging habitat. Heronries in the North-East are relatively small; half of the 28 counted during the atlas period comprised just one or two nests and only two were large - both of them beside productive estuaries and coastal marshland, at Newburgh (about 25 nests) and Findhorn Bay (24 nests).

Changes in distribution

The early heronry surveys were inventories. They did not involve systematic search and rarely documented numbers. Nevertheless, it appears that throughout the 20th century, as persecution, pollution and severe winter weather have sequentially decreased, Grey Herons increased in both their distribution and numbers. In the most comprehensive of comparisons, the number of occupied recording units in Aberdeenshire/Aberdeen City increased between 1981–84 and 2002–06 by 55%, perhaps because Heron numbers have increased with the series of mild winters, although an effect of increased coverage and effort cannot be ruled out.

Grey Heron, Maryculter, April 1998. © *Ed Duthie*

Population and trends

In the North-East, as elsewhere in Scotland, both the number and size of heronries have apparently increased, though levelling off in recent years (Marquiss 2007). In the 1928–29 survey there were 29 occupied nests in nine heronries, records increasing in 1954 to 92 nests in 17 heronries (Garden 1958). These figures are meagre compared with those of the 1981–84 atlas, when breeding was confirmed in 42 recording units and the total population was reckoned at 200–250 pairs. Over the last decade, 25 heronries have been counted, with the average annual counts at each heronry totalling 177 occupied nests. During the period 2002–06, atlas records confirmed breeding in 48 tetrads and suggested probable breeding in another 22. If we assume that, on average, tetrads contained single heronries and that those counted were not biased towards larger colonies, then the overall population for the region is at least 340 pairs, and could be 500.

Author: *Mick Marquiss*

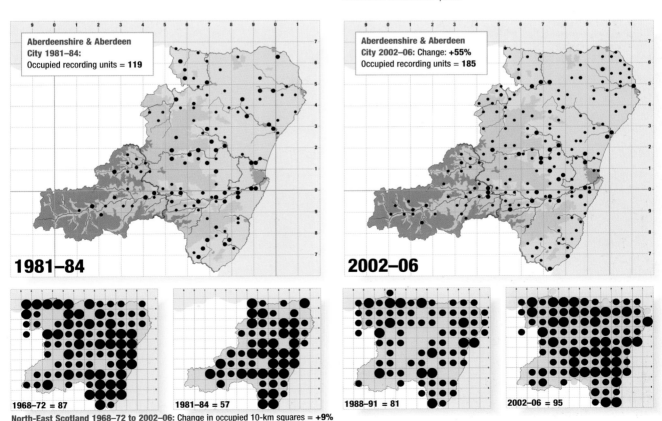

Aberdeenshire & Aberdeen City 1981–84: Occupied recording units = **119**

1981–84

1968–72 = 87   1981–84 = 57

Aberdeenshire & Aberdeen City 2002–06: Change: **+55%** Occupied recording units = **185**

2002–06

1988–91 = 81   2002–06 = 95

North-East Scotland 1968–72 to 2002–06: Change in occupied 10-km squares = +9%

Spoonbill

Platalea leucorodia

Occasional visitor in spring and summer. Estimated population in North-East Scotland: **0 pairs**

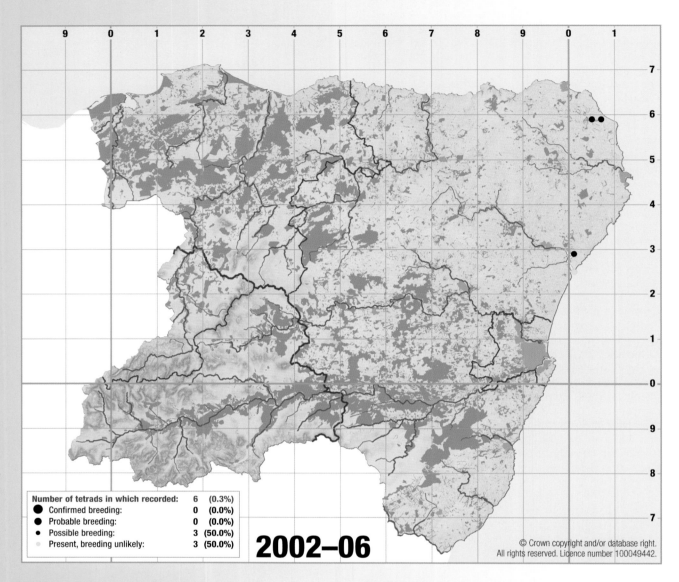

Number of tetrads in which recorded:	6	(0.3%)
● Confirmed breeding:	0	(0.0%)
● Probable breeding:	0	(0.0%)
• Possible breeding:	3	(50.0%)
◦ Present, breeding unlikely:	3	(50.0%)

2002–06

Habitat and breeding biology

In their European range, Spoonbills are found in coastal lowlands or alluvial river basins. Here they seek their invertebrate food in shallow water among fine sediments. They breed colonially, sometimes at ground level in dense reedbeds but also at heights up to 5 m in waterside scrub or small trees.

Scottish distribution and status

The Spoonbill is a scarce passage migrant in Scotland with occurrences peaking in May–July and in October. They have been recorded in many parts of Scotland but there is a large bias towards southern and eastern coastal counties, especially Dumfries & Galloway, Lothian, Angus & Dundee, North-east Scotland and Orkney (Clugston in *BS3*). There were suggestions of breeding behaviour in Scotland in 1998 and 2000, and in 2008 a pair successfully raised three young in Dumfries & Galloway.

Distribution and status in North-East Scotland

During the period 1970–2006, Spoonbills were recorded in North-East Scotland in 25 years, involving a total of around 50 birds (Phillips 1997, *NESBRs*, *MNBRs*). However,

some duplicate sightings of individual birds may have been involved. Only two of these were in Moray (Cook 1992). Most recent records, of adult and immature birds, have been at Loch of Strathbeg or, less frequently, the Ythan estuary. The great majority arrived in May or June and a few have remained for a prolonged period such as the first year bird at Loch of Strathbeg from 23rd April–7th September 2003 (*NESBR* 2003). Although single birds are usually involved, there has been more than one on several occasions; most notably three at Loch of Strathbeg in June–August 1996 (*NESBR* 1996) and four there in late June 1999 (*NESBR* 1999). During 2002–06, seven or eight birds were seen, all in the vicinity of the Ythan estuary or Loch of Strathbeg.

Three colour-ringed birds have originated in the Netherlands and, if colonies there continue to increase, we might expect more visiting Spoonbills in North-East Scotland and perhaps a breeding attempt - on current evidence, Loch of Strathbeg seems the most likely location.

Author: *Dominic Funnell*

See photograph on page 123.

Green-winged Teal, Dumfries & Galloway, November 2010. © *Richard Pittam*

Bittern, Loch of Strathbeg, February 2003. © *Harry Scott*

Little Egret, Loch of Strathbeg, January 2008. © *Sam Alexander*

Spoonbill, Loch of Strathbeg, May 2003. © *Harry Scott*

Black-necked Grebe, Lincolnshire, May 2010. © *Trevor Gunby*

Avocet, Ythan estuary, May 2005. © *Chris Jones*

Black-tailed Godwit, Iceland, June 2004. © *John Chapman*

Whimbrel, Iceland, June 2004. © *Sam Alexander*

Little Grebe
Tachybaptus ruficollis

Scarce resident. Estimated population in North-East Scotland: ***100–200 pairs*** (10% of Scottish population, 2% of UK)

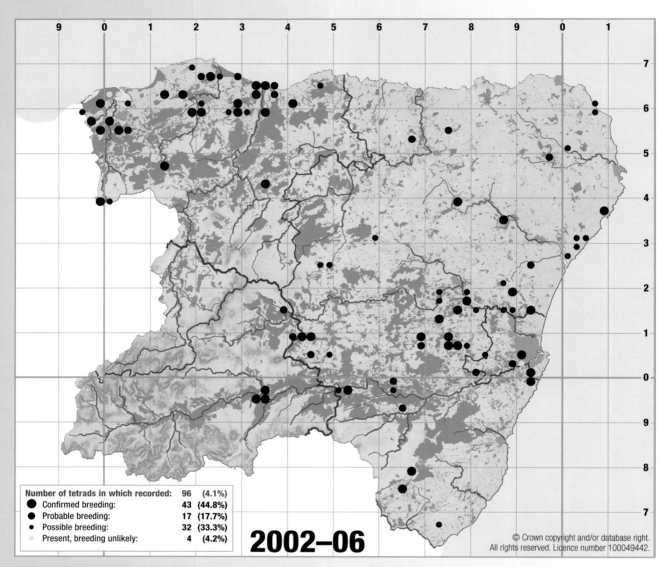

Number of tetrads in which recorded:	96	(4.1%)
● Confirmed breeding:	43	(44.8%)
● Probable breeding:	17	(17.7%)
● Possible breeding:	32	(33.3%)
○ Present, breeding unlikely:	4	(4.2%)

2002–06

Habitat and breeding biology

Little Grebes utilise a variety of small, shallow water bodies, primarily below 400 m, preferring waters with a dense growth of marginal and submerged aquatic vegetation. Due to generally fast-flowing rivers, breeding Little Grebes in North-East Scotland are primarily birds of small lochs and ponds, usually on pools of less than half a hectare in size (*NES 1st Atlas*), but sometimes also on rivers. At the Loch of Strathbeg

Little Grebe, Sutherland, June 1992. © *Ed Duthie*

reserve, for example, nesting regularly takes place on the Savoch Burn, with birds rarely using the loch itself during the breeding season. The nest is a floating structure anchored to vegetation growing beneath the surface, allowing some protection against rising or falling water levels. The breeding season is relatively late, with the 4–6 eggs usually laid in mid to late May and the first chicks appearing between June and August. Second broods are regularly recorded and third broods may be possible in Scotland (Mitchell in *BS3*).

Scottish distribution and status

Little Grebes are locally distributed across lowland areas of Scotland with the largest concentrations in the south and east. Small numbers are found west and north as far as the Outer Hebrides and Orkney. The Scottish population is estimated to be between 650–2,250 pairs, with indications of an increase in recent years (Mitchell in *BS3*).

Distribution and status in North-East Scotland

The majority of records are from lowland Moray, and the areas along the major river systems in Aberdeenshire, particularly the Don, Dee and Ythan. In Buchan, they are sparsely distributed, mostly on small lochs near the coast; no doubt the lack of suitable ponds is a limiting factor, although they are adaptable in using small ponds on golf courses and newly created farm ponds once these become suitably vegetated. Many small water bodies are not used consistently; in Moray, 31 sites have held Little Grebes in the breeding season since 1997 although only 10–15 are occupied every year (*MNBR*s). Although Little Grebes can sometimes be found on their breeding sites all year round, many of the smaller water bodies, especially in the west, are abandoned for the winter, when the birds move onto the rivers or down to the coast.

Little Grebe, Dunecht, June 2010. © *John Chapman*

Changes in distribution

The Little Grebe has increased its distribution markedly since 1968–72 when only 24 1-km squares were occupied (*BTO 1st Atlas*). The situation was little changed in 1988–91 (*BTO 2nd Atlas*) but by 2002–06 there were 43 occupied 10-km squares, with breeding confirmed in 27 of these. The range expansion is even better demonstrated within Aberdeenshire/Aberdeen City where the number of occupied recording units has increased almost fourfold since 1981–84. Most of the increase has been in the Dee and Don catchment areas, including within the City of Aberdeen. There has also been a marked expansion northwards into the Buchan plain, but with limited confirmation of breeding in this area. Although only comparable at a 10-km square level, there has also been a significant infilling of the range within Moray.

Population and trends

Little Grebes can be secretive in the breeding season and, due to their preference for small water bodies, it is likely that many pairs will go unrecorded in most years. During 2002–06, 92 tetrads showed some form of breeding activity. Many of these tetrads contain only a single suitable site, often with only one pair of birds, but other sites, such as Loch Oire and Loch Park in Moray, can hold at least four pairs (*MNBR*s). It may therefore be reasonable to estimate that the population falls within the range of 100–200 breeding pairs. The increases in range, and presumed related rise in the regional population, will have been aided by habitat creation and the recent trend towards milder winters, as the Little Grebe is prone to suffering in harsh weather conditions.

Author: *David Parnaby*

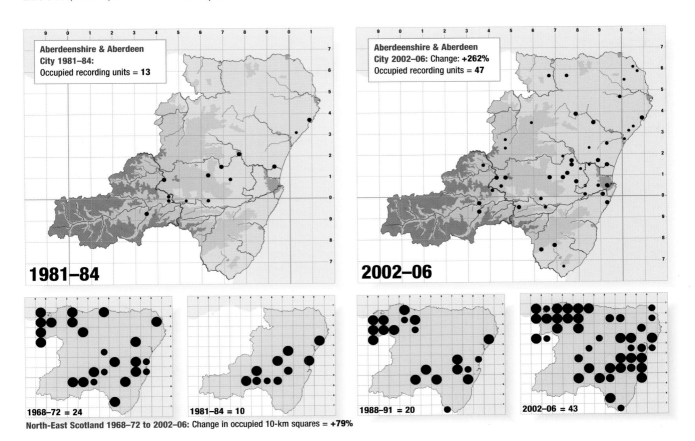

North-East Scotland 1968–72 to 2002–06: Change in occupied 10-km squares = **+79%**

Great Crested Grebe

Podiceps cristatus

Very rare summer visitor and breeder. Few in winter. Estimated population in North-East Scotland: **3–5 pairs** (1% of Scottish population, <1% of UK)

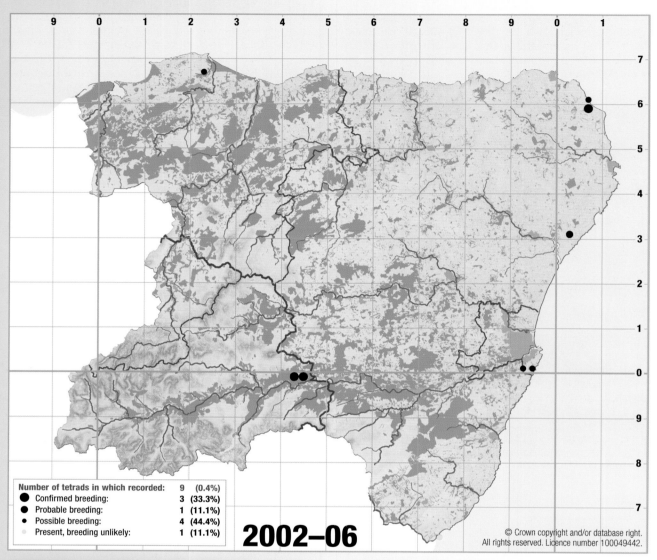

Number of tetrads in which recorded:	9	(0.4%)
● Confirmed breeding:	3	(33.3%)
● Probable breeding:	1	(11.1%)
● Possible breeding:	4	(44.4%)
Present, breeding unlikely:	1	(11.1%)

2002–06

Great Crested Grebe, location and date unknown. © *John Edelsten*

Habitat and breeding biology

Great Crested Grebes breed on large natural shallow lowland freshwater bodies fringed with aquatic vegetation. Nest sites consist of a floating platform and are generally on the vegetated fringes or amongst emergent vegetation at the loch edge. Birds can arrive back as early as January but most return in late February to mid March and have left by late November. Breeding success is generally poor with few chicks fledging successfully; predation, and wet weather in summer months leading to high water levels, are probably significant factors. It has been suggested that due to the low productivity of the breeding population, numbers of this species are supplemented by immigration (*NES 1st Atlas*).

Scottish distribution and status

This is a relatively scarce breeding species, with a scattered distribution on suitable waters in the central lowlands with smaller numbers throughout south-west and east Scotland. The Scottish population is estimated at 310–365 pairs with the largest concentration found at Loch Leven (Perth & Kinross) where there were 35–40 pairs in 2003. Since the 1970s there has been some indication of an increase but numbers now appear relatively stable (Murray & Ogilvie in *BS3*).

Great Crested Grebe, Sand Loch, May 1990. © *Ed Duthie*

Distribution and status in North-East Scotland

In North-East Scotland, Great Crested Grebes are on the northern edge of their breeding range in Britain and only just maintain a breeding presence in the region. The distribution of breeding pairs probably reflects the number of suitable water bodies in the area. During 2002–06, only Loch of Strathbeg and Loch Kinord hosted successful breeding pairs.

Changes in distribution

The small North-East Scotland breeding population has colonised, and subsequently abandoned, suitable waters since the first pair nested, at Loch Spynie in 1913. Here, breeding continued until 1929 (Baxter & Rintoul 1953) and single pairs bred in 1954–56, 1984–87 and 1990–98 (Cook 1992, *MNBR*s). At Loch of Strathbeg, breeding commenced in 1920 and there were four pairs in 1936 (Baxter & Rintoul 1953). They bred again in 1968–72 (*BTO 1st Atlas*) but did not do so between 1976–92. In 1993, breeding recommenced and has continued since. At Loch Kinord, breeding was recorded in 1929, 1935, 1948 (Baxter & Rintoul 1953) and again in 2005–06. Up to three pairs bred at Loch Davan in the 1930s (Baxter & Rintoul 1953) and this continued sporadically with the last pair present in 1988 (*NESBR*s). Great Crested Grebes bred at Sand Loch (Collieston) during 1968–72 (*BTO 1st Atlas*) and 1–2 pairs continued to do so until 1989 (*NES 1st Atlas*, *NESBR*s). The only other site where breeding is known to have taken place is Loirston Loch, in 1995; a pair was also present there in 1996–97 (*NESBR*s).

Population and trends

During 2002–06 the North-East Scotland breeding population varied between 3–5 pairs - the maximum at Loch of Strathbeg was five pairs in 2004, and at Loch Kinord a single pair bred in 2005 and 2006. This had been exceeded in recent years only in 1999 when Loch of Strathbeg held six pairs (*NESBR* 1999). The population in the region did not reflect the increase that the national population underwent from the 1970s and the local increase at Loch of Strathbeg was possibly due to changing water quality. Eutrophication of the loch has resulted in turbid water and declining aquatic vegetation. Great Crested Grebes appear to adapt to these conditions as their feeding technique is little hampered by water turbidity (Hagemeijer & Blair 1997) and changes in fish populations may also benefit them. Evidence suggests that the Great Crested Grebe will always be a scarce breeding species in the region although enough suitable waters exist to permit a slightly larger population to become established in the future.

Author: *Scott Paterson*

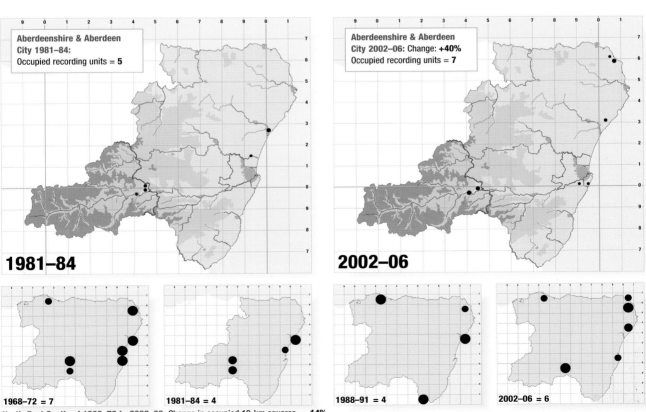

Aberdeenshire & Aberdeen City 1981–84:
Occupied recording units = **5**

1981–84

Aberdeenshire & Aberdeen City 2002–06: Change: **+40%**
Occupied recording units = **7**

2002–06

1968–72 = 7

1981–84 = 4

1988–91 = 4

2002–06 = 6

North-East Scotland 1968–72 to 2002–06: Change in occupied 10-km squares = -14%

Slavonian Grebe
Podiceps auritus

Very rare breeder. Winter visitor. Estimated population in North-East Scotland: **0–1 pair** (0–5% of Scottish and UK population)

Amber list; Schedule 1; Annex 1; Scottish BAP list

Number of tetrads in which recorded:	7	(0.3%)
● Confirmed breeding:	2	(28.6%)
● Probable breeding:	3	(42.9%)
● Possible breeding:	2	(28.6%)
○ Present, breeding unlikely:	0	(0.0%)

Slavonian Grebe, Moray, July 2006. © *Ian Francis*

Habitat and breeding biology

Slavonian Grebes usually breed on small, shallow waters ranging from eutrophic pools and gravel pits in the lowlands to nutrient-poor upland lochans, though larger lochs such as Loch Ruthven near Inverness may also be used. Usually, breeding sites have extensive fringing vegetation, but more rarely, including the most recent North-East Scotland breeding site, artificial pools with little marginal vegetation are occupied. Birds return to breeding sites at the end of March or in early April. The nest is usually a floating mound of water weed attached to aquatic vegetation such as sedges or reeds. Where suitable vegetation is lacking, the artificial provision of cut willow or Gorse at the water's edge has proved acceptable and artificial floating rafts have been used abroad. The mean clutch size in Scotland is 3.9 eggs and repeat clutches are often laid if the nest fails, generally due to flooding or predation (Summers in *BS3*).

Scottish distribution and status

The current Scottish breeding distribution is centred around the inner Moray Firth, especially in Inverness District but also in Ross & Cromarty, Badenoch & Strathspey and Moray & Nairn. Elsewhere during the 20th century, Slavonian Grebes have bred in Caithness, Sutherland, North-east Scotland and Perth & Kinross. During the period 1978–2004, the population has fluctuated within the range 30–80 pairs but since 1984 there has been a steady decline in the number of occupied lochs (Summers in *BS3*). Recently, the population has fared even worse, with only 23 pairs in Scotland in 2009 (S. Benn pers. comm.).

Distribution and status in North-East Scotland

During 2002–06, Slavonian Grebes bred on several artificial pools in north Moray. Pairs were also present for brief periods at other sites, including Loch Spynie and a single bird was at Meikle Loch in Aberdeenshire, but there was no evidence of a breeding attempt at these localities.

Changes in distribution

Slavonian Grebes first bred in Moray, at Loch Oire, in the 1950s. This site held 6–7 pairs in the 1970s but numbers dwindled and the last breeding took place here in 1995 (Cook 1992, *MNBRs*). Birds were first seen at the most recent breeding site in 1979 or 1980 but breeding does not appear to have been proved until 1986, after which it continued until the last unsuccessful attempt in 2007. In Aberdeenshire, breeding occurred at two well-separated upland sites in Donside and upper Deeside in 1960–62 (Thom 1986) and in 1974 (*NES 1st Atlas*) but not since.

Population and trends

During the 1970s-mid 1980s, breeding took place only at Loch Oire where there were seven pairs in 1971 and 1976, but this had reduced to two pairs by 1986. After a brief resurgence to 4–5 pairs in 1988–89, the last two pairs bred, unsuccessfully, in 1995. The most recent nesting population grew steadily from 1–2 pairs in the late 1980s to 3–5 through the 1990s, peaking at seven pairs in 2003, eight in 2004 and six in 2005. During 2002–04, a total of 21 young was raised, but this dropped to zero during 2005–07 due, at least in part, to the attention of egg-collectors. Single pairs appeared in 2008 and again, briefly, in 2009 but no breeding took place. The Slavonian Grebe may now be close to being lost as a breeding species in North-East Scotland.

Authors: *Charlie Gervaise & Martin Cook*

Slavonian Grebe, Moray, July 2010. © *Allan Adam*

Black-necked Grebe   *Podiceps nigricollis*

Occasional probable breeder. Passage migrant. Estimated population in North-East Scotland: 0 pairs

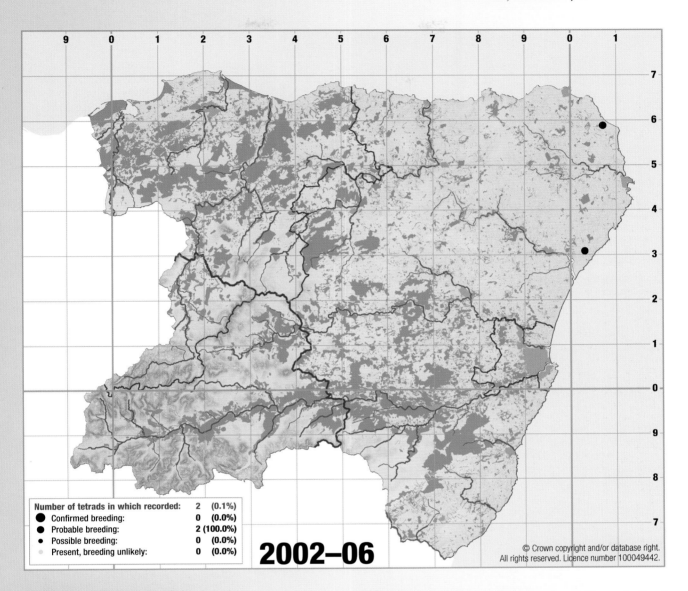

Number of tetrads in which recorded: 2   (0.1%)
- ● Confirmed breeding: 0   (0.0%)
- ● Probable breeding: 2 (100.0%)
- • Possible breeding: 0   (0.0%)
- Present, breeding unlikely: 0   (0.0%)

2002–06

Habitat and breeding biology
Black-necked Grebes breed on shallow eutrophic lochs containing emergent aquatic vegetation for nest sites and areas of open water in which to feed. They often associate with colonies of Black-headed Gulls. Pairs arrive at Scottish breeding sites from late March to early May and clutches of, usually, 3–5 eggs are laid from late May to July (Leitch in *BS3*).

Scottish distribution and status
Breeding was first confirmed in Scotland in Lothian in 1930. Subsequently, a range expansion took place with pairs breeding in at least five other recording areas by 1965. Between 1992–2003, breeding was proved in Angus & Dundee, Perth & Kinross, Fife, Borders and Dumfries & Galloway. The population varied between 8–17 pairs in these years but dropped to seven pairs in 2004 and only a single pair in 2005 (Leitch in *BS3*). Elsewhere in Scotland, Black-necked Grebes are uncommon passage migrants and winter visitors.

Distribution and status in North-East Scotland
Black-necked Grebes are rare visitors to North-East Scotland and have never been proved to breed. Between 1974–2006, 36 birds were recorded (only one of these in

Moray) with no records in 12 of these years. The majority of records were of single birds on freshwater close to the coast, with Meikle Loch and Loch of Strathbeg the favoured sites. Most appear between late April–early June or in August–September and stay only briefly (Cook 1992, Phillips 1997, *NESBR*s, *MNBR*s). This pattern was maintained during 2002–06. Records most relevant to potential breeding occurred in 1996, when two birds were at Loch of Strathbeg between 6th–12th May (with a different two at Meikle Loch on 12th May) (*NESBR* 1996), and in 2004 when two were at Loch of Strathbeg between 8th–26th May (*NESBR* 2004). The habitat may be suitable for breeding at both of these sites but following the steep decline in the breeding population elsewhere in Scotland, the omens for a start to breeding in North-East Scotland do not appear good at present.

Author: *Dominic Funnell*

See photograph on page 123.

Honey-buzzard

Pernis apivorus

Very rare summer migrant breeder. Passage migrant. Estimated population in North-East Scotland: **1+ pairs** (6% of Scottish population, 2% of UK)

Number of tetrads in which recorded:	8	(0.3%)
● Confirmed breeding:	0	(0.0%)
● Probable breeding:	1	(12.5%)
● Possible breeding:	6	(75.0%)
○ Present, breeding unlikely:	1	(12.5%)

Honey-buzzard, Ythan Estuary, September 2008. © *Micky Maher*

Habitat and breeding biology

Honey-buzzards require habitats which provide ample supplies of their staple summer food; the nests of social wasps and bumble-bees. Within such areas they occupy mature forests with clearings, as well as mixed landscapes with woods and farmland. In Highland Scotland, the majority of nests have been found in mixed coniferous and deciduous forest, and here the favoured nesting trees are Beech and Pedunculate Oak. In coniferous plantations, three-quarters of located nests were in Douglas Fir. The clutch, usually of two eggs, is laid in late May or early June. Highland breeding success is good with most breeding pairs rearing two young (Etheridge in *BS3*).

Scottish distribution and status

Since 1976, Honey-buzzards have bred regularly in the SOC recording areas of Highland (chiefly Ross & Cromarty, Inverness District and Badenoch & Strathspey), Moray & Nairn and Perth & Kinross. Occasional or possible breeding has also been noted in Aberdeenshire and four other regions in the south of Scotland. Accurate information on breeding numbers is not known but it seems very likely that 15–20 pairs nest annually in Scotland and there are possibly as many as 50 pairs (Etheridge in *BS3*).

Distribution and status in North-East Scotland

During 2002–06, Honey-buzzards were seen in seven tetrads. In two areas, birds were reported from two adjacent tetrads in Moray forests where breeding has been confirmed within the last 15 years. In one of these areas only a single bird was seen while in the other there were several sightings of a pair and, in view of previous and subsequent events, it is very likely that breeding did take place. The remaining three records were of single birds seen in possible breeding habitat in widely separated forests in Aberdeenshire. The only other Honey-buzzard reported during 2002–06 was a coastal migrant at Newtonhill in June 2004 (*NESBR* 2004).

Changes in distribution

Historically, breeding was first recorded in North-East Scotland at Abergeldie prior to 1840 (MacGillivray 1855) and at Ballogie in 1867 (Sim 1903). There were 21 further reports of single birds in Aberdeenshire between 1864–1913, many of which were shot. More recently the species has been an occasional, less than annual, visitor with most records being of single birds on passage during May–June and August–September (Phillips 1997). Breeding in recent times was first confirmed in a heavily forested area of Moray in 1977 and one or two pairs have continued to breed in this area ever since, most recently in 2009. At a second site, one pair bred in 1992–94 and probably continued to do so until 1998. In a third forest, a nest with young was found in 1986 and a single bird was seen in the same area in 1990. There has been no confirmation of breeding in Aberdeenshire since 1867 (Phillips 1997). In Moray, away from known breeding sites, there have been only two recent inland records and a single coastal migrant, at Burghead in June 1985.

Population and trends

It is only known with certainty that one locality in North-East Scotland, in Moray, currently holds a breeding pair annually. However, Honey-buzzards can be secretive nesters and locating new pairs is time-consuming and requires experience in the species' breeding behaviour. It would appear that extensive suitable habitat is available in North-East Scotland and the presence of further undetected pairs is perfectly possible.

Author: *Martin Cook*

Honey-buzzard, Moray, August 2009. © *Roy Dennis*

Forest of Birse

This large area of moorland, farmland and woodland (broad-leaved and coniferous) holds a very diverse range of breeding birds. Open-ground species include Teal, Red Grouse, Black Grouse, Merlin, seven wader species including Golden Plover, Cuckoo, Short-eared Owl, Skylark, Whinchat and Ring Ouzel. The area used to be good for breeding Hen Harriers but they are rarely present now. Peregrines can sometimes be seen here. Woodland species include Sparrowhawk, Woodcock, Tree Pipit, Redstart, Spotted Flycatcher and Common Crossbill. August 2007 © *Paul Chapman*

Red Kite

Very rare re-introduced resident. Estimated population in North-East Scotland: **5 pairs** (4% of Scottish population, <1% of UK)

Amber list; Schedule 1; Annex 1; Scottish BAP list

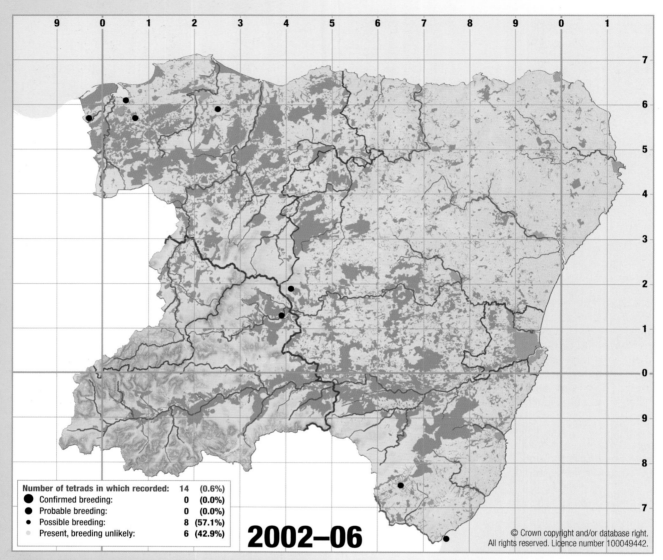

Number of tetrads in which recorded:	14	(0.6%)
● Confirmed breeding:	0	(0.0%)
● Probable breeding:	0	(0.0%)
• Possible breeding:	8	(57.1%)
○ Present, breeding unlikely:	6	(42.9%)

2002–06

Red Kite, Skene, January 2010. © *John Young*

Habitat and breeding biology

As an adaptable and generalist species, the Red Kite has few specialist habitat requirements, and is recorded in a variety of habitats in Scotland. A lowland mosaic of farmland and woodland, which provides suitable carrion, invertebrates and small mammals, is probably the most productive habitat for Red Kites. The species builds its nests in large trees of a variety of species usually at a height of 12–15 m (Carter 2001). Nests are constructed, or taken over from other species, in early spring and are lined with a variety of debris including sheep's wool and even scraps of clothing material (Orr-Ewing in *BS3*). Egg laying commences in early April with a usual clutch size of three eggs. Most of the incubation is carried out by the female.

Scottish distribution and status

After a 120-year absence, re-introductions started within Scotland in 1989 and since then populations have been established in the Black Isle, the Stirling and Perth area, Dumfries & Galloway and recently near Aberdeen. In 2009, the Scottish population was estimated to contain 137 breeding pairs, generally found close to release areas (RSPB Scotland).

Red Kite, near Garlogie, June 2009. © *Ewan Weston*

Distribution and status in North-East Scotland

The main concentration of the 14 sightings during 2002–06 was in mid Deeside and Donside, where there is abundant carrion and Rabbits. Most of these birds were identified by their wing-tags as immature birds from the Black Isle population, and were seen several times. They were most likely to have been completing their moult over the summer. After an initial juvenile dispersal, which can be of some considerable distance, Red Kites generally return to their natal area to breed. The birds at St Cyrus and Fettercairn were likely to be from the Stirling re-introduction, which were dispersing through Angus. So far, the re-colonisation of Moray has not materialised.

Changes in distribution

Red Kites were common across the UK, including North-East Scotland, until their human-induced extinction in the late 19th century. The re-colonisation across the former Scottish range has been entirely dependent on re-introductions. The increase in occurrence of Red Kite sightings in the North-East is associated with the re-introduction which started on the Black Isle in 1989. Despite an initial run of sightings in the early 1990s, the species did not colonise North-East Scotland and in recent years, prior to the re-introduction described below, there were only around five sightings annually.

Population and trends

Illegal persecution remains one of the main causes of mortality in Scottish Red Kites, which could limit the population yet again (Orr-Ewing in *BS3*). Since the end of the fieldwork period for this atlas, RSPB Scotland began a re-introduction project on the outskirts of Aberdeen. In total, 101 birds were released at Easter Anguston Farm near Peterculter. These birds were taken from donor nests in existing populations in the Chilterns, Northamptonshire, Central Scotland and the Black Isle. The three-year project started in 2007, and the first pair laid eggs in 2008, although the nest failed. In 2009 there were at least five breeding attempts distributed as shown in the map below, with seven young reared. If all goes well, by the time a future North-East Scotland breeding bird atlas is carried out there will be a healthy and expanding Red Kite population.

Author: *Jenny Lennon*

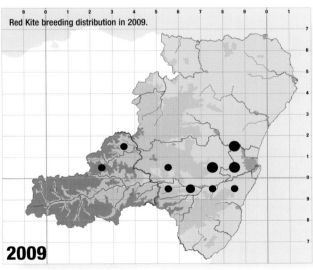

Red Kite breeding distribution in 2009.

2009

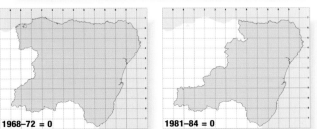

1968–72 = 0

1981–84 = 0

North-East Scotland 1968–72 to 2002–06: Change in occupied 10-km squares = **Gain**

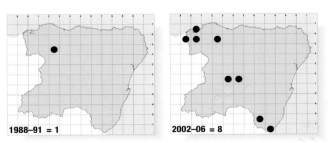

1988–91 = 1

2002–06 = 8

Marsh Harrier

Circus aeruginosus

Very rare migrant breeder. Passage migrant. Estimated population in North-East Scotland: **0–3 breeding females** (10–25% of Scottish population, <1% of UK)

Amber list; Annex 1; Schedule 1; Scottish BAP list

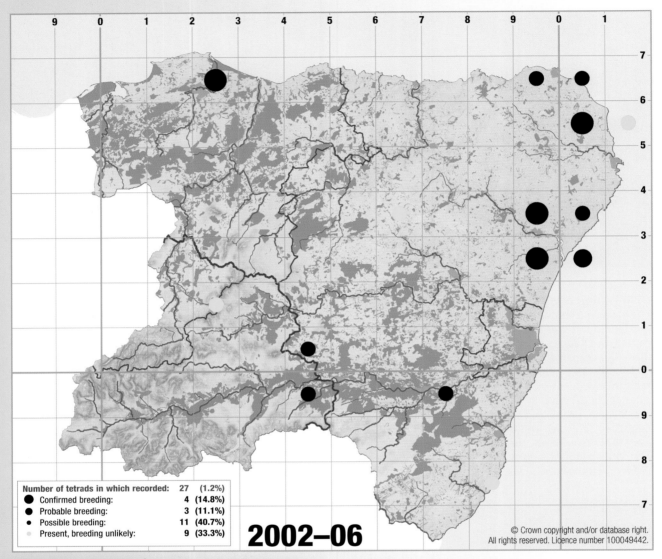

Number of tetrads in which recorded:	27	(1.2%)
● Confirmed breeding:	4	(14.8%)
● Probable breeding:	3	(11.1%)
● Possible breeding:	11	(40.7%)
● Present, breeding unlikely:	9	(33.3%)

2002–06

Habitat and breeding biology

The Marsh Harrier is largely a summer visitor to Scotland. Spring passage commences in March and autumn passage is usually over by the end of September, with very few birds occurring in winter. Some passage birds are Scandinavian (Bell in *BS3*). In North-East Scotland, since 2000, arrival dates have ranged from 13th March to 23rd April, with last records from 4th September to 9th November. Scottish breeding pairs have exclusively used reedbeds for nesting, ranging from extensive areas adjacent to large rivers to smaller stands at inland lochs, especially if fertile agricultural land is adjacent (Bell in *BS3*). On one occasion in North-East Scotland, a male was suspected to have bred with two females using nest sites separated by *c*.1 km. Since breeding was first recorded in 2000, pairs in our area have fledged a total of 20 young. However, there is no evidence of young birds returning to their natal area to breed in North-East Scotland and very few instances of this are known from elsewhere in Scotland. All breeding birds disperse south to England, continental Europe and Africa, but there is no specific indication of particular wintering areas for birds from North-East Scotland.

Marsh Harrier, Newburgh, June 2001. © *Rab Rae*

The Breeding Birds of North-East Scotland

Marsh Harrier, Tay reedbeds, July 2006. © *Joyce Moyes*

Scottish distribution and status

The Scottish breeding population is around 3–9 breeding females, found widely scattered across Scotland but centred on the Tay reedbeds between Perth and Dundee. North-East Scotland has been the most regular nesting area away from the Tay. At other times, Marsh Harriers occur on passage, especially in the spring (Bell in *BS3*). In the UK in 2005, a national survey found 363–429 breeding pairs, of which seven were in Scotland (Holling *et al.* 2008).

Distribution and status in North-East Scotland

During the 2005 national survey, three pairs bred in North-East Scotland - the maximum number that has nested in any single year. They were found in eastern and northern lowland areas, and almost all records annually are concen-

Marsh Harrier, Newburgh, May 2001. © *Rab Rae*

trated around Loch of Strathbeg, the Ythan estuary and Loch Spynie. Some of our breeding birds may originate from the Tay estuary area, as there have been numerous sightings since 1991 of birds marked with unique wing tags fitted on nestlings from breeding sites in that area, though no tag has been seen on a breeding adult. Continental origins are also possible (see below).

Changes in distribution

There have been no changes in the locations and habitats used by passage and breeding Marsh Harriers in the area over the last 15 years. However, a pair built a nest near Dinnet (mid Deeside) in 1980; sadly, the male bird, which had been ringed as a chick in the Netherlands, was poisoned (*NES 1st Atlas*). There are still occasional records from the Muir of Dinnet area.

Population and trends

Marsh Harriers in North-east Scotland have shown a long-term slow increase since the early 1960s (Phillips 1997) with the first record in Moray in 1969 (Cook 1992); birds were present very regularly during summer at several potential nesting sites throughout the 1990s. This culminated in the first successful breeding in 2000, when four young were fledged. Since then, their fortunes have varied, with breeding failures in 2001, 2003, 2004 but two pairs rearing eight young in 2002 and three pairs rearing six young (two successful nests) in 2005, when successful breeding first took place at Loch Spynie. In 2006, one pair reared two young at Loch Spynie, but from 2007 to 2009, there was no confirmed breeding in the area, with very few birds even seen at the Ythan estuary.

Author: *Ian Francis*

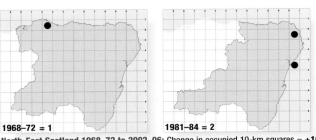

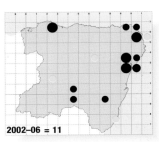

1968–72 = 1   1981–84 = 2   1988–91 = 1   2002–06 = 11

North-East Scotland 1968–72 to 2002–06: Change in occupied 10-km squares = **+1000%**

Hen Harrier

Circus cyaneus

Rare breeder. Few in winter. Estimated population in North-East Scotland: **18–22 pairs** (3% of Scottish population, <3% of UK)

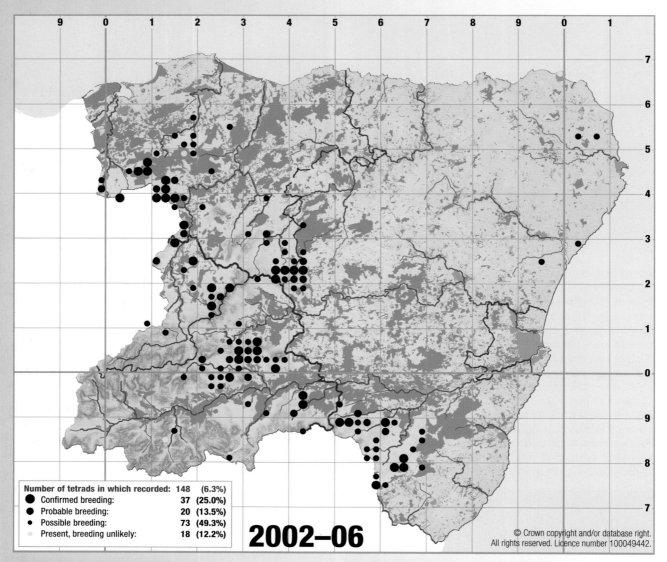

Number of tetrads in which recorded:	148	(6.3%)
● Confirmed breeding:	37	(25.0%)
● Probable breeding:	20	(13.5%)
● Possible breeding:	73	(49.3%)
● Present, breeding unlikely:	18	(12.2%)

2002–06

Habitat and breeding biology

Hen Harriers breed on upland Heather moors, particularly those managed for Red Grouse sport shooting, and on areas of moorland with regenerating Scots Pine. They nest on the ground, usually in deep Heather at altitudes of 200–550 m. The majority return to breeding areas in North-East Scotland in mid March to mid April, and both sexes display over potential nesting sites. Established pairs will utilise the same general area for nesting in successive years if unmolested. They are single-brooded and normally vacate breeding areas by the end of July, but occasional successful repeat nesting can result in families on territory until the end of August.

Scottish distribution and status

Hen Harriers are sparingly distributed across the southern uplands and eastern highlands, with good numbers in Orkney, the Uists and Argyll (Etheridge in *BS3*). In 2004, 633 territorial pairs were estimated for Scotland. Increases, since previous surveys in 1988–89 and 1998, were found in most areas, apart from the south and east Highlands. Declines in these latter areas were attributed to the recognised conflict between driven Red Grouse shooting interests and breeding Hen Harriers (Sim *et al.* 2007).

Distribution and status in North-East Scotland

Hen Harriers were found around the Cairn o' Mount, on mid Deeside, upper Donside, the Cabrach, Fiddich and Livet areas, the Ladder and Cromdale Hills, and fragmented former 'grouse moor' in west Moray. In addition, there were some records from low ground, but breeding on lowland raised bogs, coastal moorland or low-intensity farmland, all habitats that are utilised in other parts of their European range (*BWP*), was not confirmed. They were largely absent as breeders in the upper Cairngorms straths, and overall much suitable breeding habitat was unoccupied, with many territories on 'grouse moors' not occupied in subsequent years.

Changes in distribution

The Hen Harrier was possibly extinct as a breeding species in North-East Scotland at the end of the 19th century, but had re-colonised part of the south-east of the region by the early 1960s, as was the case across much of mainland Scotland by the mid 1970s (Watson 1977, Picozzi 1978). Apart from west Moray, numbers have decreased in the 21st century, such that the species is now a rare breeder across much of Aberdeenshire and east Moray (*MNBR*s, NESRSG annual reports). The 64% increase in 10-km square distribution, between 1968–72 and 2002–06, has masked the recently reported declines. For example, many territories on 'grouse moors' were only occupied for one or two years, resulting in the cumulative range distribution disguising a poorer annual situation. However, not all declines were associated with 'grouse moor' management, and some loss of breeding areas and hunting habitat occurred after extensive areas of commercial conifer plantations reached the thicket stage, such as east of the Cairn o' Mount road to Netherley, north Morven, at Clashindarroch and in west Moray.

Population and trends

Members of the North-East Scotland Raptor Study Group (NESRSG) monitor around 60 former breeding areas annually. In 2004, additional suitable habitat was also covered, as part of a national survey. Despite the increased effort, only 14 pairs were located in Aberdeenshire, similar to the average of 12 pairs (range 9–18) located during 1999–2006. In Moray, the 2002–06 population was considered relatively stable at 9–12 breeding pairs. Little has been published on numbers in North-East Scotland but two studies highlight the declining trend well.

The first study, covering 120 km^2 around Glen Dye and Drumtochty Forest (formerly in Kincardineshire, now Aberdeenshire) during 1970–74 located at least 15 breeding pairs in 1974 (Picozzi 1978). All of Kincardineshire was surveyed in 1988–89 and 1995 as part of a national survey and a study on Hen Harrier dispersion respectively. Three breeding pairs were located in 1988–89, but none in 1995. Further national surveys in 1998 and 2004 located one and two breeding pairs respectively over the same area.

The second study covered the Ladder Hills SSSI/SAC at Glenlivet, Moray where, on average, seven pairs bred annually in 1991–99 with as many as 12 in 1994 (NESRSG annual reports). Classification of the Ladder Hills as an SPA for Hen Harriers was deferred in 2000–03 while further population survey, prey availability and habitat suitability was assessed. In 2004, this assessment concluded 'there are large areas of

Hen Harrier, Deeside, 1982. © *Graham Rebecca*

breeding habitat with suitable nest sites across the site and no evidence of lack of prey' (SNH 2004). Despite the habitat and prey suitability, there was only one breeding pair in 2001, three in 2002 and none in 2000 and 2003–06 (Hardey & Craib 2001, Hardey *et al.* 2002, 2003, NESRSG annual reports). Further, in 2007, 11 km^2 in the Ladder Hills/Lecht area were fully surveyed with no Hen Harriers located, and it was noted that although habitat within the SSSI/SAC was still suitable for Hen Harriers there had been more intensive burning of suitable areas of longer Heather (Francis in *MNBR* 2007). These studies show how Hen Harriers can fluctuate in areas where Red Grouse sport shooting is the primary land-use.

Author: *Graham Rebecca*

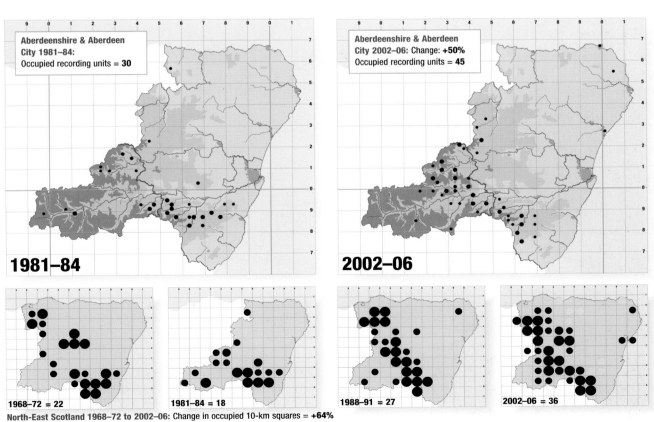

Aberdeenshire & Aberdeen City 1981–84: Occupied recording units = 30

1981–84

Aberdeenshire & Aberdeen City 2002–06: Change: **+50%** Occupied recording units = **45**

2002–06

1968–72 = 22

1981–84 = 18

1988–91 = 27

2002–06 = 36

North-East Scotland 1968–72 to 2002–06: Change in occupied 10-km squares = **+64%**

Goshawk

Accipiter gentilis

Rare resident. Estimated population in North-East Scotland: **50–60 pairs** (42% of Scottish population, 13% of UK)

Schedule 1

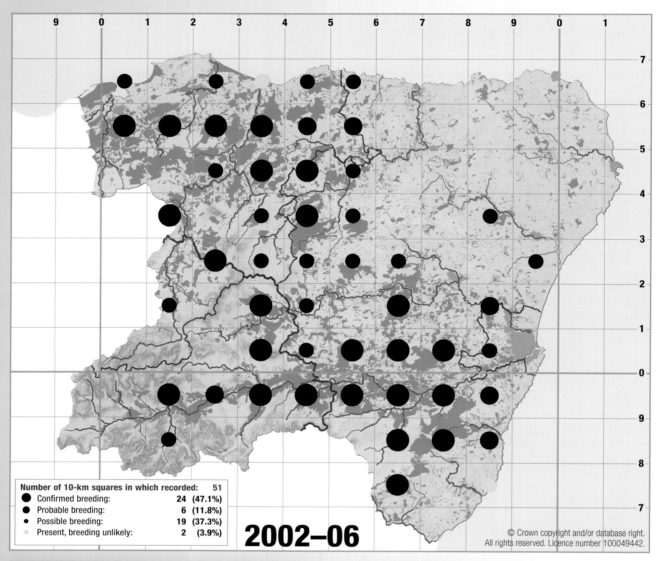

Number of 10-km squares in which recorded: 51
- ● Confirmed breeding: 24 (47.1%)
- ● Probable breeding: 6 (11.8%)
- • Possible breeding: 19 (37.3%)
- ○ Present, breeding unlikely: 2 (3.9%)

2002–06

Goshawk, Dyce, March 2008. © *Ed Duthie*

Habitat and breeding biology

Goshawks are wide-ranging birds of heavily wooded landscapes, hunting predominantly in forest but also across open country particularly where, between flights, they can perch in copses or scattered trees. In North-East Scotland they mainly nest in the lower canopy of mature conifers within large forests but, as elsewhere, they sometimes use smaller woodlots of less than 50 ha. They are resident, using the same woods year round, although shifting their hunting activity to exploit local abundance in their prey - most importantly pigeons, followed by corvids, Rabbits and game birds respectively. They refurbish nests in March and lay eggs in April; young hatch in May, fledge by July and disperse in August and September.

Scottish distribution and status

The last recorded native Scottish pair bred in 1883 and re-colonisation was from captives mainly imported from Fennoscandia in the early 1970s (Marquiss & Newton 1982, Petty 1996) and first proven breeding was in 1972. By the late 1970s there were settled birds in the Borders, Grampian, Highland, Argyll and Clyde, although numbers were sustained in only two regions. The breeding population has since spread and is now centred on

Goshawk, Aberdeenshire, June 1995. © *Gavin Legge*

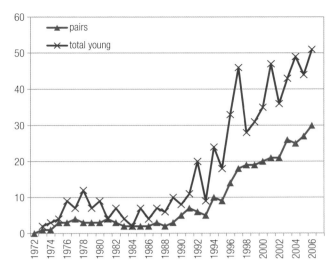

Figure 1. Goshawk pairs found and young produced, 1972–2006, in North-East Scotland south of Rhynie (data, M. Marquiss, G. Legge & J. Young).

Southern Scotland and the North-East, with a few pairs elsewhere (Petty in *BS3*). The number of Scottish breeders in 2000–04 was estimated at 130 pairs and increasing, probably reaching 150 by 2006. In 1994, there were about 400 pairs in the UK (Petty 1996).

Distribution and status in North-East Scotland

During the 2002–06 Atlas period, birds were located in 49 10-km squares, with evidence of breeding in 27 of these. There were few records from the Cairngorms and Buchan so the breeding population is currently restricted to the most wooded terrain in the region. Though widespread, the population is at very low density; within intensively monitored areas, most occupied 10-km squares only contained one breeding pair. The main influence on distribution is persecution. There are reasonably stable numbers in state forests but persistent gaps in the current distribution are adjacent to managed grouse moor and near places where Pheasants or Red-legged Partridges are released in large numbers. Both adult and dispersing juvenile Goshawks are attracted to artificially high densities of such vulnerable prey (Kenward 2006) and some are illegally killed when caught in cage traps set legally to control corvids (Petty 2002, Marquiss *et al.* 2003). Although annual productivity of Goshawks is very high in the North-East, at 2.44 young/pair (Marquiss & Legge 2003), many of these potential recruits are lost before they settle to breed.

Changes in distribution

Four casual sight records between 1969 and 1972 included birds near Forres and Banchory. There were, at that time, unconfirmed reports of breeding in Moray, Huntly and beside Mintlaw, but the first proven nest was found near Banchory in 1973. From intensive searching of woodlands in the late 1970s and early 1980s, it seemed that breeding birds were by then widespread although very few in number. At that time there were pairs near Forres, Elgin, Huntly, Inverurie, Banchory and Edzell, and a single near Mintlaw. The current geographical spread is similar despite substantial population increase.

Population and trends

Since the early 1970s, Goshawks have slowly increased at about 5% per year (Figure 1) except in the mid 1980s when numbers temporarily fell and re-extinction seemed possible. In 2006, about half of North-East Scotland was intensively searched and contained 31 pairs. By extrapolation to all occupied squares, the breeding population of the whole region could have been 56 pairs. Assuming average productivity and that few birds breed in their first year, there were probably about 200 individuals in the North-East in autumn 2006. The increase in breeding birds is substantially less than elsewhere (Marquiss *et al.* 2003). By analogy with similar landscapes across western Europe we anticipate much higher densities and considering the configuration of available nesting woodland, the breeding population could ultimately stabilise at about 140 pairs. There would be an even larger population if, as well-wooded terrain is occupied to capacity, new recruits start to use sub-optimal habitat in farmland and urban environments (Rutz *et al.* 2006). Realistically, this is unlikely as long as illegal killing continues because areas with plentiful food and no breeding birds persistently attract further victims.

Author: *Mick Marquiss*

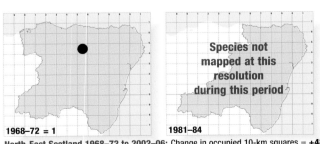

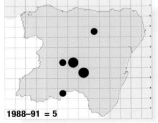

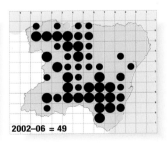

1968–72 = 1   1981–84 Species not mapped at this resolution during this period   1988–91 = 5   2002–06 = 49

North-East Scotland 1968–72 to 2002–06: Change in occupied 10-km squares = **+4800%**

Sparrowhawk

Accipiter nisus

Scarce resident. Passage migrant. Estimated population in North-East Scotland: *500–1,000 pairs* (8% of Scottish population, 2% of UK)

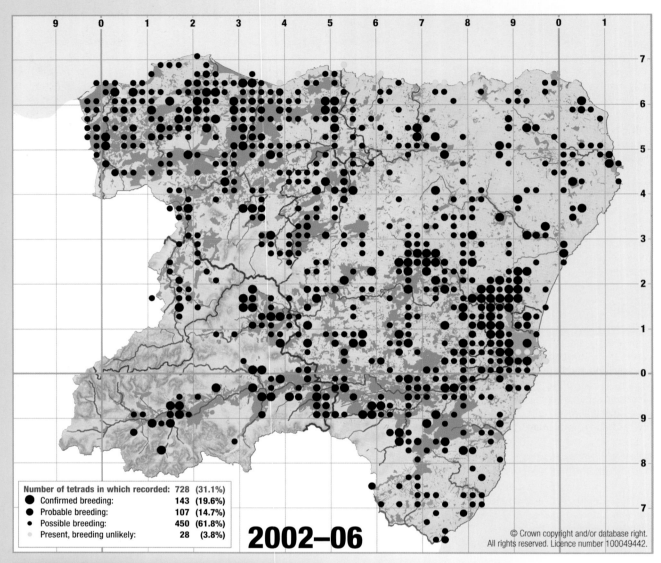

Number of tetrads in which recorded: 728 (31.1%)
- ● Confirmed breeding: 143 (19.6%)
- ● Probable breeding: 107 (14.7%)
- ● Possible breeding: 450 (61.8%)
- · Present, breeding unlikely: 28 (3.8%)

2002–06

Sparrowhawk, Drum, 1977. © *Graham Rebecca*

Habitat and breeding biology

Sparrowhawks are small, bird-eating raptors that hunt most parts of the North-East from sea level to the tree-line at about 600 m. They use cover to approach their songbird prey, hunting predominantly in woodland but also over open country including moorland, open farmland and shoreline. Males take smaller prey than females and favour thicker cover, but both sexes use forest edges and farmland with scattered woodlots, copses and hedges. Sparrowhawks also use towns and villages, hunting parks and gardens in addition to the surrounding countryside (Newton 1986). In North-East Scotland they mainly nest in the lower canopy of thick coniferous woodland, on the periphery of large forests, in small farmland woods and in shrubby urban parkland. Here, Sparrowhawks are resident, displaying in March, refurbishing nests in April and laying eggs in May; their young hatch in June, fledge in July and disperse in August.

Scottish distribution and status

Sparrowhawks are widely distributed as resident breeding birds across most of Scotland wherever there is woodland, although they are absent in moorland and mountain areas and on islands devoid of trees. Breeding densities are broadly correlated with the densities of songbirds that are

The Breeding Birds of North-East Scotland

their main prey, which in turn are correlated with elevation and land productivity. The Scottish breeding population in 2000–04 was estimated as 8,000–12,000 pairs (Newton in *BS3*). Migrants from Scandinavia arrive in Scotland in September to November and leave in April and May, but wintering numbers are unknown.

Distribution and status in North-East Scotland

Sparrowhawks are secretive and breeding is not always easy to confirm. Nevertheless, the tetrad-scale distribution during the atlas period is broadly correlated with elevation and the presence of nesting habitat - well distributed over the North-East and absent only in the uplands of the Cairngorms. The scatter of breeding records might coarsely represent relative abundance, as the pattern of fewer observations across less wooded areas is consistent with fewer breeding territories on open farmland where woods are scattered and small. It is also interesting that there seem to be more records on the edges of large forests than within, consistent with the lower densities of small birds deep within forests. The very highest concentration of Sparrowhawk records is at low elevation on the fringes of villages and around Aberdeen. This pattern may reflect hawk density or it might simply result from the greater observer effort there. North-East Scotland has some of the highest elevation Sparrowhawk breeding sites in the UK, in birch woodland at 380 m in Glen Gairn, and in semi-natural Scots Pine in Glen Derry (440 m) and Glen Quoich (510 m). In such high elevation Cairngorms woodlands, there are few prey birds during the winter and hawks which have presumably wintered on lowland nearby, return to breed late, laying eggs in early June and fledging young in August (pers. obs.).

Changes in distribution

As elsewhere in Britain, Sparrowhawks were scarce in the lowland farmland of North-East Scotland during the late 1950s and early 1960s associated with persistent organochlorine pollution (J. Oswald pers. comm.) but there is no local quantitative evidence for it. It is also thought that over

the last 20 years, Sparrowhawks have changed their fine-scale breeding distribution with fewer nests in large forest blocks and more in thicket stage plantations, small woods in farmland, and in urban habitats (pers. obs.). This could be the result of interaction with medium-sized raptors as Goshawks have colonised and Buzzards become ubiquitous. More plausibly, it could be because of changes in woodland structure as plantations have matured and been harvested, or because of widespread decline in woodland songbird populations and their increase in gardens. Unfortunately, we cannot distinguish between these explanations because the Sparrowhawk breeding population has not been well monitored. Distribution changes shown in consecutive atlases are no more enlightening. Although the 2002–06 atlas recorded presence in more 10-km squares than formerly, the tetrad distribution is similar to previous atlases, which suggests that presence in more 10-km squares is an artefact of the greater coverage and more records in the recent atlas.

Population and trends

In the 1970s, breeding densities (nests per 100 km^2) of Sparrowhawks in the well-wooded parts of Deeside were 89 near Crathes, 49 around Banchory, 45 at Ballater and 21 in Mar Forest. In well-wooded parts of Moray, beside Forres, there were 59 nests per 100 km^2, and 94 in plantations set amongst predominantly arable farmland near Mintlaw (Newton 1986, in *BS3*). These measured densities suggest there were then 1–4 nests/occupied tetrad. There have been no large-scale surveys for breeding density since. From 1994–2006, the mean number of Sparrowhawks seen on BBS squares in North-East Scotland halved, suggesting decline - but the sample was small. Nevertheless, with substantial decline in songbird populations it is possible that there are far fewer hawks now - less than two nests/occupied tetrad. Given the paucity of information we can only guess that the current population of the region is of the order of 500–1,000 pairs.

Author: *Mick Marquiss*

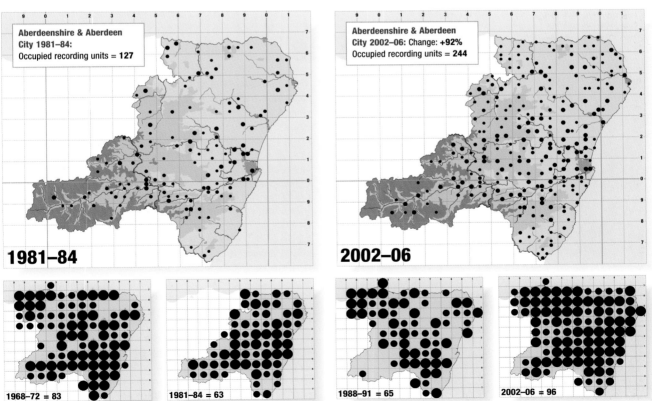

1981–84

2002–06

North-East Scotland 1968–72 to 2002–06: Change in occupied 10-km squares = +16%

Buzzard

Buteo buteo

Common resident. Estimated population in North-East Scotland: **2,300 pairs** (13% of Scottish population, 6% of UK)

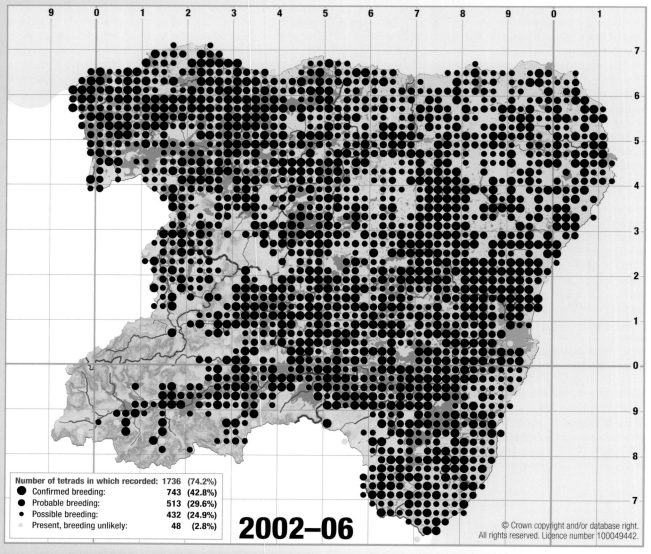

Number of tetrads in which recorded:	1736	(74.2%)
● Confirmed breeding:	743	(42.8%)
● Probable breeding:	513	(29.6%)
● Possible breeding:	432	(24.9%)
· Present, breeding unlikely:	48	(2.8%)

2002–06

Buzzard, Bettyhill, Sutherland, 1979. © *Graham Rebecca*

Habitat and breeding biology

Buzzards are found in a variety of habitats, with densities being highest in areas with greatest prey availability and low persecution. They are now a species typical of open countryside with small woods and shelterbelts. Continuous enclosed woodland is avoided, as are urban areas and high mountains. Nests are built in trees, on crags, cliffs or even, occasionally, on the ground, and are found at varying heights, from only a few metres to tens of metres. In woods, they tend to be located towards the edges rather than in the centre and in a variety of tree species (Martinez-Padilla 2006). The nests, usually built from woody material, are often re-used and can become up to 1 m in diameter and height (Martinez-Padilla 2006). Clutch size (1–5 eggs) and brood size (typically 1–4 chicks) are largely dependent on the available prey in the territory, nests near large Rabbit populations being more successful than those where the main available prey is small birds and rodents (Graham *et al.* 1995, Halley 1993). Incubation lasts for 33–35 days and young are in the nest for 50–55 days before fledging (*BWP*).

Scottish distribution and status

Buzzards are distributed widely throughout Scotland, with the exception of Shetland, much of Orkney and some of the smaller islands. They are largely absent from mountainous areas, however, particularly the north-west Highlands and the Grampians. Highest densities occur in Dumfries & Galloway, Argyll, Skye, and the Great Glen up into Inverness-shire (Holling in *BS3*). The distribution of Buzzards in Scotland has changed markedly over the last few decades. The species underwent a large decline and contraction of range from the mid 19th century, when persecution was intense. Numbers were greatly reduced, but small populations remained in refuges less affected by deliberate killing. From the 1960s onwards the species has gradually spread back into much of its former range. The breeding population was estimated at 15,000–20,000 pairs in 2007 (Holling in *BS3*).

Distribution and status in North-East Scotland

Buzzards breed in most parts of North-East Scotland, where they are particularly associated with lightly-wooded countryside which provides nest sites and plentiful prey. They penetrate the uplands along wooded glens but avoid the highest ground. They are increasingly appearing in more populated localities but still avoid urban areas, notably central Aberdeen. The density is also lower over much of Buchan where a shortage of nesting woods is perhaps a limiting factor. Nesting Buzzards in mid Deeside fed their young on a wide variety of prey, most commonly Rabbits but the diet also included pigeons, Pheasants and hares (Martinez-Padilla 2006). Their fondness for carrion causes mortality through traffic collisions and makes them susceptible to illegal killing by entering baited crow cages or feeding from poisoned bait.

Changes in distribution

The spread in the distribution of Buzzards in North-East Scotland has been similar to that of the rest of Scotland. The North-East experienced some of the most intense

persecution, especially in relation to game bird management. In the 20th century, prior to the Second World War, Buzzards were almost entirely absent as breeding birds, with only occasional nests and pairs found (A. Watson pers. comm.). A slow recolonisation and increase began after that time. Since the 1960s the range has expanded enormously. In 1968–72, Buzzards were found in 61 10-km squares, and proved to breed in 35 of them (*BTO 1st Atlas*). By 2002–06, 105 squares were occupied with confirmed breeding in 98. The spread is demonstrated even more dramatically by the comparative maps of Aberdeenshire/Aberdeen City for the two local Atlas periods where a 254% increase in occupied recording units during the intervening 20 years is evident. During that period, Buzzards have spread out of their Deeside and upper Donside strongholds to colonise the entire North-East, with the exception of the highest uplands.

Population and trends

Clearly the increased distribution of Buzzards in the North-East has been accompanied by an increase in numbers. There has, however, been no local systematic monitoring to give an indication of the size of the population. The Scottish population estimate was derived using densities of between 0.25–0.5 pairs/km^2 (Holling in *BS3*) which converts to 1–2 pairs/tetrad. If we apply this range to the 1,256 tetrads where breeding was probable or confirmed, and assume 1 pair/tetrad in the 432 where breeding was possible, then a median population estimate of around 2,300 pairs in North-East Scotland is obtained. Although nine of the 24 tetrads where Buzzard territories were counted during 2002–06 contained 3–4 pairs, conversely, densities are very low in large forests, on Heather moorland and on the fringes of the Cairngorms, and not all tetrads where possible breeding was recorded would actually hold nesting birds.

Author: *Ewan Weston*

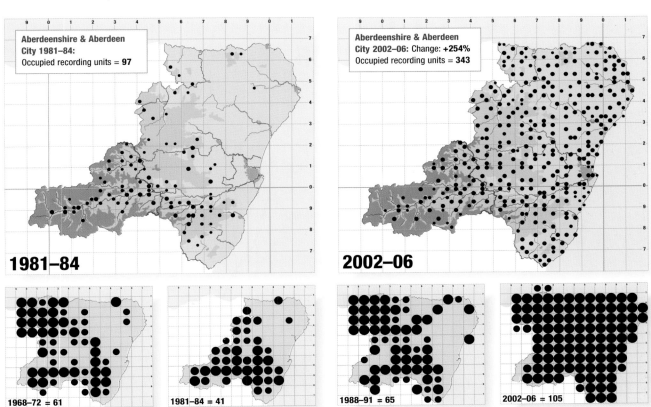

Aberdeenshire & Aberdeen City 1981–84: Occupied recording units = **97**

1981–84

Aberdeenshire & Aberdeen City 2002–06: Change: +254% Occupied recording units = **343**

2002–06

1968–72 = 61   1981–84 = 41

1988–91 = 65   2002–06 = 105

North-East Scotland 1968–72 to 2002–06: Change in occupied 10-km squares = +72%

Golden Eagle

Aquila chrysaetos

Rare resident. Estimated population in North-East Scotland: **17–20 occupied territories**, 10–15 breeding pairs (4% of Scottish and UK population)

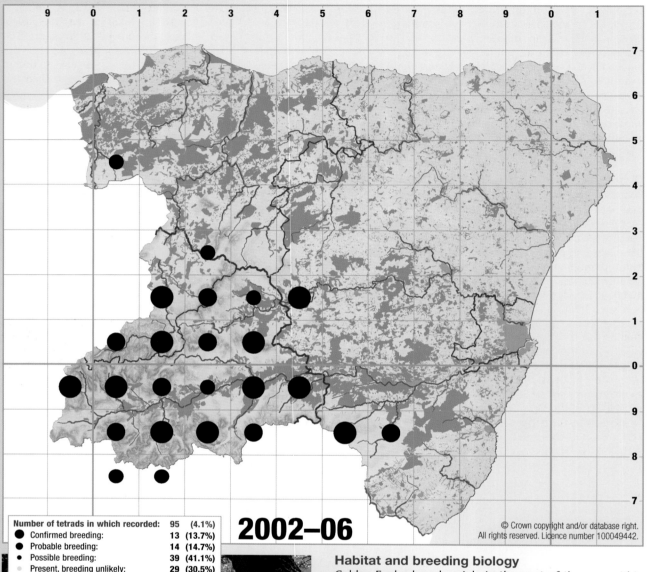

2002–06

Number of tetrads in which recorded:	95	(4.1%)
● Confirmed breeding:	13	(13.7%)
● Probable breeding:	14	(14.7%)
● Possible breeding:	39	(41.1%)
● Present, breeding unlikely:	29	(30.5%)

Golden Eagle, Ballater, April 2007. © *Rab Rae*

Habitat and breeding biology

Golden Eagles breed mainly in the west of the area within the Cairngorm mountain range, where they occupy both cliff and tree eyries. Birds are pair and site faithful, and display can be seen in suitable weather almost any time of year. Eggs are laid in late March and early April. Some nest sites in North-East Scotland are as high as 1,000 m, among the highest in the country, and many fail due to late snowfalls. The chicks generally hatch in early May and the young fledge 10–12 weeks later, in July. Breeding success averages 0.6 chicks/pair, which is above the national average of 0.36/pair (Eaton *et al.* 2007). Food items recorded at eyries reflect the available prey, but the remains of Red Grouse, Mountain Hares and Rabbits are found at most nests. Roe Deer calves and Fox cubs are not uncommon, while Ptarmigan are regular prey items in the higher nests.

Scottish distribution and status

Golden Eagles are widely distributed in most of upland Scotland north of the central belt. The 2003 national survey revealed 442 pairs (Eaton *et al.* 2007) and this population is considered to be stable or possibly increasing, although continued persecution in the east is restricting their distribution here (Whitfield *et al.* 2003).

Distribution and status in North-East Scotland

The distribution of Golden Eagles has changed little in the last 100 years (Sim 1903); the birds are still largely confined to the west of the area where 'deer forest' is the primary land use. Here, eagles were traditionally tolerated because they killed grouse that could ruin the deer stalking. There have been a few pairs outwith the Cairngorm massif in recent years on Donside and in Moray. These were all on grouse moors and all home ranges have now been abandoned with some adult birds known to have been killed while others have simply disappeared. The North-East Scotland eagle population has a long history of study, and detailed breeding records going back to 1944 are available for most territories. Many of the 'deer forest' territories show continuous occupation for the whole period with some pairs producing twins for 20 consecutive years. No grouse moor territories have similar continuous occupation for such periods. A strong body of local evidence reinforces the conclusions of Whitfield *et al.* (2008) that illegal persecution is the main factor restricting the spread of Golden Eagles in this area. North-East Scotland Raptor Study Group records since 1944 also show that when left to breed successfully, Golden Eagles in our area have a better breeding performance than average for Scotland. Yet this productivity has not led to an increase - there is still the same number of breeding eagles now as there were in 1944. There is certainly enough suitable habitat and prey to support at least twice the current breeding numbers.

Changes in distribution

There has been no permanent change in the distribution of Golden Eagles in North-East Scotland although pairs have temporarily set up territories and bred, notably on Donside grouse moors where two pairs established themselves as successful breeders for several years before disappearing on the arrival of new gamekeepers. There are no vacant territories on the high deer forests to the west of the area but there are many on the lower grouse moors of the east, though birds seldom occupy these vacant areas for more than a season.

Population and trends

The Golden Eagle population in North-East Scotland has been fairly stable since 1944 at around 17 pairs occupying territories. In addition, there are usually a further three unpaired birds occupying vacant territories. Of the 17 pairs, only 10–15 lay eggs in any year and usually only around 10–12 regularly rear young (North-East Scotland Raptor Study Group).

Author: *Robert Rae*

Golden Eagle, East Cairngorms, May 1985. © *Ed Duthie*

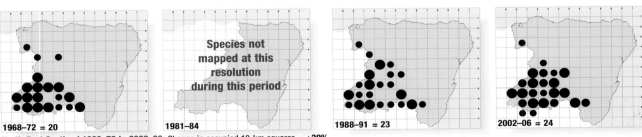

1968–72 = 20

1981–84   Species not mapped at this resolution during this period

1988–91 = 23

2002–06 = 24

North-East Scotland 1968–72 to 2002–06: Change in occupied 10-km squares = +20%

Chapter 3. The breeding birds of North-East Scotland: species accounts

Osprey

Pandion haliaetus

Rare summer migrant breeder. Passage migrant. Estimated population in North-East Scotland: **30 pairs** (16% of Scottish population, 15% of UK)

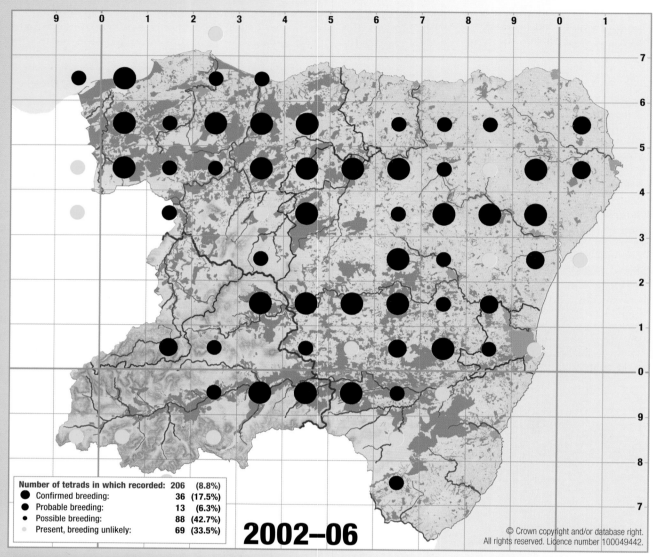

Number of tetrads in which recorded:	206	(8.8%)
● Confirmed breeding:	36	(17.5%)
● Probable breeding:	13	(6.3%)
● Possible breeding:	88	(42.7%)
● Present, breeding unlikely:	69	(33.5%)

2002–06

Osprey, Finland, June 2008. © *John Chapman*

Habitat and breeding biology

Ospreys return from wintering areas in West Africa (and, increasingly, Spain) during late March or early April and are then present throughout the summer, with birds usually seen until mid September and occasionally into October. Established breeders normally return directly to nests from previous years and refurbish them. Most nests are in conifer trees and are often some distance from water. New nests may be built, when nests are robbed or storm damaged, and as the number of pairs increases or pairings change. Eggs are laid in mid to late April or early May, with young hatching after around five weeks of incubation and first flights occurring eight weeks or so after that, usually in late July. Broods range from one to three young, with an average for Aberdeenshire of 1.4 young fledging per occupied nest (Francis 2007), slightly lower than the 1.6 average for Scotland (Dennis in *BS3*). One of the main influences on Osprey breeding success is the weather in June and July, particularly when there are small chicks in the nest. Long periods of cold wet weather can cause numerous breeding failures. Later in the summer, adults and fledged birds may range more widely and sometimes several birds can be seen at favoured areas such as the Ythan estuary. Certain stocked fisheries and stretches of river are visited frequently for feeding.

Scottish distribution and status

The Osprey is an increasing breeding summer visitor to much of mainland Scotland (Dennis in *BS3*). Most birds are found in northern, central and eastern areas, though there are now small but growing numbers in southern Scotland. The densest populations are in Tayside, several areas of Highland Region, and in Moray and Aberdeenshire. The Scottish population in 2007 was estimated at 182–200 pairs (Dennis in *BS3*).

Distribution and status in North-East Scotland

As elsewhere in Scotland, Ospreys often breed in loose colonies or clusters, and in our area there are clear concentrations in west Moray, east Moray, the Deveron, Donside and the Ythan catchment. Deeside has only a few breeding pairs. However, there is a scattering of pairs away from these clusters and Ospreys can be seen more or less anywhere in the area during the summer. It is also becoming increasingly difficult to find all possible Osprey sites so it is likely that a few pairs remain undetected.

Changes in distribution

In Scotland, there was a clear spread from the original nesting areas in Strathspey outwards to the north (into Moray), south and then east to Aberdeenshire. Nests in our area have been well distributed ever since first colonisation, but Moray then Donside were favoured early on, as was the Ythan, whereas nesting in the Deveron catchment occurred generally later. There is now infill occurring across the whole area, but south Moray, the upper third of Deeside and the Howe of the Mearns still hold no known nests.

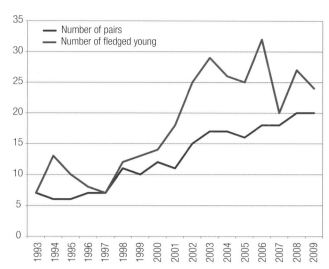

Figure 1. Ospreys in Aberdeenshire 1993–2009.

Population and trends

The first nesting pair in Moray in recent historic times was in 1966 (Cook 1992). In Aberdeenshire, nesting took place later, in 1977 (*NES 1st Atlas*). During the atlas period numbers rose to 29 known pairs in 2006 (with 48 young fledged) and in 2008, there were 31 pairs of Ospreys in North-East Scotland. The graph shows the trend for Aberdeenshire, which typifies the increase. There are now as many Ospreys breeding in North-East Scotland as there were in the whole country in 1983 (Dennis 2008) and this trend of slow expansion seems likely to continue.

Author: *Ian Francis*

Osprey, Donside, July 2009. © *Ewan Weston*

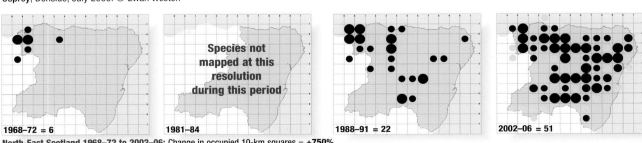

1968–72 = 6

1981–84   Species not mapped at this resolution during this period

1988–91 = 22

2002–06 = 51

North-East Scotland 1968–72 to 2002–06: Change in occupied 10-km squares = +750%

Kestrel

Falco tinnunculus

Scarce resident. Passage migrant. Estimated population in North-East Scotland: *800–900 pairs* (11% of Scottish population, 2% of UK)

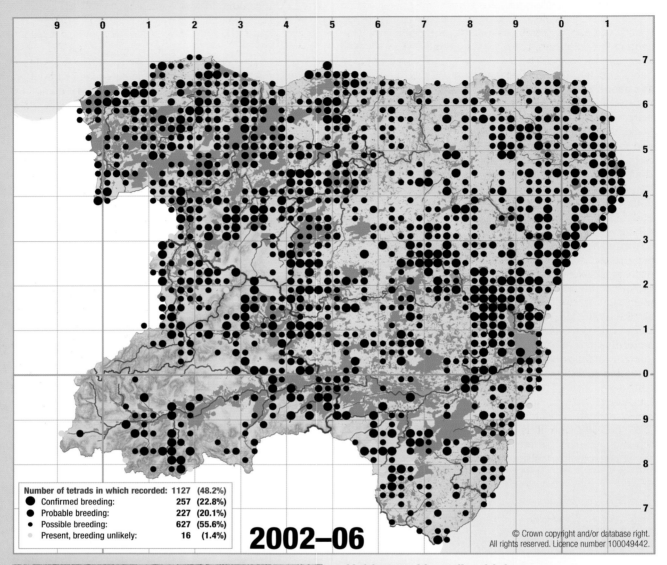

Number of tetrads in which recorded:	1127	(48.2%)
● Confirmed breeding:	257	(22.8%)
● Probable breeding:	227	(20.1%)
● Possible breeding:	627	(55.6%)
● Present, breeding unlikely:	16	(1.4%)

2002–06

Kestrel, Glen Isla, Angus, 1980. © *Bruce Anderson*

Habitat and breeding biology

Kestrels are found in a diverse range of largely open habitats, from coastal cliffs to upland areas. Common nest sites are rocky ledges, tree holes, buildings and old stick nests of other birds, while nestboxes are readily used. Unusually for the mainland, birds also occasionally nest on the ground in North-East Scotland, as was recorded on Donside in 2000. Following fledging in late June or July, family parties of Kestrels remain together for a few weeks before the young disperse. Kestrel breeding performance is often linked to the abundance of the Field Vole, its preferred prey in upland grassland habitats, which has a three- to four-year cycle.

Scottish distribution and status

The Kestrel is widely distributed across Scotland, but commonest in the south and east. The Scottish population has recently been estimated at 7,500–7,800 pairs (Riddle in *BS3*), but is declining rapidly. BBS data indicate that the population decreased by 56% during the period 1994–2007, the largest decline of any species for which a trend could be calculated (Risely *et al.* 2008). This decline may have started earlier, as a 9% decrease in occupied 10-km squares was recorded between 1968–72 and 1988–91. The reduction has largely been attributed to habitat degradation in

The Breeding Birds of North-East Scotland

farmland, although increasing competition with other raptors may also be a factor.

Distribution and status in North-East Scotland
The Kestrel has a patchy distribution covering most of the region, with possible, probable or confirmed breeding recorded in 48% of tetrads. Favoured areas include the Urie and lower Don valleys, the coastal strip north of Balmedie, and much of Moray. These areas contain suitable hunting habitat, such as unimproved grassland and mixed farmland, and offer shelter belts, plantations or cliffs as nesting sites. Kestrels are largely absent as a breeding species from the high mountains of the Cairngorms, and have little presence in extensive areas of forest or upland moorland. They are also sparsely distributed in the intensively agricultural areas of the Mearns and much of the Buchan plain, where prey and/or nest sites are likely to be limiting.

Changes in distribution
The proportion of recording units in Aberdeenshire/ Aberdeen City which contain Kestrels increased by 33% between 1981–84 and 2002–06. The increases have largely been in the north and east of the region, on the Buchan plain, around the River Urie and in the vicinity of Aberdeen, while the overall distribution in the south and west of the region has changed relatively little. It is not clear whether all of the increases are due to a genuine range expansion, to better recording or to population fluctuation. It was noted that a lack of confirmed breeding records from the Buchan plain in 1981–84 was partly due to under-recording, although agricultural intensification was also considered to be a likely factor here and in south Kincardine (*NES 1st Atlas*). This latter factor is unlikely to have changed substantially in favour of Kestrels since 1981–84, although it is possible that agri-environment schemes or nestbox provision may have benefited the species in some agricultural areas.

Population and trends
Although the 2002–06 data indicate an increase relative to 1981–84, BBS data suggest that the local population may now be in decline, with such a trend apparent in the average maximum number of birds recorded per square between 1994 and 2006. However, this is set against widely fluctuating numbers based on a relatively small sample size. Kestrel breeding density and performance can vary significantly in response to vole populations, and they are also susceptible to cold winters, when prolonged snow cover inhibits hunting. These factors make the estimation of Kestrel populations difficult. Using the recent population estimate for Scotland (Riddle in *BS3*), and the proportion of land area comprising the region, a population estimate of 800–900 pairs can be derived for North-East Scotland. However, as has been suggested for Fife, the number of pairs may halve between good and poor vole years (Elkins *et al*. 2003). It should be noted that the Kestrel population level in North-East Scotland in 1981–84 was considered to have been depressed by a number of cold winters, so data from this time may represent a low baseline against which to compare.

Author: *Hugh Addlesee*

Kestrel, Newburgh, May 2003. © *Rab Rae*

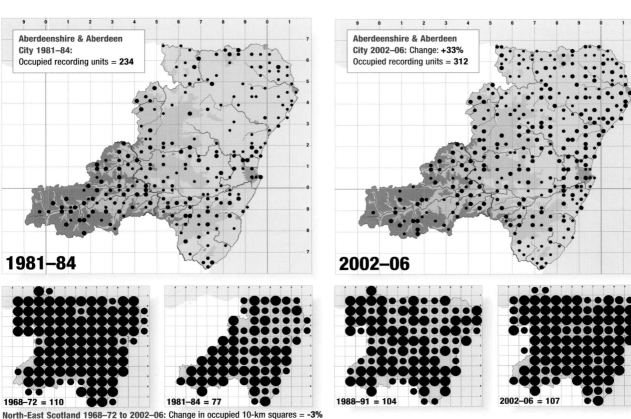

Aberdeenshire & Aberdeen City 1981–84:
Occupied recording units = **234**

1981–84

Aberdeenshire & Aberdeen City 2002–06: Change: +33%
Occupied recording units = **312**

2002–06

1968–72 = 110

1981–84 = 77

1988–91 = 104

2002–06 = 107

North-East Scotland 1968–72 to 2002–06: Change in occupied 10-km squares = **-3%**

Merlin

Falco columbarius

Rare resident. Passage migrant. Estimated population in North-East Scotland: **75–85 pairs** (10% of Scottish population, 6% of UK)

Schedule 1; Annex 1; Scottish BAP list

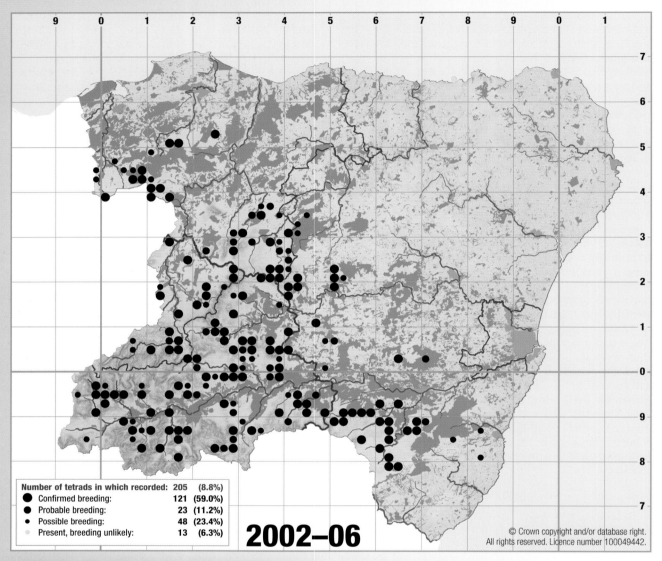

Number of tetrads in which recorded:	205	(8.8%)
● Confirmed breeding:	121	(59.0%)
● Probable breeding:	23	(11.2%)
● Possible breeding:	48	(23.4%)
○ Present, breeding unlikely:	13	(6.3%)

2002–06

Merlin, Deeside, 1982. © *Graham Rebecca*

Habitat and breeding biology

Merlins breed on upland Heather moors, in open Scots Pine forest and in young conifer plantations, mainly within a 200–650 m altitude range. A study during 1980–89, over the area covered by the North-East Scotland Raptor Study Group (NESRSG) (Aberdeenshire, Kincardineshire and Banffshire) recorded 292 breeding attempts. 89% of nests were on the ground in Heather, 7% in old Carrion Crow nests in trees and 4% on crags, with clutch size averaging 4.4 for 195 nests (Rebecca *et al.* 1992). Merlins return to breeding territories in late March to mid April with most pairs commencing egg-laying in early to mid May; the mean first egg-laying date for 340 clutches from Deeside during 1980–2003 was 8th May (Rebecca 2006). Incubation takes 27–28 days per egg and young fledge at 26–28 days (*BWP*, Rebecca 2006). Hence, most broods fledge in early to mid July. Territories are then vacated by late July to mid August, coinciding with an increase in Merlin records on low altitude farmland, estuaries and other coastal habitats (*NESBRs*, *MNBRs*).

Scottish distribution and status

Merlins are widely distributed across the southern uplands, upland regions of north and west Scotland, Orkney, Shetland and the Inner and Outer Hebrides (*BTO 1st* and *2nd Atlases,*

Dickson & Heavisides 2007). An estimate of around 800 breeding pairs was given for Scotland in 1993–94, following a combination of full and partial regional surveys and calculated extrapolation (Rebecca & Bainbridge 1998).

Distribution and status in North-East Scotland

Rebecca *et al.* (1992) gave details of 81 breeding areas from the NESRSG area in 1980–89 and assessed that the largely low-density population was probably stable. Numbers varied between 1–5 pairs/10-km square, with some alternate nest sites up to 3.5 km apart. Many other 10-km squares were unoccupied and illegal persecution of Merlins occurred on three sporting estates, which may have been the reason why other suitable areas were devoid of Merlins. Further survey of the NESRSG area in the 1990s, culminated in approximately 100 breeding territories, covering 130 1-km squares, being identified (Rebecca & Cosnette 2003). Annual survey and monitoring of territories also occurs in Moray (*MNBR*s) where the population is estimated at 25–30 pairs (J. Craib pers. comm.).

Changes in distribution

Historically, Merlins bred on lowland raised bogs and coastal moorland in North-East Scotland, but none were found in recent surveys of these areas (Rebecca *et al.* 1992, I. Francis & G. W. Rebecca unpublished). However, their 10-km square distribution increased steadily between 1968–72 and 2002–06. This probably indicated an increase in Merlins, as the British population estimate doubled between 1983–84 and 1993–94 (Rebecca & Bainbridge 1998). However, an increase in survey coverage and observer quality and commitment should also be considered (Cosnette & Rebecca 1997). For example, two study areas were established in Aberdeenshire in 1980 and 1986 covering 215 km^2 on lower Deeside and 237 km^2 on upper Donside respectively (Rebecca & Cosnette 2003). A degree of distributional stability in Aberdeenshire was found between 1981–84 and 1993–96, with Merlins recorded in 30 10-km squares in both study periods and in 59 and 56 recording units respectively (Rebecca 1990, Cosnette & Rebecca 1997). Merlins then increased to 82 occupied atlas recording units in 2002–06. However, few Merlins are now found east of the Cairn o' Mount road where commercial conifer plantations are now at the thicket stage (Rebecca 2006). The direct, due to habitat change, and indirect effects of commercial afforestation, such as increased predation risk and lack of prey availability may also be reasons for some of the declines in Moray in the 1990s. Excessive Heather burning was believed to have caused declines in upper Donside in the mid 1990s (Rebecca & Cosnette 2003) but numbers recovered by 2005–06. In contrast, decreases in the 21st century, with no obvious causes, were recorded in mid Donside, Glen Tanar, Forest of Birse and the Glen Livet and Cabrach areas, and breeding is no longer regular on the Hill of Fare or Bennachie.

Population and trends

Detailed surveys in Aberdeenshire and Moray during 1980–2006 resulted in approximately 130 confirmed Merlin breeding territories being located (Rebecca & Cosnette 2003, J. Craib pers. comm.). The NESRSG monitor some of these annually, and 46–64 breeding pairs were located during 1999–2006 (*NESBR*s, *MNBR*s). All territories have never been checked in a single year and some remote areas were rarely visited. Allowing for alternate breeding areas (Rebecca & Cosnette 2003) and extrapolating a minimum population for the remote areas rarely visited, gave an annual estimate of 75–85 breeding pairs. We also consider that numbers were relatively stable in Aberdeenshire in 2002–06 but that Merlins have decreased in Moray in the late 1990s to 2006.

Authors: *Brian Cosnette & Graham Rebecca*

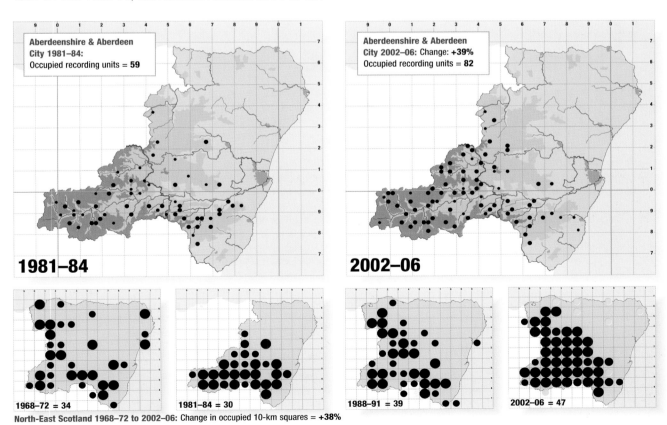

Aberdeenshire & Aberdeen City 1981–84:
Occupied recording units = **59**

1981–84

Aberdeenshire & Aberdeen City 2002–06: Change: +39%
Occupied recording units = **82**

2002–06

1968–72 = 34   1981–84 = 30   1988–91 = 39   2002–06 = 47

North-East Scotland 1968–72 to 2002–06: Change in occupied 10-km squares = +38%

Hobby

Falco subbuteo

Occasional probable breeder. Summer visitor and passage migrant. Estimated population in North-East Scotland: **0 pairs**

Schedule 1; Scottish BAP list

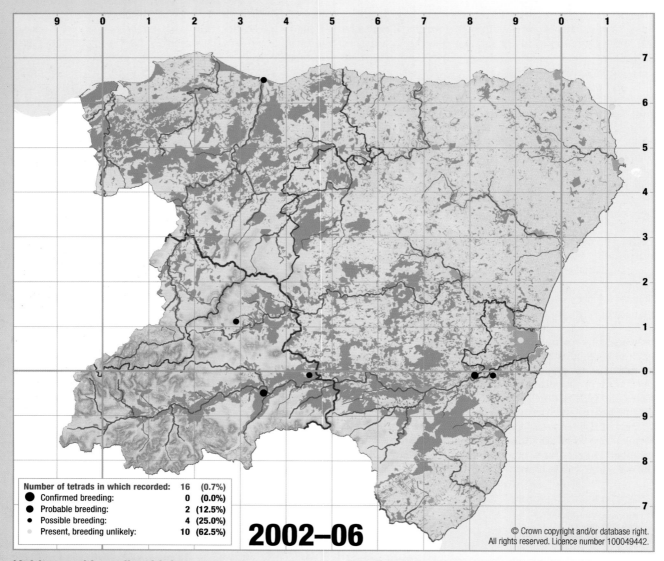

Number of tetrads in which recorded: 16 (0.7%)
- ● Confirmed breeding: 0 (0.0%)
- ● Probable breeding: 2 (12.5%)
- • Possible breeding: 4 (25.0%)
- · Present, breeding unlikely: 10 (62.5%)

2002–06

Habitat and breeding biology

The Hobby is a relatively late-arriving migrant, with birds returning to British breeding sites between late April and mid May. Typically, they use disused corvid or raptor nests at forest edges and in scattered clumps of trees and woodland copses. Adjacent feeding habitats include open country, heathland, farmland and wetland, where prey items may be more abundant. Eggs are laid in mid June and young fledge in mid August. Late in the breeding season they are more usually associated with wetlands and sand pits where prey is plentiful. September is the peak month for southward migration.

Scottish distribution and status

Hobbies remain scarce passage migrants to Scotland although they are being recorded with increasing frequency. Migrants have been recorded in all Scottish recording areas except Clyde Islands and Upper Forth with almost one third of all sightings being in the Northern Isles and the majority of the others in eastern Scotland and Dumfries & Galloway. In the 20th century, a pair probably bred in Perth & Kinross in 1977, and since 1990 breeding has been suspected on a number of occasions but only proved in Fife in 1994 and Strathspey in 2001–03 (Crooke in *BS3*).

Distribution and status in North-East Scotland

The North-East accounts for the second highest number of Scottish records, after the Northern Isles; May–June and September are the peak months for observations which suggests that most records relate to birds on migration, possibly to Fennoscandia. Birds are seen mainly at coastal sites such as Loch of Strathbeg, although inland records are becoming more common. Despite the increase in such inland occurrences, often during the breeding season, there is no proven breeding for the region. In 2004, a pair was seen regularly at a Deeside locality between mid June and late August which was strongly suggestive of a breeding attempt, although no conclusive evidence was found. Elsewhere on Deeside a single bird showed signs of anxiety in early June 2003 but there was no further indication of breeding. Hobbies were also seen on Deeside in June 2007 and in May and June 2008, and a juvenile was photographed at Dinnet on 3rd October 2008 (*NESBR* 2007, 2008).

Changes in distribution

There has been a notable increase in observations in the region since the mid 1970s–1980s when the species was described as rare, averaging around one record each year, although four individuals were seen in 1977 (*NES 1st Atlas*).

Hobby, Dinnet, October 2008. © *Bob Humphreys*

Between 2002–06, a total of 24 individuals was reported, with eight in 2003 being the best year. Although coastal sightings of non-staying single birds predominate, inland reports, mainly from Deeside, are now more frequent than previously.

Population and trends

In view of the increase in the number of breeding pairs in Britain (Clements 2001) and Norway (Hagemeijer & Blair 1997) in recent years, it is perhaps not surprising that observations in Scotland and the North-East are also becoming more frequent. Given that the species in Scotland is at the northern edge of its range, any warming of the climate is likely to increase the abundance of insect prey, and consequently the chance of Hobbies successfully raising young should be improved. There has been a small but significant increase in inland observations in recent years and if the trend continues, it is very possible that breeding will be confirmed in the future.

Author: *Andrew Thorpe*

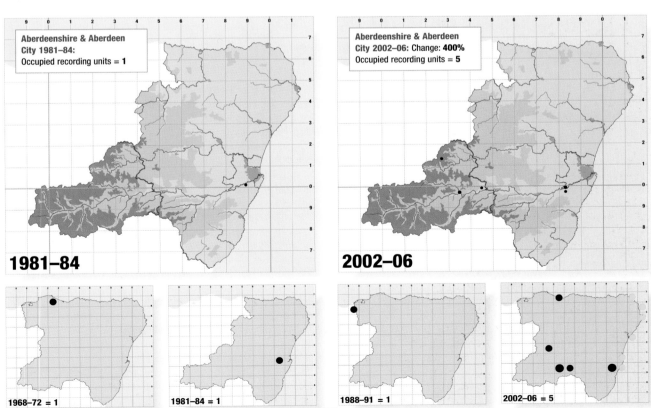

Aberdeenshire & Aberdeen City 1981–84:
Occupied recording units = 1

1981–84

Aberdeenshire & Aberdeen City 2002–06: Change: 400%
Occupied recording units = **5**

2002–06

1968–72 = 1

1981–84 = 1

1988–91 = 1

2002–06 = 5

North-East Scotland 1968–72 to 2002–06: Change in occupied 10-km squares = +400%

Peregrine

Falco peregrinus

Rare resident. Estimated population in North-East Scotland: **50 pairs** (8% of Scottish population, 4% of UK)

Schedule 1; Annex 1; Scottish BAP list

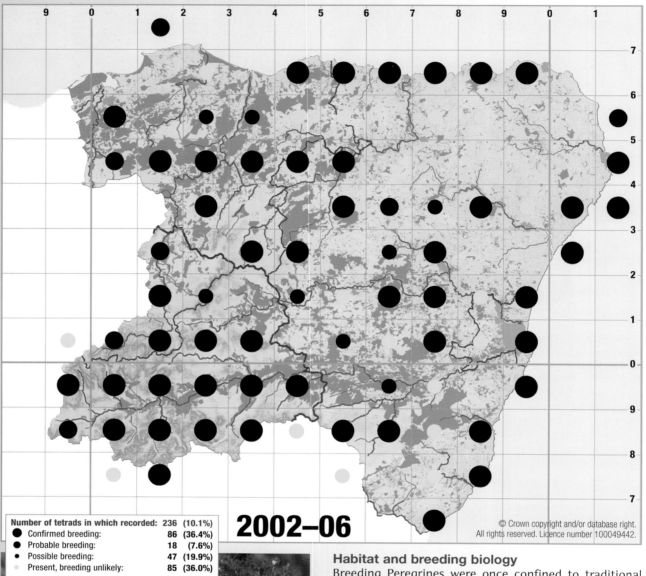

2002–06

© Crown copyright and/or database right.
All rights reserved. Licence number 100049442.

Number of tetrads in which recorded:	236	(10.1%)
● Confirmed breeding:	86	(36.4%)
● Probable breeding:	18	(7.6%)
● Possible breeding:	47	(19.9%)
○ Present, breeding unlikely:	85	(36.0%)

Peregrine, Cabrach, 1982. © *Graham Rebecca*

Habitat and breeding biology

Breeding Peregrines were once confined to traditional cliffs on the coast, and in the uplands where eyries were sited on secure ledges high on crags. As the inland population increased in the 1980s and 90s, they occupied most moorland and mountain areas and started to breed on smaller crags, sand banks and on steep Heather slopes. Many of these new sites were on grouse moors and have now been deserted. Despite this, breeding birds continued to spread into new habitats and they now breed in lowland quarries and even in urban areas. Breeding sites are occupied from January onwards, with eggs laid from mid March on the coast but as late as early May in the uplands. Incubation takes 28–33 days and the young fledge after 5–6 weeks (Hardey in *BS3*). Away from their nesting areas, Peregrines can be seen hunting over almost all open habitats including coastal marshes and estuaries.

Scottish distribution and status

Peregrines are scarce but widespread breeders, found in most upland areas of Scotland and most cliff-bound coasts. They breed in the Outer Hebrides and Orkney but not in Shetland. The Scottish breeding population in 2007 was

The Breeding Birds of North-East Scotland

estimated to be about 600 pairs, with a winter population of between 2,000 and 2,500 birds (Hardey in *BS3*).

Distribution and Status in North-East Scotland

Peregrines breed in low numbers from corries on the edge of the Cairngorms down to coastal cliffs. They are present in the hills around upper Deeside, especially on Invercauld and Mar Lodge estates, but numbers have declined in this area. Away from Deeside, Peregrines are distributed thinly over much of the uplands and in parts of the lowlands where suitable cliffs or quarries exist. Along the coast, Peregrines now breed wherever cliffs provide secure nest sites, but they can be difficult to locate here. They are centred on three stretches of coastline; the north coast between Buckie and Rosehearty, the east coast from Peterhead to Collieston, and south from Aberdeen. Their adaptability is reflected in the fact that a pair also breeds on a building in the centre of Aberdeen. The winter population is believed to be approximately 350–400 birds and at this time of year, they can be found anywhere, although they tend to be near breeding sites or in places where there is abundant avian prey such as around estuaries or river valleys.

Changes in distribution

As inland numbers increased up to the 1990s, most moorland and mountain areas were reoccupied but many grouse moor sites have since been deserted. However, the increase at non-grouse moor and coastal sites has been sustained. In 1968–72, Peregrines were found in suitable breeding habitat in 25 10-km squares and were proved to nest in 15 of these, all of which were inland (*BTO 1st Atlas*). By 1988–91, 37 10-km squares were occupied and breeding was proved in 22, two of these being on the north Aberdeenshire coastal cliffs (*BTO 2nd Atlas*). During 2002–06, Peregrines were located in suitable breeding habitat in 63 10-km squares, and breeding was proved in 48

Peregrine, Whinnyfold, April 2008. © *Ed Duthie*

of these. The most striking increase has been on the coast where 16 squares contained nesting pairs; here, most traditional sites are now occupied.

Population and Trends

Over the last 200 years, breeding numbers in Scotland and in the North-East have been influenced by levels of persecution and, during the mid 20th century, by diminished breeding success due to the effects of pesticide residues (Ratcliffe 1993). The Scottish population peaked in 1991 (Hardey in *BS3*) but not until 1999 in North-East Scotland, when there were over 70 occupied sites. A subsequent decline saw the inland breeding population of North-East Scotland fall by 18% between the national surveys of 1991 and 2002, during which period a 42% increase took place in the coastal population (Crick & Ratcliffe 1995, Banks *et al.* 2003). The inland decrease was associated with the loss of birds breeding on grouse moors, which has been more marked than that at other, less productive, inland sites (Figure 1). The inland decline has been compensated to some extent by the coastal increase but these pairs rear fewer young than successful inland pairs. In 2006, the North-East Scotland Peregrine population contained about 50 breeding pairs.

Author: *Jon Hardey*

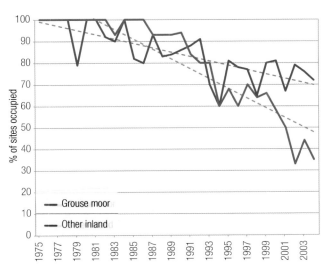

Fig 1. Percentage occupancy of grouse moor and other inland nesting sites 1975–2004

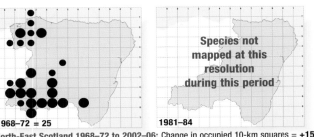

1968–72 = 25

1981–84

1988–91 = 37

2002–06 = 63

North-East Scotland 1968–72 to 2002–06: Change in occupied 10-km squares = **+152%**

Water Rail

Rallus aquaticus

Scarce resident. Winter visitor and passage migrant. Estimated population in North-East Scotland:
125–175 pairs (11% of Scottish population, <11% of UK)

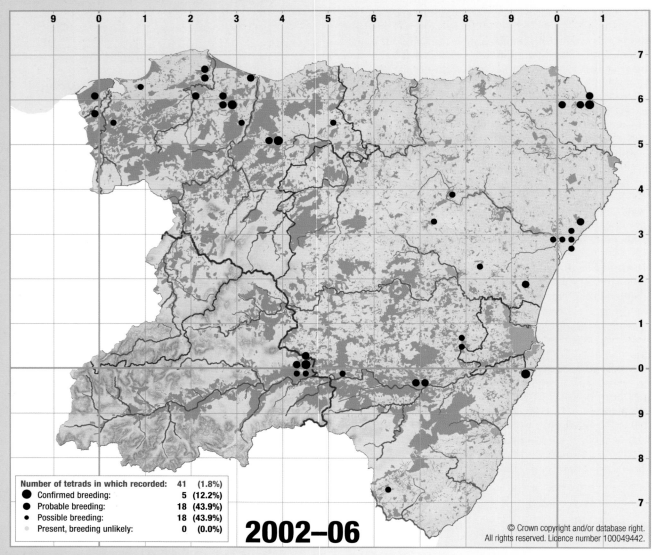

Number of tetrads in which recorded:	41	(1.8%)
● Confirmed breeding:	5	(12.2%)
● Probable breeding:	18	(43.9%)
• Possible breeding:	18	(43.9%)
Present, breeding unlikely:	0	(0.0%)

2002–06

Habitat and breeding biology

Water Rails breed in a variety of wetland habitats including freshwater and estuarine reedbeds, loch-side vegetation and extensive bog areas and ditches, where there is dense vegetation over, or adjacent to, water. They are elusive and secretive birds which are easily missed in summer, even when sites are visited regularly. Defended territories can be as small as 100 m^2 and birds can be present in relatively restricted areas of suitable habitat, sometimes at densities hitherto unsuspected. Eggs are laid mainly in April and May with an average clutch size of 7–8 eggs. After three weeks incubation the eggs hatch and the young leave the nest immediately, fledging after a further eight weeks.

Scottish distribution and status

The Water Rail is a scarce but locally common breeding species, primarily in lowland areas of Scotland. The main populations are found in the Tay estuary, the Clyde basin, Islay, Insh marshes (Badenoch & Strathspey) and in parts of the Borders and Moray & Nairn (Wood in *BS3*). The true size of many of these populations has only been revealed through the use of tape luring and it is likely therefore that, in areas where this has not been attempted, significantly large populations may remain to be discovered. In

2007 the Scottish population was estimated at 1,250–1,400 pairs (Wood in *BS3*).

Distribution and status in North-East Scotland

Water Rails have a very localised distribution due to their habitat requirements, and the map reflects suitable habitat which has been carefully checked. Four general areas are evident: the Moray coastal plains where wetlands remain, the Loch of Strathbeg, along the valley of the river Dee, and the vicinity of the Ythan estuary and Forvie. Key sites in Moray are Loch Spynie and the Lein marshes at Kingston. On Deeside, the distribution centres on Lochs Davan and Kinord, and on Loch of Leys at Banchory. Other significant sites in Aberdeenshire are Loch of Strathbeg and Wartle Moss near Rothienorman.

Changes in distribution

Much caution has to be exercised when interpreting changes in distribution because comparable techniques and levels of effort have not been used over recent decades. Comparison of 10-km square occupancy reveals an apparent increase from 12 squares in 1968–72 (*BTO 1st Atlas*) and eight in 1988–91 (*BTO 2nd Atlas*) to 25 in 2002–06. In Moray, where Water Rail distribution has been given special attention in recent years (Young & Cook 2001), the apparent increase from one occupied 10-km square in each of the earlier surveys to eight in 2002–06 is almost certainly artificial. Similar caution must be attached to the increase from seven to 23 occupied recording units in Aberdeenshire/Aberdeen City over the last 30 years. Historically, little was known about the status of Water Rails in Scotland (Wood in *BS3*) so all comparisons are difficult. Nonetheless, it is clear that over the last hundred years significant areas of wetland have been drained and it is probable that much suitable habitat has been lost.

Population and trends

The only available population estimate is based on fairly comprehensive survey work in Moray in 1996–2000 and a selection of counts from Aberdeenshire sites. During the period 1996–2006, eight North-East sites held more than two pairs, or calling birds, in spring or summer (Table 1). In addition, 13 calling birds were located at 11 other sites in Moray, and nine birds at eight sites in Aberdeenshire. Assuming that calling birds represent pairs, and that the populations given in Table 1 are typical for the sites, then the known Water Rail population in North-East Scotland amounts to 86–91 pairs. However, use of tape luring in Moray has revealed that the species is far more numerous than was previously believed so it is likely that the numbers

Water Rail, Loch of Strathbeg, January 2003. © *Sam Alexander*

Table 1. Sites holding more than two pairs or calling birds during 1996–2006.

Site	Population (Year); Source
Loch Spynie and marshes:	25–30 pairs (1996–99); Young & Cook 2000
Loch of Strathbeg:	8 calling birds (2001); *NESBR* 2001
Loch Davan:	6 calling birds (2002); *NESBR* 2002
Lein, (Kingston):	6 pairs (2000); Young & Cook 2000
Loch of Leys (Banchory):	5 calling birds (1999, 2004); *NESBR* 1999, 2004
Loch Kinord:	5 calling birds (2003); *NESBR* 2003
Ordie and Black Mosses (Dinnet):	5 calling birds (2002); *NESBR* 2002
Wartle Moss (Rothienorman):	4 calling birds (1999); *NESBR* 1999

at known sites in Aberdeenshire could be much higher than thought, and some smaller sites may have been overlooked. It is certainly quite possible that the true size of the North-East population lies in the range of 125–175 pairs. It is difficult to make any real comment on trends due to the changes in survey techniques and previous low detection of pairs, but there is no evidence of any notable change in population in the last 20–30 years.

Author: *Alastair Young*

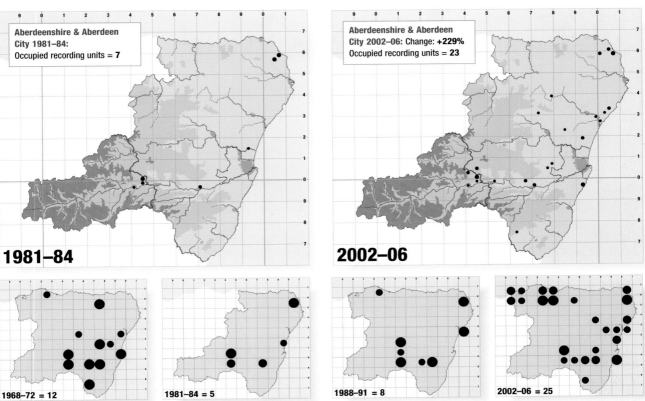

Aberdeenshire & Aberdeen City 1981–84: Occupied recording units = 7

1981–84

Aberdeenshire & Aberdeen City 2002–06: Change: +229% Occupied recording units = 23

2002–06

1968–72 = 12

1981–84 = 5

1988–91 = 8

2002–06 = 25

North-East Scotland 1968–72 to 2002–06: Change in occupied 10-km squares = +108%

Spotted Crake

Porzana porzana

Occasional probable summer migrant breeder. Passage migrant. Estimated population in North-East Scotland: *0–2 pairs* (5% of Scottish population, 1% of UK)

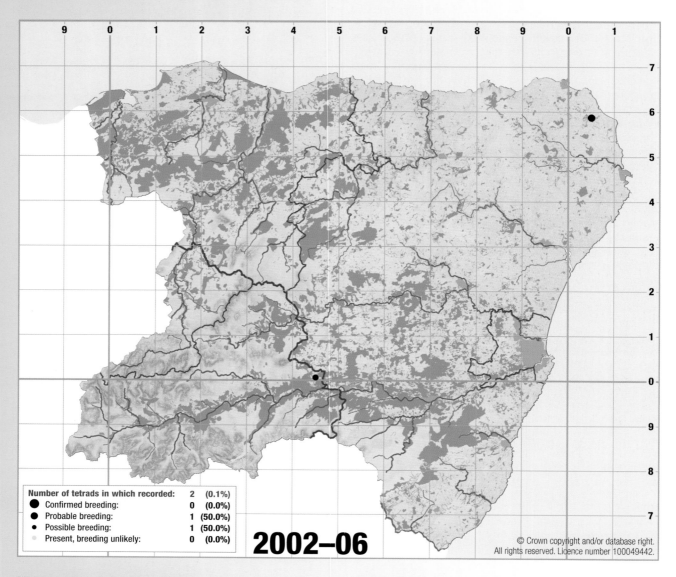

Number of tetrads in which recorded:	2	(0.1%)
● Confirmed breeding:	0	(0.0%)
● Probable breeding:	1	(50.0%)
● Possible breeding:	1	(50.0%)
Present, breeding unlikely:	0	(0.0%)

2002–06

Habitat and breeding biology

Spotted Crakes in North-East Scotland occupy sites that are typical of the species elsewhere in the country. Eight of nine potential breeding localities (where singing birds have been present in the past) are extensive fens or marshy wetlands with high summer water levels, dominated by sedge beds or other very wet fen vegetation, sometimes with patchy Common Reed and always with scattered willows. The remaining site is a marginal waterside fen. Nothing is known of their breeding ecology here and the relationship between singing activity and breeding biology is not clear. Singing birds have been recorded in the area from 16th May to 16th June, and occasionally in July - though in Scotland they have been recorded from mid April to the end of July. There has been one instance in North-East Scotland where breeding was considered likely though not confirmed; a bird giving alarm calls and suspected to have young on 28th June 1990 (Bourne 1992).

Spotted Crake habitat, Deeside, May 2010. © *Ian Francis*

Scottish distribution and status

The Spotted Crake is a rare breeding bird in Scotland, with a population of 10–33 pairs (Francis & Stroud in *BS3*). It has a scattered distribution across the country, reflecting its very localised habitat requirements of extensive wet, sedge-dominated fens. It is also a rare migrant, especially through Orkney and Shetland (Francis & Stroud in *BS3*), and predominantly in autumn.

Spotted Crake, Norfolk, September 2009. © *Bob Humphreys*

Distribution and status in North-East Scotland

During 2002–06, there were only two records. One sang for one night only at a site in Deeside on 30th May 2005, and one sang every night from 30th May to 8th June 2005 at the Loch of Strathbeg. There was no further evidence of breeding there but a single adult bird was reported on 7th August. These were the first singing birds in the area since 2001, when one also sang at Loch of Strathbeg from 30th May to 16th June. In 1999, during the national census, seven singing birds were found at four traditional sites in Aberdeenshire (the highest total ever recorded) and one sang in Moray at Loch Spynie for one night only on 25th May 1999. One was also recorded here in 1997, but that was the first record in Moray for 14 years; prior to that there were only six other records in Moray last century (Cook 1992). From 1989 to 1998, 1–5 singing birds were detected annually in Aberdeenshire at 1–4 sites (nine sites used in total), making the area one of the most important for Spotted Crakes in the UK during the 1990s (Francis & Thorpe 1999). Occasional migrants are recorded in the area, mainly in autumn.

Changes in distribution

Singing males have used the same sites throughout the 1980s to 1990s, though some are now becoming overgrown through vegetation succession, which may be a factor in the apparent reduction in the number of singing birds.

Population and trends

Prior to 1989, there were few records in North-East Scotland and since 2005 there have been no records. The period from 1989 to 2005 appears to have seen unusually high numbers of Spotted Crakes, and this long-term increase followed by a recent decrease has been reflected in Scotland and the UK as a whole (Holling *et al.* 2007a). During the 1999 census, around 33 singing males, around half the British total, were recorded in Scotland, with seven of these in North-East Scotland. However, since then numbers in all areas have dropped, and in 2005, there were 13 singing males in Scotland (two in our area) and in the UK there was a maximum of 21 singing males at 19 sites (Holling *et al.* 2008). The reasons for such changes are unknown.

Author: *Ian Francis*

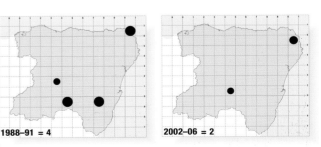

1968–72 = 1   1981–84 = 0   1988–91 = 4   2002–06 = 2

North-East Scotland 1968–72 to 2002–06: Change in occupied 10-km squares = +100%

Corncrake

Crex crex

Occasional summer migrant breeder. Passage migrant. Estimated population in North-East Scotland: 0 pairs

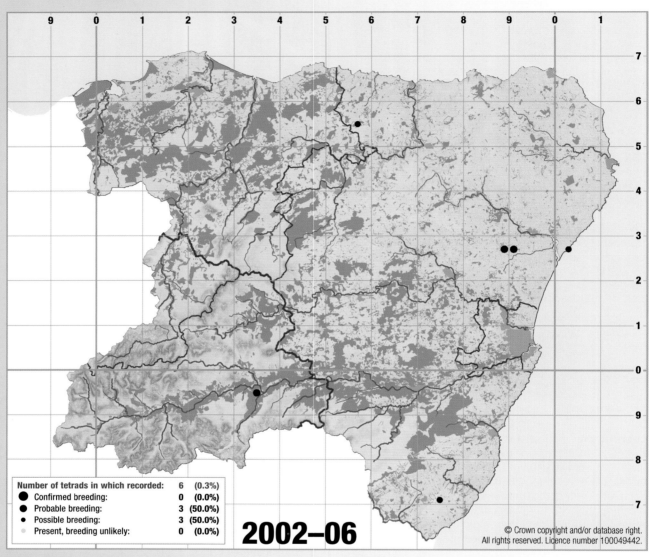

Number of tetrads in which recorded: 6 (0.3%)
● Confirmed breeding: 0 (0.0%)
● Probable breeding: 3 (50.0%)
● Possible breeding: 3 (50.0%)
● Present, breeding unlikely: 0 (0.0%)

2002–06

Habitat and breeding biology

The few Corncrakes that have recently been reported in the region usually occur in the agricultural lowlands of Aberdeenshire. Singing is heard from spring cereal, un-grazed grassland and extensively managed fields. Males sing predominantly at night but once paired become less vocal (Green in *BS3*). During recent years, most birds recorded in North-East Scotland are heard singing during mid to late summer. It is not known how many attract females.

Scottish distribution and status

The Scottish breeding population is mainly found on the Outer Hebrides and the Argyll islands. Small numbers are found on Orkney, Skye, the Lochaber islands and the west mainland. Corncrakes declined rapidly during 1978–93 but since that time there has been a partial recovery of the population in response to conservation management schemes (O'Brien *et al*. 2006). The breeding population was estimated at *c*.1,220 singing males in 2007 (Holling *et al*. 2010).

Distribution and status in North-East Scotland

Corncrakes have undergone severe declines during the last century, largely in response to changing agricultural practices (Green in *BS3*). There were only five individuals recorded in Aberdeenshire during 2002–06. One of these was a bird flushed from suitable habitat at the coast in 2004 but which was probably a migrant. Another bird was seen briefly in suitable habitat near Cornhill in May 2005. The only confirmed territorial activity was noted in 2002 near Ballater, where a bird sang for weeks in a weedy set-aside field until it was cut (J. Robertson, per A. Watson pers. comm.) and in 2006 near Pitmedden. Here, a bird sang intermittently from set-aside and once from Oil-seed Rape (in two tetrads) between 8th June and 7th July. Additionally in 2006, a bird sang for one week near Laurencekirk in August.

Changes in distribution

During the late 19th century, Corncrakes regularly bred in almost every county in Britain (Holloway 1996). In Scotland it was considered to have one of the broadest distributions of any species (Green in *BS3*). In parts of Aberdeenshire, declines occurred during agricultural intensification in the 1960s. Singing birds were 'common' on arable land near Bucksburn in the mid 1950s but these became extinct during the 1960s (B. Pirie pers. comm.). After near extinction in Moray in the late 1940s, a period of slow recovery was noted until the1960s with 6–12 calling males annually. In the period 1968–72 probable breeding was recorded in six 10-km squares in Aberdeenshire and a further six in Moray (*BTO 1st Atlas*). During 1981–84, possible breeding was recorded only from Rora in 1982 (*NES 1st Atlas*), and during the national Corncrake survey in 1978–79 no birds were recorded in any part of North-East Scotland (Cadbury 1980).

Population and trends

Since the last confirmed breeding in North-East Scotland, Corncrakes have been reported in summer in 13 out of the 21 years up to 2006. The majority of these records have come from Aberdeenshire. Most reports involve one or two singing birds but in 1996, there may have been up to five. There have been no reports from Moray since 1993. The most recent confirmed breeding was from a site near Aberdeen in 1985. Some birds may be overlooked due to their nocturnal habits, but on current knowledge, the Corncrake cannot be regarded as an annual breeding species in the region.

Author: *Hywel Maggs*

Corncrake, North Uist, May 2009. © *Ian Hay*

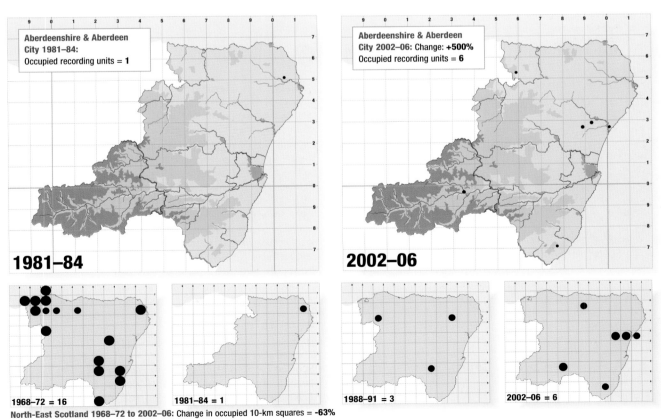

Aberdeenshire & Aberdeen City 1981–84:
Occupied recording units = **1**

1981–84

Aberdeenshire & Aberdeen City 2002–06: Change: **+500%**
Occupied recording units = **6**

2002–06

1968–72 = 16

1981–84 = 1

1988–91 = 3

2002–06 = 6

North-East Scotland 1968–72 to 2002–06: Change in occupied 10-km squares = -63%

Moorhen

Gallinula chloropus

Scarce resident. Winter visitor. Estimated population in North-East Scotland: **500–750 pairs** (4% of Scottish population, <1% of UK)

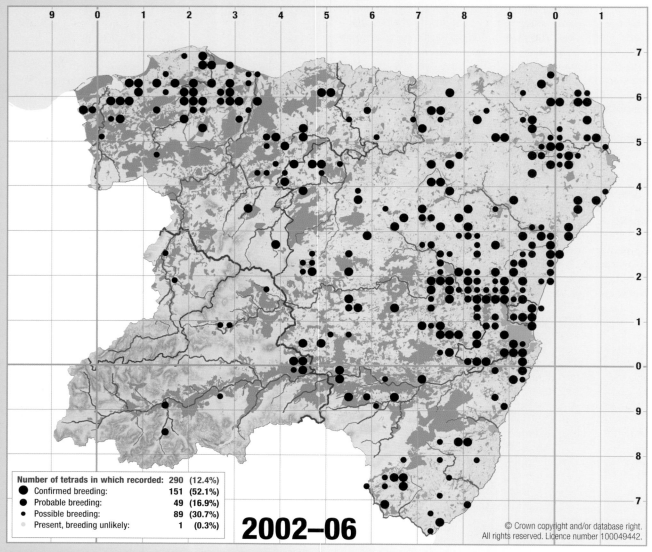

Number of tetrads in which recorded:	290	(12.4%)
● Confirmed breeding:	151	(52.1%)
● Probable breeding:	49	(16.9%)
● Possible breeding:	89	(30.7%)
Present, breeding unlikely:	1	(0.3%)

2002–06

Moorhen, Corgarff, May 2009. © *Harry Scott*

Habitat and breeding biology

Moorhens breed on a broad range of still or slow-moving lowland freshwater bodies including lochs, reservoirs, ponds, rivers and drainage channels (Taylor in *BS3*). Nests are built on or near water, usually in emergent vegetation sometimes on the ground or in a bush. The clutch generally contains 5–9 eggs (exceptionally 2–13) and is laid from April onwards. Incubation takes around three weeks, the precocial young are tended by both parents for a further seven to ten weeks until fledged and independent. Second clutches are sometimes laid and nests with eggs can occasionally still be found in August.

Scottish distribution and status

The Moorhen is a common and widespread resident species with the highest densities in the south and east. It is absent from most upland areas and much of the north-west, apart from a few island populations in the Outer Hebrides and Argyll. There is strong evidence of an increase in the Scottish population during the first half of the 20th century, followed by a contraction of its range in the latter part of that century. The current population is estimated at 10,000–25,000 pairs (Taylor in *BS3*).

Distribution and status in North-East Scotland

Moorhens are commonly found in suitable habitat throughout the region. They tend to occur in low-lying areas particularly in the Moray and Buchan plains as well as east Aberdeenshire in the lower Dee, Don and Ythan valleys. Further inland from these areas, their occurrence is more patchy and usually associated with the larger river systems where suitable habitat may be found along the valleys, for example around the Lochs Davan and Kinord at Dinnet. Upstream from here, the river gradient and water flow increase so there is little suitable habitat and Moorhen occurrence is scarce, a pattern found along several of our river systems. They have, in the past, bred as high as 490 m near Loch Builg (Nethersole-Thompson & Watson 1974) and may still breed in the Tomintoul area.

Changes in distribution

During 1968–72, Moorhens were found in 89 of the 10-km squares within our region (*BTO 1st Atlas*). By 1988–91 they were no longer found in many of these, particularly on the Buchan plain and the total fell to 69 (*BTO 2nd Atlas*). Drainage of wet fields and small water bodies is a likely cause of this decline (*NES 1st Atlas*) although differences in observer coverage may have had an impact; in 2002–06 the number of occupied 10-km squares had moved back up to 77. Between the two regional atlases, Moorhens extended their range in Aberdeenshire/Aberdeen City from 130 recording units in 1981–84 to 146 in 2002–06. Their return to some previously occupied areas is perhaps largely due to creation or restoration of habitats such as fishing lochs or ornamental ponds. Along the major river systems their distribution has remained broadly unchanged.

Population and trends

The increase in the Scottish Moorhen population during the first half of the 20th century is perhaps as a result of intense predator control. This was followed by a contraction of the range in the latter part of that century, for which the presence of Mink and the recovery of the Otter may be locally responsible. Improved drainage of many areas would have resulted in a population decrease in the North-East towards the end of this period. The recent long term trend in the UK is of a slow increase, a pattern mirrored in the results of the BBS in our area since 1994. This, together with their return to many previously occupied areas, particularly on the Buchan plain, indicates an increasing population in the North-East. Extrapolation of our population from national population estimates is fraught with difficulty and Moorhens are regularly under-recorded (Taylor in *BS3*). In North-East Scotland in 2002–06, Moorhens were recorded in 289 tetrads with breeding confirmed in 151 of those. The Moorhen is a sedentary species and it is likely therefore that breeding took place in the great majority of occupied tetrads. Most sites appear to hold only 1–2 pairs, but some tetrads include more than one site so an estimate of 500–750 pairs in North-East Scotland seems reasonable.

Author: *Richard Schofield*

Moorhen, Ord Dam, Peterculter, 1976. © *Graham Rebecca*

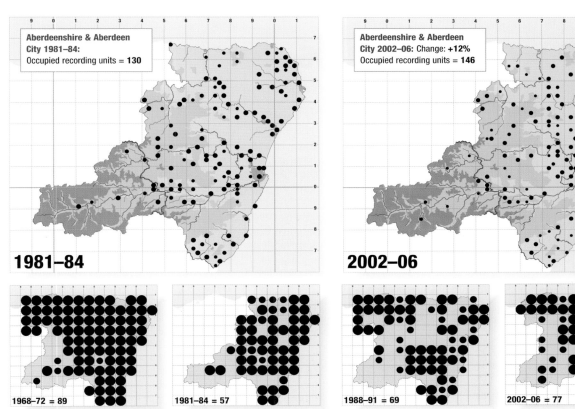

Aberdeenshire & Aberdeen City 1981–84:
Occupied recording units = **130**

1981–84

Aberdeenshire & Aberdeen City 2002–06: Change: +12%
Occupied recording units = **146**

2002–06

1968–72 = 89   1981–84 = 57   1988–91 = 69   2002–06 = 77

North-East Scotland 1968–72 to 2002–06: Change in occupied 10-km squares = -13%

Coot

Fulica atra

Scarce resident. Winter visitor and passage migrant. Estimated population in North-East Scotland: **100–200 pairs** (8% of Scottish population, <1% of UK)

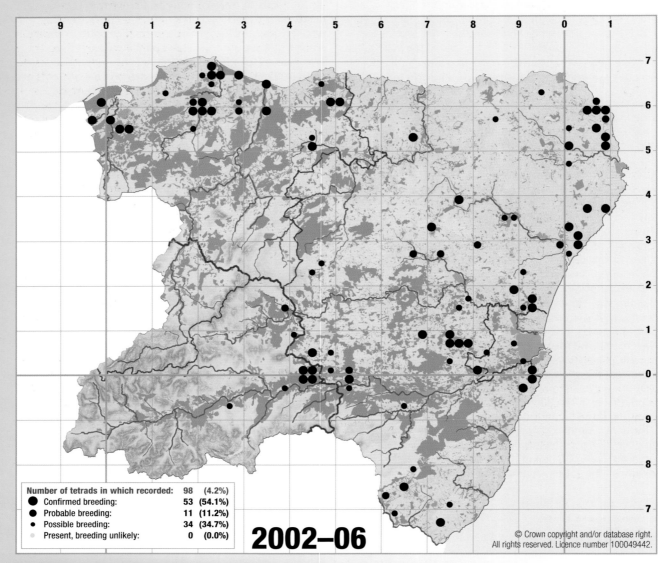

Number of tetrads in which recorded:	98	(4.2%)
● Confirmed breeding:	53	(54.1%)
● Probable breeding:	11	(11.2%)
● Possible breeding:	34	(34.7%)
● Present, breeding unlikely:	0	(0.0%)

2002–06

Coot, Banffshire, 1980s. © *John Edelsten*

Habitat and breeding biology

Coots prefer nutrient-rich lochs and rivers with a good growth of both emergent and submerged vegetation (Murray & Taylor in *BS3*). Man-made ponds and reservoirs which meet these criteria are frequently used, however they shun faster flowing rivers, and deep, nutrient-poor waters. In our region they are therefore mostly birds of lowland waters. Pair formation generally occurs prior to establishing territory. Bulky nests are built using both dead and living plant material, usually concealed amongst vegetation in shallow water. The usual clutch contains 4–8 eggs and is laid in April. Incubation takes three weeks and the precocial young are tended by both parents for a further eight to nine weeks until fledged and independent. Second clutches are sometimes laid.

Scottish distribution and status

The Coot is a common resident, usually at low densities, in the lowlands of eastern and southern Scotland. It is absent from most upland areas and many islands, although it can be found in Orkney, the Outer Hebrides and some of the Inner Hebrides of Argyll. There is good evidence of a decline in some localities, however the population appears to be generally stable in its core areas. The current Scottish population is estimated at 1,500–2,500 pairs (Murray & Taylor in *BS3*).

Coot, Aboyne Loch, May 2009. © Harry Scott

Changes in distribution

Coots were recorded in 50 10-km squares in 1968–72 (*BTO 1st Atlas*) but only in 33 in 1988–91 (*BTO 2nd Atlas*). However, this apparently substantial range reduction is likely, at least in part, to reflect differences in coverage; 47 occupied squares were found in 2002–06, suggesting little change over the last 40 years. At the level of occupied recording units in Aberdeenshire/Aberdeen City, there was a small increase from 49 in 1981–84 (*NES 1st Atlas*) to 58 in 2002–06. It is relatively easy to prove that Coots are breeding, with bulky nests and obvious downy chicks on open water bodies, so it is likely that this increase is genuine; habitat creation or restoration in areas such as the Cloddach gravel pits and Cruden Bay brick pits might be a part of the explanation.

Population and trends

There is good evidence that Coots colonised Scotland in the 19th century as happened in other north European countries *e.g.* Norway and Finland. In the mid 20th century there was a range contraction which was also apparent in Moray and Banff & Buchan (Murray & Taylor in *BS3*). Since then, Coots have expanded their range again in North-East Scotland. Their recent history in the region is very similar to that of Moorhens, similarly influenced by the effects of predation and drainage. Their population probably mirrors these trends as Coot breed only in small numbers on any water in our region. Even at the large and seemingly suitable Loch of Strathbeg, breeding pairs are usually numbered in single figures, whilst at many of the smaller lochs only one or two pairs are present. Coots were recorded in 97 tetrads with breeding confirmed in 53 of those, from which an estimate of 100–200 breeding pairs can be derived.

Author: *Richard Schofield*

Distribution and status in North-East Scotland

Most lowland freshwater bodies of at least 1 ha hold breeding Coots, but such waters are scarce in our region (*NES 1st Atlas*). The majority occur on the Moray and east Buchan plains, Slains, Skene and mid Deeside. Coots were found on these core sites in all survey periods. Smaller waters are also used although many of these are quite new in origin and inadequately vegetated. The occasional use of many of these localities explains the variations between surveys. Upland waters are rarely suitable and during 2002–06 the highest altitudes at which Coots were recorded were 320 m near Balmoral, where they possibly bred, and 270 m in Glen Buchat, where they probably did so.

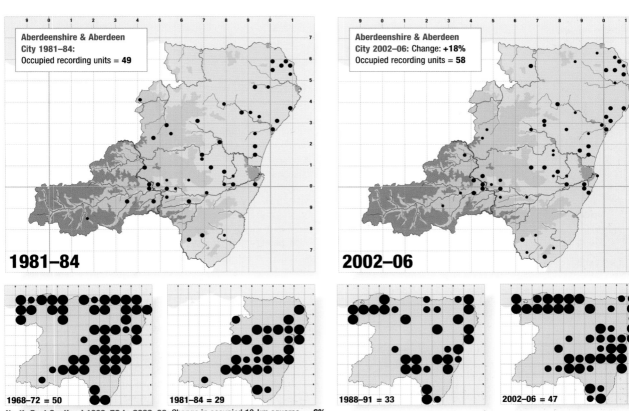

Aberdeenshire & Aberdeen City 1981–84:
Occupied recording units = **49**

1981–84

Aberdeenshire & Aberdeen City 2002–06: Change: **+18%**
Occupied recording units = **58**

2002–06

1968–72 = 50   1981–84 = 29   1988–91 = 33   2002–06 = 47

North-East Scotland 1968–72 to 2002–06: Change in occupied 10-km squares = **-6%**

Occasionally present in summer. Passage migrant. Estimated population in North-East Scotland: **0 pairs**

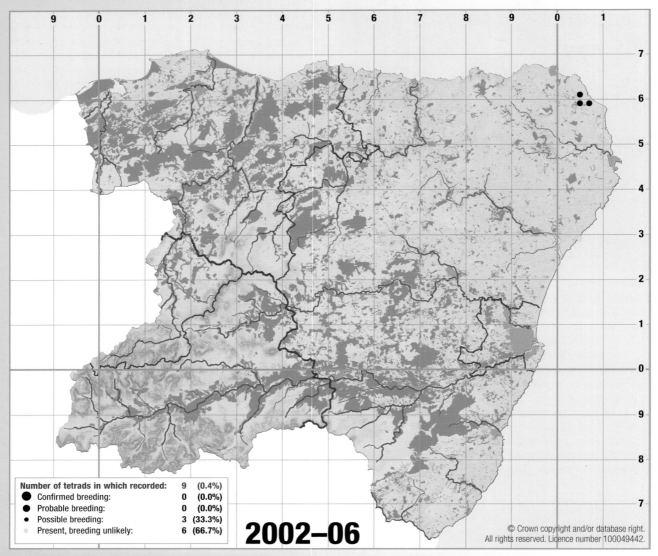

Number of tetrads in which recorded:	9	(0.4%)
● Confirmed breeding:	0	(0.0%)
● Probable breeding:	0	(0.0%)
● Possible breeding:	3	(33.3%)
● Present, breeding unlikely:	6	(66.7%)

2002–06

Crane, Dinnet, May 2009. © *Harry Scott*

Habitat and breeding biology

Over their European breeding range, Cranes occupy large undisturbed wetland habitats including treeless moorlands with bogs and pools, swampy forest clearings and marshes with reeds. The nest is a large pile of vegetation in which eggs are laid in late April–early May (*BWP*). On passage in Scotland, Cranes often appear in open, cultivated, countryside.

Scottish distribution and status

Cranes are uncommon passage migrants in Scotland, recorded most frequently in eastern and northern parts of the country. There have been *c*.272 records, of 373 birds, since the early 19th century. The number of records has increased substantially since 1995; the great majority are seen in April and May. Evidence from archaeological excavations includes chick bones found in Orkney, indicating that they bred in the past and may even have been widespread in Scotland (K. Morton pers. comm.). There has been only one possible recent breeding attempt, at Killimster Moss (Caithness) in 1997 (Betts & Schofield in *BS3*).

Crane, St. Fergus, April 2006. © *Ian Francis*

Distribution and status in North-East Scotland

During the period 1962–96 there were 18 records of single birds on passage, with nine arriving during April–May and six during August–October (Cook 1992, Phillips 1997, *NESBR*s, *MNBR*s). Most interestingly during this period, in 1987, two birds in second summer plumage remained in the Strypes-Teindland Mains area (Moray) from 25th May until at least 28th July, occasionally displaying. In 1988 one bird was at Teindland Mains for a month from mid May and it, or another, was seen around neighbouring areas of Moray from 23rd September until 19th November (Cook 1992). Since 1996, Cranes have become more frequent visitors with records in most years and at least two birds together in eight years. In 2000, two birds were in the Loch of Strathbeg area throughout much of the summer and were seen displaying. During 2002–06, birds were seen annually except in 2003. Most were singles but in 2002 there were three at Cuttyhill (Rora) in late March, four at Loch of Strathbeg on 7th April and 26th May and two in the Roseisle–Kinloss area (Moray) on 15th–17th March. In 2004, one bird spent the summer at Loch of Strathbeg. In 2005, two were at Longside on 5th June. In 2006 two were seen in various locations in north-east Buchan between 30th March and 15th April, with some display noted at Loch of Strathbeg, and a single individual was present on the Buchan mosses during part of the summer. Following the recovery of the western European population over the last 50 years, many more birds are now travelling the spring migration route from France to Sweden. The increase in spring records in North-East Scotland is likely to be as a consequence of this greater passage and there is a possibility that breeding will take place here in the future.

Author: *Dominic Funnell*

Crane habitat, Loch of Strathbeg, September 2009. © *Duncan Goulder*

Oystercatcher

Haematopus ostralegus

Common resident and migrant breeder. Winter visitor. Estimated population in North-East Scotland: **5,000–10,000 pairs** (8% of Scottish population, 7% UK)

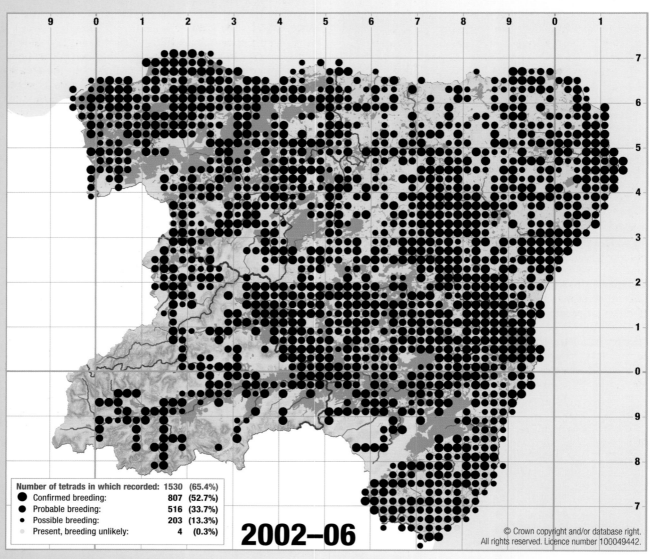

Number of tetrads in which recorded:	1530	(65.4%)
● Confirmed breeding:	807	(52.7%)
● Probable breeding:	516	(33.7%)
● Possible breeding:	203	(13.3%)
○ Present, breeding unlikely:	4	(0.3%)

2002–06

Oystercatcher, Aberdeen, June 2005. © *Paul Baxter*

Habitat and breeding biology

Oystercatchers are widespread breeders in North-East Scotland. They prefer open areas such as farmland and waste ground with short vegetation permitting early detection of the approach of predators. They also nest in dune slacks and on river and coastal shingles. Many breed on flat gravel-covered rooftops in the city of Aberdeen. This was first noted in the mid 1960s and the habit has spread to several small towns in the area. For example, roof-breeding birds were first recorded in Elgin in the mid 1970s, in Forres and Turriff in the 1990s and in Ellon and Inverurie in 2000, although they were possibly present earlier in these places (Duncan *et al.* 2001). Nesting on flat roofs gives the birds the same open habitat as on the ground with the added benefit of freedom from ground predators. The Oystercatcher is one of the few waders that can carry food to their young - essential for roof nesting. They also sometimes occupy unusual sites such as on stone walls, an ornamental pedestal, flower pots, flower beds, traffic islands (A. Duncan pers. obs.) and even shallow hollows in trees (Dougall *et al.* 1989). Breeding sites are occupied usually in February, laying starts about mid April and the young are mostly fledged by the end of June.

The Breeding Birds of North-East Scotland

Scottish distribution and status

Oystercatchers breed virtually throughout Scotland with particularly high densities found in the Northern Isles, North-East Scotland and the southern isles of the Outer Hebrides. They formerly nested exclusively on the coast but in the early 1800s they began breeding inland, including in North-East Scotland. There was an increase in both breeding range and population during the 20th century, and the present Scottish breeding population is estimated to be between 84,500 and 116,500 pairs (O'Brien in *BS3*).

Distribution and status in North-East Scotland

Oystercatchers have an extensive range through North-East Scotland from the coast to the uplands where pairs breed up to 450–500 m in the glens around Braemar and south from Tomintoul. All tetrads in Aberdeen City hold breeding pairs, where the number of roof nesting pairs has increased and levelled off since this behaviour was first noted in the 1960s (Table 1, A. Duncan and R. Duncan unpublished data). They are conspicuously absent from large tracts of forestry. The patchy distribution through the Buchan plain and westwards towards the Moray border is hard to explain but may partly be accounted for by late fieldwork visits after nesting pairs had failed and moved away. Birds start to move inland from late January or early February, arriving a little later in the uplands. They gather in flocks around lochs, floodwater or on river banks, before pairs move off to breeding territories. Ringing recoveries and sightings of marked birds show that Oystercatchers from North-East Scotland move south and west in winter to north-west England, Wales, Ireland and as far as France and Iberia; others winter on local coasts (Duncan 1991, Cook 1992).

Changes in distribution

Comparison of the distribution maps between 1981–84 and 2002–06, shows that there has been virtually no change in the distribution of breeding Oystercatchers in the area in the intervening 20 years. However, small, local changes occur. Birds are displaced from open areas taken over for building development and from urban sites where buildings are demolished or the roofs renewed. Afforestation would remove sites but there is no information on this.

Population and trends

North-East Scotland contains a range of Oystercatcher breeding habitats with correspondingly different population densities. This contributes to the difficulty of producing a valid population estimate for the whole area. During 2002–06, Atlas fieldworkers counted or estimated the number of breeding pairs in 35 tetrads at an average of 3.3 pairs/tetrad. This suggests a total of 5,049 pairs in the 1,530 tetrads where breeding was considered at least possible. In Aberdeen City in 1993 the density was 10.8 pairs/tetrad (Duncan *et al.* 2001) and during 2002–06, in one area of optimal habitat, tetrad density exceeded 15 pairs so it is not impossible that the North-East Scotland breeding population lies towards the upper end of a range of 5,000–10,000 pairs. O'Brien (1994) estimated 16,600 pairs, with wide confidence limits, in 1992–93. The BBS has indicated a decline in the Scottish Oystercatcher population of 27% during 2004–07 (Risely *et al.* 2008) and the same survey in North-East Scotland suggests that the local population has fallen by at least a similar margin.

Author: *Alistair Duncan*

Table 1. Number of breeding pairs of Oystercatchers in Aberdeen.

	Ground nesting	Roof nesting	Total
1978	0	30	30
1986	23	74	97
1988	16	107	123
1993	30	205	235
2001	51	216	267
2005	37	190	227

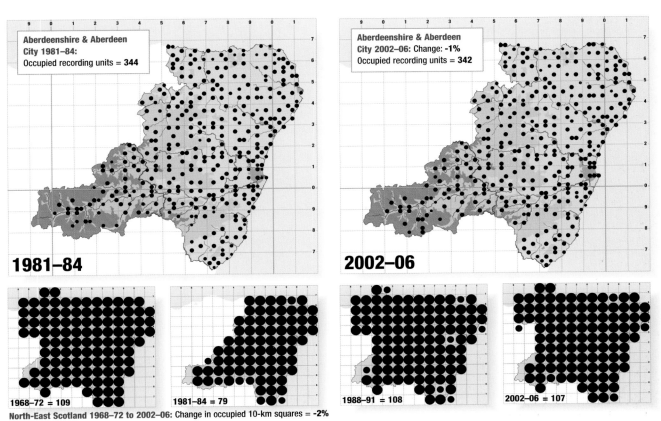

Aberdeenshire & Aberdeen City 1981–84:
Occupied recording units = **344**

1981–84

Aberdeenshire & Aberdeen City 2002–06: Change: **-1%**
Occupied recording units = **342**

2002–06

1968–72 = 109

1981–84 = 79

1988–91 = 108

2002–06 = 107

North-East Scotland 1968–72 to 2002–06: Change in occupied 10-km squares = -2%

Avocet

Recurvirostra avosetta

Occasional visitor, mostly in spring. Estimated population in North-East Scotland: 0 pairs

Amber list; Schedule 1; Annex 1

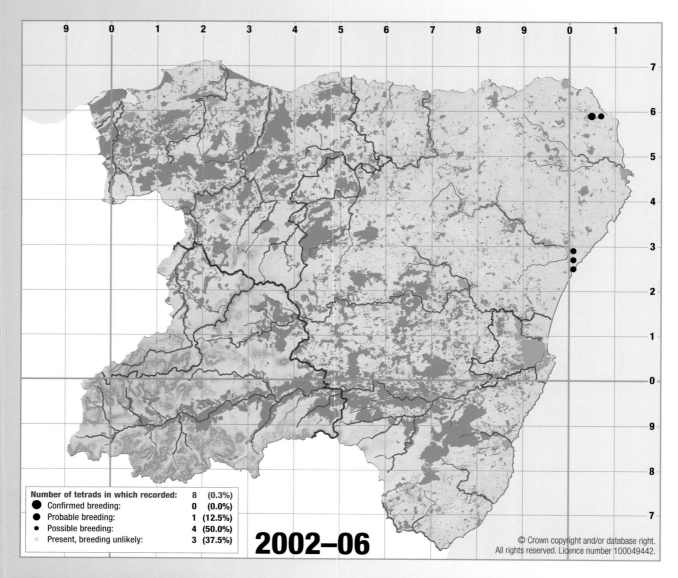

Number of tetrads in which recorded: 8 (0.3%)
- ● Confirmed breeding: 0 (0.0%)
- ● Probable breeding: 1 (12.5%)
- • Possible breeding: 4 (50.0%)
- Present, breeding unlikely: 3 (37.5%)

2002–06

Habitat and breeding biology
In England, breeding Avocets favour shallow, brackish coastal lagoons where they nest on low islands, either in the open or among sparse vegetation (*BTO 2nd Atlas*). In Scotland, migrant birds are most often found on tidal mud flats or shallow freshwater pools such as those in front of the Starnafin visitor centre at Loch of Strathbeg.

Scottish distribution and status
Avocets are rare migrants to Scotland, mostly occurring in April or May. Since 1968 they have been seen almost annually. Most are found on the east side of the country with Lothian, North-east Scotland and Shetland receiving the most records. Only five of the 106 Scottish records have been inland (Clugston in *BS3*).

Distribution and status in North-East Scotland
Approximately 39 Avocets have been seen in North-East Scotland since 1974, with 24 of these in the months of April or May (Phillips 1997, Cook 1992, *NESBR*s, *MNBR*s). During 2002–06 there were around eight records, all in April or May, involving at least 13 birds; in some instances it was hard to determine whether new or long-staying birds were involved.

All were around the Loch of Strathbeg area or the Ythan estuary (*NESBR*s). The largest group was of three birds at Strathbeg on 6th April 2002. In 2006, a pair displayed at Strathbeg between 12th–14th April and the same, or another, pair was there on 21st April (*NESBR* 2006). The English breeding population is continuing to increase and expand northwards, having reached Leighton Moss (Lancashire) in 2001 (Brown & Grice 2005) and Durham in 2006 (Holling *et al*. 2009), so there is a real possibility that birds from northern England, or from Europe, might one day breed in North-East Scotland. Indeed a colour-ringed bird at Strathbeg in 2002 had been ringed as a chick in Suffolk in 1997. Loch of Strathbeg RSPB reserve is probably most likely to play host to any future breeding attempt.

Author: *Dominic Funnell*

See photograph on page 123.

Ythan estuary and Sands of Forvie

A major wetland and coastal complex, and famous for decades of research by ornithologists at Aberdeen University, the Ythan estuary and Sands of Forvie National Nature Reserve is one of the best birding sites in eastern Scotland. The breeding birds of this Special Protection Area are very diverse, and include some nationally important populations, such as the UK's largest Eider colony and Scotland's largest Sandwich Tern colony. Other nesting species around the estuary include Greylag and Canada Geese, Shelduck, Black-headed Gull (a large colony), Common, Arctic and Little Terns, four species of owl and a wide range of song birds. Seabirds and Rock Pipits nest on the cliffs around Collieston, Red Grouse are still present in very small numbers on the coastal heath and Corn Buntings nest in farmland just to the north. As with the Loch of Strathbeg, the potential exists here for southern species such as Little Egret, Spoonbill, Avocet and Bearded Tit to colonise in future. May 2007 © *Ian Francis*

Little Ringed Plover

Charadrius dubius

Very rare summer migrant breeder. Estimated population in North-East Scotland: *2–10 pairs* (27% of Scottish population, <1% of UK)

Schedule 1

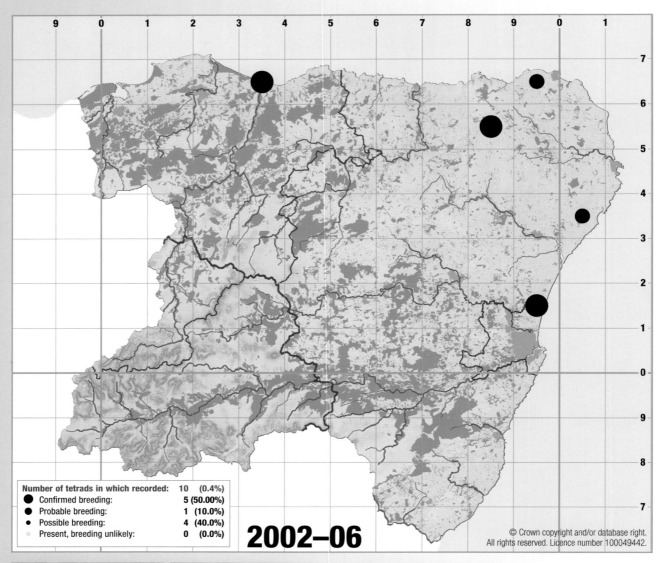

Number of tetrads in which recorded:	10	(0.4%)
● Confirmed breeding:	5	(50.00%)
● Probable breeding:	1	(10.0%)
● Possible breeding:	4	(40.0%)
● Present, breeding unlikely:	0	(0.0%)

2002–06

Little Ringed Plover, near Aberdeen, May 2006. © *Chris Jones*

Habitat and breeding biology

Little Ringed Plovers are summer visitors, normally arriving from the second half of April onwards, when the males' distinctive butterfly display flight can be seen over suitable breeding habitat. They nest in sand and gravel pits, dune slacks and on river shingle but new and temporary areas of gravelly ground created during the development of other man made sites such as landfill, housing and industrial estates are also used. Breeding attempts are prone to disturbance and predation but females frequently re-lay. Two broods are normally attempted. Young fledge by the end of July and the majority of breeding birds have departed by the end of August.

Scottish distribution and status

Little Ringed Plovers first bred in Scotland (in Clyde) in 1968 (Nisbet in *BS3*). There has since been a slow and steady expansion from central Scotland northwards up the eastern side of the country. They have now become established as scarce but annual breeders in south, central and eastern Scotland. There has been a notable increase in breeding numbers in recent years, with 22 pairs located in 2006–07 (Conway *et al.* 2008).

Distribution and status in North-East Scotland

Prior to 1992, single birds at Auchmacoy in 1977 and Starnafin in 1991 were the only two records but an unprecedented five birds in 1992 heralded an almost annual occurrence thereafter *(NESBRs)*. Breeding was first recorded in Aberdeen in 1995 in a gravelly overspill car park of the Exhibition Centre on the outskirts of the city and the same pair returned to breed there in 1996. Also in 1996, breeding was recorded for the first time in Moray, on the shingles of the lower River Spey. The Little Ringed Plover has now become established as a regular breeding species in the North-East though numbers fluctuate between years. Breeding has taken place at six or seven sites, and on at least two occasions single males have paired and bred with two females. Ringed males have returned to the same breeding site in consecutive summers and some sites have now become traditional. Most breeding has taken place in the vicinity of Aberdeen or the lower Spey but in 2005 a pair showed distraction displays at Little Byth, although no chicks were seen, and in 2008 at least one pair bred in coastal dunes in north Aberdeenshire *(NESBR* 2008).

Changes in distribution

Little Ringed Plovers have bred almost annually in the North-East since 1995 but the distribution has expanded only slightly around the north of Aberdeen. There remains only the single site in Moray.

Population and trends

There are three or four regular breeding sites in the North-East and the number of breeding females has fluctuated from none in 1998 up to 6–7 in 2005. Some sites have been occupied for several years in succession while others only intermittently. Taking into account the possibility of a few overlooked pairs, the population in North-East Scotland probably fluctuates within the range 2–10 pairs. Breeding success locally and elsewhere contributes to the local population - birds ringed as chicks in Moray and Tayside have been found breeding in Aberdeenshire. Disturbance, predation and competition with Ringed Plovers may all affect breeding distribution and success but there is no shortage of potential breeding sites and numbers may be expected to increase slowly if Little Ringed Plovers continue to expand their breeding range in Scotland.

Author: *Raymond Duncan*

Little Ringed Plover, lower River Spey, June 2003. © *Martin Cook*

Little Ringed Plover, lower River Spey, July 2008. © *Martin Cook*

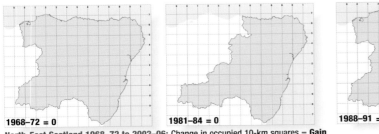

1968–72 = 0   1981–84 = 0

North-East Scotland 1968–72 to 2002–06: Change in occupied 10-km squares = **Gain**

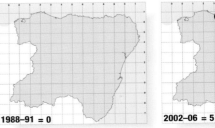

1988–91 = 0

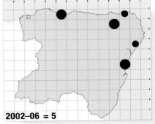

2002–06 = 5

Ringed Plover

Charadrius hiaticula

Scarce resident and migrant breeder. Passage migrant. Estimated population in North-East Scotland: *130–150 pairs* (4% of Scottish population, <2% of UK)

Amber list

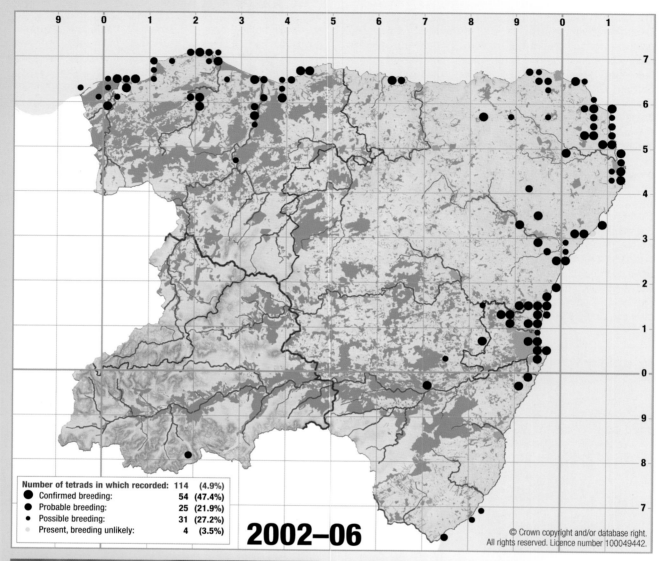

Number of tetrads in which recorded: 114 (4.9%)

	Breeding status		
●	Confirmed breeding:	54	(47.4%)
●	Probable breeding:	25	(21.9%)
•	Possible breeding:	31	(27.2%)
·	Present, breeding unlikely:	4	(3.5%)

2002–06

Ringed Plover, Finnmark, June 2008. © *Harry Scott*

Habitat and breeding biology

Ringed Plovers breed mainly in areas of sand and shingle along the coasts of North-East Scotland. Smaller numbers are found inland in similar habitats such as river shingles, lochs, industrial sites and gravel pits. Adults arrive on the breeding sites in mid-late February although first clutches, normally of four eggs, are not started until mid-late April. Incubation, shared by both adults, lasts for 21–27 days and is followed by a three week fledging period. In the event of predation, second and third replacement clutches can be laid through to late July or early August. Loss of eggs and, especially, chicks can be very high due to disturbance and predation; at Kingston in recent years less than 5% of eggs have produced fledged young (pers. obs.).

Scottish distribution and status

The most recent national breeding survey, in 2007, found about 3,350 pairs in Scotland (Conway *et al*. 2008). These are scattered around the coast-line of the country with notable concentrations in the southern islands of the Outer Hebrides as well as in Orkney and Shetland. Inland nesting is now widespread on the mainland, although mostly at low density (Buxton in *BS3*).

Distribution and status in North-East Scotland

The distribution of Ringed Plovers is mainly coastal although few are to be found along the cliff-bound coastline that predominates between Buckie and Rosehearty, between Peterhead and Collieston and southwards from Aberdeen. The majority of inland breeding takes place within 10 km of the coast, where natural sites include river shingles and the gravelly margins of lochs. Occasionally, breeding may take place in the uplands; during the Atlas period a pair probably bred above 500 m at the head of Glen Callater. Pairs can also be found in artificially created flat, dry habitats with only sparse vegetation such as in the industrial estates of the Aberdeen area, gravel pits and airfields including those at Aberdeen, Crimond and Kinloss. In 2003 a pair bred on a roof-top in Altens (*NESBR* 2003). In the Buckie area, forest nurseries have held a few pairs in recent years, where the ground is unplanted or holds only tiny trees; this was also found in the Mearns (S. Alexander pers. comm.).

Changes in distribution

Comparison of the range in North-East Scotland between 1968–72 and 2002–06 shows an increase of one third in occupied 10-km squares, with breeding in more non-coastal squares. In Aberdeenshire/Aberdeen City, between 1981–84 and 2002–06, the number of occupied recording units has more than doubled. When considered separately, the number of occupied coastal units has remained almost constant (18 in 1981–84, 22 in 2002–06) while the number inland has increased nearly six-fold from five to 29. This increase is likely to be due in part to an expansion of industrial sites and, to an unknown extent, to increased observer coverage.

Population and trends

Little up-to-date information on breeding densities is available; estimates of 6–8 pairs at RAF Kinloss (A. J. Lawrence pers. comm.) and nearly 30 pairs around Aberdeen City in 2005 (*NESBR* 2005) are exceptional and a mean density of two pairs/tetrad seems more realistic

overall. Applying this figure to the 54 tetrads in which breeding was confirmed, and assuming an additional one pair per tetrad for the 25 tetrads in which breeding was 'probable', gives a total of 133 pairs in North-East Scotland. A few breeding pairs in the 31 tetrads in the 'possible' category may raise the total close to 150 pairs, compared with the 102 pairs located during the 1984 survey (Prater 1989). As suggested above, much of the increase may be attributable to an increase in inland breeding. With the Scottish Outdoor Access Code permitting wider public access to areas of the countryside where Ringed Plovers nest, human interference may have a significant affect on future numbers. So too will changes in land use which allow breeding areas to become covered in vegetation; this has happened at Kingston and Cloddach Quarry in Moray. It may well be that areas not favoured by the public or having restricted access, such as industrial estates in Aberdeen and RAF bases in Moray, could in future hold an important proportion of our nesting Ringed Plovers.

Author: *Peter Gordon Smith*

Ringed Plover, St Cyrus, May 2008. © *Harry Scott*

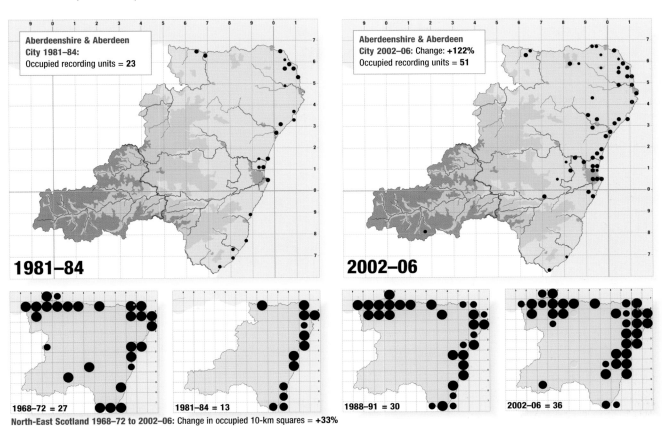

Aberdeenshire & Aberdeen City 1981–84:
Occupied recording units = **23**

1981–84

Aberdeenshire & Aberdeen City 2002–06: Change: **+122%**
Occupied recording units = **51**

2002–06

1968–72 = 27   1981–84 = 13   1988–91 = 30   2002–06 = 36

North-East Scotland 1968–72 to 2002–06: Change in occupied 10-km squares = +33%

Dotterel

Charadrius morinellus

Scarce summer migrant breeder. Passage migrant. Estimated population in North-East Scotland: ***200+ males*** (30–40% of Scottish and UK population)

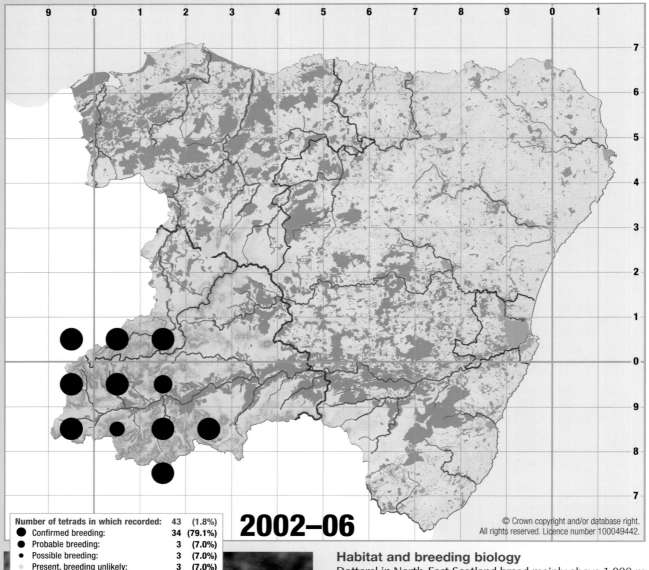

Number of tetrads in which recorded:	43	(1.8%)
● Confirmed breeding:	34	(79.1%)
● Probable breeding:	3	(7.0%)
● Possible breeding:	3	(7.0%)
○ Present, breeding unlikely:	3	(7.0%)

2002–06

Dotterel, Cairngorms, June 2010. © *Dave Pullan*

Habitat and breeding biology

Dotterel in North-East Scotland breed mainly above 1,000 m on dry, exposed mountain tops but can nest on lower ridges or hills that provide similar habitat, sometimes as low as 650 m. They occupy both predominantly vegetated sites and also bare stony areas often with tussocks of Three-leaved Rush, grasses, Woolly-hair Moss and lichens. They usually avoid steep slopes and areas of peat. The first Dotterel arrive at the end of April or early-mid May (usually 10th–20th) and initially gather in flocks of up to 30 birds on breeding hilltops. Pairs are then established and break off from the flocks prior to laying eggs. Dotterel generally lay a clutch of three eggs from late May onwards and these are incubated by the male only, with the first chicks hatching from late June and fledging in late July. The breeding grounds are generally abandoned by late August. Birds breeding in Scotland one year have been found breeding in Norway in subsequent years and chicks from Norway have been found breeding in Scotland, suggesting that we share the same population (Whitfield in Wernham *et al.* 2002)

Scottish distribution and status

Dotterel have been known to breed on the higher ground of the Cairngorms for over 100 years (Gordon 1903). Breeding

Dotterel may be found throughout the central and north-west Highlands wherever suitable habitat occurs. This is mainly above 1,000 m but can be as low as just a few hundred metres on the north Sutherland coast. The population appears to have declined from c.840–980 breeding males in 1987–88 to around 630 (510–755) in 1999, but may show major fluctuations from year to year (Whitfield 2002).

Distribution and status in North-East Scotland

The tops of the Cairngorms and the higher hills surrounding these are the main breeding areas for Dotterel in North-East Scotland. Here, the birds occupy the flat, broad tops and shoulders of the hills where suitable habitat is found. Although several hundred metres lower than the main breeding areas, the higher Strathdon hills hold occasional

Dotterel, An Socach, June 2004. © *Ian Francis*

breeding males, where they nest on the exposed wind clipped ridges that occur here; however they are not regular on any of these hills. Nowhere in any part of their range in North-East Scotland could Dotterel be described as common, with nests seldom closer than 200 m apart. Whitfield (2002) recorded a density of 2.17 males/km^2 in the East Highlands, which included all of the high ground in North-East Scotland together with the rest of the central Cairngorms.

Changes in distribution

There has been no obvious change in the distribution of the Dotterel population in North-East Scotland over the past century. Birds are still breeding where Seton Gordon (1912) and Sim (1903) found them in the late 1800s, and are present on most suitable hills despite increased human recreation pressure. Though the number of occupied recording units was slightly higher in 2002–06 than in 1981–84 (possibly due to better coverage), there is no strong indication of long-term change in distribution.

Population and trends

The population in North-East Scotland was estimated at 200+ incubating males by Watson & Rae (1987) and around 432 males were estimated by Whitfield (2002) to be present in the larger East Highlands area in 1999. Applying Whitfield's East Highlands average density figure of 2.17 males/km^2 to the 43 tetrads (172 1-km squares) where Dotterel were present in North-East Scotland in 2002–06 gives a figure of 373 males - probably too high (because not every 1-km square in a tetrad may contain suitable habitat) but suggesting that an estimate of 200+ males is not unrealistic. There were marked reductions in numbers in the East Highlands between 1987–88 and 1999. Numbers do, however, fluctuate from year to year - this is believed to be related to invertebrate food supply, which in turn is linked to weather conditions (Whitfield 2002, Shaw *et al.* 2006).

Author: *Robert Rae*

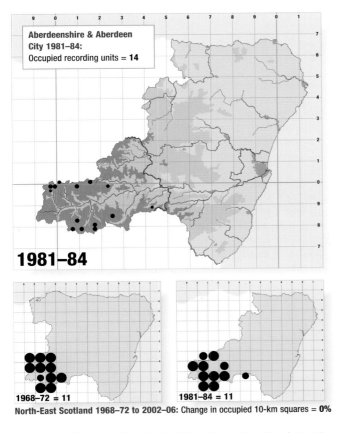

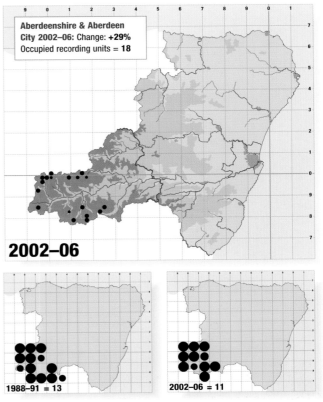

North-East Scotland 1968–72 to 2002–06: Change in occupied 10-km squares = **0%**

Golden Plover
Pluvialis apricaria

Common resident and summer migrant breeder. Passage migrant and winter visitor. Estimated population in North-East Scotland: **1,600 pairs** (11% of Scottish population, 7% of UK)

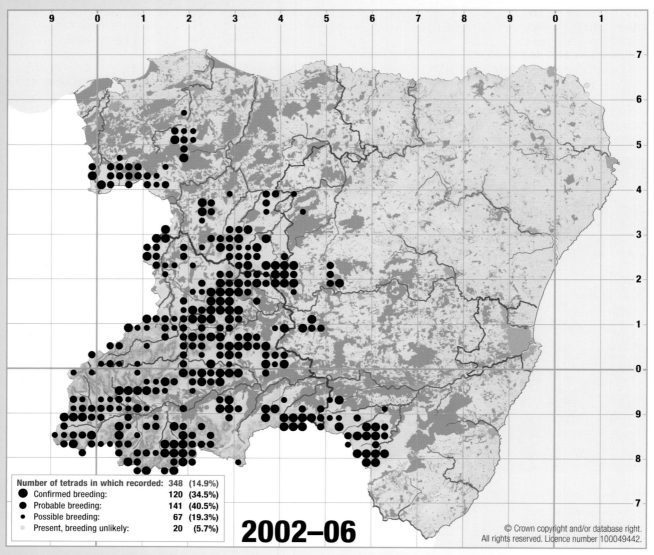

Number of tetrads in which recorded:	348	(14.9%)
● Confirmed breeding:	120	(34.5%)
● Probable breeding:	141	(40.5%)
● Possible breeding:	67	(19.3%)
Present, breeding unlikely:	20	(5.7%)

2002–06

Golden Plover, Deeside, May 2005. © *Ian Francis*

Habitat and breeding biology

The Golden Plover's preferred habitats are large, flat hill-top areas, exposed ridges with short wind-clipped Heather, peat bogs or grass. Lower hill shoulders can also provide similar habitat, particularly where Heather burning associated with grouse moors provides habitat for a few years before becoming unsuitable again when the Heather grows tall. Birds can arrive back on the breeding grounds as early as late February in mild, snow-free winters, but late March or early April is more usual. They gather in small groups of up to ten birds. At this time the display flight of the Golden Plover can be heard high overhead; the male sings one of the most beautiful and evocative of all bird songs while flying butterfly-like on stiff wings. Golden Plovers are pair and site faithful, though different pairs can nest sequentially in the same breeding range in the same summer *e.g.* in Deeside (Parr 1979). The usual clutch of four eggs is laid from early April onwards on the lower hills to early June on the higher tops of the Cairngorms. The first chicks hatch 28–30 days later and fledge three to four weeks after hatching. Both parents incubate and attend the chicks. The breeding grounds are generally abandoned in late August.

Scottish distribution and status

Golden Plovers breed throughout Scotland, mainly in the uplands of the north and west but down to sea level on the north coast and in the Western and Northern Isles. They are also present, generally at lower densities, in the Southern Uplands. Population trends are variable across the country following apparent declines between 1968–72 and 1988–91 (Thompson in *BS3*), and BBS trends for 1995–2007 indicate a non-significant 12% decline (Risely *et al.* 2009). The Scottish population is estimated to be around 15,000 pairs and the UK population around 19,900 pairs (Thompson in *BS3*).

Distribution and status in North-East Scotland

North-East Scotland is rich with suitable habitat for breeding Golden Plovers, from the Durris, Birse and Glen Dye hills in the south-east, west to the Cairngorms and north through the Ladder Hills to the moors around Dava and Glenlatterach in Moray. Golden Plovers can nest from around 250 m at Dava Moor in north-west Moray to well over 1,000 m in upper Deeside. Off-duty birds can also often be seen feeding on nearby tops as well as hill pastures such as those of the

Golden Plover, Glas Maol, July 2010. © *Harry Scott*

Cabrach. The peat bogs on the Ladder Hills hold the highest densities of breeding Golden Plovers in the area.

Changes in distribution

The number of occupied recording units in Aberdeenshire declined by around 12% from 1981–84 to 2002–06, with sites lost at lower altitude and on eastern moorlands. From the late 1970s, forestry plantations encroached onto breeding grounds such as those in the Durris region, removing much breeding habitat (Parr 1992). Prior to this, breeding Golden Plovers could also be found on lower ground such as the floodplain above the Linn of Dee at Mar Lodge (330 m), and by the roadside on the old military road between Crathie and Cockbridge.

Population and trends

The population in North-East Scotland probably declined over the last 30 years but appears to be largely stable now. Surveys in the North-East suggested a 37% decline during the 1980s to 1990s (Sim *et al.* 2005). However, there has been no further detectable decline in numbers on a small study area on the Ladder Hills over the last 15 years, with the number of pairs fluctuating between four and six on one hill throughout the period (pers. obs.) and, in a wider area here, numbers increased slightly between 1997 and 2007 following no clear change from 1988–89 to 1997 (Francis 2008). Breeding densities of 1–8 pairs/km² seem typical of Scottish uplands (Thompson in *BS3*). Work on the Moray moors in 1989 by NCC (Shepherd *et al.* 1989) estimated *c.*6 pairs/tetrad. Sim *et al.* (2005) recorded densities in North-East Scotland equal to 2.4–7.2 pairs/tetrad. Thirty-one estimates across the North-East during 2002–06 gave an average of 3 pairs/tetrad. From these sources, assuming a mid-point of *c.*4.5 pairs /tetrad and applying this to the 348 tetrads where breeding was at least considered possible in 2002–06, gives an estimate of around 1,600 pairs in North-East Scotland.

Author: *Robert Rae*

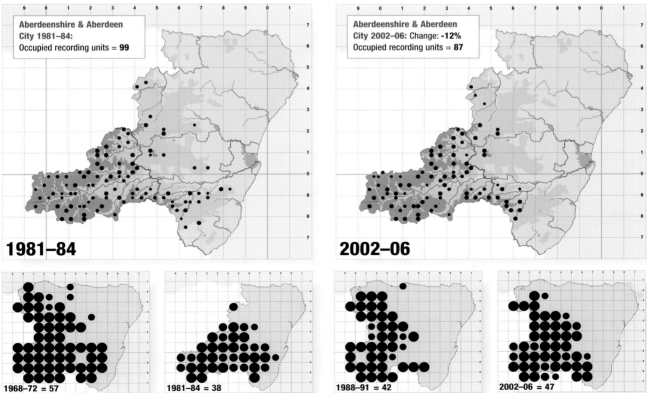

Aberdeenshire & Aberdeen City 1981–84:
Occupied recording units = **99**

1981–84

1968–72 = 57

1981–84 = 38

Aberdeenshire & Aberdeen City 2002–06: Change: **-12%**
Occupied recording units = **87**

2002–06

1988–91 = 42

2002–06 = 47

North-East Scotland 1968–72 to 2002–06: Change in occupied 10-km squares = **-18%**

Lapwing

Vanellus vanellus

Common resident and summer migrant breeder. Passage migrant. Estimated population in North-East Scotland: **3,400 pairs** (4% of Scottish population, 2% of UK)

Red list; UK and Scottish BAP lists

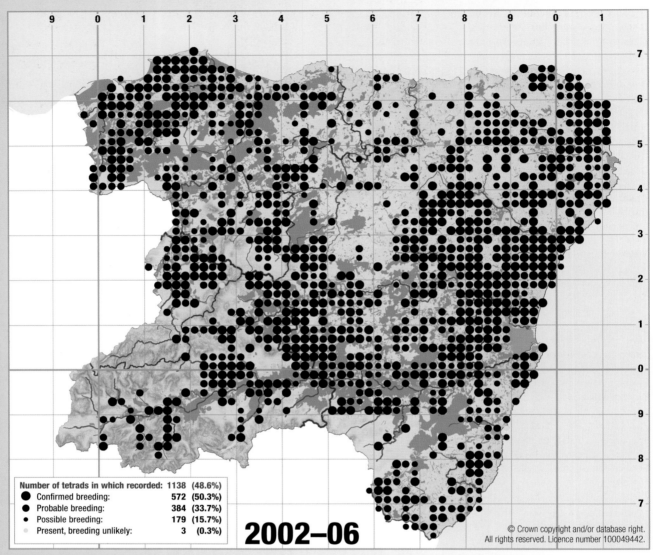

Number of tetrads in which recorded: 1138 (48.6%)		
● Confirmed breeding:	572	(50.3%)
● Probable breeding:	384	(33.7%)
● Possible breeding:	179	(15.7%)
· Present, breeding unlikely:	3	(0.3%)

2002–06

Habitat and breeding biology

Lapwings nest on all types of grassland from river valleys to uplands, in ploughed fields and in spring-sown crops (O'Brien in *BS3*, Picozzi *et al*. 1996) and need short vegetation for nest sites and open ground with all-round visibility away from trees. Suitable invertebrate-rich chick rearing habitat close by is critical, particularly wet ground with a short sward. Lapwings return to nest and begin their distinctive tumbling display flights from mid-late February to May. Pairs either breed singly or in loose colonies of up to 30 pairs; these help to defend against predators such as crows but are becoming rarer, with an increase in single, more vulnerable pairs. Four eggs are usually laid in April, and birds failing during incubation can re-lay on into May and even early June. Spring Barley fields are often favoured as nest sites but these nests are vulnerable to agricultural operations, which can result in a loss of 26% of nests (BTO nest record data).

Scottish distribution and status

Lapwings are still widely distributed, with an estimated breeding population of 91,200 (71,500–105,600) pairs in the mid 1990s (O'Brien in *BS3*). However, there was a decline on Scottish BBS plots of 38% between 1994–2007 (Risely *et al*. 2008) and other indicators suggest range contraction and population decline (O'Brien in *BS3*).

Distribution and status in North-East Scotland

In the North-East, Lapwings are also widely distributed (1,138 occupied tetrads), but are absent from forested, urban and upland moorland areas. Gaps in their distribution, particularly in the Deveron catchment, may be due to more

Lapwing, Drum, 1978. © *Graham Rebecca*

intensive livestock farming and lack of suitable nesting sites, though it is possible that some areas were under-recorded during atlas fieldwork. They extend into upland straths west of Braemar and in Strathdon (Grampian FWAG 2006) but in all areas there are concentrations in suitable habitat scattered amidst areas with few birds. A survey of Lapwings in North-East Scotland in 1996 (Francis 1997) found eight sites in Aberdeenshire and Moray holding more than 10 pairs/km^2.

Changes in distribution

Occupied recording units declined from 320 in 1981–84 Atlas (*NES 1st Atlas*) to 295 in 2002–06, with reductions spread fairly evenly over the area, though areas south of Huntly show larger losses. At the 10-km square scale, the distribution has shown a slight contraction since 1968–72. Lapwing populations are affected by changes in agricultural practices, particularly the widespread drainage of damp fields, faster farm machinery and high stocking rates resulting in nest losses (Winspear & Davis 2005). In parts of North-East Scotland, mixed farming with cereals and nearby pasture is now less common, and forage crops, such as Turnips, which provide good habitat have been largely replaced by silage. Afforestation has also replaced some wet fields and allowed refuges for common predators such as crows and Foxes. Ironically, participation in agri-environment schemes designed to help wildlife may have contributed to the decline as restrictions in grazing intensity have led to a spread of dense Soft Rush in some formerly suitable fields. This may have led to declines within areas such as the Cairngorms Straths (Picozzi *et al.* 1996).

Population and trends

During 2002–06, 1,138 tetrads were occupied, but the population is larger than this. Atlas fieldworkers estimated numbers in 88 tetrads, possibly those with higher than average populations, and counts averaged 4.8 pairs/tetrad (range 1–22 pairs) which, if replicated across all occupied tetrads, would give an upper estimate of 5,462 pairs in the

Lapwing, Logie Coldstone, May 2004. © *Harry Scott*

area. In fact, 2–3 pairs were recorded most frequently, suggesting a more realistic population estimate in our area of perhaps up to 3,400 pairs. BBS data in North-East Scotland suggest a decline between 1994 and 2006, reflecting the wider decline in Scotland. O'Brien (1994) estimated 4,400–14,800 pairs in lowland Grampian in 1992–93, which if adjusted for the Scottish 38% decline since 1994 suggests a current population of 2,728–9,176 pairs - encompassing the estimate resulting from fieldwork for this atlas. The 3.7% of Scottish and 2.2% of UK population (156,000 pairs - Baker *et al.* 2006) that our 3,400 pairs represents, probably underestimates the true proportion, since both of these country-wide estimates are at least 10 years out of date. Across the area, local numbers have varied, against a background of general decline. A site in Glenbuchat, Donside, held 11 pairs in 1992 and 1997 (Francis 1997) but this had declined to one pair in 2005. Conversely, a 100 ha area around Tomintoul and the 205 ha Dee floodplain near Braemar saw slight increases from 1996 to 2005 and numbers have remained stable at Loch of Strathbeg (RSPB Aberdeen, unpublished data).

Author: *Nicky Penford*

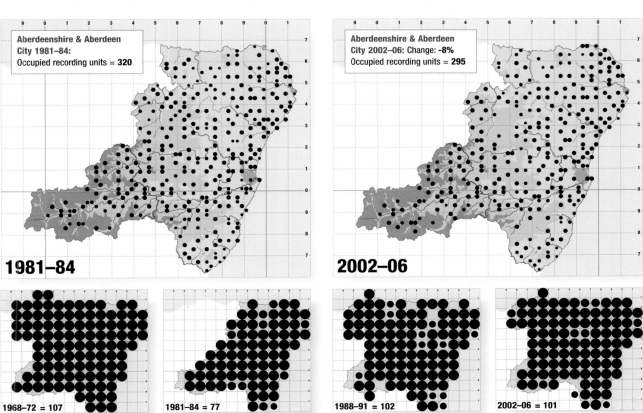

Aberdeenshire & Aberdeen City 1981–84: Occupied recording units = **320**

1981–84

Aberdeenshire & Aberdeen City 2002–06: Change: **-8%** Occupied recording units = **295**

2002–06

1968–72 = 107

1981–84 = 77

1988–91 = 102

2002–06 = 101

North-East Scotland 1968–72 to 2002–06: Change in occupied 10-km squares = **-6%**

Temminck's Stint

Calidris temminckii

Occasional probable breeder. Passage migrant. Estimated population in North-East Scotland: **0 pairs**

Red list

Number of tetrads in which recorded:	1	(0.0%)
● Confirmed breeding:	0	(0.0%)
● Probable breeding:	0	(0.0%)
• Possible breeding:	1	(100.0%)
˙ Present, breeding unlikely:	0	(0.0%)

Temminck's Stint, Finnmark, June 2009. © *Harry Scott*

Habitat and breeding biology

The Temminck's Stint is primarily an Arctic breeder where it occupies sheltered coastal habitats, breeding on flat grassy islands or sandy shores. It also nests among dwarf plant communities in the uplands to 1,200 m or more (*BWP*). The few Scottish breeding sites, usually close to a river or loch, have included sparsely-vegetated open terrain, the fringe of a pine forest, and a coastal meadow (Kalejta-Summers in *BS3*). In Scotland, breeding birds arrive from mid May to June and the clutch, usually of four eggs, is laid from mid June into July. The breeding strategy, over the Arctic range at least, is unusual; the female lays two clutches, the first of which is incubated by her mate and the second, after she has mated with a different male, is incubated by herself. The eggs hatch after about three weeks and each brood is reared by its own parent.

Scottish distribution and status

Temminck's Stints are rare breeders in Scotland with a maximum population, in the late 1970s–early 1980s, of ten pairs. Since then, numbers have dwindled and, despite the presence of pairs in some years, no breeding has been confirmed since 1993. Up to five sites were occupied between 1968–2002, in Clyde, Badenoch & Strathspey, Ross & Cromarty and Caithness (Kalejta-Summers in *BS3*). The species is a little more familiar as a passage migrant, chiefly in May–June but with a smaller autumn passage in August–September. Most are seen in eastern Scotland, especially in Shetland, Caithness, North-east Scotland and Lothian.

Distribution and status in North-East Scotland

During the period 1975–2007, 55 migrants were seen, seven in Moray and the others in the North-east Scotland recording area. Of these, 28 were in May, eight in June, 11 in July and only eight in the August–October autumn passage period. In addition, possible breeding activity has taken place at two sites. In 1978, two were seen displaying near the Ythan estuary on two dates in late May. In 1979, at a site in Moray, a singing Temminck's Stint was present on 30th May and a bird sang and displayed between 9th–16th June; a second bird was seen on 10th June (*SBR* 1979). In 1980, a bird sang and displayed on 1st June and 16th June, and the following year, song was heard on 7th June. In 1982, a bird displayed between 16th May–11th June (*SBR* 1982) but again breeding could not be confirmed. Following a gap of three years, two were seen on 7th July 1986 and, relevant to this Atlas period, two were present on 18th May 2005 and one was there ten days later (*MNBR* 2005). There was nothing to suggest that the 2005 birds were anything other than migrants, but clearly this remains a potential breeding site.

Author: *Martin Cook*

Culbin Bar and Sands

The vegetation on the sandy Culbin Bar is dominated by Marram Grass with stands of low-growing conifers. Breeding species include Skylark and Meadow Pipit, with a few species such as Robin, Wren and possibly Stonechat in the scrub. Sandy areas hold Oystercatcher and Ringed Plover and there may be Eider broods on the sheltered water inside the bar. Culbin Forest, which borders the Sands, holds a wide range of woodland species including Buzzard, Sparrowhawk, Great Spotted Woodpecker, Tree Pipit and Jay. There is a large population of Crested Tits, and two or three species of crossbill may be found. September 2010 © *Martin Cook*

Pectoral Sandpiper

Calidris melanotos

Passage migrant, may have bred. Estimated population in North-East Scotland: **0 pairs**

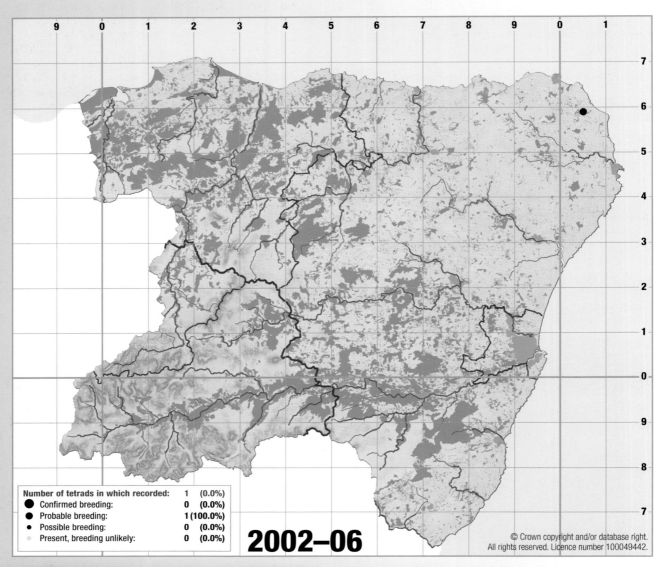

Number of tetrads in which recorded: | 1 | (0.0%)
- ● Confirmed breeding: 0 (0.0%)
- ● Probable breeding: 1 (100.0%)
- ● Possible breeding: 0 (0.0%)
- Present, breeding unlikely: 0 (0.0%)

2002–06

Pectoral Sandpiper, Marywell Pool, Aberdeen, October 2003. © *Harry Scott*

Habitat and breeding biology

Pectoral Sandpipers breed on arctic tundra in Canada, Alaska and eastern Siberia, favouring areas with a continuous grass or sedge cover and a well-drained nest-site, often near the shore of lakes or pools (*BWP*). As scarce migrants in Scotland, they are usually encountered at the edge of freshwater pools and lochs, often among vegetation (Murray in *BS3*).

Scottish distribution and status

There were only four records in the first half of the 20th century but Pectoral Sandpipers began to occur more often in the 1950s and 1960s and have been recorded annually in Scotland since 1973. The majority of records have been in North-east Scotland, the Outer Hebrides and the Northern Isles, mainly in the period July to October with a peak in the first two weeks of September. There has been an increase in spring records since 2000. In autumn 2003 there was an unprecedented influx, with 38 birds recorded in Scotland, including about 11 in North-east Scotland (Murray in *BS3*, *NESBR* 2003). It has been suggested that the regularity with which Pectoral Sandpipers occur in Europe in autumn may be at least partly attributed to a flyway of Siberian birds heading for wintering grounds in Africa (Lees & Gilroy 2004). It would therefore be expected that the exceptional passage in autumn 2003 would be followed by a substantial return in spring 2004. This did, indeed, occur with 16 birds reported in Scotland during April–June (Murray in *BS3*). Birds were found on three different Hebridean islands during June 2004, raising the possibility of a breeding attempt; indeed one pair displayed and held territory (Holling *et al.* 2007). Other events, relevant to North-East Scotland, are described below.

Distribution and status in North-East Scotland

During 1973–2006, around 70 Pectoral Sandpipers were recorded in North-East Scotland. Only nine were in the May–June spring period with the remainder during July–October with September the peak month. During 1973–1990, birds were seen in only eight years, but since then they have become almost annual and especially numerous since 1999; about 50 individuals have been found in the eight-year period 1999–2006. The majority of records are from the Loch of Strathbeg RSPB reserve, with birds favouring the shallow pools at Starnafin Farm and Tower Pool. Other favoured locations are Slains pools and Meikle Loch. Only nine have been seen in Moray.

In 2004, events at Loch of Strathbeg suggested the possibility of a breeding attempt there. There is, however, some confusion in the literature as to the significance of these events. *NESBR* 2004 states "a single bird was at Loch of Strathbeg 18–23 May, followed by two birds, a male and female, at the same location on 6 June. The male was observed displaying during the evening over the reserve". Holling *et al.* (2007) relates the *NESBR* 2004 records and gives additional information: "In early July an adult and very fresh juvenile were seen together, remaining until October", commenting that "it seems very likely that breeding did occur at this site". *BS3*, in response to Holling *et al.* (2007), states that "This is the only confirmed breeding record" (for Scotland) (Murray in *BS3*). So, was breeding by Pectoral Sandpipers confirmed at Loch of Strathbeg in 2004 or not? There was in fact no conclusive evidence and no written description of the juvenile bird was submitted to the North-east Scotland Rarities Committee. Furthermore, the only record of the adult and juvenile together was on 21st July; birds recorded into the autumn were likely to have been new arrivals (H. Maggs pers. comm.). Although the observations fulfil the atlas criteria for 'probable breeding' there is no certainty that the juvenile was raised at Loch of Strathbeg and the level of conclusive evidence required for a first Scottish, British and (possibly) Western Palearctic breeding record was not obtained. This is now the agreed position of the North-east Scotland Recorder, the local Records Committee and RSPB staff at Loch of Strathbeg at the time.

Author: *Scott Paterson*

Habitat used by Pectoral Sandpiper, Loch of Strathbeg, September 2009. © *Duncan Goulder*

Purple Sandpiper

Calidris maritima

Very rare breeder. Winter visitor and passage migrant. Estimated population in North-East Scotland: **1–2 pairs** (50% of Scottish and UK population)

Number of tetrads in which recorded:	1	(0.0%)
● Confirmed breeding:	0	(0.0%)
● Probable breeding:	1	(100.0%)
• Possible breeding:	0	(0.0%)
Present, breeding unlikely:	0	(0.0%)

Purple Sandpiper, Cairngorms, May 2004. © *Derek McGinn*

Habitat and breeding biology

The tiny Scottish population of Purple Sandpipers breeds above 1,000 m in arctic-alpine habitats, usually associated with Three-leaved Rush and Stiff Sedge heaths. Typically, there are areas of bare ground and boulders nearby, together with burns or wet flushes. Adults arrive back at breeding sites in mid-late May. In a study conducted between 1987 and 1993, five nests each contained a clutch of four eggs. Most clutches hatched between mid June and early July; two late nests hatching on 20th July and 28th July were considered to be repeat clutches. In ten out of 11 broods, the young were attended only by the male. Most fledged young had vacated the breeding areas by early August (Smith & Summers 2005).

Scottish distribution and status

Purple Sandpipers were first found breeding in Scotland in 1978 and since that time, up to 2007, the population has fluctuated between 1–5 pairs (Summers in *BS3*). There has been no evidence of a population increase over the past 30 years. Pairs are secretive during incubation, however, and may be overlooked.

Purple Sandpiper, Cairngorms, June 1990. © *Ed Duthie*

Purple Sandpiper, Cairngorms, June 1990. © *Ed Duthie*

Distribution and status in North-East Scotland

A pair of Purple Sandpipers was found in suitable nesting habitat in North-East Scotland on 3rd June 1978. Subsequently this pair hatched out three young of which at least one fledged. This was the first recorded breeding by Purple Sandpipers in the UK (Dennis 1983). Breeding at this locality continued; in 1980 a recently fledged juvenile was seen in early August, and on the same day there were two single adults at different places well away from the juvenile (A. Watson pers. comm.). In 1981, four broods of chicks were found but fledging success was not known (Dennis 1983) and in 1982, a nest with four eggs was found on 4th June (A. Watson pers. comm.). In the late 1980s–early 1990s, up to three pairs bred annually in an area of *c*.4 km² and at least one brood of large chicks was seen in most years (Smith & Summers 2005). Since that time, birds have been regularly present in summer; most recently in 2009 when at least one, and probably two, pairs bred.

Author: *Martin Cook*

Lochnagar and the Mounth

This photograph illustrates well the conditions that can face birds that breed in high altitude alpine habitats in North-East Scotland; substantial snow patches can last well into June and conditions are always harsh. Lochnagar (1,155 m) is the highest point on the mountains known as the Mounth, which run from Carn Ealar on Mar Lodge eastwards to Mount Keen and Cairn o' Mount. This large area of high ground holds breeding Red Grouse, Ptarmigan, Red-throated Diver, Golden Eagle, Merlin, Peregrine, Golden Plover, Dotterel, Dunlin, Short-eared Owl, Wheatear, Ring Ouzel, Raven, Twite and Snow Bunting. April 2008 © *Ian Francis*

Dunlin

Calidris alpina

Scarce summer migrant breeder. Winter visitor and passage migrant. Estimated population in North-East Scotland: *350–500 pairs* (5% of Scottish population, <5% of UK)   **Red list** (*schinzii* subspecies); Scottish BAP list

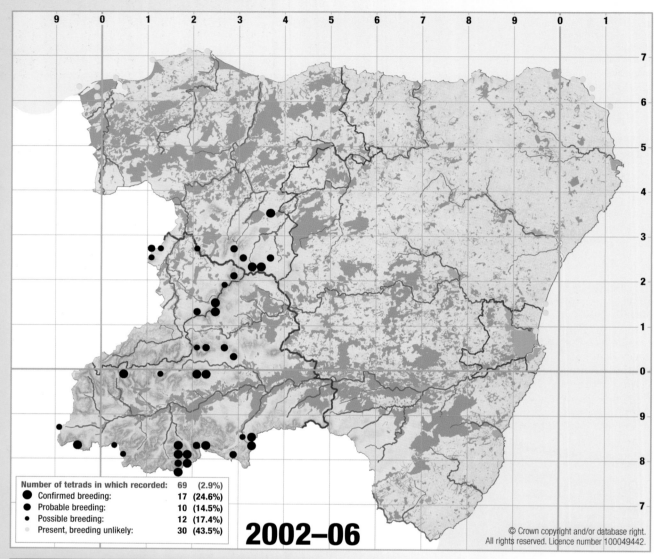

Number of tetrads in which recorded:	69	(2.9%)
● Confirmed breeding:	17	(24.6%)
● Probable breeding:	10	(14.5%)
● Possible breeding:	12	(17.4%)
Present, breeding unlikely:	30	(43.5%)

2002–06

Dunlin, Greenland, June 2008. © *Ed Duthie*

Habitat and breeding biology

North-East Scotland's breeding Dunlin belong to subspecies *C. a. schinzii*, most of which breed on peatlands at around 500–800 m altitude where they frequently nest in the company of Golden Plovers; this association has earned Dunlin the name 'plover's page'. Wet blanket bog with pools is particularly favoured, and often several pairs may breed in close proximity forming a loose colony. Some also nest on the high tops on drier grassy ridges with wet flushes (for example on An Sgarsoch at 1,000 m), where Ptarmigan or Dotterel may be nearest neighbours. Dry stony areas are avoided. Birds arrive from early May when they can be seen in small flocks with Golden Plovers. Dunlin are site and pair faithful (*BWP*) and by mid May pairs can be found together on their previous year's territory prior to egg laying. Four eggs are laid generally from mid May and first chicks hatch from about 10th June, fledging in late June or early July. During incubation, Dunlin can be very inconspicuous and elusive. Chicks are tended by the pair when they first hatch but by the male alone after the first week and, in contrast to the incubation period, Dunlin with chicks are extremely demonstrative and can fly to an intruder from 100 m or more, uttering alarm calls. Both adults and chicks leave the breeding grounds by the end of July.

Scottish distribution and status

Dunlin breed in suitable habitat throughout Scotland, including the blanket bogs and high tops preferred in the North-East but also on lower ground in the north and west where good habitat reaches down to sea level. The highest numbers are found in the Flow Country of Sutherland and Caithness and in the Outer Hebrides where they breed at high densities on the machair. There are considered to be 8,000–10,000 pairs in Scotland (Insley in *BS3*). The UK population was estimated at 9,150–9,900 pairs by Baker *et al.* 2006 (based on 1980s figures) but a higher estimate has been made of 18,000–33,500 pairs (BirdLife International, quoted in *BS3*).

Distribution and status in North-East Scotland

During 2002–06, most Dunlin were found on tops within the Cairngorms National Park, along the Mounth and north to the Ladder Hills. They have previously been found further east as far as the Cairn o' Mount (Rae & Watson 1998). Most cursory surveys overlook Dunlin (see below) and this applies to the current atlas fieldwork, which, despite finding more Dunlin than in 1981–84, does not fully reflect the probable true distribution (see map for 1987–97 in Rae & Watson 1998).

Changes in distribution

Some higher-ground sites have been deserted, due possibly to drainage or to overgrazing by Red Deer, but now the distribution is probably stable. Dunlin formerly bred on the coast of Aberdeenshire, in particular in dune slacks around St. Fergus and south-east of Loch of Strathbeg. Three to five pairs regularly bred here from the 1970s to the mid 1980s, when the nesting area was drained (Rae & Watson 1998). During 1968–72 they also bred to the west of Rosehearty (*BTO 1st Atlas*) but although the habitat still appears to be suitable no birds have been recorded here in recent years. Coastal breeding also took place at Findhorn in 1970 (Cook 1992).

Dunlin, Glen Gairn, June 2003. © *Harry Scott*

Population and trends

Numbers in the uplands appear to vary annually with fluctuating water levels, and though the range may have contracted in some high-ground areas there is no compelling evidence to suggest a major change in numbers. Sim *et al.* (2005) reported a 36% decline in Dunlin in North-East Scotland over a 10–15 year period prior to 2002–06 (non-significant due to a small number of plots), but cursory moorland surveys do not detect Dunlin well (Rae & Watson 1998). In 2002–06 Dunlin occupied breeding habitat in 39 tetrads, implying a population much less than the 436 pairs estimated in 1987–97 by Rae & Watson (1998). Some adjustments are needed to this earlier figure, however, since some of the 10-km squares included were in nearby parts of Angus and Perth. On the other hand, the survey did not fully cover all areas in the North-East and the estimate was considered 'minimal' (Rae & Watson 1998). This detailed survey suggests that the species is much more widespread and numerous than was indicated during 1968–72, 1981–84 and 1988–91 (*BTO 1st* and *2nd Atlas*, *NES 1st Atlas*), and the range was also probably under-recorded in the 2002–06 atlas fieldwork. There seems no reason to revise Rae & Watson's estimate and a current breeding population of 350–500 pairs of Dunlin in North-East Scotland is suggested.

Author: *Robert Rae*

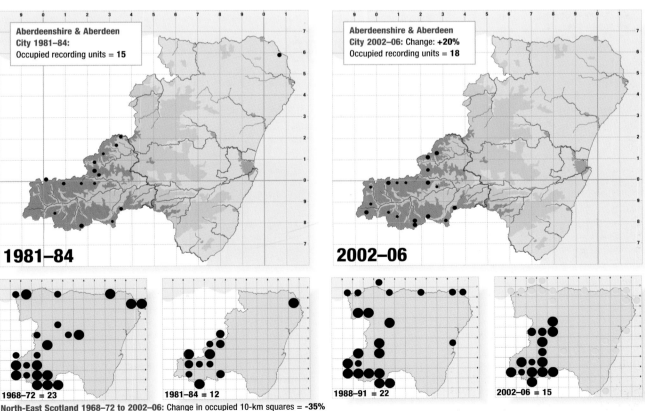

Aberdeenshire & Aberdeen City 1981–84:
Occupied recording units = **15**

1981–84

Aberdeenshire & Aberdeen City 2002–06: Change: **+20%**
Occupied recording units = **18**

2002–06

1968–72 = 23

1981–84 = 12

1988–91 = 22

2002–06 = 15

North-East Scotland 1968–72 to 2002–06: Change in occupied 10-km squares = -35%

Ruff

Philomachus pugnax

Occasional in breeding habitat. Passage migrant. Estimated population in North-East Scotland: **0 pairs**

Red list; Schedule 1; Annex 1; Scottish BAP list

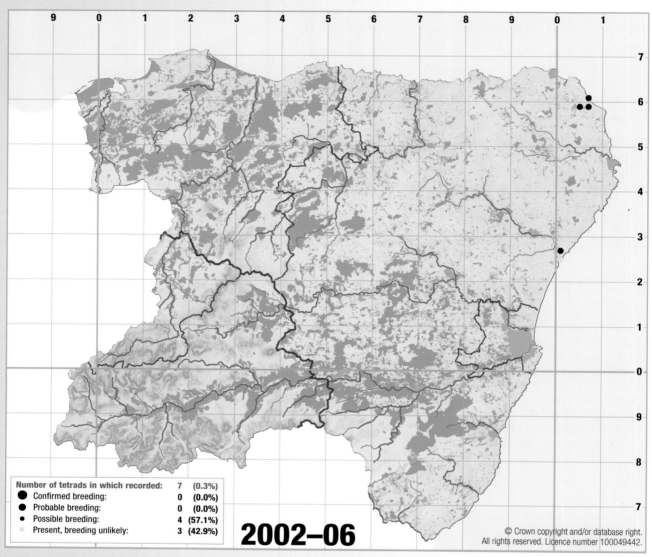

Number of tetrads in which recorded:	7	(0.3%)
● Confirmed breeding:	0	(0.0%)
● Probable breeding:	0	(0.0%)
• Possible breeding:	4	(57.1%)
Present, breeding unlikely:	3	(42.9%)

2002–06

Habitat and breeding biology

In their arctic and sub-arctic breeding grounds, Ruff prefer littoral margins, estuaries and marshland with small lakes and shallow water. They nest among drier patches of vegetation such as sedges (*BWP*). In England the main breeding habitat is low-lying, wet grassy meadows (*BTO 2nd Atlas*).

Scottish distribution and status

In Scotland, Ruff are frequent passage migrants, primarily in autumn, with the majority of records from southern and eastern counties and the Northern Isles. Following probable instances in 1976 and 1977, breeding was first proved in Scotland in 1980, in Sutherland. Since then, breeding has taken place in the Outer Hebrides and the Northern Isles. Up to two pairs have bred in any one year although this is by no means an annual occurrence (Clark in *BS3*).

Distribution and status in North-East Scotland

Ruff are common passage migrants to North-East Scotland, primarily coastal in the spring but often inland in the autumn. They are more frequent in Aberdeenshire than in Moray. Spring passage is light and very variable with birds arriving at any time from April through to mid May. There were a few spring occurrences during 2002–06 but the only

case in which any breeding behaviour was observed was in mid May 2005 when a male and female were present at Loch of Strathbeg (*NESBR* 2005) and some display was seen.

Author: *Dominic Funnell*

Ruff, Finnmark, June 2009. © *Harry Scott*

Speymouth

Downstream from Garmouth viaduct, the River Spey divides into several channels with shingle islands between them. Colonies of Arctic and Common Terns breed, along with Black-headed and Common Gulls. Sandwich and Little Terns have also bred. Other species nesting on the shingle include Oystercatcher, Common Sandpiper, Ringed Plover and, in recent years, Little Ringed Plover. Broods of Shelduck and, occasionally, Red-breasted Merganser appear around the rivermouth – where a flock of moulting Goosanders congregates in summer. This is an excellent site to watch fishing Ospreys. Riverside vegetation holds Sedge Warbler, Whitethroat and Reed Bunting while Chiffchaff, Blackcap and Garden Warbler sing in riverine woodland. June 2009 © *Martin Cook*

Snipe

Gallinago gallinago

Common resident and migrant breeder. Winter visitor and passage migrant. Estimated population in North-East Scotland: *1,500–3,000 pairs* (5% of Scottish population, 4% of UK)

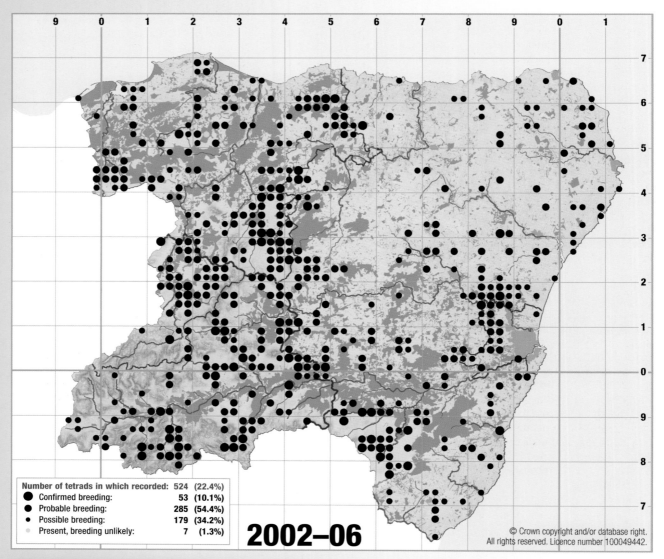

Number of tetrads in which recorded:	524	(22.4%)
● Confirmed breeding:	53	(10.1%)
● Probable breeding:	285	(54.4%)
● Possible breeding:	179	(34.2%)
· Present, breeding unlikely:	7	(1.3%)

2002–06

Snipe, Glen Finglas, May 2008. © *Gina Prior*

Habitat and breeding biology

The vibrating sound of display high above their breeding grounds, known as 'drumming', is a clear indicator of breeding Snipe. Their 'chooka chooka' call is less well known, but both are characteristic sounds of nesting areas, often at dawn or dusk or after rain. They require soft wet ground, marshy areas or boggy moorland. Birds arrive in breeding areas in February and March. Nests are usually placed in deep cover, often in a clump of dead grass which frequently forms a tent over the incubating bird; eggs are normally laid from early April onwards on lower ground, but not until early May on higher hill ground. The normal clutch of four eggs is laid at 24-hour intervals and they hatch after about 19–22 days; the brood of hatched chicks is then usually divided between male and female, and they are able to fly after around 20–24 days (*BWP*).

Scottish distribution and status

Breeding Snipe are widespread in Scotland but are scarce or absent from the highest mountains and from intensively farmed lowlands. The greatest densities are found in widely scattered parts of mainland Scotland and in the northern and western Isles, where the subspecies is *G. g. faeroeensis*; elsewhere, including North-East Scotland, the subspecies is

The Breeding Birds of North-East Scotland

G. g. gallinago (O'Brien in *BS3*). The Scottish breeding population is estimated at 34,000–40,000 pairs, with numbers fluctuating substantially and showing no clear long-term trend (O'Brien in *BS3*).

Distribution and status in North-East Scotland

Snipe are now largely confined to the uplands between 250–700 m (sometimes to 800 m, such as around the Cairnwell and Glen Muick) and these areas probably hold the bulk of our breeding birds. Here they inhabit sheep walk, deer forest, grouse moor and any damp unimproved pasture; any moorland fieldworker knows how widely they are scattered in moorland flushes. In the lowlands, Snipe are now uncommon due to lack of suitable habitat but where this still exists (even temporarily) it is readily occupied. For example, at Pitmedden, near Ellon, a blocked drain allowed colonisation of a field for a couple of years until it was repaired and the birds again disappeared. Lowland Snipe are thinly scattered but a concentration of breeding birds was found along the lower Don area between Inverurie and Aberdeen.

Changes in distribution

Snipe were formerly fairly common with several pairs often breeding close together in damp field corners across the area. Land drainage undoubtedly led to a decline in numbers. However, there were 97 occupied 10-km squares in both the 1968–72 and the 2002–06 atlases, indicating little change in distribution at that resolution. Comparison of the 1981–84 and 2002–06 Aberdeenshire/Aberdeen City maps shows a 41% increase in occupied recording units, with an even greater increase in the north-east lowlands. Recording effort no doubt influenced these figures, but it seems most likely that a scattering of breeding sites has been maintained across the lowlands, perhaps influenced by small-scale environmental schemes on farms, but former high densities of breeding birds have reduced. This may mirror the decline noted in the 1970s and 80s for Scotland, followed by a more recent increase (O'Brien in *BS3*).

Snipe, Glen Muick, May 2004. © *Harry Scott*

Population and trends

There is no reliable information about numbers or population change, with evidence for both declines and local increases. Snipe are difficult to survey and most estimates are likely to be inaccurate. On lowland farmland in the north-east, Snipe appear to have declined in numbers and in some areas have largely disappeared, although upland populations appear to be more stable. In Scotland, BBS data indicate an increase of some 58% between 1994 and 2007, but this survey method does not count Snipe well. There may have been some local increases. On a 2 km^2 upland floodplain near Braemar, Snipe increased from six to 18 pairs between 1996 and 2008 following ditch blocking, and on 1 km^2 of upland farmland near Tomintoul they increased from two to seven pairs between 1996 and 2005 (both RSPB data). There are estimated still to be many tens of pairs across six areas on Mar Lodge estate (pers. obs.). Using densities from South-east Scotland (Murray *et al.* 1998) and those in some tetrads during this atlas (*e.g.* 10 tetrads held 3–15 displaying birds but most had fewer than this), a range of 2–5 pairs/occupied tetrad for the North-East Scotland uplands may be reasonable. Lowland tetrads are mostly likely to contain very restricted suitable habitat leading to one pair/occupied tetrad at best. The breeding population in North-East Scotland may perhaps be around 1,500–3,000 pairs; a more precise estimate is not possible.

Author: *Robert Rae*

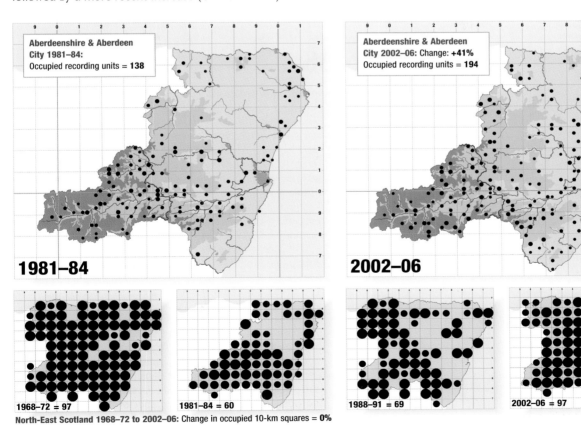

Aberdeenshire & Aberdeen City 1981–84:
Occupied recording units = **138**

1981–84

Aberdeenshire & Aberdeen City 2002–06: Change: **+41%**
Occupied recording units = **194**

2002–06

1968–72 = 97   1981–84 = 60   1988–91 = 69   2002–06 = 97

North-East Scotland 1968–72 to 2002–06: Change in occupied 10-km squares = **0%**

Woodcock

Scolopax rusticola

Common resident and migrant breeder. Winter visitor and passage migrant. Estimated population in North-East Scotland: *2,000–4,000 males* (8% of Scottish population, <8% of UK)

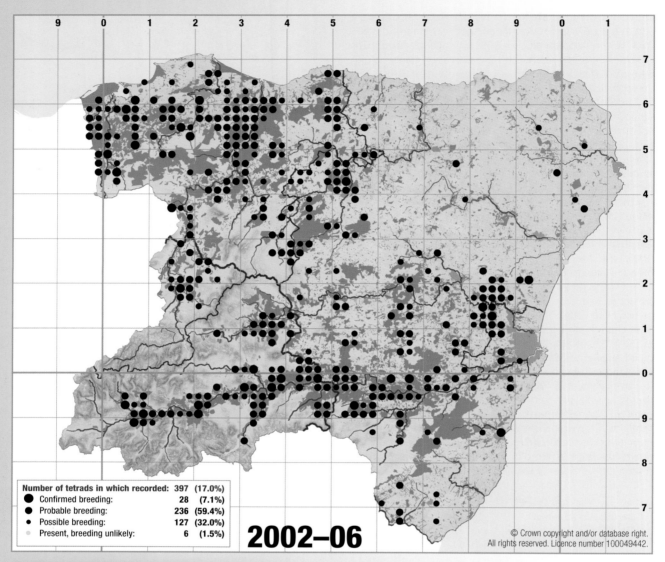

Number of tetrads in which recorded:	397	(17.0%)
● Confirmed breeding:	28	(7.1%)
● Probable breeding:	236	(59.4%)
● Possible breeding:	127	(32.0%)
○ Present, breeding unlikely:	6	(1.5%)

2002–06

Woodcock, Banchory Devenick, April 1979. © *Ed Duthie*

Habitat and breeding biology

Breeding Woodcock prefer open, mature woodland or younger plantations with clearings and damp patches, but may nest in Heather or Bracken at the edge of heathland. Deciduous or mixed woodland is preferred to conifers, with birch being a favourite in North-East Scotland, where thickets provide cover for nesting. The courtship 'roding' flights of males, seen at dusk and dawn, make use of clearings and forest rides and have been noted to pass close to incubating females. Roding commences in early March and may continue until July. Most clutches, usually of 3–4 eggs, are laid in late March and early April. After 22 days incubation the young hatch and are led by the female to more open areas, where earthworms and arthropods are important food items. The family group splits up after about four weeks.

Scottish distribution and status

A widespread resident throughout Scotland, the Woodcock prefers wooded river valleys but will use higher ground with suitable habitats. The 2003 Breeding Woodcock Survey (Hoodless 2005) revealed that 46% of the 78 woods studied had roding birds. Highest breeding numbers were in Borders, Lothian, Moray, Nairn and Inverness, with certain localities favoured, such as Strathspey birch woods with

5.0–10.1 males/km^2 and Tentsmuir Forest with 8.1 males/km^2. North-East Scotland (excluding Moray) had lower numbers. The Scottish population was estimated to contain 24,000–56,500 males in 2007 (Hoodless in *BS3*).

Distribution and status in North-East Scotland

The breeding distribution map emphasises probable and confirmed breeding along the major river systems. The valleys of the Dee, much of the Don, the upper Deveron, the Spey and the Findhorn all have the moist woodland preferred for breeding. Birds were recorded up to the tree line at an altitude around 400 m at Spittal of Glenmuick, Glen Lui, Glen Quoich, Cock Bridge and near Tomintoul. Areas showing high concentrations of probable breeding records, such as central Moray and north-west of Aberdeen City, are likely to reflect dedicated evening fieldwork to record roding birds, and this raises the possibility of under-recording elsewhere. Moray has a rich woodland heritage and three main river valleys, hence the widespread occurrence of Woodcocks. It is probably the lack of woodland with a suitable structure and ungrazed ground cover that explains the scarcity of Woodcock in north Aberdeenshire; only eight probable or possible breeding records came from an area of around 180 km^2.

Changes in distribution

In 1968–72, 84% of 10-km squares in North-East Scotland were occupied (*BTO 1st Atlas*), but a decrease had occurred in Aberdeenshire by 1981–84 (*NES 1st Atlas*). This was maintained in 1988–91 when Woodcocks were not recorded in 42 of the 10-km squares in North-East Scotland where they had been present in 1968–72. The authors suggested that the decrease was partly due to the timed tetrad recording method (with emphasis on day-time fieldwork), but also thought that many commercial forests were at the inappropriate thicket stage (*BTO 2nd Atlas*). The 2002–06 survey showed an increase of 33% in occupied recording units in Aberdeenshire/Aberdeen City compared with 1981–84, most

of these being in central Aberdeenshire and around Huntly. Unlike 1981–84, breeding was at least possible in four east Buchan squares in 2002–06 but there were no records near the north coast between Banff and Pennan.

Population and trends

Counts of roding males provide the most appropriate method for estimating the breeding population, as the species is otherwise secretive (Hoodless in *BS3*). The Breeding Woodcock Survey used this method and found that deciduous and mixed woodland contained an average density of 2.5–3.7 males/km^2 and conifer forests averaged 0.6–1.2 males/km^2, although some optimal areas held up to 13 males/km^2. These figures may be applied to the same woodland types in North-East Scotland to estimate the Woodcock population. Data from the Forestry Commission in 2008 for their own and private woodland, but excluding woods under 2 ha, gave a deciduous/mixed area of around 270 km^2 and conifer area of 1,279 km^2. This gives a male population of 1,442–2,534 for the larger woodlands. In addition the woods and thickets under 2 ha could contain a further 20%, as these often provide wet conditions and are undisturbed by commercial operations, so the total rises to 1,730–3,041 males. As the species is generally under-recorded, the population range of males is probably between 2,000–4,000 birds. Threats include reduced winter feeding when permanent pasture is converted to arable use, and free-range dog walking in forests. However, the current wet summers may help chick survival by maintaining their invertebrate food supplies on the forest floor, as should the increase in deciduous trees planted in new and restocked forests.

Author: *Ian Suttie*

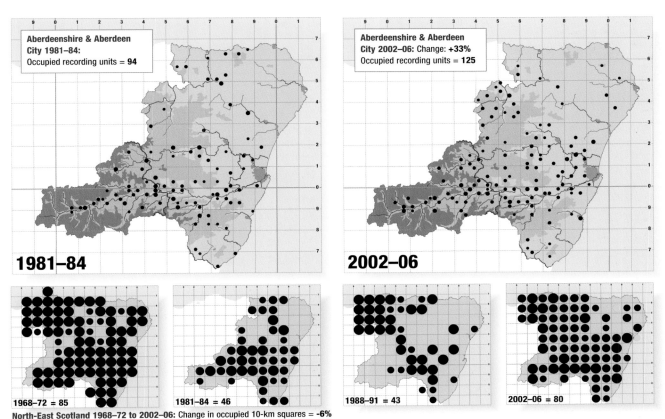

1981–84   Aberdeenshire & Aberdeen City 1981–84: Occupied recording units = 94

2002–06   Aberdeenshire & Aberdeen City 2002–06: Change: +33% Occupied recording units = 125

1968–72 = 85   1981–84 = 46   1988–91 = 43   2002–06 = 80

North-East Scotland 1968–72 to 2002–06: Change in occupied 10-km squares = -6%

Black-tailed Godwit

Limosa limosa

Occasional in breeding habitat. Passage migrant. Estimated population in North-East Scotland: **0 pairs**

Red list; Schedule 1; UK and Scottish BAP lists

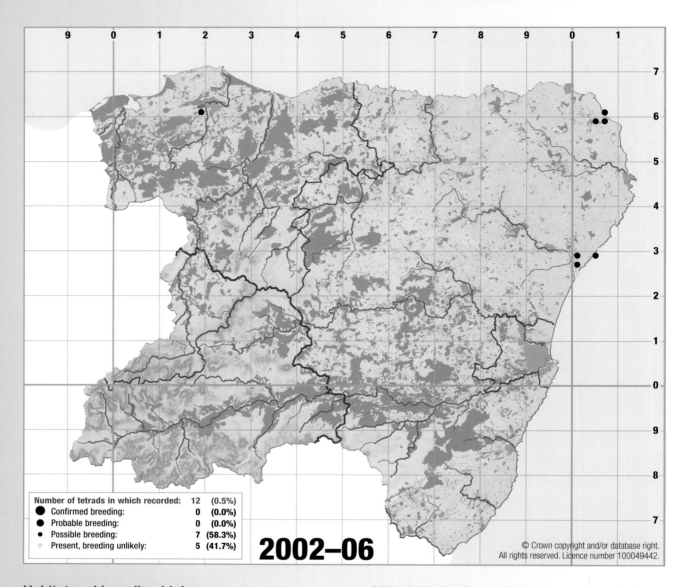

Number of tetrads in which recorded:	12	(0.5%)
● Confirmed breeding:	0	(0.0%)
● Probable breeding:	0	(0.0%)
• Possible breeding:	7	(58.3%)
· Present, breeding unlikely:	5	(41.7%)

2002–06

Habitat and breeding biology

In Britain, Black-tailed Godwits of nominate race *limosa* breed in lowland wet grasslands such as poorly drained marginal farmland. Birds breeding in northern Scotland, considered to be of the Iceland race *islandica*, occupy fens or small marshes, often at the edge of moorland (E. Meek, P. Ellis pers. comm.). These birds usually return to their breeding grounds in late April or early May and 3–4 eggs are laid from mid May onwards (Hatton in *BS3*).

Scottish distribution and status

Black-tailed Godwits are primarily passage migrants and there is a small but increasing winter population. The first confirmed successful breeding in Scotland was in Caithness in 1946, followed by Shetland in 1949 and Orkney in 1973. Today the breeding population is largely confined to the Northern Isles with around 5–11 pairs annually (Hatton in *BS3*).

Distribution and status in North-East Scotland

In spring, in Aberdeenshire, Black-tailed Godwits are annual migrants in small numbers on the Ythan estuary and at Loch of Strathbeg, with peak counts of 39 in 2002

and 37 in 2003. Smaller numbers are seen along the Moray coast, with Findhorn Bay the most favoured site. Although most flocks move quickly on, a few birds pause for longer, especially at the Loch of Strathbeg where fen-type habitats could perhaps support a future breeding attempt. Autumn passage is more protracted, between July and October, and involves greater numbers of birds; the largest flocks seen during 2002–06 were 160 in Findhorn Bay in July 2006 (*MNBR* 2006) and 136 on the Ythan estuary in September 2002 (*NESBR* 2002). During 1975–1984, flocks of ten or more were seen only twice in spring and twice in autumn (*NES 1st Atlas*) so it would appear that the species has increased substantially in North-East Scotland since that time.

Author: *Dominic Funnell*

See photograph on page 123.

Whimbrel

Numenius phaeopus

Occasional in breeding habitat. Passage migrant. Estimated population in North-East Scotland: 0 pairs

Red list; Schedule 1

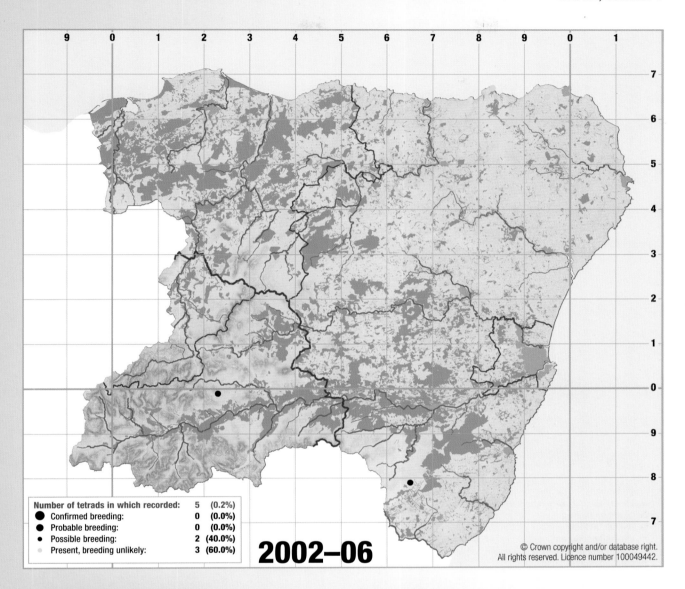

Number of tetrads in which recorded:	5	(0.2%)
● Confirmed breeding:	0	(0.0%)
● Probable breeding:	0	(0.0%)
• Possible breeding:	2	(40.0%)
○ Present, breeding unlikely:	3	(60.0%)

2002–06

Habitat and breeding biology

The habitat of the main Scottish breeding population, in Shetland, includes heathlands, blanket bog and grazed acid grassland. Here, birds arrive back on territory from the last week in April and into May. The usual clutch consists of four eggs and the first chicks hatch in the third week of June. Most territories are vacated by the first week in August (Ellis in *BS3*).

Scottish distribution and status

The Scottish Whimbrel population was estimated, in 2007, at 400–500 pairs. Of these, over 95% are found in Shetland, with a few pairs in Orkney, the Outer Hebrides and the far north of the mainland. The evidence suggests that breeding numbers are declining (Ellis in *BS3*).

Distribution and status in North-East Scotland

Whimbrels are primarily migrants, passing through North-East Scotland on their way to northerly breeding grounds including Iceland, Scandinavia and north-west Russia. Spring passage is generally light, peaking in the first half of May, while far larger numbers move through in late summer with the main concentration during mid July–late

August. Most passage birds follow the coast although individuals and small groups are occasionally seen or heard passing over the uplands. As far as is known, Whimbrels have never attempted to breed in North-East Scotland. Buckland *et al.* (1990) state that a few birds have been recorded "very rarely in suitable breeding habitat in summer" but give no further detail. During 2002–06 there were two records of single adults in apparently suitable breeding habitat. In 2003 a bird was calling for several minutes on Arnbarrow Hill near Cairn o' Mount on 18th May and in 2005, on 29th May, a bird dropped in and displayed mildly at Tom a'Bhealaidh, north of Balmoral; nothing could be found here on 12th June. A breeding attempt in North-East Scotland is not impossible but under current circumstances seems unlikely.

Author: *Martin Cook*

See photograph on page 123.

Curlew

Numenius arquata

Common migrant breeder. Winter visitor and passage migrant. Estimated population in North-East Scotland: *3,000–5,000 pairs* (7% of Scottish population, 4% of UK)

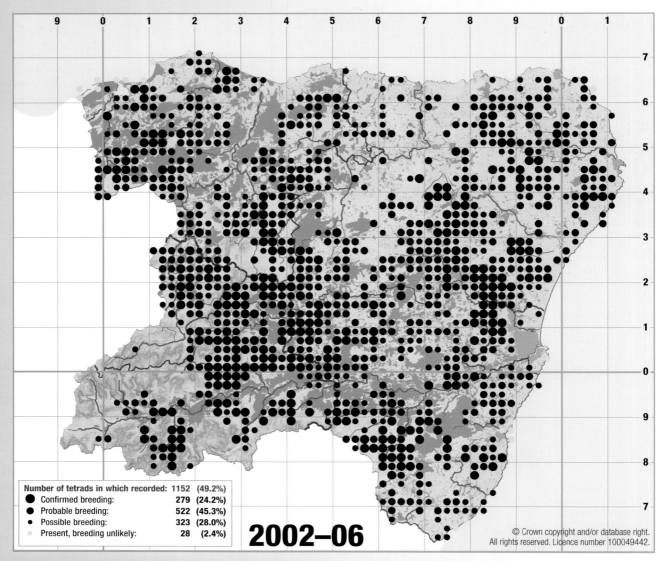

Number of tetrads in which recorded:	1152	(49.2%)
● Confirmed breeding:	279	(24.2%)
● Probable breeding:	522	(45.3%)
• Possible breeding:	323	(28.0%)
Present, breeding unlikely:	28	(2.4%)

2002–06

Curlew, Fair Isle, July 2007. © Paul Baxter

Habitat and breeding biology

The Curlew is a widespread breeding bird, favouring the stock-farmed uplands where rushy pastures, Heather moorland, peat mosses and unimproved grassland provide moist feeding habitats. At lower levels it also nests in improved grassland down to near the coast and may use arable land. Pre-breeding flocks gather on low ground with suitable feeding in late February then head inland, weather permitting, to reach traditional breeding localities during March. After courtship, which includes the male's melodious display flights, clutches are completed by early May and the eggs hatch after about 28 days. Both parents tend the young, though adult females may leave the breeding areas first, the males and young birds following to the coast during July.

Scottish distribution and status

In 1988–91, Curlews were present in almost 90% of all Scottish 10-km squares (*BTO 2nd Atlas*) and a survey in farmed land found them present in 59% of randomly selected 1-km squares on the mainland (O`Brien *et al.* 2002). High breeding densities occur in southern and eastern Scotland as far north as Caithness and the Northern Isles, where there is an abundance of unimproved moorland and wetland, but Curlews are absent from the less fertile

Curlew, Sutherland, May 1999. © *Ed Duthie*

and mountainous parts of the north and west Highlands and the Outer Hebrides. The Scottish breeding population is estimated to contain *c.*58,800 pairs (Bainbridge in *BS3*).

Distribution and status in North-East Scotland

During 2002–06, Curlews either probably or certainly bred in every complete 10-km square in North-East Scotland, the favoured areas being the damp grasslands of central Aberdeenshire, the moors and high pastures of upper Donside and westwards to Glenlivet and Strath Avon. Gaps in distribution occur where there are commercial forests *e.g.* the Spey valley, south-west of Huntly, Fetteresso and Deeside. Other gaps occur where intensive agriculture follows the river valleys of the Deveron and Ythan. The highest breeding densities were in the altitude range 250–450 m but the species was recorded from sea level to

around 600 m in the hills, where breeding was confirmed near the Glenshee ski area and near Faindouran Lodge in Glen Avon. Many other territories at 400–500 m were occupied in Glen Ey, Glen Derry and the Gairn valley.

Changes in distribution

Since 1968–72, the distribution in terms of occupied 10-km squares has remained virtually unchanged. In Aberdeenshire/Aberdeen City there was a small decline in terms of occupied recording units from 1981–84 to 2002–06. It is possible that birds in cereal farming areas benefited for almost 20 years from the presence of uncut grass under the set-aside scheme; with the ending of this scheme in 2007, they may persist in the new crops as Baxter & Rintoul (1953) noted when Curlews lost traditional grassland sites to war-time ploughing.

Population and trends

Population densities ranging from 1–10+ pairs were estimated for 45 tetrads in North-East Scotland during 2002–06, with an average density of 2.6 pairs/tetrad. Applying this density to the 1,127 tetrads where breeding was considered to be at least possible suggests a total population of 2,930 pairs. In a number of instances, however, tetrad densities were given as minima, so this could be an underestimate of the population, which may therefore be more safely placed within the range of 3,000–5,000 pairs. O'Brien (1994) estimated 3,550 pairs for the lowlands, with wide confidence limits, in 1992–93. BBS data for Scotland as a whole reveal a population decline of 48% between 1994–2007 (Risely *et al.* 2008) and this trend is supported by that observed in the limited number of BBS squares which hold Curlews in North-East Scotland. Many factors could be causing this decrease: intensification of agriculture, upland afforestation, drainage of wetlands, reduced hill livestock numbers and increased predation by Foxes and the crow family.

Author: *Ian Suttie*

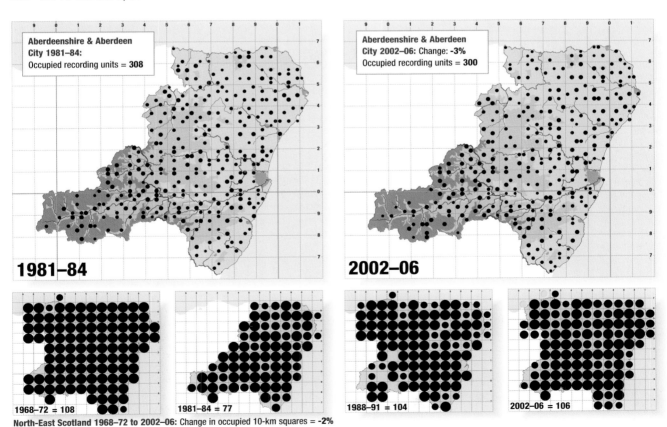

Aberdeenshire & Aberdeen City 1981–84:
Occupied recording units = **308**

1981–84

1968–72 = 108   1981–84 = 77

Aberdeenshire & Aberdeen City 2002–06: Change: **-3%**
Occupied recording units = **300**

2002–06

1988–91 = 104   2002–06 = 106

North-East Scotland 1968–72 to 2002–06: Change in occupied 10-km squares = **-2%**

Common Sandpiper

Actitis hypoleucos

Common summer migrant breeder. Passage migrant. Estimated population in North-East Scotland: **1,100–1,200 pairs** (5% of Scottish population, <5% of UK)

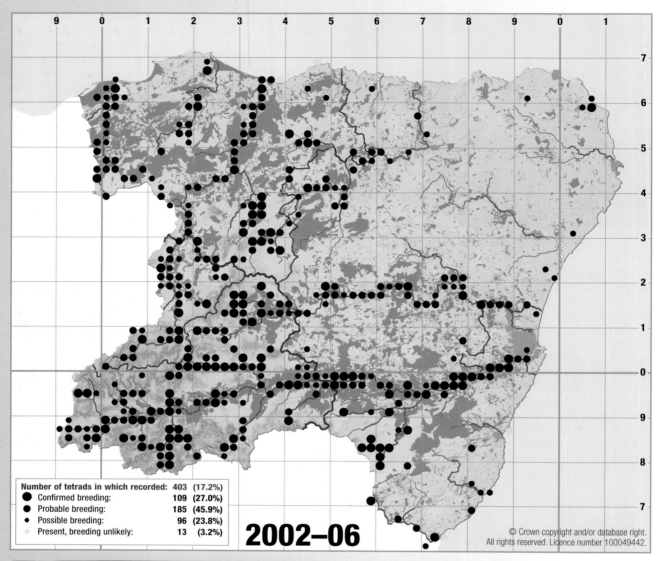

Number of tetrads in which recorded:	403	(17.2%)
● Confirmed breeding:	109	(27.0%)
● Probable breeding:	185	(45.9%)
● Possible breeding:	96	(23.8%)
Present, breeding unlikely:	13	(3.2%)

2002–06

Common Sandpiper, Loch Kinord, June 2008. © *Harry Scott*

Habitat and breeding biology

During the breeding season, Common Sandpipers are closely associated with rivers, burns and lochs. They are particularly common in upland riparian and loch-side locations with birds present up to 660 m altitude. Occupied waterways are usually shallow or with broken water and also with a shallow gradient. Nest sites are usually set back from the riverbank in short vegetation and nests may be hidden by grass tufts or overhanging branches. Birds usually arrive inland at breeding sites in mid to late April and the breeding sites are usually vacated by mid to late July.

Scottish distribution and status

Common Sandpipers are widely distributed across upland Scotland but are very scarce or absent from the slow-flowing rivers of the agricultural lowlands of eastern Scotland. Particularly high densities are found in the north-west and in the Outer Hebrides (Dougall & Yaldon in *BS3*). They are commonly found on the coast during spring and (especially) autumn passage periods. The Scottish population was estimated at 19,000–24,000 pairs in 2007. Since the 1950s the breeding range in Scotland has generally contracted (Dougall & Yaldon in *BS3*) and BBS data indicate a 14% population decline during 1994–2007 (Risely *et al.* 2008).

Distribution and status in North-East Scotland

The distribution of Common Sandpipers in North-East Scotland mirrors the distribution of the main rivers and their tributaries. In particular there are strong breeding populations along the Rivers Dee and Don where breeding birds occur from near the river mouths right up to high altitudes in the Cairngorm mountains. Birds are present but less common in the lower reaches of the Rivers Deveron and North Esk but numbers increase in the upper reaches of these rivers. Breeding pairs are common along the lower sections of the Rivers Lossie, Spey and Findhorn - even breeding on the estuaries of the Spey and Findhorn. Common Sandpipers are conspicuously scarce breeders in the north-east corner of the region, which includes the Ugie and Ythan river systems. The habitat in this area is more agricultural and lower lying than much of the rest of the North-East region. Factors which may effect Common Sandpiper occupation in this area are intensive grazing of river margins, decreased water quality and increased disturbance.

Changes in distribution

There was an apparent contraction in the distribution of Common Sandpipers in North-East Scotland between 1968–72 and 1981–84. For example, of six 10-km squares in Buchan where breeding was confirmed in 1968–72 none yielded evidence of breeding in 1981–84 (Buckland *et al.* 1990). However, data from 2002–06 suggest that the breeding range of the Common Sandpiper may have recently expanded - the distribution of breeding records has increased in the lower Don, Dee and North Esk. In 1981–84, no breeding records were recorded from within 3 km of the mouth of the River Dee. In 2002–06 there were many more breeding records on the Deveron around Huntly and breeding took place again at Loch of Strathbeg. Increases in Common Sandpiper distribution in these areas is likely to be due to positive changes in water quality, agricultural practices or riverside disturbance.

Population and trends

There is no detailed survey information available for the Common Sandpiper in North-East Scotland, so only a broad estimate of breeding population size can be made. During 1999–2006, pairs were counted along eight stretches of river in Moray (totalling 35 km), including the Avon, Spey, Lossie and Findhorn, as well as the Dorback and Builg Burns (*MNBRs*). The mean density was 1.5 pairs/km. Data collected in 2002–06 data indicated that breeding was at least possible in 389 tetrads. On the assumption that 2 km of waterway flow through each occupied tetrad, and applying an average density of 1.5 pairs/km, then the North-East Scotland population may lie in the range 1,100–1,200 pairs. There is no evidence to determine whether the North-East has shared in the recent Scottish population decline.

Author: *Shaila Rao*

Common Sandpiper, Dinnet, May 2005. © *Harry Scott*

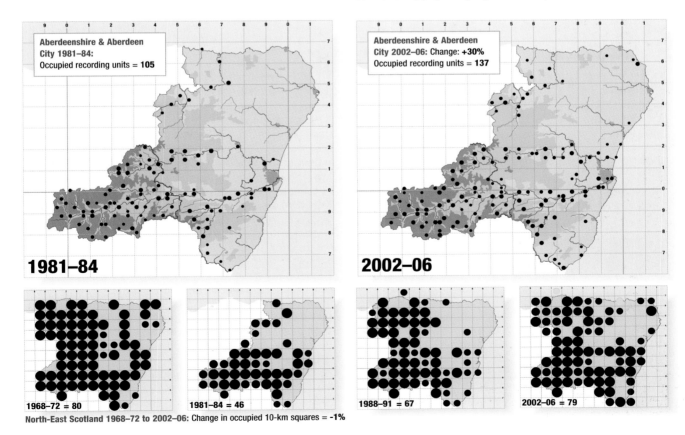

Aberdeenshire & Aberdeen City 1981–84:
Occupied recording units = **105**

1981–84

Aberdeenshire & Aberdeen City 2002–06: Change: **+30%**
Occupied recording units = **137**

2002–06

1968–72 = 80   1981–84 = 46   1988–91 = 67   2002–06 = 79

North-East Scotland 1968–72 to 2002–06: Change in occupied 10-km squares = **-1%**

Greenshank

Tringa nebularia

Occasional in breeding habitat, former breeder. Passage migrant. Estimated population in North-East Scotland: usually **0 pairs** (last bred 1996)

Schedule 1

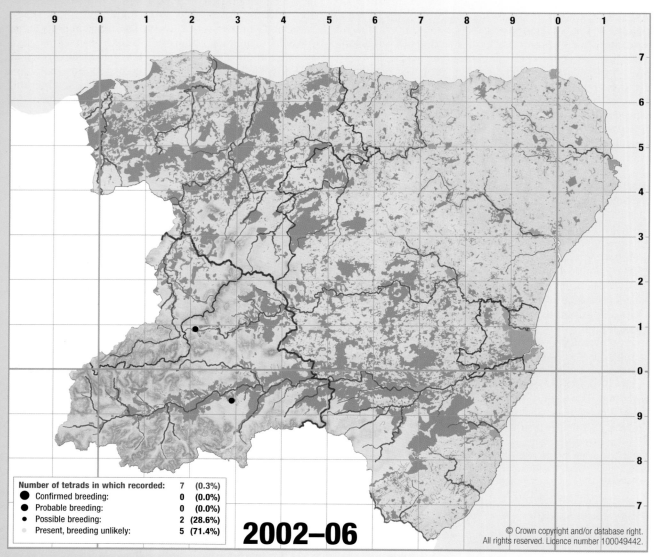

Number of tetrads in which recorded: 7 (0.3%)
- ● Confirmed breeding: 0 (0.0%)
- ● Probable breeding: 0 (0.0%)
- • Possible breeding: 2 (28.6%)
- · Present, breeding unlikely: 5 (71.4%)

2002–06

Habitat and breeding biology

Most Greenshanks in Scotland breed on peatlands - either extensive blanket bog with thick peat or boulder-strewn thin peat (Thompson in *BS3*). In North-East Scotland they were mostly in terrain with hillocks formed by glaciers or glacial rivers. Here, the hillocks dammed water to form present-day lochs and pools, and the nearby stony streams and fertile alluvium provided good feeding. A few pairs on such terrain nested near big pines and a very few elsewhere on blanket bog.

Greenshank, Borgie, May 1998. © *Ed Duthie*

Scottish distribution and status

In Scotland, Greenshanks are widely distributed as breeders on moorland, particularly north of the Great Glen, although there are outlying populations in Inverness-shire and north Perthshire (Thompson in *BS3*). The national population was estimated at 730–1,480 territories in 1995 (Hancock *et al.* 1997), considered to be an increase on numbers estimated in the late 1960s, and thought to have stabilised, though with local declines and fluctuations (Thompson in *BS3*).

Status and distribution in North-East Scotland

Greenshanks in North-East Scotland are at the eastern margin of their Scottish distribution as breeding birds (Nethersole-Thompson & Nethersole-Thompson 1979). There were only two records of possible breeding during 2002–06, one in Strath Don and one near Ballater. In both cases these involved single birds in or near suitable breeding habitat. Passage birds occur at inland locations in both spring and autumn.

Changes in distribution

The first records of breeding in North-East Scotland were in the 1920s and breeding Greenshanks were probably absent before then. By the late 1940s, small numbers bred in upper Deeside. The only annual study there, in 1969–73, was by

Robert Moss, whose notes were published by Nethersole-Thompson & Nethersole-Thompson (1979). In mid Deeside, there were records from 1976, and two pairs reared young in 1980 and one pair in 1981 (*NES 1st Atlas*; Jenkins & Chapman 2007). Deeside birds decreased greatly in the 1970s and 1980s. The last known breeding records were in 1992 in upper Deeside and 1996 in mid Deeside, and all former haunts have now been abandoned. Possible causes are fewer aquatic invertebrates owing to acidic pollution, overgrazing and trampling by increased Red Deer numbers, more Sheep Ticks (owing to increased deer), fewer of the wide muirburn fires that characterised deer-forest management in the 1940s and 1950s, disturbance by more tourists, predation (by increased numbers of crows, gulls, Foxes and Mink), and reforestation involving dense tall Heather with trees and scrub.

Population and trends

Numbers in upper Deeside reached at least 17 pairs in the late 1940s (A. Watson, unpublished collation of evidence). Writing of the Cairngorms massif between Aviemore and Braemar, Watson (1966) stated that most glens had one or two pairs each, although there were fewer in the mid 1960s on the Dee side of the hills than in the 1940s. Breeding birds declined further to 10 pairs in 1973, and observations revealed only one pair in 1988 and three later years to 1996. They are now absent. Although the habitat in some places seems suitable, Greenshanks now appear to have declined to extinction as breeding birds in North-East Scotland, as illustrated in the atlases.

Author: *Adam Watson*

Greenshank, Borgie, May 1996. © *Ed Duthie*

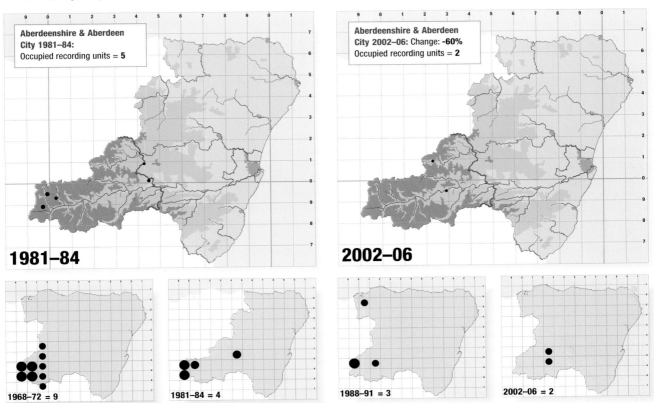

Aberdeenshire & Aberdeen City 1981–84:
Occupied recording units = 5

1981–84

Aberdeenshire & Aberdeen City 2002–06: Change: **-60%**
Occupied recording units = **2**

2002–06

1968–72 = 9

1981–84 = 4

1988–91 = 3

2002–06 = 2

North-East Scotland 1968–72 to 2002–06: Change in occupied 10-km squares = -78%

Redshank

Tringa totanus

Scarce resident and migrant breeder. Winter visitor and passage migrant. Estimated population in North-East Scotland: *100–200 pairs* (1% of Scottish population, <1% of UK)

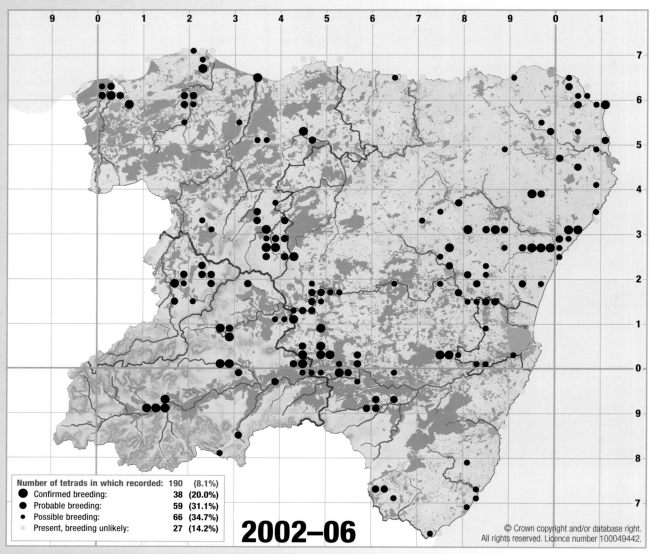

Number of tetrads in which recorded:	190	(8.1%)
Confirmed breeding:	38	(20.0%)
Probable breeding:	59	(31.1%)
Possible breeding:	66	(34.7%)
Present, breeding unlikely:	27	(14.2%)

2002–06

Redshank, Iceland, June 2007. © *Sam Alexander*

Habitat and breeding biology

Redshanks return to their breeding areas from March onwards, when records of displaying birds are usually first reported each year. They require wetter fields than other waders such as Lapwing and Curlew, though the timing of their breeding is similar, with egg laying in April and early May, and most chicks hatching in late May and early June. By early July the birds have started to leave the breeding areas and flocks start to build up in coastal locations such as the Ythan estuary. There is some evidence that at least some of these North-East breeders move south-east as far as the Wash and south-west to north-west England and north Wales (Clark 2002).

Scottish distribution and status

The Redshank is considered a widespread and relatively common breeding species across Scotland with the main strongholds in Orkney, Shetland and the Outer Hebrides, especially on the Uists where breeding densities up to 15 pairs/km² have been found. On the mainland, average densities are 2 pairs/km² on damp pasture, 0.7 pairs/km² on rough grazing and only 0.2 pairs/km² on the Caithness Flows. The Scottish breeding population is estimated at 11,700–15,500 pairs (Thompson in *BS3*).

Redshank, Forvie, May 1976. © *John Massie*

Distribution and status in North-East Scotland

The main strongholds for breeding Redshanks in North-East Scotland are wet fields along the main rivers, especially the Dee, Don, Ythan and Deveron. Rather fewer breed in coastal fields and marshes. There is a small scattering across some of the wet areas within the intensive arable farmland of the Buchan plain and some find breeding areas within the margin between the coastal zone and the more intensive agriculture. Some pairs attempt to breed on silage fields near early wet patches but are, like Lapwing, seldom successful because of early rolling. Other pairs are thinly distributed across North-East Scotland in upland grazing areas and rough pasture around the main mountain fringe, where these areas are sufficiently poorly drained to include wet ground (*e.g.* in fields around Cabrach and Corgarff).

Changes in distribution

There has been a substantial retraction of occupied range since 1981–84, with the greatest changes in the north-west and south-west of the area. In the 16 10-km squares west of Fraserburgh and north of Huntly, the number of occupied recording units dropped from 21 in 1981–84 to only five in 2002–06. In the 13 10-km squares west of Ballater the drop was from 16 to four occupied recording units - a decline of 75%. A smaller, but still substantial, decline in occupied recording units in the main river valleys means that, overall, only 87 occupied units were found during 2002–06 compared with 136 during 1981–84, a decline of 36% in the area occupied by breeding Redshanks. The distribution of coastal pairs seems to have remained more stable since 1981–84.

Population and trends

A summary of the comments on tetrad record cards submitted for this atlas suggests that an average of 1.3 pairs/occupied tetrad was found in 22 tetrads during 2002–06. Applying this average density to the 97 tetrads in which breeding was probable or confirmed in the same period, suggests a total population of around 126 pairs. Allowing also for a number of pairs in the 'possible breeding' tetrads, it is probably safe to say that the population lies within the range of 100–200 pairs. In view of the range retraction described above, it is clear that Redshanks have declined markedly in North-East Scotland in line with the trend elsewhere. BBS data for the UK suggest a 12% decline nationally during 1994–2007 (Risely *et al.* 2008). O'Brien (1994) estimated 150 pairs (confidence limits 1–450) in lowland North-East Scotland in 1992–93; in view of recent declines it seems possible that at that time numbers were in fact at the higher end of his range.

Author: *Hugh Insley*

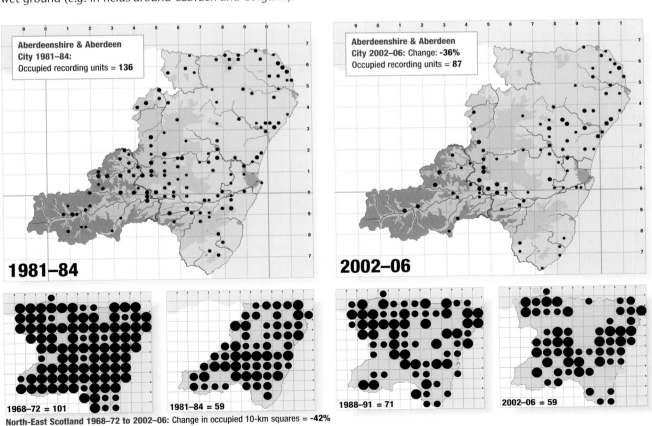

Aberdeenshire & Aberdeen City 1981–84: Occupied recording units = **136**

1981–84

Aberdeenshire & Aberdeen City 2002–06: Change: **-36%** Occupied recording units = **87**

2002–06

1968–72 = 101   1981–84 = 59   1988–91 = 71   2002–06 = 59

North-East Scotland 1968–72 to 2002–06: Change in occupied 10-km squares = -42%

Kittiwake

Rissa tridactyla

Very common resident and migrant breeder. Passage migrant. Estimated population in North-East Scotland: **70,000 pairs** (25% of Scottish population, 18% of UK)

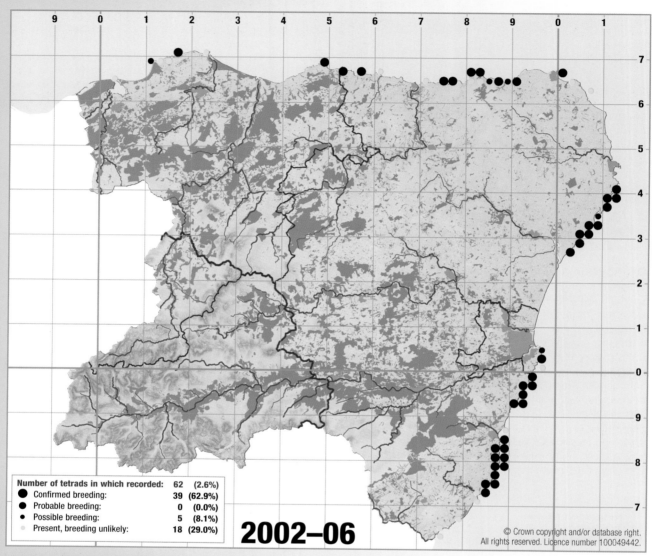

Number of tetrads in which recorded:	62	(2.6%)
● Confirmed breeding:	39	(62.9%)
● Probable breeding:	0	(0.0%)
● Possible breeding:	5	(8.1%)
Present, breeding unlikely:	18	(29.0%)

2002–06

Habitat and breeding biology

Kittiwakes breed colonially on sea cliffs and very occasionally on buildings. Birds appear at the colonies from the end of February, with nest building commencing in late April. Up to three eggs are laid from mid May onwards, although this may be delayed into June if food supplies are scarce. Incubation takes 25–32 days and fledging occurs five to six weeks after hatching (Heubeck in *BS3*). Colonies are usually deserted by the end of August although large numbers can still be found roosting on piers and beaches at this time. Otherwise the Kittiwake is a pelagic species.

Scottish distribution and status

Colonies exist around much of the Scottish coast although only thinly on the west of the mainland. The largest colonies are on the high sea cliffs of the Northern Isles, and north and east coasts. Kittiwakes increased in numbers throughout most of the 20th century but there has been a significant recent decline (Heubeck in *BS3*). This decline has been strtongest in the Northern Isles where, between 1985–88 and1998–2002, the number of breeding pairs fell by 41% (from 125,788 to 74,400), compared with 11% for the rest of Scotland (from 233,637 to 207,813) (Seabird Colony Register, Seabird 2000). The total Scottish

population was last censused in 1998–2002, when 282,213 apparently occupied nests were found (Seabird 2000).

Distribution and status in North-East Scotland

Kittiwakes can be found breeding almost continuously along the east coast between Inverbervie and Stonehaven, from Newtonhill almost to the City of Aberdeen, and from Forvie to Boddam. In all these areas the cliffs are at least 30 m high offering the greatest protection from predators as well as an abundance of suitable nesting sites. Colonies along the north Aberdeenshire and Moray coasts tend to be smaller and more scattered, reflecting the coastal topography. The first use of a man-made structure as a nesting site in the North-East appears to be at Fraserburgh where there is a small colony of 20–30 pairs on the south pier at the entrance to the harbour (R. Duncan pers. comm.). Large colonies at the high cliffs of Troup Head, Bullers of Buchan and Fowlsheugh hold the majority of pairs. Success at these colonies varies; whilst numbers declined at Fowlsheugh between 1970 and 1986, colonies elsewhere along the east coast increased (Buckland *et al*. 1990).

Changes in distribution

Despite the 12% decrease in apparently occupied nests in North-East Scotland between 1985–88 (Seabird Colony Register) and 1998–2002 (Seabird 2000), Kittiwakes have expanded their breeding range in our region, occupying 22 recording units in Aberdeenshire/Aberdeen City in 2002–06 compared with 18 in 1981–84. Along the north Aberdeenshire coast three new colonies have appeared including the one on the harbour pier at Fraserburgh. The picture is mixed along the east Aberdeenshire and Kincardine coasts, with birds abandoning sites in three recording areas yet colonising four new ones. In Moray, the colonies at Covesea and Portknockie have been occupied since at least the mid 20th century and the only new breeding site since then is at Burghead where a few pairs have nested intermittently since 1993 (*MNBRs*). Decreasing food availability or increased predation may both cause movement between colonies or to new ones (Heubeck in *BS3*).

Population and trends

The general increase which occurred throughout most of the last century may be partly explained by the cessation of shooting and egg collecting as well as the fishery expansion (Lloyd *et al.* 1991). The North-East Kittiwake population (apparently occupied nests) was counted during three national seabird censuses. In 1969–1970 there were 66,910 (Operation Seafarer), in 1985–88 there were 80,525 (Seabird Colony Register) and in 1998–2002 there were 70,843 (Seabird 2000). Nationally, the population increased by 4% between the first two surveys and then decreased by 21% between the second and third compared with an increase of 20% and a decrease of 12% in the North-East. In the late 1980s, as the Shetland population decreased, numbers in Orkney increased and there is evidence that the same happened here - over 110,000 apparently occupied nests were counted at just the three main colonies in 1992. The recent decline is most likely to be due to a decrease in food availability during the breeding season. There is a growing consensus that this is linked to climate and oceanographic changes (Heubeck in *BS3*). Numbers at the key colonies continued their decline through 2007 (R. Mavor pers. comm.). At the two Moray colonies (Covesea and Portknockie) numbers have fluctuated from year to year but show a general increase throughout the last fifteen years, to 800 nests in 2009 (*MNBRs*).

Author: *Richard Schofield*

Kittiwake, Crawton, May 2008. © *Ed Duthie*

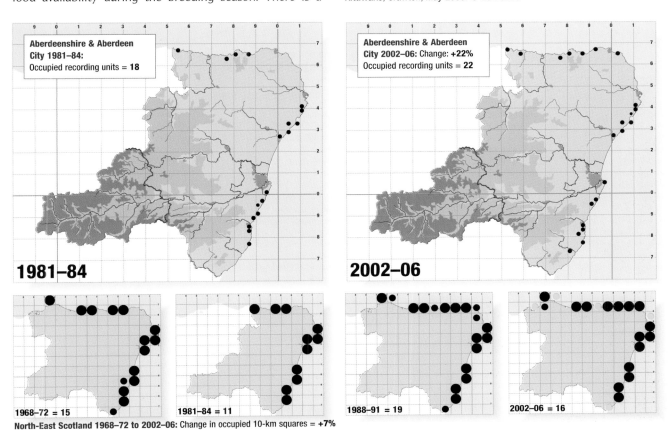

Aberdeenshire & Aberdeen City 1981–84:
Occupied recording units = **18**

1981–84

Aberdeenshire & Aberdeen City 2002–06: Change: **+22%**
Occupied recording units = **22**

2002–06

1968–72 = 15

1981–84 = 11

1988–91 = 19

2002–06 = 16

North-East Scotland 1968–72 to 2002–06: Change in occupied 10-km squares = **+7%**

Black-headed Gull   *Chroicocephalus ridibundus*

Common resident and migrant breeder. Winter visitor and passage migrant. Estimated breeding population in North-East Scotland: ***1,000–2,500 pairs*** (4% of Scottish population, 1% UK)   Amber list

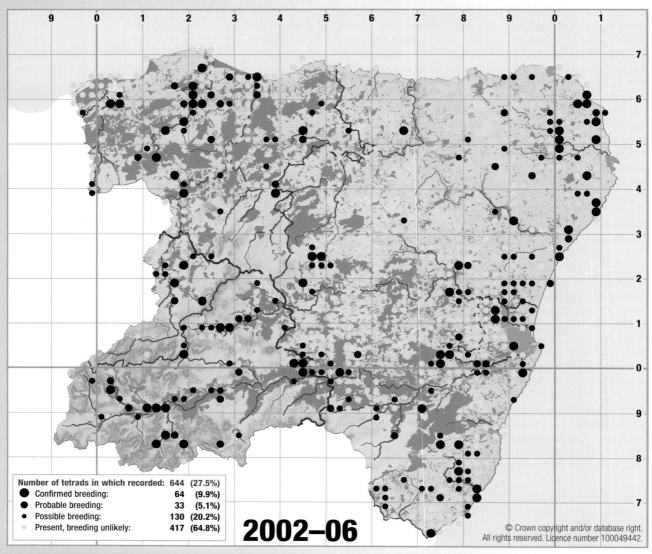

Number of tetrads in which recorded:	644	(27.5%)
● Confirmed breeding:	64	(9.9%)
● Probable breeding:	33	(5.1%)
● Possible breeding:	130	(20.2%)
○ Present, breeding unlikely:	417	(64.8%)

2002–06

Black-headed Gull, Banffshire, 1980s. © *John Edelsten*

Habitat and breeding biology

In North-East Scotland, Black-headed Gulls nest inland and coastally. Most inland colonies are at low altitudes in marshes, on islands in lochs or on river shingles. Others, however, breed on higher ground, occasionally with other gulls, on mosses and upland heaths. Coastal colonies are mostly in sand dunes or on flat ground in undisturbed, fenced enclosures. Breeding areas are occupied from late February onwards, later in the uplands than near the coast. The clutch of 2–3 eggs is laid from late April with most young fledging in late June or early July (Tasker in *BS3*).

Scottish distribution and status

Colonies are found in most parts of Scotland from south-west, central and eastern areas to the Outer Hebrides and the Northern Isles. Breeding does not take place, however, in the north-west Highlands (Tasker in *BS3*). In 1969–70 there were estimated to be 18,226 pairs along the Scottish coast, in 1985–88 9,554 pairs along the coast and 25,105 inland, and in 1998–2002 there were 6,888 pairs along the coast, and 36,303 inland. Combined totals were therefore 34,659 in 1985–88 and 43,191 in 1998–2002 (Mitchell *et al.* 2004, Tasker in *BS3*). The most recent survey, at least, missed many of the inland sites on Deeside reported by

The Breeding Birds of North-East Scotland

Buckland *et al.* (1990) and which were still present during 2002–06, though reduced in size.

Distribution and status in North-East Scotland

Black-headed Gull colonies are scattered over much of the North-East, but most commonly in lowland marshes, along river valleys and close to the coast. They avoid cliff-bound coastlines and most coastal colonies are at river mouths or in the dunes of the east coast. Away from colonies, feeding birds are encountered widely throughout the North-East, even occasionally in the mountains at altitudes approaching 1,000 m.

Changes in distribution

At the 10-km square level, the number of squares where breeding was considered to be at least possible has remained little changed since 1968–72 (*BTO 1st Atlas*). However, the number of squares where breeding was proved has fallen substantially from 55 in 1968–72 to 40 in 2002–06. At a more detailed scale, the number of recording units in Aberdeenshire/Aberdeen City where breeding was proved has changed very little since 1981–84 (*NES 1st Atlas*) but the distribution across the North-East has altered. In 1981–84, breeding was proved in 25 recording units in and around Deeside while in the same area in 2002–06 only 14 recording units held colonies. Conversely, the Buchan area between Newburgh and Fraserburgh held only five colonies in 1981–84 (assuming thorough coverage) but there were 11 in 2002–06.

Population and trends

There have been three national seabird surveys since the 1960s in which the North-East Scotland Black-headed Gull population was counted. In 1969–70 only coastal areas were counted, revealing 2,253 pairs (Operation Seafarer). In 1985–88 there were 1,999 coastal pairs and 723 inland (Seabird Colony Register) and in 1998–2002 there were 692 coastal pairs and 422 inland (Seabird 2000). These last counts, however, missed many, often large, colonies on

Deeside (*NES 1st Atlas*, pers. obs.). It is likely that the current population in the North-East lies in the range 1,000–2,500 pairs, but there is much uncertainty. Many colonies have declined in recent years. In Moray a colony at Darnaway fell from 1,375 in 1958 to 40 in 1990 (Cook 1992). On Deeside there were hundreds of pairs at the Lochs of Park and Leys in the 1970s which left following drainage in the 1980s. There were still hundreds into the 1990s at Kerloch and Finzean and Tillypronie, and thousands near Ordie between Loch Davan and the Black Moss in the Dinnet National Nature Reserve, which first declined slowly and then finally departed suddenly in 2003 (H. Kruuk pers. comm., pers. obs.). All the mid Deeside colonies were abandoned by 2006 (Jenkins & Chapman 2009). Elsewhere there have been up to 1,516 pairs on the Sands of Forvie and 900 on islands in the Loch of Strathbeg in 1999, 200 at Corgarff in 2000, over 100 regularly at Craig Castle, 450+ in Kirkhill Industrial Estate, Dyce in 1999 (which left following disturbance) and 68 in Aberdeen City in 2001 - but the numbers have fluctuated.

Various factors may be implicated in the decline. Changes in agriculture involving the use of pesticides and fertilisers, and the timing of crops, may be important for all gulls, and drainage and other developments have affected some colonies. At RAF Kinloss, 500 pairs were "discouraged" as a bird-strike hazard in the 1960s. While there has been some predation at colonies (probably by Mink or Foxes) the mortality has not been large, but the disturbance, especially at night and early in the season, may have been significant. The weather may also be important - the situation needs further study.

Author: *W.R.P. Bourne*

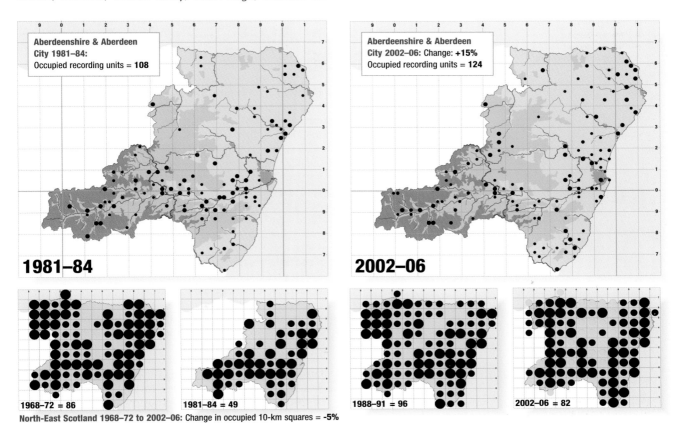

North-East Scotland 1968–72 to 2002–06: Change in occupied 10-km squares = -5%

Mediterranean Gull
Larus melanocephalus

Occasional possible breeder. Visitor in other seasons. Estimated population in North-East Scotland: **0 pairs**

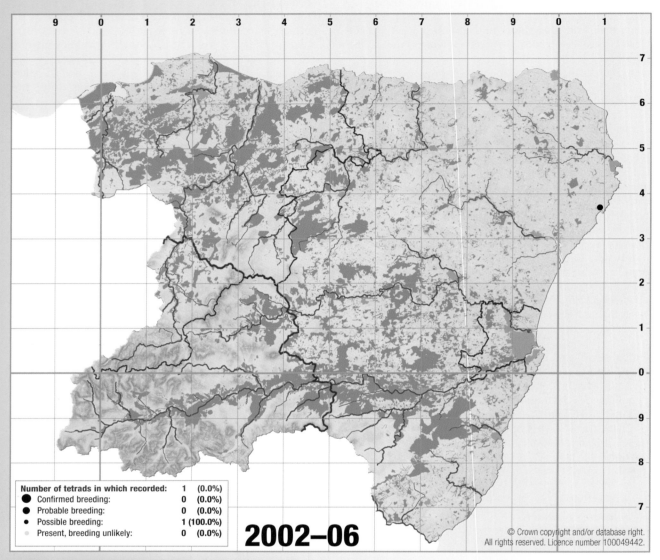

Number of tetrads in which recorded:	1	(0.0%)
● Confirmed breeding:	0	(0.0%)
● Probable breeding:	0	(0.0%)
• Possible breeding:	1	(100.0%)
Present, breeding unlikely:	0	(0.0%)

2002–06

Mediterranean Gull, Fife, March 2009. © *Mike Thrower*

Habitat and breeding biology

Mediterranean Gulls first nested in Britain in 1978 and there was a slow but steady increase over the next 20 years, with around 100 pairs in 2000. Between 2003–05 the pace of increase quickened and by 2005 there were 243–262 pairs (Holling *et al.* 2008). Most breeding takes place in Black-headed Gull colonies in coastal wetlands along the southern and eastern coasts of England between Hampshire and Norfolk. During the initial phase of colonisation there were regular instances of hybrid pairs with Black-headed Gulls, sometimes producing young. This was presumably a consequence of the difficulty experienced by pioneer individuals in locating a mate.

Scottish distribution and status

The first Scottish record of a Mediterranean Gull was in North-East Scotland, at Girdle Ness in October 1972. Since that time the species has become an increasingly frequent visitor with most birds seen between mid July and late April. Most records have come from the east coast and Ayrshire (Shaw in *BS3*). Breeding has never been proved in Scotland but single adults have been seen in Black-headed Gull colonies on four occasions and also in two Common Gull colonies (Shaw in *BS3*).

Common Gull colony, Tips of Corsemaul, July 2006. © *Nicky Penford* Mediterranean Gulls (left) have been seen in gull colonies on several occasions but breeding has not been confirmed.

Distribution and status in North-East Scotland

During the breeding season, single adult Mediterranean Gulls have been seen in gull colonies on five occasions. In 1986 and 1987, in the Correen Hills Common Gull colony, one bird appeared to have a territory and a nest, although eggs were never seen (M. Tasker pers. comm.). In 1997 one was associating with a Common Gull in a mixed colony of Black-headed and Common Gulls at Dyce on 23rd March (*NESBR* 1997) and the following year one was in the same colony on 30th May (*NESBR* 1998). Most recently, and during the Atlas period, one was seen on several dates apparently paired to a Black-headed Gull in a colony of that species at Cruden Bay. Breeding was not, however, proved (*NESBR* 2002). At other seasons, Mediterranean Gulls remain scarce but increasingly frequent visitors. It is to be hoped that this may lead eventually to successful breeding. This is most likely to be detected by a thorough annual examination of Black-headed Gull colonies.

Author: *Martin Cook*

Common Gull, Lecht, May 2009. © *Rab Rae*

Common Gull

Larus canus

Common resident. Winter visitor and passage migrant. Estimated population in North-East Scotland:
7,000–9,000 pairs (22% of Scottish population, <22% of UK)

Amber list

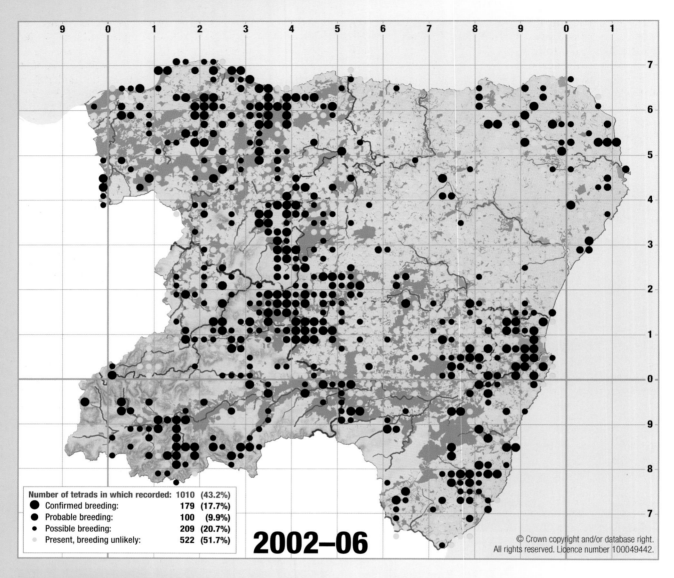

Number of tetrads in which recorded: 1010 (43.2%)
- ● Confirmed breeding: 179 (17.7%)
- ● Probable breeding: 100 (9.9%)
- ● Possible breeding: 209 (20.7%)
- ● Present, breeding unlikely: 522 (51.7%)

2002–06

© Crown copyright and/or database right.
All rights reserved. Licence number 100049442.

Habitat and breeding biology

Common Gulls breed on high heathy hilltops, lower mosses and Heather moorland, and around wet places at all levels including river shingles. Some disperse to hawk over high moorland, but most now feed on lower pasture after silage is cut, behind the plough on agricultural land and by scavenging along the shore. They have recently also started to nest in forest nurseries, on large buildings around distilleries, in towns and in the fenced enclosures associated with petroleum and gas developments and storage sites. Other nest sites have included rock-faces in quarries, graveyards and the tops of hedges. Upland breeding colonies are re-occupied from early March onwards, although birds move out if adverse weather returns. Clutches of 2–3 eggs are laid in late April–May and incubation lasts for 24–25 days. Colonies are abandoned as soon as the chicks fledge (Tasker in *BS3*).

Scottish distribution and status

Breeding areas are widespread in Scotland, mostly to the north of the central lowlands, and include the Outer Hebrides and the Northern Isles (Tasker in *BS3*). The largest colonies are in North-East Scotland on upland Heather moors surrounded by extensive agricultural land. The most recent

national survey of 1998–2002 found 20,467 nests near the coast and a further 27,646 inland - a total of 48,113 (Seabird 2000). Since that time, however, the main Mortlach Hills colonies have declined by *c*.12,000 nests. Due to the national importance of these colonies, this has probably reduced the estimated Scottish population to *c*.36,000 nests now.

Distribution and status in North-East Scotland

The traditional breeding sites in short Heather on the central Correen and Mortlach Hills may once have held some of the largest colonies in the world, numbering many thousands, in the 1980s (Bourne & Smith 1977, Tasker *et al.* 1991). Smaller colonies occur widely, especially in wet places in the hills and behind the north-west and north-east coasts, and on other outlying northern heathy hilltops and mosses (Bourne 2004, 2008). A few breed beside small rivers or on islands in lochs in the high uplands such as Loch Etchachan at 900 m. Birds were first reported nesting on rooftops in Altens Industrial Estate, Aberdeen, in 1984 (Sullivan 1985); there were 142 pairs in Aberdeen in 1993–95 and 280 in 1999–2002, with 27 in Elgin in 2000. In 2002, 15–20 pairs nested on Milne's High School in Fochabers and this colony has persisted; they have also colonised distillery warehouse roofs in Moray.

The Breeding Birds of North-East Scotland

Changes in distribution

The past status of this and other gulls is difficult to determine owing to wholesale misidentification (Holloway 1996). It was thought not to breed by Thomas Edward (1856–60). When Common Gulls were first reported in the Correen and Mortlach Hills in the 1880s they were said to have been present for about 15 years (Wilson 1890). They are reported by local people still to have been there in the 1940s, when many outlying hill sites were also found at Monaughty near Pluscarden, east past Wishach Hill, Aultmore, Ordiequish, Hill of Towie, The Balloch (over 1,000 pairs), Cuminestown, Greeness Hill, Waggle Hill (much reduced by egg-collecting since the 1930s), and Fetteresso (Watson 1998 and *in litt.*). They were also present on the Teindland and Fordyce Hills (A. J. M. Smith and M. J. Imber pers. comm.) and later the Moss of Dunphail among other places (Cook 1992). Some were also found on mosses at Mulben and Kellas Moor near Elgin at that time (Watson 1998), and at St Fergus Moss in 1972 (Bourne & Dixon 1974). Most of these birds have since been displaced by forestry and other development. They may have reinforced the central colonies - the population of the Correen Hills was reported to have increased five times between the 1940s and 1980s. This area was by then already half-afforested, and the rest overgrown, and the birds left after bad breeding seasons in the late 1990s. Some of these birds may have returned to a former site at Bluemill (Boultenstone)

Table 1. Estimated pairs of Common Gulls at larger North-East Scottish colonies (Tasker in Mitchell *et al.* 2004, Tasker in *BS3*, M. Smedley pers. comm., I. Francis pers.comm. (for Bluemill)). (*Survey methods have varied, and these numbers may not be directly comparable*)

	Correen Hills	Mortlach Hills	Bluemill	Total
1988–89	24,500	16,200	returning?	40,700
1995	6,400	21,700	2,200+	30,300
1998	extinct	17,900	3,200	21,100
2003	extinct	6,565	1,000	7,565+
2007–08	extinct	6,045	300	6,345+

(Bourne 2004, Tasker in Mitchell *et al.* 2004), but evidence for redistribution of birds between colonies is lacking.

Population and trends

Estimated numbers at the main colonies are given in Table 1. By 2000, the Mortlach Hills colony had declined considerably (pers. obs.); in 2003, there were 6,565 pairs and by 2007–08 numbers had dropped further, to 6,045 (M. Smedley pers. comm.). At Bluemill, a maximum of 1,500 birds was counted in 2005 although a nest or pair count was not undertaken (*NESBR* 2005). If we assume a total of 1,000–2,000 pairs elsewhere then a very rough estimate for the current North-East population might lie in the range 7,000–9,000 pairs. However, a detailed re-survey of the main Common Gull colonies is required, and there were indications that all the big colonies were reduced in numbers in 2009 following a series of bad breeding seasons (pers. obs.). A parallel decrease has occurred at the smaller colonies, the number of occupied 10-km squares where breeding was proved declining from 77 in 1968–72 (*BTO 1st Atlas*) to 48 in 1988–91 (*BTO 2nd Atlas*) and 60 in 2002–06. It is likely that incomplete observer coverage was a factor in 1988–91. It is also the case though that some new colonies have formed in recent years (*e.g.* Lecht ski area, *c.*200 pairs in 2009 and Tillypronie, *c.*500 pairs in 2009 and growing). However, these new sites are insufficient to compensate for losses at the main colonies.

The reasons for the general decline may be much the same as for the other gulls (Bourne 2008). Exposed nests on the higher hills often fail with bad weather early in the season, as on the Correen Hills in 1993 and 1994 before the birds left, and north Corsemaul in the Mortlach hills in 2007–09. There may be some adult mortality then, possibly due to exposure or botulism. Chicks may also starve later in the season during droughts, which may drive earthworms deep, and this was followed by mortality along the shore in 2004 (Bourne 2004).

Author: *W.R.P. Bourne*

See photographs on page 211.

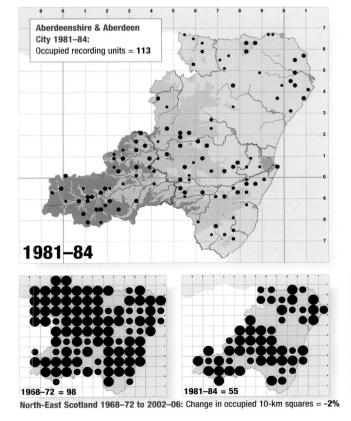

1981–84

1968–72 = 98   1981–84 = 55

North-East Scotland 1968–72 to 2002–06: Change in occupied 10-km squares = **-2%**

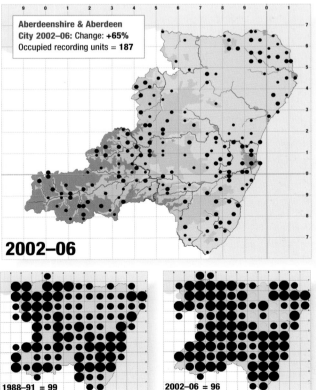

2002–06

1988–91 = 99   2002–06 = 96

Lesser Black-backed Gull

Larus fuscus

Scarce summer migrant breeder. Passage migrant. Estimated population in North-East Scotland: **200–300 pairs** (1% of Scottish population, <1% of UK

Amber list

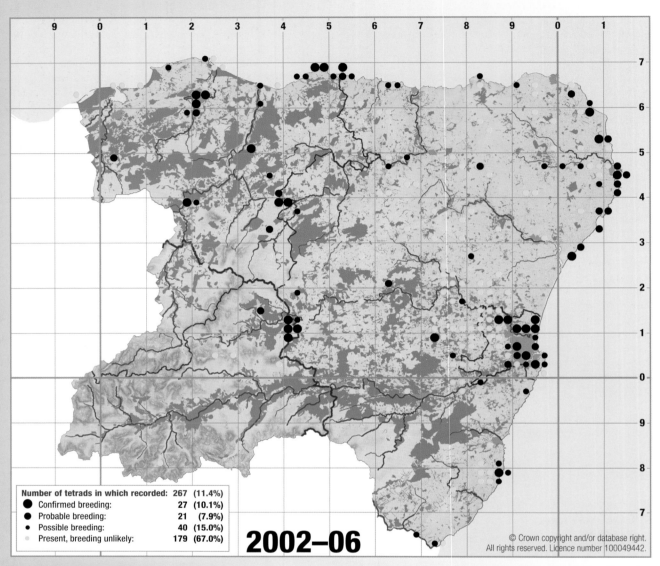

Number of tetrads in which recorded: 267 (11.4%)
- ● Confirmed breeding: 27 (10.1%)
- ● Probable breeding: 21 (7.9%)
- • Possible breeding: 40 (15.0%)
- ∙ Present, breeding unlikely: 179 (67.0%)

2002–06

Habitat and breeding biology
Lesser Black-backed Gulls breed along the coast and also inland on moorland, often in association with Common Gulls and a few Herring Gulls. In recent times they have nested on buildings, sometimes close to town centres, and on distillery warehouse roofs. Birds move back to the North-East from mid February onwards and most egg laying takes place in the second half of May.

Scottish distribution and status
The breeding range extends around most of the Scottish coast but numbers are largest in the south and west. During 1998–2002, the largest colonies (containing more than 500 pairs) were in Ayrshire, Dumfries & Galloway and around the Firth of Forth, with a large inland colony, of 2,270 pairs, at Loch Leven (Monaghan in *BS3*). The Scottish population has increased steadily over the last 40 years; on the coast there were 12,031 pairs in 1969–70, 19,524 in 1985–88 and 21,565 (with 3,492 inland) in 1998–2002 (Calladine in Mitchell *et al.* 2004, Monaghan in *BS3*).

Distribution and status in North-East Scotland
The Lesser Black-backed Gull has a restricted breeding range in the North-East, with proved breeding almost equally divided between coastal and inland tetrads. Coastal presence in 2002–06 was focussed around Findochty to Cullen, St. Fergus to Cruden Bay, and the Fowlsheugh seabird colony, south of Stonehaven. Coastal breeding also took place around Aberdeen but here the emphasis was on urban nesting within the city. Urban breeding is also well-established in Elgin but most other inland sites, such as the Tips of Corsemaul (Mortlach Hills) and Bluemill/Boultenstone areas, are on moorland. Many pairs have also nested on Auchroisk distillery warehouses near Keith. As the map reveals, birds wander widely in the North-East, away from breeding colonies. These include non-breeders, but the concentration to the west of Aberdeen suggests that breeding birds from the city are moving inland to feed.

Changes in distribution
Lesser Black-backed Gulls were first noticed on the coast with Herring Gulls two miles south of Whinnyfold in June 1873 (Sim 1903), but not reported on the coast again until 1950. They were first noticed inland with other gulls in the Huntly district in the 1880s (Wilson 1890). Many were

Lesser Black-backed Gull, Isle of May, June 2007. © *John Anderson*

found nesting with them on the Balloch and the Waggle Hills and a hundred on Wishach Hill in the 1940s (Watson 1998). A well-established colony of hundreds was found with other gulls behind the coast on St. Fergus Moss in the early 1970s, when many were also breeding on the rougher ground in the big inland gulleries on the Correen and Mortlach Hills inland (Bourne & Smith 1977, Bourne 2004), and a few elsewhere. These colonies reached hundreds in the 1980s, but nearly all have now gone, leaving only occasional pairs inland. They were nesting on Aberdeen roofs by 1987 (*NESBR* 1987) and in Elgin from 1990 (*MNBR* 1990).

Population and trends

There were estimated to be 69 coastal pairs in 1969–70 (Cramp *et al.* 1974) and 105 in 1985–88 when there were also 193 inland, mostly in the Mortlach Hills (110) and the Correen Hills (81) (Seabird Colony Register). During 1998–2002, there were 154 apparently occupied nests in Aberdeen City, mostly on roof tops (compared with 57 in 1993 - *NESBR* 1993), 28 on Elgin roof tops, 24 along the coast and 101 in the Mortlach Hills (Seabird 2000). The Mortlach Hills colony, centred on Tips of Corsemaul, has continued to decline, with only about 20 pairs in 2003, 5 in 2005, 3 in 2006 and possibly 1–2 pairs in 2009 (*MNBR* 2003, 2005, 2006). The current population of North-East Scotland is probably in the range 200–300 pairs.

Author: *W.R.P. Bourne*

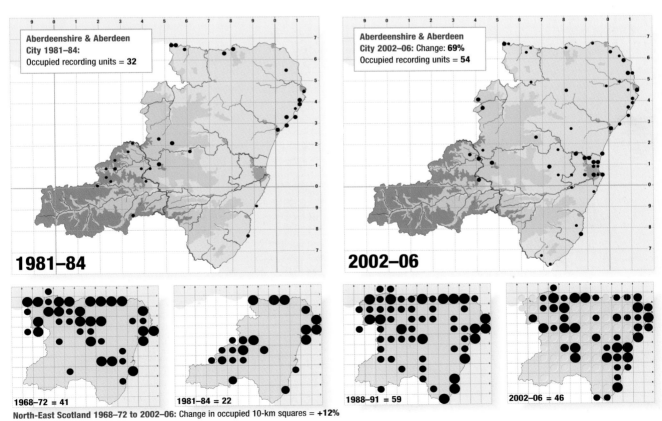

Aberdeenshire & Aberdeen City 1981–84:
Occupied recording units = **32**

1981–84

Aberdeenshire & Aberdeen City 2002–06: Change: 69%
Occupied recording units = **54**

2002–06

1968–72 = 41

1981–84 = 22

1988–91 = 59

2002–06 = 46

North-East Scotland 1968–72 to 2002–06: Change in occupied 10-km squares = +12%

Herring Gull　　　　　　　　　　　*Larus argentatus*

Very common resident. Winter visitor and passage migrant. Estimated breeding population in North-East Scotland: **16,000 pairs** (22% of Scottish population, 12% of UK)　　Red list; UK and Scottish BAP lists

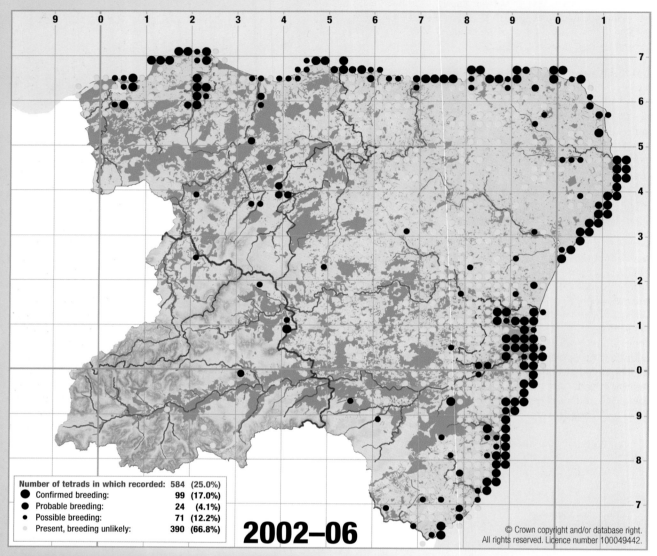

Number of tetrads in which recorded:	584	(25.0%)
● Confirmed breeding:	99	(17.0%)
● Probable breeding:	24	(4.1%)
● Possible breeding:	71	(12.2%)
● Present, breeding unlikely:	390	(66.8%)

2002–06

Herring Gull, Peterhead, July 2010. © *Harry Scott*

Habitat and breeding biology

Herring Gulls are typically coastal breeders, nesting on cliffs and stacks, but in North-East Scotland they only infrequently build their nests on level ground such as dunes and shingles. A few pairs sometimes breed inland, usually associated with Common Gull colonies on short Heather moorland. Increasingly, however, they nest on roofs of buildings in towns near the coast and even on distillery warehouse roofs well inland. The clutch, typically of three eggs, is generally laid in early or mid May and incubation lasts for around 28 days, with chicks fledging about six weeks later (Monaghan in *BS3*).

Scottish distribution and status

There are Herring Gull colonies all around the coast of Scotland including the Western and Northern Isles and smaller outlying islands. There are also several inland colonies though these are generally small. There are around 13 major colonies exceeding 500 pairs; seven of these lie on the east coast between Troup Head and the Firth of Forth, while three others are around the Firth of Clyde (Monaghan in *BS3*). During 1998–2002, a total of 71,659 nests was counted around the Scottish coast, with another 471 inland (Seabird 2000).

Distribution and status in North-East Scotland

Herring Gulls breed all around the coast of North-East Scotland wherever there are rocky coastlines or cliffs. Unoccupied stretches of shore reflect the absence of such habitat, such as between Lossiemouth and Buckie, and between Aberdeen and the Ythan estuary. The most densely occupied parts of the range lie between Peterhead and Collieston, and between Aberdeen and Inverbervie. Rooftop nesting is responsible for the sizeable population in Aberdeen and this is now taking place in many coastal towns, such as Lossiemouth, where there were 78 pairs in 2000, and in central Elgin, 9 km from the coast, where there were 75 pairs in 2000. Inland breeding in natural sites is now rare, and during 2002–06 this was proved only at Inchloan, near Durris, and Craig Glas on Donside where there were several pairs. However, a number of distillery warehouses in Moray do hold small colonies, as far inland as Dufftown. Non-breeding, or feeding, birds range widely through the lowlands of North-East Scotland in summer, but they are unusual in the uplands.

Changes in distribution

In the 1830s the Herring Gull was possibly a comparatively scarce breeder along the shore (MacGillivray 1852) where, being a large and formerly prized bird, it was hunted and its eggs were taken. Its increase appears to have begun with the passage of the Bird Protection Acts in the second half of the 19th century (Horn 1881, Wilson 1890, Holloway 1996), when it began to take over the role of scavenger as other species were eliminated by gamekeepers. Following its adoption of apparently new scavenging habits, such as feeding behind fishing boats and around towns and garbage dumps inland, vast numbers were nesting on the cliffs by the 1950s and overflowing their tops (pers. obs.). There has been a decline in recent decades, during which the birds have largely stopped breeding on level ground and taken to nesting on buildings. They have been nesting on Aberdeen rooftops since at least 1969 (Bourne & Smith 1978) and many hundreds were doing so by the late 1970s (pers. obs.).

Herring Gull, Fowlsheugh, May 1974. © Sam Alexander

Population and trends

Despite the increase in range, the breeding population of Herring Gulls in North-East Scotland has declined substantially over the last 40 years. The coastal breeding population was estimated to be 43,940 pairs in 1969–70, 19,034 in 1985–88, and 15,853 pairs (with 50 inland) in 1998–2002 (Monaghan in *BS3*, Seabird 2000). In the latter survey, 629 pairs were in Moray, 6,671 in Banff & Buchan, 853 in Gordon, 4,227 in Kincardine & Deeside, and 3,522 in the City of Aberdeen (B. Madden & S.F Newton in Mitchell *et al.* 2004). The City of Aberdeen total represents a large increase over the 1,987 pairs which were counted there in 1993. The general decline may be partly due to improved street hygiene (with the adoption of wheelie bins), changes in agriculture, and a reduction of fish discarded at sea. The birds have also been affected by botulism due to eating stale food contaminated by *Clostridium botulinum* (Macdonald & Standring 1978). The change from level ground to buildings for nesting, not only in towns but in places well inland such as Auchroisk distillery near Rothes, is presumably partly due to reduced human persecution and partly to a need to avoid other predators, especially Foxes (Watson 1998).

Author: *W.R.P. Bourne*

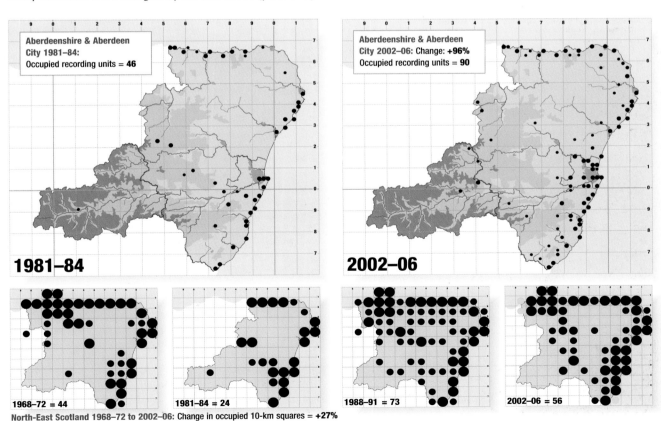

Aberdeenshire & Aberdeen City 1981–84:
Occupied recording units = **46**

1981–84

Aberdeenshire & Aberdeen City 2002–06: Change: +96%
Occupied recording units = **90**

2002–06

1968–72 = 44   1981–84 = 24   1988–91 = 73   2002–06 = 56

North-East Scotland 1968–72 to 2002–06: Change in occupied 10-km squares = **+27%**

Great Black-backed Gull

Larus marinus

Rare resident breeder. Winter visitor. Estimated population in North-East Scotland: *80–90 pairs* (<1% of Scottish and UK populations)

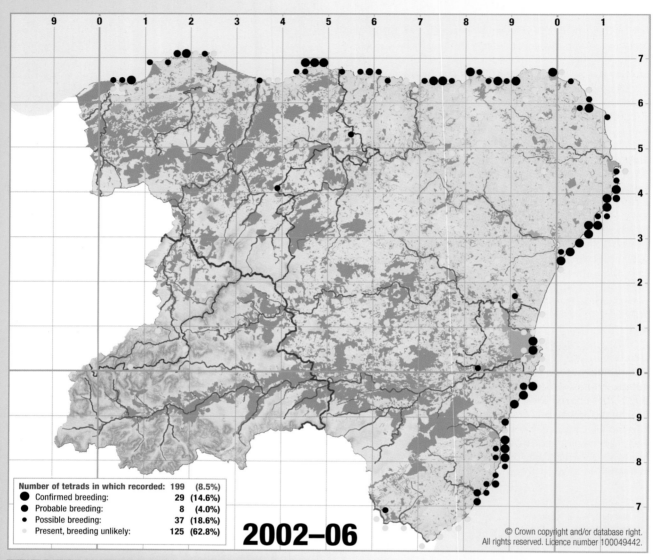

Number of tetrads in which recorded:	199	(8.5%)
● Confirmed breeding:	29	(14.6%)
● Probable breeding:	8	(4.0%)
● Possible breeding:	37	(18.6%)
○ Present, breeding unlikely:	125	(62.8%)

2002–06

Great Black-backed Gull, Brora, June 1979. © *Ed Duthie*

Habitat and breeding biology

In North-East Scotland, Great Black-backed Gulls nest primarily on coastal cliffs, either as single pairs or in small groups. Nests are often located on the highest point of a stack or rocky outcrop. A few pairs sometimes breed in coastal dunes, on roofs in towns and occasionally with other gull species in moorland colonies. Elsewhere in northern Scotland in the past, colonies have contained hundreds of pairs. Territories are established in February and March with eggs laid in the second half of April. Usually, the clutch contains three eggs, which are incubated for about 28 days. The young fledge in July, around 43 days after hatching (Zonfrillo in *BS3*).

Scottish distribution and status

Most Great Black-backed Gulls nest on the west and north coasts of Scotland, with fewer scattered along the east coast. In the 1960s and 1970s some colonies were very large, including over 1,500 pairs on North Rona (Love & Stevenson 2006) and there were two colonies of 1,000+ and 600 pairs on Hoy, with two other Orkney colonies of 500–800 pairs (J. Williams pers. comm.). All of these colonies are now greatly reduced, with only 300–400 pairs remaining on North Rona (Murray 2009). During 1998–2002, a total of 14,773 coastal pairs was counted in Scotland (Seabird 2000).

Distribution and status in North-East Scotland

During 2002–06, breeding activity was confined to the coast where the distribution closely mirrors the cliff-bound sections of coastline. Breeding was proved, or probable, on the cliffs at Covesea, Portknockie, between Macduff and Fraserburgh, and more widely down the east coast south from Peterhead. A few nesting pairs also occupied flat ground at RAF Kinloss and Sands of Forvie, while breeding was also noted on an island in Loch of Strathbeg and on Aberdeen rooftops. Great Black-backed Gulls were also widely reported from inland areas. Such records referred to birds feeding inland, most of which are likely to have been immature or non-breeders.

Changes in distribution

The species is reported to have bred on an island in the Loch of Strathbeg in the 19th century (Edward 1854, Horn 1881), when it was seen along the cliffs at all seasons (Sim 1903). In recent times at least, breeding was not confirmed until 1963, at Collieston (*NES 1st Atlas*). A few pairs were present at the gulleries inland on the Waggle Hills and Ordiequish in the 1940s (Watson 1998), and at St. Fergus Moss in the 1970s. A nest with three eggs was found in the gullery on the Correen Hills in 1977, and they were present (and probably shot) in the Mortlach Hills gullery in the 1990s. Inland, there were two nests on roofs in Aberdeen in 1993, and one nest in Elgin in 2000. They bred at the Loch of Strathbeg again in 2001 and at Forvie in 2003, when there were four nests.

Population and trends

The breeding population in North-East Scotland has been counted during three national surveys since the 1960s. In 1969–70 there were 48 coastal pairs; not 68 as 20 of the 22 in 'Morayshire' were in fact on Nairn Bar, just outside Moray (Cramp *et al.* 1974, R. Mavor pers. comm.). In 1985–88 there were 43 coastal nests and eight inland - four at the Moss of Dunphail and four in the Mortlach Hills (Seabird Colony Register). In 1998–2002 there were 83 nests

Great Black-backed Gull, Shetland, July 1985. © *John Edelsten*

including nine in the City of Aberdeen and one on an Elgin rooftop. Coastal nests during this period were found in Moray (10), Banff & Buchan (37), Gordon (5) and Kincardine & Deeside (21) (Seabird 2000). Together, this leads to an estimate of 80–90 pairs in North-East Scotland.

Author: *W.R.P. Bourne*

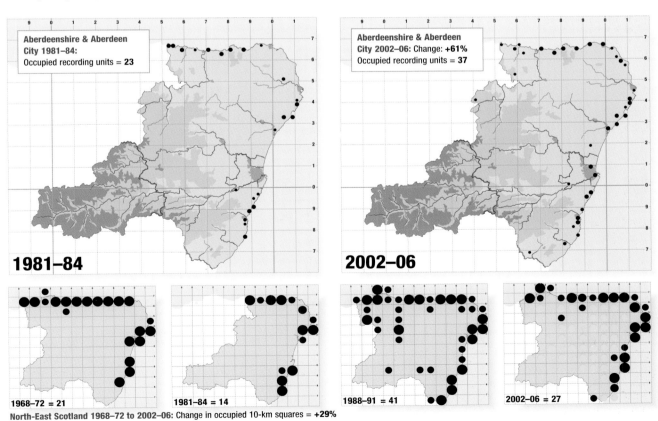

Aberdeenshire & Aberdeen City 1981–84:
Occupied recording units = 23

1981–84

Aberdeenshire & Aberdeen City 2002–06: Change: +61%
Occupied recording units = 37

2002–06

1968–72 = 21

1981–84 = 14

1988–91 = 41

2002–06 = 27

North-East Scotland 1968–72 to 2002–06: Change in occupied 10-km squares = +29%

Little Tern
Sternula albifrons

Rare summer migrant breeder. Estimated population in North-East Scotland: **20–35 pairs** (9% of Scottish population, 1% of UK)

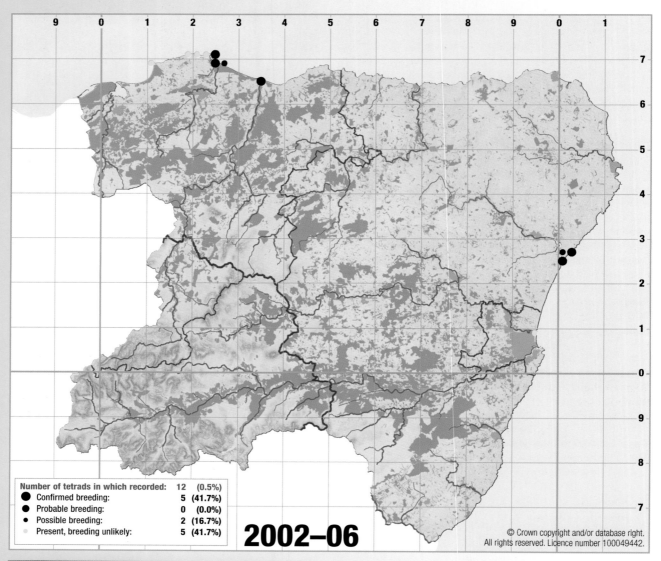

Number of tetrads in which recorded:	12	(0.5%)
● Confirmed breeding:	5	(41.7%)
● Probable breeding:	0	(0.0%)
• Possible breeding:	2	(16.7%)
Present, breeding unlikely:	5	(41.7%)

2002–06

Little Tern, Montrose, July 2007. © *John Anderson*

Habitat and breeding biology

The Little Tern is an entirely coastal species, usually seen inshore near suitable breeding sites. Nest sites are on open sandy or shingle beaches and spits, often close to the high water mark. Clutches are commonly lost to high tides or to predation, which often follows disturbance by human activity. Scattered scrapes are made in sand or among pebbles and are not usually closely associated with other tern species. Clutches, usually of two eggs, are laid in May and incubated for 18–22 days. The young are independent by mid July. Productivity has been measured at 0.30 fledged chicks/pair over 17 years at Forvie between 1986–2004 (Mavor *et al.* 2006).

Scottish distribution and status

During 2000–04, Little Terns nested at about 23 sites around Scotland, notably on the Argyll islands, the Outer Hebrides and down the east coast between Orkney and Lothian. The only colonies containing 50 or more apparently occupied nests were on Tiree and at the Ythan estuary (Sands of Forvie). A comparison of the Seabird Colony Register (1985–88) (Lloyd *et al.* 1991) and Seabird 2000 surveys showed a 44% population decrease in east Scotland but a 4% increase in Argyll and the Western Isles.

Little Tern, St Cyrus, May 2007. © *Harry Scott*

Distribution and status in North-East Scotland

Little Terns bred at three sites during 2002–06. The largest colony is at a protected site at the Ythan estuary, within Forvie National Nature Reserve. In Moray there is a small colony on the exposed sandy beach at Lossiemouth, and a very few pairs sometimes breed on the shingle at Speymouth, occasionally as far upstream as the Garmouth viaduct. The first Little Terns are seen at Aberdeen or the Ythan in mid–late April; usually a little later on the Moray coast. Throughout the period May to July, Little Terns are commonly seen plunge diving for sand eels and small fish inshore, especially from Donmouth to the Ythan, and also to the west of Lossiemouth. Departure from the North-East is usually between late July and mid August, but can be earlier if clutches fail.

Changes in distribution

Traditionally, the largest Little Tern colonies in North-East Scotland have been at Forvie, on the Ythan, and St. Cyrus. The Forvie colony thrived between the mid 1950s and early 1970s when it was temporarily deserted due to disturbance (*NES 1st Atlas*). Breeding resumed there soon afterwards and has continued ever since. Despite once being one of the largest colonies in Britain, with 158 pairs in 1974 (*NES 1st*

Atlas), St Cyrus was abandoned after 1987, probably as a result of Fox predation and disturbance by dogs. In Moray, a colony at Findhorn held 40 pairs in 1958 but this dwindled to extinction by 1980 (Norman & Saunders 1969, Cook 1982). Although it was a traditional Little Tern breeding site, Lossiemouth was abandoned during the 1980s with breeding resuming there in 1994. Speymouth was first occupied in 1986 and a very few pairs have nested irregularly since. In the past, Little Terns have bred at a number of other North-East sites in small numbers but these have suffered from a lack of protection and the extensive measures such as restrictions on public access, predator control and electric fences which currently help to maintain the Forvie colony. The extent of suitable breeding habitat has not changed significantly in North-East Scotland, but the availability of food, especially sand eels, has been suggested as an important factor influencing when Little Terns colonise an area (Perrow *et al.* 2003).

Population and trends

The colony at Forvie has fluctuated considerably in size over the years with up to 67 pairs during the mid 1950s–early 1970s (*NES 1st Atlas*), 60–74 pairs during 1976–79 (*NES 1st Atlas*) and 20–30 pairs, on average, between 1980–98. Numbers then increased again to 76 pairs in 2002 before dropping sharply to 29 in 2003 and 19 between 2004 and 2006. Since then, the site has supported around 20 pairs with variable breeding success. The Lossiemouth colony has fluctuated between 1–12 nests since its reoccupation in 1994. The maximum count of adults has been 30 in 2006 and 2008. Productivity has recently been poor as the beach is fully exposed to rough seas and subject to much human disturbance. On the shingles at the mouth of the Spey, up to three pairs breed - none in some years. Combining the data from all extant colonies, the annual breeding population in recent years has varied in the range 20–35 pairs.

Author: *Annabel Drysdale*

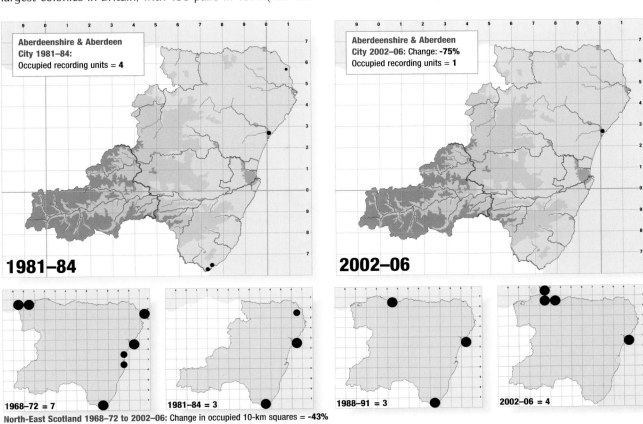

Aberdeenshire & Aberdeen City 1981–84:
Occupied recording units = **4**

1981–84

Aberdeenshire & Aberdeen City 2002–06: Change: -75%
Occupied recording units = **1**

2002–06

1968–72 = 7

1981–84 = 3

1988–91 = 3

2002–06 = 4

North-East Scotland 1968–72 to 2002–06: Change in occupied 10-km squares = -43%

Sandwich Tern
Sterna sandvicensis

Scarce summer migrant breeder. Passage migrant. Estimated population in North-East Scotland: **790–830 pairs** (74% of Scottish population, 7% of UK)

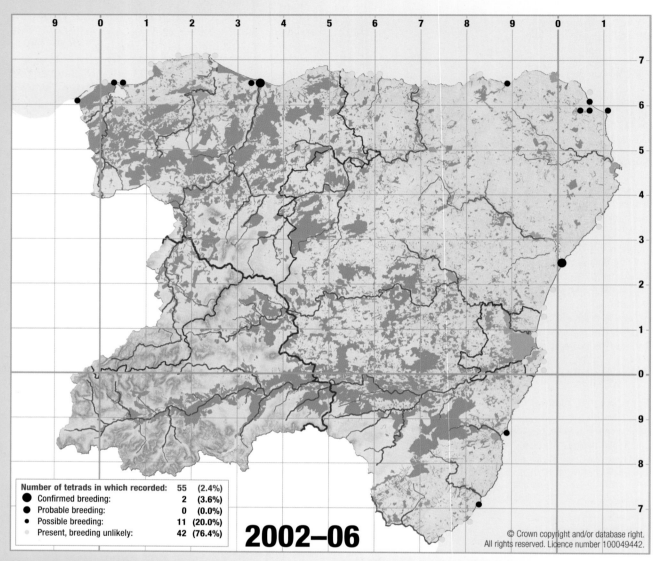

Number of tetrads in which recorded:	55	(2.4%)
Confirmed breeding:	2	(3.6%)
Probable breeding:	0	(0.0%)
Possible breeding:	11	(20.0%)
Present, breeding unlikely:	42	(76.4%)

2002–06

Habitat and breeding biology

The habitats occupied by the main breeding colonies at the Loch of Strathbeg and Forvie National Nature Reserve are very different. The former colony was located on a muddy island of quaking Reed Canary Grass often subject to flooding. At Forvie NNR, apart from the period from 1954–58 when breeding took place on Heather moorland west of Rockend, the terns breed among sand dunes vegetated with Marram Grass, often on bare sand. This followed years of breeding in the same place on a substrate of mud and sand with low vegetation. The few pairs which have bred at Speymouth in recent years have nested among low vegetation on shingle bars and islands in the river. At the main colonies, egg-laying usually begins during the first week of May but, where there are few breeders, laying takes place later in May or even in June. In highly synchronised, early colonies, the breeding period extends to 60 days with young fledging at age 27–35 days from the third week in June onwards. Occasionally, however, the season extends to 90 days with fledging in late July–early August.

Scottish distribution and status

During 2002–04, Sandwich Terns bred on the east coast of Scotland on the Isle of May and in Orkney but mainly in North-East Scotland at Forvie NNR. A scatter of former breeding sites extends from the Firth of Forth to Shetland. Although the colony at Loch of Strathbeg was lost subsequent to flooding of the island breeding site in 2000, those at Forvie NNR and in Orkney have remained fairly stable. Since the 1990s, substantial numbers have bred at Loch Ryan (Dumfries & Galloway) but further north on the west coast breeding is extremely rare (Smith in *BS3*).

Distribution and status in North-East Scotland

Sandwich Terns may be found all along the coast of the North-East, often flying close inshore, from mid March to October. There is now only one major breeding site, at Forvie NNR, following the demise of the Loch of Strathbeg colony in 2000. The only other breeding locality during 2002–06 was on the River Spey shingles at Garmouth viaduct where one pair bred unsuccessfully in 2005, and possibly did so in 2006 (*MNBR* 2005, 2006). Post-breeding dispersal into North-East waters from more southerly colonies takes place rapidly after fledging, with young birds continuing to be fed by at least one parent (Smith 1975, Cook 1992). This results in large gatherings along the Moray coast e.g. 266 at Culbin Bar in September 2003 and 259 at Portgordon in September 2004 (*MNBR* 2003, 2004).

Changes in distribution

Sandwich Terns were first recorded breeding in North-East Scotland in 1887 when there were 32 nests on Culbin Bar (Harvie-Brown & Buckley 1895). They first bred at Forvie in 1912, and did so again in 1932 (BTO ringing records), 1935 and 1936 (Baxter & Rintoul 1953). They bred again at Forvie, west of Rockend, in 1954 and probably did so prior to this (V.

Sandwich Tern, Newburgh, August 2008. © *Ed Duthie*

C. Wynne-Edwards pers. comm.). When this colony began to disintegrate in 1956 due to the increase in Fox predation, some of the terns moved to the present breeding sites in the south of Forvie sands while others may have moved to the Nairn Bar, where 267 pairs bred in 1958 (Thom 1986). However, with increased protection measures of breeding terns in the Forvie colony, numbers gradually increased. When Fox predation once again became a problem there, a proportion of the breeding population moved to the island in the Loch of Strathbeg in 1984; they continued to breed there until 2000 (Smith in *BS3*). The Forvie colony was deserted in the mid 1990s but a substantial colony had returned by 1999. In 1994, seven pairs nested on a shingle bar at the mouth of the River Spey and there were ten nests in 1995; no young were reared in either year (*MNBR* 1994, 1995).

Population and trends

In 1960, when the National Nature Reserve was created at Forvie, numbers of Sandwich Terns had settled at around 250 pairs. With close protection the total breeding population gradually increased to well over 1,000 pairs with 2,100 pairs in 1971 when failed breeders from further north were thought to have added to an existing large Forvie colony (Bourne & Smith 1978). During the period 1975–1983 numbers at Forvie varied between 825–1,670 pairs but fell to 331 pairs in 1984 when the Loch of Strathbeg colony became established. Following a period of absence in the mid 1990s, four pairs of Sandwich Terns returned to Forvie in 1997 and the colony increased annually until, by 2003, 1,008 pairs were nesting. During 2004–06, the population fluctuated between 790–830 pairs; more recently there were c.900 pairs in 2007 and 670 in 2008. The Loch of Strathbeg colony was occupied between 1984 and 2000, during which time numbers ranged from 700 pairs (in 1984 and 1985) to 121 in 1990, but had recovered to 923 pairs by 1994.

Author: *Alistair Smith*

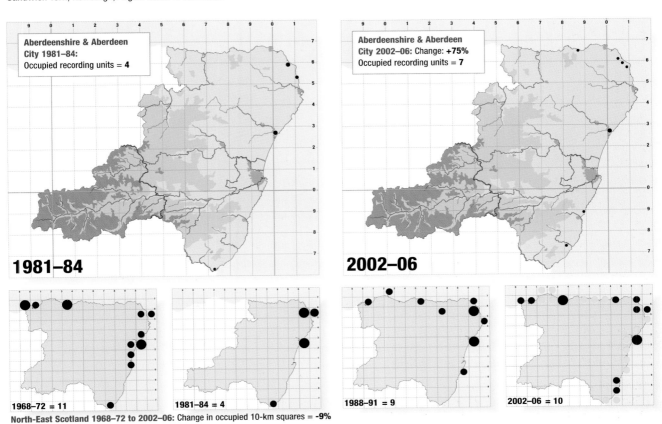

Aberdeenshire & Aberdeen City 1981–84:
Occupied recording units = **4**

1981–84

Aberdeenshire & Aberdeen City 2002–06: Change: **+75%**
Occupied recording units = **7**

2002–06

1968–72 = 11

1981–84 = 4

1988–91 = 9

2002–06 = 10

North-East Scotland 1968–72 to 2002–06: Change in occupied 10-km squares = -9%

Loch of Skene

The only water body of any size near Aberdeen, Loch of Skene is an important winter roost for Pink-footed and Greylag Geese and gulls, and is designated as a Special Protection Area. Its breeding birds include Mute Swan (several pairs), Greylag Goose, Mallard, Little Grebe, Tufted Duck (in the past up to 50 pairs, now much reduced), summering Goldeneye, numerous pairs of Coot, and a range of other ducks present in the breeding season. Common Gulls and Common Terns sometimes nest on small islands holding shooting butts. The loch edges and adjacent fields hold Heron, Moorhen, Water Rail, Oystercatcher, Lapwing, Curlew, Sedge Warbler and Reed Bunting. June 2006 © *Ian Francis*

Loch Spynie

The loch, surrounded by extensive reedbeds, is the premier freshwater site in Moray. The reeds hold a small breeding population of Bearded Tits, many Sedge Warblers and Reed Buntings, and there is a large population of Water Rails. Marsh Harriers have bred in recent years. Nesting wildfowl include Mallard, Tufted Duck and several pairs of Mute Swan. Little Grebes are regular breeders although Great Crested Grebes have been, at least temporarily, lost. An artificial island attracts a small colony of Common Terns and Black-headed Gulls. There is a heronry in the woods beside the loch, where other species include Blackcap, Chiffchaff and Spotted Flycatcher. August 2010 © *Martin Cook*

Common Tern

Sterna hirundo

Scarce summer migrant breeder. Passage migrant. Estimated population in North-East Scotland:
200–400 pairs (6% of Scottish population, 3% of UK)

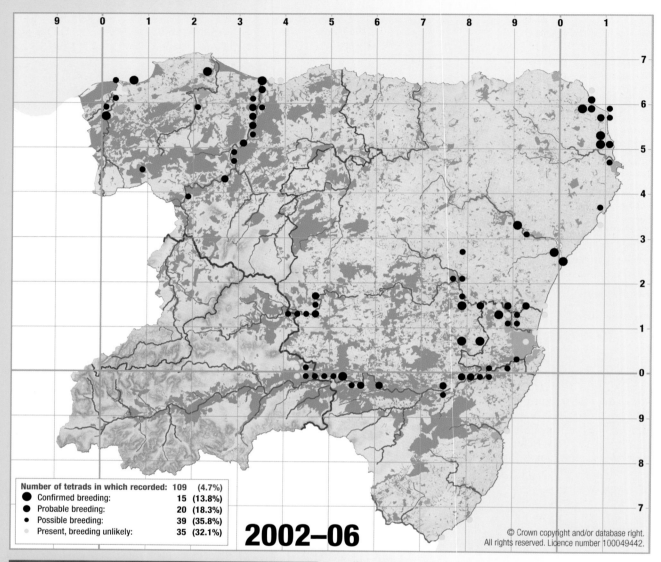

Number of tetrads in which recorded:	109	(4.7%)
● Confirmed breeding:	15	(13.8%)
● Probable breeding:	20	(18.3%)
● Possible breeding:	39	(35.8%)
● Present, breeding unlikely:	35	(32.1%)

2002–06

Common Tern, Aberdeen, September 2007. © *John Chapman*

Habitat and breeding biology

In Scotland, most Common Terns nest coastally on small off-shore islets and skerries, with smaller scattered populations breeding on mainland coastal sites such as beaches, or inland on shingle bars on the main rivers. They will use man-made habitats such as construction yards and docks, and can be attracted to lochs by the provision of nesting rafts. Pairs will breed individually but they are more usually colonial, such colonies occasionally exceeding 1,000 pairs (Mitchell *et al*. 2004). In North-East Scotland, all Common Terns breed on mainland sites, with a few large, well-established colonies in dune slacks. Shingle bars and associated inland riverine habitats, are still used widely by small colonies or single pairs. An increasing number of colonies breed on non-natural structures, such as artificial islands (*e.g.* at Loch Spynie and Loch of Strathbeg), and in industrial sites such as Kirkhill Industrial Estate, Dyce. Roof tops have been used for nesting here as well as at St. Fergus gas terminal (*NESBR* 2005, W. R. P. Bourne pers. comm.).

Scottish distribution and status

The main colonies are to be found on the west and east coasts with smaller numbers in the far north and south-west (Craik in *BS3*). During the Seabird 2000 census in 1998–2002, a Scottish total of 4,784 apparently occupied nests was found. The species has always been prone to shifting colonies, which has obscured accurate trends but overall the Scottish population declined by 30% in the 15 years between 1984 and 1999 (Mitchell *et al*. 2004).

Distribution and status in North-East Scotland

The population is distributed unevenly with the bulk of pairs breeding in three reasonably-sized coastal colonies on the north-east coast, at Sands of Forvie, St. Fergus Gas Terminal and Loch of Strathbeg. Smaller numbers breed in scattered colonies up to 50 km inland along the Rivers Findhorn, Spey, Ythan, Dee and Don, and there is a regular population to the west of Aberdeen. Occasionally, small numbers will breed elsewhere such as islands on inland lochs (e.g. Loch of Skene). Many of these smaller colonies persist for just a few seasons. Common Terns typically return to the area in late April with adults settling at colonies in late May or early June. Colonies are largely vacated by early August when flocks, often in association with other terns and gulls, build up on the coast. Numbers fall rapidly in September though birds are regularly seen in the first half of October. These include birds from outside the area (Norman in Wernham et al. 2002). There is no firm evidence of change in arrival or departure dates.

Changes in distribution

Nationally there appears to have been a contraction in coastal distribution through the loss of coastal colonies (BTO 2nd Atlas) and this is the case in North-East Scotland, where the number of occupied 10-km squares fell from 47 in 1968–72 (BTO 1st Atlas) to 37 in 1988–91 (BTO 2nd Atlas) and 31 in 2002–06. The main sites at Loch of Strathbeg, Sands of Forvie and St. Fergus have been occupied at least intermittently since the early 20th century or earlier (Bourne 1978). However, nesting at St. Cyrus has not occurred in recent years and some smaller colonies appear to have been lost from the north coast, such as between Cullen and Portsoy (NES 1st Atlas). Inland there appears to have been some consolidation on industrial sites to the west of Aberdeen and on sites specifically managed for this species such as Loch Spynie where the species was attracted to breed in 1999 through the provision of a nesting platform. Along the River Dee there was an increase from eight to 14 occupied recording units between

1981–84 and 2002–06. In the 1970s, Common Terns were sometimes found in Common Gull colonies such as Tips of Corsemaul and in the Correen Hills where breeding was proved (Bourne & Smith 1978).

Population and trends

The largest colonies are generally counted annually. However, the riverine populations are less well covered and make up a smaller percentage of the population. All coastal populations have been counted regularly through national censuses.

Table 1. Numbers of coastal breeding Common Terns (apparently occupied nests) in North-East Scotland (Mitchell et al. 2004).

Year	1969–70	1985–88	1998–2000	% change (1969–70 to 1998–2000)
Total	563	447	338	-40

A long-term historic decline appears to be continuing at present. Numbers on the lower River Spey collapsed from 500 pairs in 1972 to around 30 pairs in the early 1990s and the formerly large colony at Sands of Forvie has declined from several hundred pairs in the 1960s to fewer than 100 since the1990s. Disturbance and predation are implicated in these declines. Until recently, numbers have been maintained at those sites offering some protection against these factors such as Loch of Strathbeg and St. Fergus Gas Terminal. However, numbers at St. Fergus also now appear to be under pressure so additional factors such as local food availability, which is affecting many other species which breed around the North Sea, may be starting to operate. The current population probably lies within the range 200-400 pairs. The planned provision of further man-made and managed habitat such as artificial islands and rafts, in addition to anti-predator measures, will be a necessary aspect of attempts to secure the future of this species in North-East Scotland.

Author: Simon Busuttil

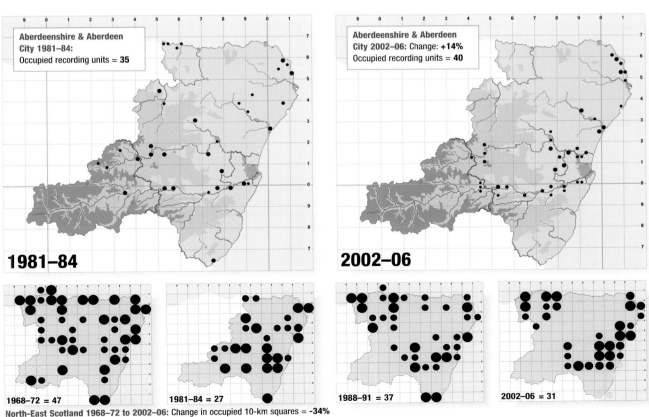

Aberdeenshire & Aberdeen City 1981–84: Occupied recording units = **35**

1981–84

Aberdeenshire & Aberdeen City 2002–06: Change: **+14%** Occupied recording units = **40**

2002–06

1968–72 = 47   1981–84 = 27   1988–91 = 37   2002–06 = 31

North-East Scotland 1968–72 to 2002–06: Change in occupied 10-km squares = **-34%**

Roseate Tern

Sterna dougallii

Occasional probable, and former, breeder. Summer visitor. Estimated population in North-East Scotland:
0 pairs

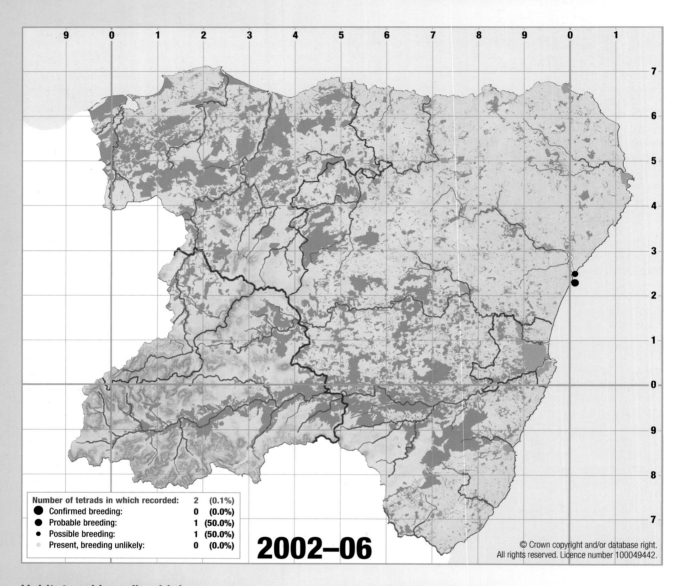

Number of tetrads in which recorded:	2	(0.1%)
● Confirmed breeding:	0	(0.0%)
● Probable breeding:	1	(50.0%)
• Possible breeding:	1	(50.0%)
Present, breeding unlikely:	0	(0.0%)

2002–06

Habitat and breeding biology

Roseate Terns nest on offshore islands and isolated beaches, often amongst other breeding tern and gull species. The clutch of 1–3 eggs is laid between late May and early July (Fairlamb in *BS3*). The few breeding attempts by this species in North-East Scotland have been confined to relatively undisturbed beaches among established tern colonies.

Scottish distribution and status

This species has maintained a precarious foothold in Scotland with a small breeding population confined mainly to islands in the Firth of Forth in recent years. Numbers of breeding pairs on these islands have declined from 450 pairs in 1957–62 to as few as two pairs in 2001 and numbers have remained low. Colonies in the Firth of Clyde have similarly declined from a peak of 155+ pairs in 1958. The last national census found a total of 14 pairs in Angus & Dundee, Fife and the Isle of May (Seabird 2000).

Distribution and status in North-East Scotland

In 1887 there were seven pairs on Culbin Bar and five nests were found (Harvie-Brown & Buckley 1895). In 1963, one pair nested at Sands of Forvie (Fairlamb in *BS3*). An adult and two juveniles were seen on the Ythan on 2nd July 1989 (*NESBR* 1989) but their origin was uncertain. A pair was present at the Ythan estuary each summer between 2002 and 2004; courtship behaviour was observed but there was no other evidence of breeding. Otherwise, the Roseate Tern has always been a scarce visitor to North-East Scotland with only 55 birds reported in the period 1968 to 2006 (Philips1997, *NESBR*s, *MNBR*s). Most records have come from coastal sites between Findhorn and St Cyrus between April–September, and usually involve one or two birds probably on passage or post-breeding dispersal. A recent increase at the breeding colony on Coquet Island in Northumberland (Holling *et al*. 2008) gives some hope that the Scottish population may recover, which may in turn lead to an increase in breeding attempts in North-East Scotland.

Author: *Scott Paterson*

The Breeding Birds of North-East Scotland

Sandwich Tern colony, Newburgh, May 2008. © *Rab Rae* Inset: **Roseate Tern**, Sands of Forvie NNR, June 1981. © *Alistair Smith* Roseate Terns are occasionally present in the Forvie tern colonies and have nested on at least one occasion.

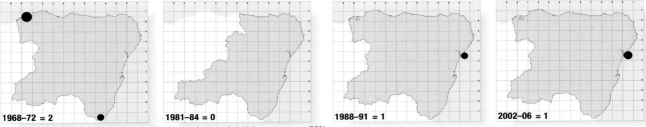

1968–72 = 2 **1981–84 = 0** **1988–91 = 1** **2002–06 = 1**

North-East Scotland 1968–72 to 2002–06: Change in occupied 10-km squares = -50%

Arctic Tern

Sterna paradisaea

Scarce summer migrant breeder. Passage migrant. Estimated population in North-East Scotland:
350–700 pairs (1% of Scottish population, <1% of UK)

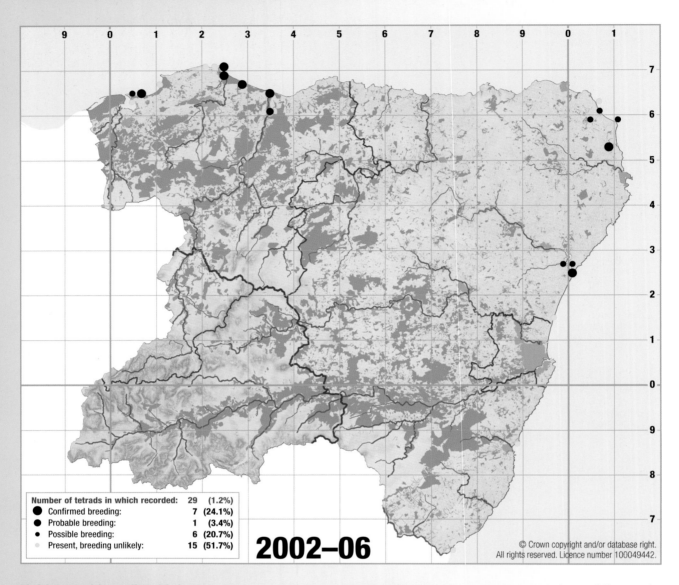

Number of tetrads in which recorded: 29 (1.2%)
- ● Confirmed breeding: 7 (24.1%)
- ● Probable breeding: 1 (3.4%)
- ● Possible breeding: 6 (20.7%)
- ● Present, breeding unlikely: 15 (51.7%)

2002–06

Habitat and breeding biology

Primarily a marine species, most Arctic Terns breed colonially in a range of coastal habitats such as rocky islets, beaches and dunes. Smaller numbers nest at inland sites such as lochs or on riverine shingle and they will breed on man-made structures such as artificial islands. Colonies can be large with several hundred or even several thousand pairs present (Craik in *BS3*), often in close association with Common Terns. Birds return to Scotland by the first week in May and breeding sites are occupied from late May, with eggs laid in June. The sites are usually vacated by August and are often abandoned earlier if breeding fails. In North-East Scotland most breeding occurs on beaches and dunes, with much smaller numbers in other habitats such as riverine shingle in the lower reaches of the River Spey.

Scottish distribution and status

During the Seabird 2000 census covering 1998–2002, 81% of Scotland's apparently occupied Arctic Tern nests were in Orkney and Shetland. The remainder of the population was predominantly in the Western Isles and along the west and north coasts. On the east coast, the Isle of May holds a major colony (Craik in *BS3*). The Scottish population was estimated at 47,306 apparently occupied nests following the Seabird 2000 census, a decrease of 34% on the previous count between 1985–88 (Mitchell *et al.* 2000).

Distribution and status in North-East Scotland

In North-East Scotland, Arctic Terns nest in three distinct coastal areas; between the Spey and Findhorn rivers including up to 5 km upstream on the Spey, on the north-east coast between St. Fergus and St. Combs, and at Sands of Forvie where they breed primarily amongst Marram Grass in low mobile dunes. Occasionally birds nest outside of these core areas. In Moray, the Findhorn colony is in vegetated dunes inside the RAF Kinloss fence, the Lossiemouth colony is in loose sand dunes, the colonies near Boar's Head Rock and at Speymouth are on coastal shingle and the Garmouth viaduct colony is on shingle islands in the Spey. The birds at St. Fergus Gas Terminal nest within the fenced area, largely secure from human disturbance. Large post-breeding gatherings occur in favoured spots on the coast (*e.g.* Rattray Head, Ythan estuary), often with other seabirds. These flocks probably include birds from outside our region.

Changes in distribution

The distribution of large colonies within North-East Scotland has been very consistent with the Sands of Forvie, St. Fergus Gas Terminal and RAF Kinloss having been occupied for many years. Re-distribution has occurred locally such as between St Fergus, Sands of Forvie and Loch of Strathbeg, probably in relation to factors such as predation, disturbance or local changes in habitat. There appears to have been some reduction in the number of small colonies in the past few decades with those at St. Cyrus and near Banff being abandoned, and a concentration at fewer large colonies, many of which now receive some measure of protection. This is evidenced by the number of occupied 10-km squares in the North-East which has declined from 17 in 1968–72 (*BTO 1st Atlas*) to 11 in 1988–91 (*BTO 2nd Atlas*) and nine in 2002–06.

Population and trends

Arctic Terns nest at a small number of sites, mostly counted annually and through regular national censuses.

Table 1. Breeding Arctic Terns (apparently occupied nests) in North-East Scotland (Mitchell *et al.* 2004).

Year	1969–70	1985–88	1998–2000	% change (1969–70 to 1998–2000)
Total	263	166	504	+91

Arctic Terns were first recorded nesting in the region in the late 19th century (Bourne & Smith 1978) though we might expect the species to have been nesting in the area prior to that time. Many records before about 1960 refer to "commic" terns rather than distinguishing between Common and Arctic Terns. Tables 1 and 2 suggest that despite a decrease in range the numbers of Arctic Terns breeding in the area in the current decade are higher than in the previous thirty years, although some of this apparent increase may be due to more rigorous monitoring of known colonies. This is in contrast

Arctic Tern, Montrose, July 2007. © *John Anderson*

Table 2. Breeding Arctic Terns (apparently occupied nests or birds incubating) at four selected colonies in North-East Scotland during 2002–06 (*NESBR* 2002–06, *MNBR* 2002–06).

	2002	2003	2004	2005	2006
RAF Kinloss	75	50	65	104	70
Garmouth viaduct	28	83	20	44	20
Sands of Forvie NNR	257	58	44	45	39
St. Fergus Gas Terminal	147	180	305	451	339
Total	507	371	434	644	468

with the fortunes of Common Terns in the region. Several of the main colonies are now protected in some way against disturbance and predation, factors that can play significant roles in declines of this species. At St. Fergus, *c.*50 pairs nested in the dune slacks in the 1970s prior to the establishment of the gas terminal, but in 1988 an additional 493 pairs were breeding, protected by the terminal's Fox-proof fence (W. R. P. Bourne pers. comm., *NES 1st Atlas*). It seems likely that food availability in the North Sea, already impacting on the bulk of the Arctic Tern population in the Northern Isles, will play an increasing role in determining the fortunes of this species in North-East Scotland.

Author: *Simon Busuttil*

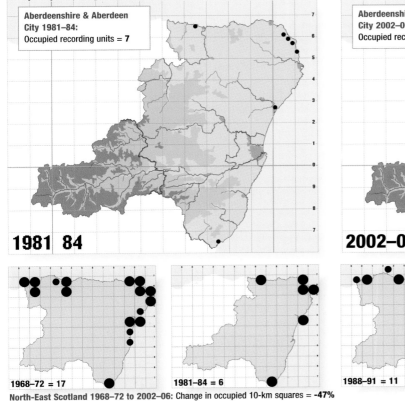

Aberdeenshire & Aberdeen City 1981–84:
Occupied recording units = **7**

1981 84

1968–72 = 17   1981–84 = 6

North-East Scotland 1968–72 to 2002–06: Change in occupied 10-km squares = **-47%**

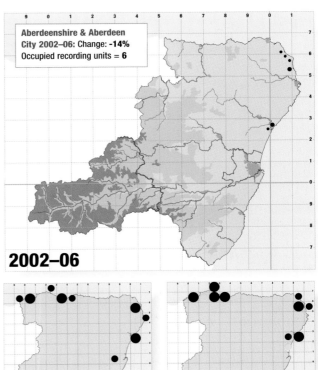

Aberdeenshire & Aberdeen City 2002–06: Change: **-14%**
Occupied recording units = **6**

2002–06

1988–91 = 11   2002–06 = 9

Guillemot

Uria aalge

Very common resident and migrant breeder. Estimated population in North-East Scotland: **100,425 pairs** (13% of Scottish population, 7% of UK)

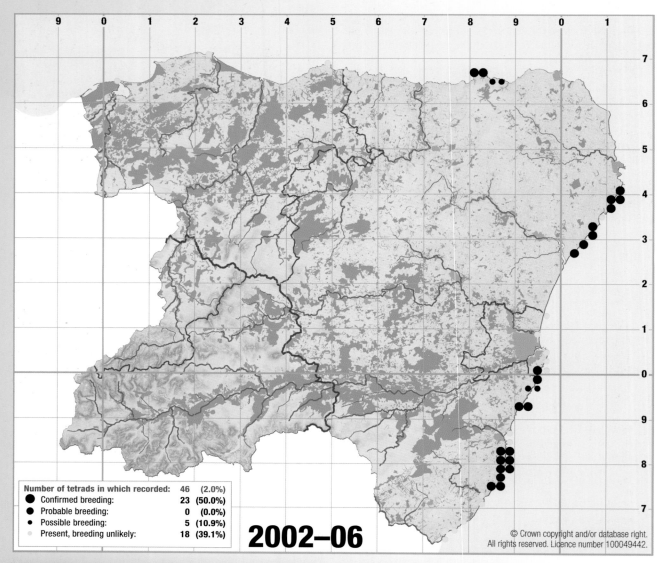

Number of tetrads in which recorded:	46	(2.0%)
● Confirmed breeding:	23	(50.0%)
● Probable breeding:	0	(0.0%)
● Possible breeding:	5	(10.9%)
Present, breeding unlikely:	18	(39.1%)

2002–06

Guillemot, Whinnyfold, May 1979. © *Sam Alexander*

Habitat and breeding biology

Guillemots breed around the coast of North-East Scotland on rocky cliffs with suitable ledges and precipitous slopes. Colonies in the region are amongst the largest in Britain, with the colony at Fowlsheugh the third largest in Scotland. Birds usually return to the cliffs from February onwards but will occasionally visit cliffs in large numbers throughout the winter. A large single egg is laid directly on to bare rock and is incubated for 32–33 days. The chick leaves the nest site after only 18–21 days and is accompanied out to sea by the male parent who feeds it for a further 6–8 weeks. The cliffs are generally empty by the end of August although birds are present offshore all year round.

Scottish distribution and status

With an estimated 1,167,841 individuals (which converts to about 780,000 pairs), Scotland is home to 75% of the British and Irish population of Guillemots (Seabird 2000). Colonies are widely distributed around the coast mainly in the north and west, with 25 sites containing over 10,000 individuals each. The total breeding population more than doubled between 1969–70 and 1998–2002 but since that time numbers have declined in some parts of Scotland (Harris & Wanless in *BS3*).

The Breeding Birds of North-East Scotland

Guillemot, Whinnyfold, June 1999. © *Stuart Rae*

Distribution and status in North-East Scotland

Guillemots breed on three main sections of cliff-bound coast in the North-East. The largest numbers, south of Stonehaven, are found between Dunnottar and Kinneff; this includes the impressive Fowlsheugh colony. Much smaller numbers breed closer to Aberdeen, at Newtonhill and between Portlethen and Cove. Further north on the east coast, Guillemots breed at Longhaven and Bullers of Buchan, with other colonies at Whinnyfold and Collieston. On the north coast of Aberdeenshire, large numbers breed at Troup Head.

Changes in distribution

The locations of the main Guillemot colonies have remained relatively unchanged since 1981–84. A few smaller colonies have, however, become established - at Collieston and between Aberdeen and Newtonhill. At Troup Head, part of the Guillemot colony has been displaced by the expanding Gannet colony.

Population and trends

The most recent complete count of Guillemots in North-East Scotland, during 1998–2002, revealed 149,889 individuals which converts to 100,425 pairs (Seabird 2000). This represents further substantial increase from 69,092 individuals counted during 1969–70 (Cramp *et al.* 1974) and 85,556 birds counted in 1985–88 during the Seabird Colony Register census (Lloyd *et al.* 1991). Since that time however, there has been evidence of a decline. At Fowlsheugh there were 62,330 individuals in 1999 (*NESBR* 1999) but this had fallen by 13.1% to 54,195 by 2006 (*NESBR* 2006). In the colonies along the Boddam to Collieston coast, numbers fell by 34% from 29,389 to 19,296 between 2001 and 2007, while at Troup Head over the same period the decline has been much greater; a fall of almost 70% from 40,559 in 2001 to 12,347 in 2007 (RSPB colony count 2007).

Author: *Scott Paterson*

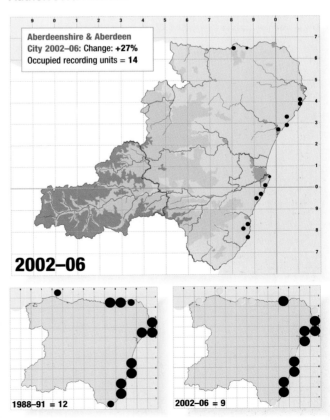

Aberdeenshire & Aberdeen City 1981–84:
Occupied recording units = 11

1981–84

Aberdeenshire & Aberdeen City 2002–06: Change: **+27%**
Occupied recording units = **14**

2002–06

1968–72 = 9

1981–84 = 8

1988–91 = 12

2002–06 = 9

North-East Scotland 1968–72 to 2002–06: Change in occupied 10-km squares = 0%

Razorbill

Alca torda

Very common resident and migrant breeder. Estimated population in North-East Scotland: **12,100 pairs** (13% of Scottish population, 6% of UK)

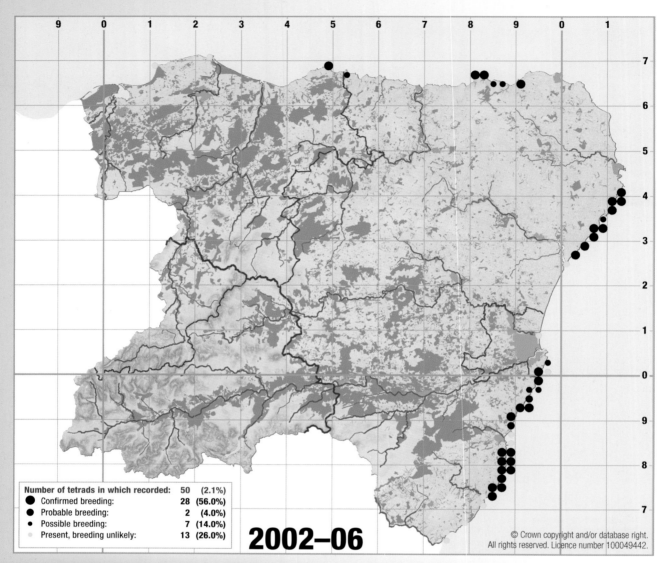

Number of tetrads in which recorded:	50	(2.1%)
● Confirmed breeding:	28	(56.0%)
● Probable breeding:	2	(4.0%)
● Possible breeding:	7	(14.0%)
Present, breeding unlikely:	13	(26.0%)

2002–06

Razorbill, Bullers of Buchan, May 2006. © *John Chapman*

Habitat and breeding biology

Razorbills breed on cliffs around the coast of North-East Scotland, nesting on ledges, in nooks and crannies, and under boulders in scattered, loose colonies. Some nest sites are lower on the cliffs than Guillemots with which the less social Razorbills often loosely associate. Birds return to colonies from February onwards and lay a single egg in late April or early May which is incubated for around 34 days. The chick leaves the cliffs at 19 days and is accompanied out to sea by the male parent. Most birds have left the cliffs by the end of August although some remain offshore in the vicinity of the colony during winter.

Scottish distribution and status

Breeding Razorbills are present in most substantial seabird colonies around much of the mainland coast, the Northern Isles and the Inner and Outer Hebrides. The two largest colonies, containing nearly one quarter of the Scottish population between them, are on Handa (Sutherland) and Berneray in the Outer Hebrides (Lauder in *BS3*). The total Scottish population between 1998–2002 was 139,186 individuals (Seabird 2000) which translates into 93,255 pairs. This represents an overall increase of 12.6% compared with the previous count in 1985–88 (Lloyd *et al.*

1991) but although nine colonies increased, three were unchanged and four declined, most seriously in Shetland.

Distribution and status in North-East Scotland
Most Razorbills breed on the east coast between Boddam and Collieston, and between Cove and Inverbervie. The largest colony, indeed the fifth largest in Scotland, is at Fowlsheugh, north of Crawton. On the north coast, the main colony is at Troup Head with a smaller colony at Quarry Head, near Rosehearty, and a few pairs at Portknockie in Moray.

Changes in distribution
At the 10-km square level, Razorbills have extended their distribution by five squares since the 1980s. This has mostly been achieved by expansion at the edges of the former range. The Aberdeenshire/Aberdeen City maps reveal that there has been in-filling within this range, most notably to the south of Aberdeen, where the number of occupied recording units has doubled. Razorbills first bred at Portknockie in 2003, and a slow expansion of this colony has continued since.

Population and trends
The Razorbill population of North-East Scotland in 1998–2002 totalled 18,070 individual birds, or approximately 12,100 pairs (Seabird 2000). This represents a substantial increase over 10,044 birds counted in 1969–70 (Cramp *et al.* 1974) and reverses the decline to 8,681 birds which was evident between 1969–70 and 1985–88 (Lloyd *et al.* 1991). More recently, however, numbers at some major colonies have declined. At Fowlsheugh numbers fell from 6,362 in 1999 to 4,280 in 2006 (*NESBR* 2006) and at Troup Head there has been a decline of nearly 70% from 3,523 birds in 2001 to 1,069 in 2007 (RSPB colony count 2007). These declines may be due to reductions in availability and quality of food (Lauder in *BS3*). Conversely, numbers along the Boddam to Collieston coast increased by 37% from 3,044 individuals to 4,179 during 2001–07.

Author: *Scott Paterson*

Razorbill, Portknockie, August 2003. © *Martin Cook*

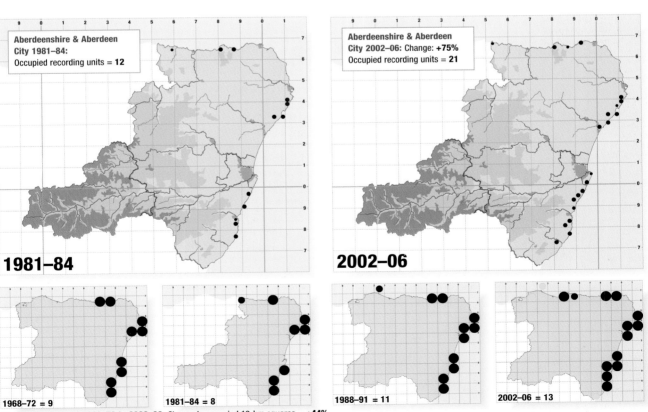

Aberdeenshire & Aberdeen City 1981–84:
Occupied recording units = **12**

1981–84

Aberdeenshire & Aberdeen City 2002–06: Change: **+75%**
Occupied recording units = **21**

2002–06

1968–72 = 9

1981–84 = 8

1988–91 = 11

2002–06 = 13

North-East Scotland 1968–72 to 2002–06: Change in occupied 10-km squares = **+44%**

Black Guillemot

Cepphus grylle

Rare resident. Estimated population in North-East Scotland: **80–100 adults** (<1% of Scottish and UK population)

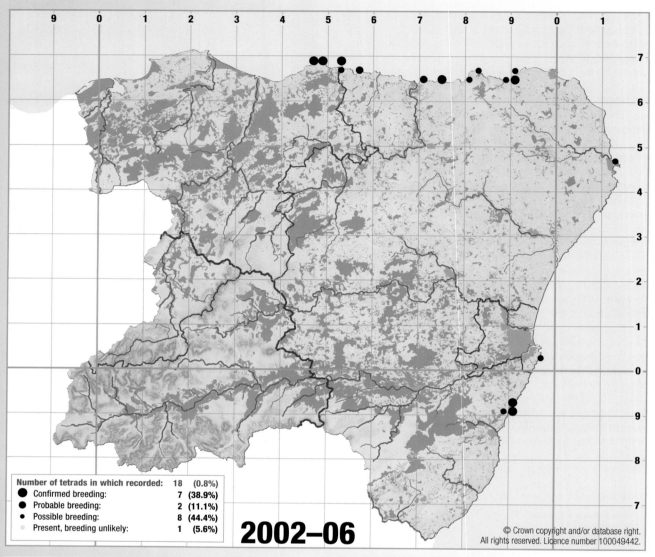

Number of tetrads in which recorded:	18	(0.8%)
● Confirmed breeding:	7	(38.9%)
● Probable breeding:	2	(11.1%)
● Possible breeding:	8	(44.4%)
Present, breeding unlikely:	1	(5.6%)

2002–06

Black Guillemot, Iceland, June 2004. © *Sam Alexander*

Habitat and breeding biology

Black Guillemots breed at low density along cliff-lined coasts, often away from large colonies of other seabirds. They nest in cracks and crevices quite low on the cliffs. Sites may be in caves and narrow inlets, sometimes among rock debris and boulders. In April, birds from a colony will gather on the sea in the early mornings and indulge in communal displays, diving and chasing, breaking into pairs and reforming into larger groups. The clutch, usually of two eggs, is laid between mid May and late June, and fledging may take place in mid July or as late as the end of August. The young are independent from the time of fledging.

Scottish distribution and status

The Scottish population breeds chiefly in loose colonies of up to 50 pairs around the western and northern coasts. There are concentrations in the Hebrides and especially in Orkney and Shetland, where an average spring density of around 7.5 birds/km of coast was estimated in the early 1980s (Walton in *BS3*). The most recent estimate put the Scottish population at 18,750 pairs (Walton in *BS3*).

Distribution and status in North-East Scotland

The breeding population is largely to be found along the Moray and north Aberdeenshire coasts from Findochty eastwards nearly to Rosehearty. In addition, a few birds breed on the cliffs at Muchalls, south of Newtonhill. Other east coast records during 2002–06 (at Peterhead and just south of Aberdeen) are unlikely to indicate breeding sites. On the north coast, the majority of the population is to be found around Portknockie where colonies are centred on Tronach Head and the Bow Fiddle Rock. Elsewhere during 2002–06, breeding was confirmed only at Logie Head (near Cullen), Stocked Head (east of Macduff) and Quarry Head (west of Rosehearty). It also probably took place at West Head (Portsoy) and at Macduff.

Changes in distribution

Comparison between the Aberdeenshire/Aberdeen City maps of 1981–84 and 2002–06 reveals very little change, especially if 'possible breeding' records are discounted. Black Guillemots formerly occurred in the breeding season up the east Aberdeenshire coast and there were colonies at Gamrie and Troup Head until the mid 19th century (Baxter & Rintoul 1953). Apart from a report by Baxter & Rintoul of 'recently recorded' breeding in Kincardineshire, the first comparatively modern record of confirmed breeding was near Portsoy in 1969. During the 1970s, sites were occupied at Pennan/Troup Head, Stocked Head/Silverford and Logie Head. Birds were first noted at Muchalls in 1981 and at Tronach Head in 1982 when they first bred there (*NES 1st Atlas*, Cook 1992). It is perhaps surprising that there has been very little further expansion of range since the early 1980s.

Population and trends

Identification and counting of discrete pairs within pre-breeding assemblies is difficult, as is locating nests. For these reasons the accepted count unit for breeding Black Guillemots is 'adults associated with a colony'; these counts

should ideally be made during the pre-breeding period in April (Walsh *et al.* 1995). In the Tronach Head/Bow Fiddle Rock area, where the first pair bred in 1982, there were never more than four adults annually in the 1980s. A marked increase began in the mid 1990s with 13 adults in 1997 and ten in 2000. Subsequently, breeding season counts in May/June revealed 22 birds in 2002, rising to 32 in 2005. An April early morning count in 2008 located as many as 57 adults, 21 at Tronach Head and 36 around the Bow Fiddle Rock and adjacent mainland cliffs. Numbers at other sites in North-East Scotland are very much lower; during 2002–06 counts of adults revealed six at West Head, four at Stocked Head, three at Quarry Head and at least five at Muchalls. Allowing for a degree of undercounting, and a few birds at Logie Head, it is likely that the current population in North-East Scotland stands at 80–100 adults.

Author: *Martin Cook*

Black Guillemot, Tronach Head, July 1988. © *Martin Cook*

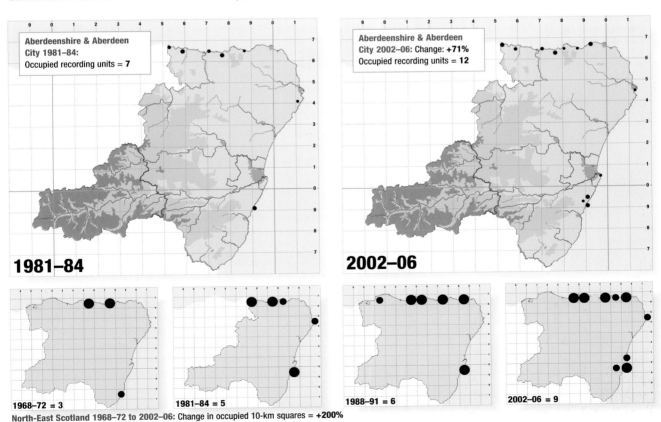

North-East Scotland 1968–72 to 2002–06: Change in occupied 10-km squares = **+200%**

Puffin

Fratercula arctica

Common summer migrant breeder. Estimated population in North-East Scotland: **2,500 pairs** (<1% of Scottish and UK populations)

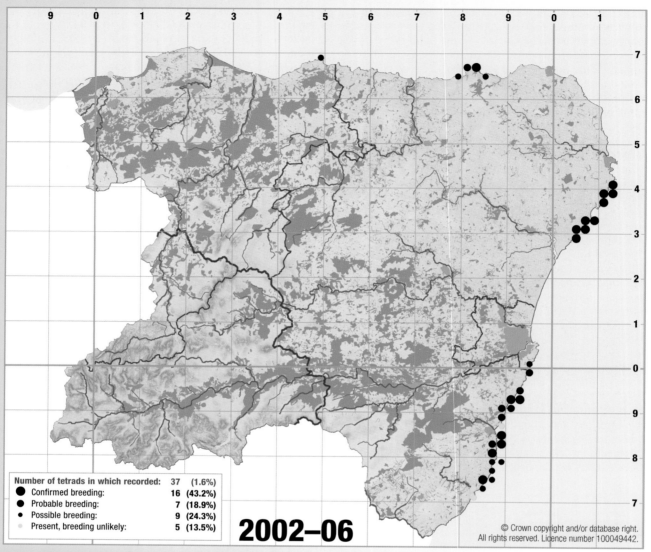

Number of tetrads in which recorded: 37 (1.6%)
- ● Confirmed breeding: 16 (43.2%)
- ● Probable breeding: 7 (18.9%)
- • Possible breeding: 9 (24.3%)
- ○ Present, breeding unlikely: 5 (13.5%)

2002–06

Puffin, Whinnyfold, June 1999. © *Stuart Rae*

Habitat and breeding biology

Puffins breed exclusively on coastal cliffs, nesting in burrows on steep grassy slopes, under boulders or in cracks on cliff faces amongst other breeding auks in colonies in North-East Scotland. They nest in scattered, loose colonies with nest sites generally located near cliff tops. Birds gather offshore from late February to early March, and return to nesting sites from late March. A single egg is laid from early April onwards and incubation takes around six weeks, with the chick leaving the nest site from late June onwards. Most Puffins have left the colonies by late July (Harris & Wanless in *BS3*).

Scottish distribution and status

Puffins are locally common, with the largest numbers breeding on offshore islands in the north and west where the largest colonies are on St Kilda, the Shiant Islands, Sule Skerry and Fair Isle. There are further major colonies in the Firth of Forth, especially on the Isle of May, and smaller colonies scattered around mainland coasts. Between 1998–2000, it was estimated that there were 493,000 pairs breeding in Scotland (Seabird 2000).

Distribution and status in North-East Scotland

Puffins breed in three main locations in North-East Scotland - between Kinneff and Cove, between Boddam and Collieston, and in the vicinity of Troup Head. The biggest concentrations are between Slains and Collieston, with notable colonies at Longhaven, Whinnyfold and the Bullers of Buchan. The largest numbers elsewhere are at Pennan Head, on the north coast, and at Kinneff in the south. Puffins can be watched at close quarters on the grassy slopes around Dunnottar Castle. Although a bird was in suitable habitat in June and July 2002 at Portknockie, there has been no other evidence relating to possible breeding in Moray, either before or since.

Puffin, Fetlar, 1996. © *John Young*

Changes in distribution

Confirmed breeding at the 10-km square level has remained almost unchanged since 1968–72. In 2002–06, however, birds were possibly or probably breeding in three to five more squares than previous atlases have revealed. At the more detailed level of occupied recording units in Aberdeenshire/Aberdeen City there has been a 57% increase to the south of Aberdeen, but little change elsewhere.

Population and trends

The Puffin is a difficult species to survey, with the location of many burrows or nest sites making them almost impossible to count accurately. Numbers are estimated according to counts of burrows or counts of individual birds on the sea and, as attendance at colonies is unpredictable, numbers of birds recorded can be very variable. The Puffin population of the region has increased from 775 burrows in 1969–70 (Cramp *et al.* 1974) to 883 in 1985–88 (Lloyd *et al.* 1991) and as many as 2,488 during 1998–2002 (Seabird 2000). This increase reflects the national trend although there are regional and local variations. There was, however, a large decline between Boddam and Collieston during 2001–07, when the number of individuals fell from 1,231 to 248. Notable counts of birds on the sea during the breeding season in 2002–06 included 300 off Kinneff on 24th April 2004, 250 off Fowlsheugh on 4th June 2004 and 450 off Slains on 30th June 2006 (*NESBR*s). Assuming that the number of burrows approximately equals the number of pairs then the North-East Scotland Puffin population during 1998–2002 was likely to have been around 2,500 pairs. However, Puffin numbers are likely to be affected by the problems responsible for the recent decline in numbers of Guillemots and Razorbills in our region. Although quantifying this decline is difficult given the practical problems in surveying Puffins, it seems likely that their numbers have declined since the Seabird 2000 survey.

Author: *Scott Paterson*

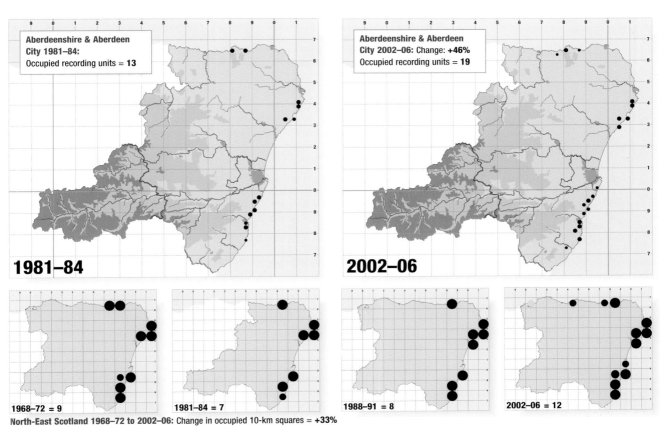

Aberdeenshire & Aberdeen City 1981–84: Occupied recording units = **13**

1981–84

Aberdeenshire & Aberdeen City 2002–06: Change: **+46%** Occupied recording units = **19**

2002–06

1968–72 = 9   1981–84 = 7   1988–91 = 8   2002–06 = 12

North-East Scotland 1968–72 to 2002–06: Change in occupied 10-km squares = +33%

Feral Pigeon/Rock Dove *Columba livia*

Common resident. Estimated population in North-East Scotland: ***7,500–12,000 pairs*** (18% of Scottish population, <10% of UK)

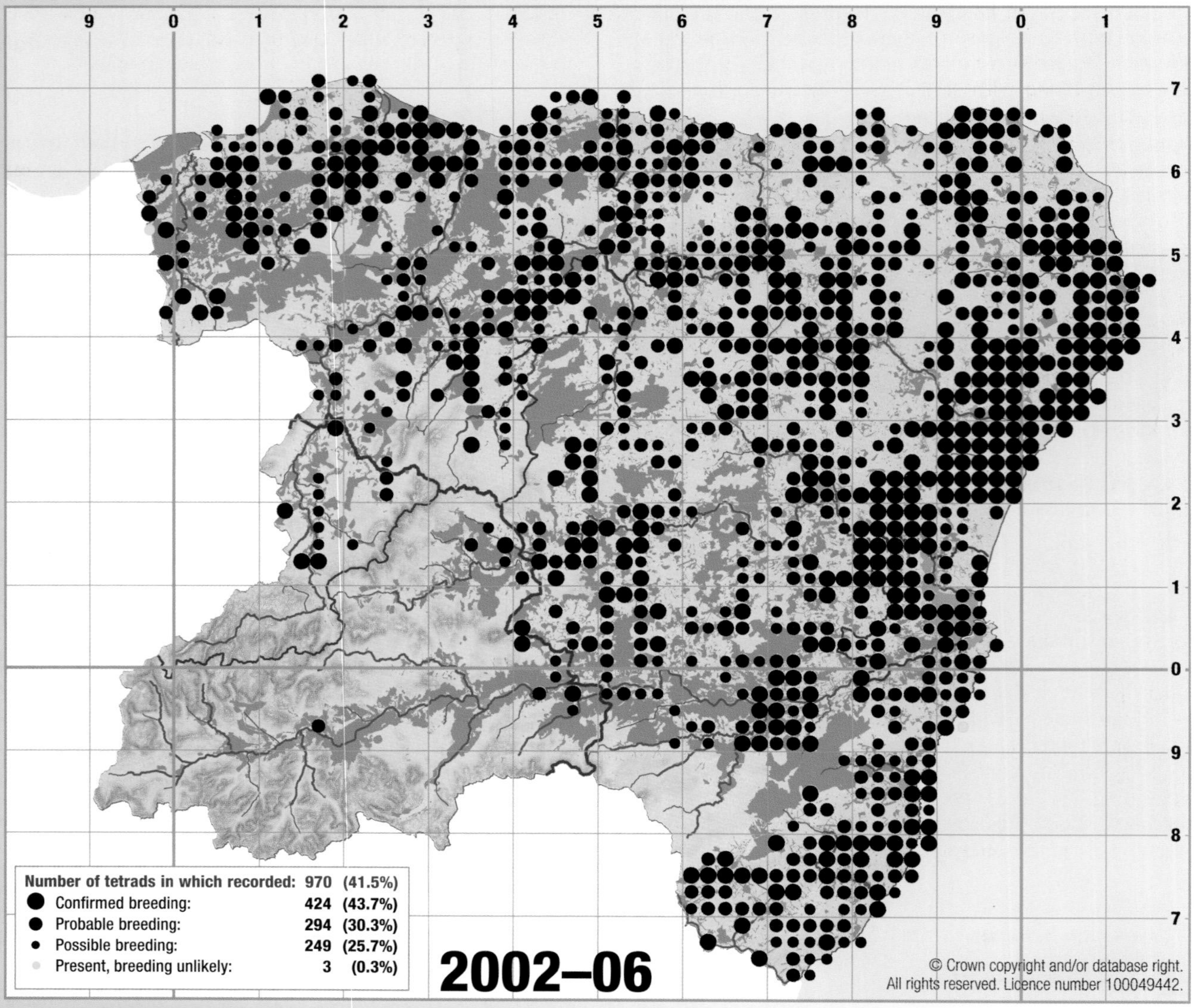
9 0 1 2 3 4 5 6 7 8 9 0 1
7 6 5 4 3 2 1 0 9 8 7
Number of tetrads in which recorded: 970 (41.5%)
● Confirmed breeding: 424 (43.7%)
● Probable breeding: 294 (30.3%)
• Possible breeding: 249 (25.7%)
· Present, breeding unlikely: 3 (0.3%)
2002–06
© Crown copyright and/or database right.
All rights reserved. Licence number 100049442.

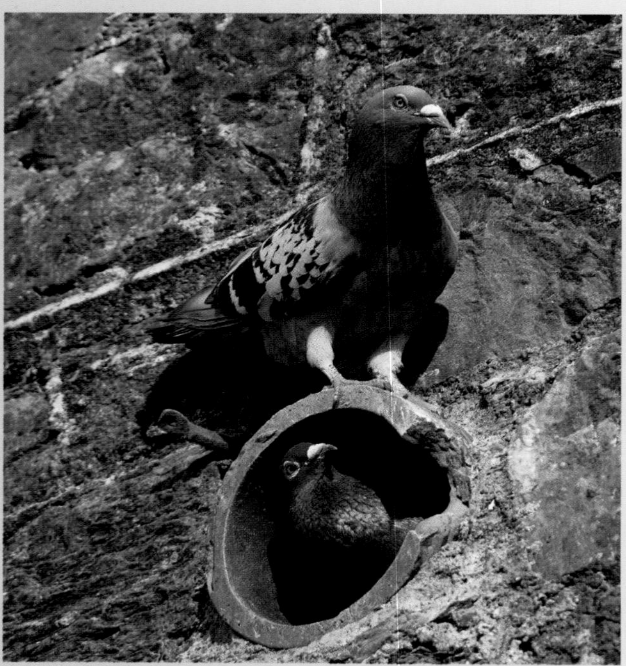

Feral Pigeon, Paignton, Devon, July 2010. © *Harry Scott*

Habitat and breeding biology

Feral Pigeons are found in a variety of habitats, although they are largely absent from the uplands. They are particularly associated with urban areas and farmland, where breeding takes place in buildings. Coastal cliffs are also commonly used for breeding and in these areas birds showing characteristics of 'pure' Rock Doves can be seen, although a wide variety of other plumages occur. Local populations of 'pure' Rock Doves are assumed to have been lost due to interbreeding with Feral Pigeons. Where conditions permit, breeding activity takes place throughout the year, although chick survival in cold conditions may be poor (Riddle 1971). During 1981–84, fledged young were noted in North-East Scotland in every month from February to October (*NES 1st Atlas*).

Scottish distribution and status

Feral Pigeons are found commonly throughout southern and eastern Scotland. 'Pure' Rock Doves predominate in the Hebrides and the Northern Isles, with the northern and western mainland occupied by a mixture of the two types. A Scottish population of 31,000–78,000 pairs has been estimated, of which less than 5,000 are thought to be 'pure' Rock Doves (ap Rheinallt in *BS3*). Over the period 1994–2007, BBS results indicate a significant 31% decline in the Scottish population (Risely *et al.* 2008).

Distribution and status in North-East Scotland

Feral Pigeons are found commonly throughout the lowlands of North-East Scotland, with inhabited areas broadly matching those of the human population below 350 m. The eastern coastal strip is particularly densely populated, along with similar areas around other larger settlements including in lower Deeside and the vicinity of Elgin. They inhabit countryside with a predominantly arable agricultural land use; the populations concentrate around the human settlements here. Many smaller villages also have breeding Feral Pigeons and their ability to adapt to areas where man has settled is shown by an isolated record of probable breeding at Braemar. There are very few lowland habitats that Feral Pigeons totally avoid, but they are generally very scarce in large woodlands, especially dense plantations. An absence from the sand dunes around Rattray Head is probably genuine, but other gaps in the distribution in the Buchan plain may be because breeding birds were only thinly distributed around farm buildings and were not detected during fieldwork. It is likely that the records shown are all of Feral Pigeon populations, with 'pure' Rock Doves unlikely to have survived in North-East Scotland. As Rock Doves and Feral Pigeons show some genetic differences (Johnston *et al.* 1988), this may be an area worthy of further study, especially as it has been suggested that the two forms may coexist in some areas (ap Rheinallt in *BS3*).

Changes in distribution

Feral Pigeons were widespread in 1968–72 (*BTO 1st Atlas*) and have undergone further range expansion since then. By 1981–84, considerable infilling of their range had taken place (*NES 1st Atlas*), presumably aided by an increasing human population as settlements, such as Ellon, increased in size. The most noticeable recent change in distribution

has been the south-westerly expansion of range, with the Deeside and Donside areas west of Alford and Aboyne seeing an increase in breeding records. This has contributed to the large increase from 66 to 90 occupied 10-km squares since 1968–72 (*BTO 1st Atlas*). Increased food supply and nesting opportunities may account for some of this spread, but it is also likely that milder winters are encouraging a longer breeding season, allowing population expansion.

Population and trends

Feral Pigeons are not well covered by the common census methods and there have been no attempts made to survey the British population. Population density will vary across the North-East, with the lowland areas capable of supporting a higher number of pairs per tetrad than the marginally populated uplands. Surveys in south-east Scotland, which contains a similar range of habitats to the North-East, suggest a density of 8–12 pairs/tetrad (Murray *et al.* 1998). Applying these figures to the 969 occupied tetrads in North-East Scotland provides an estimate of 7,500–12,000 pairs, with the vast majority (possibly all) of these pairs likely to be Feral Pigeons rather than 'pure' Rock Doves. Increases in range since 1968–72 have probably been accompanied by an overall increase in the population. Although some winter food supplies, such as stubble fields, may have diminished with changing agricultural practices, others will have increased, including the provision of seed and grain in gardens. It is also likely that racing pigeons are recruited into the population, at least in Aberdeen where ringed pigeons are frequently seen on the streets. The increase of predators in urban areas, particularly Sparrowhawk and Peregrine, appears to have had little or no impact on Feral Pigeon populations. Indeed the same buildings chosen as nest sites by Peregrines in urban areas often contain several nesting pairs of Feral Pigeons!

Author: *David Parnaby*

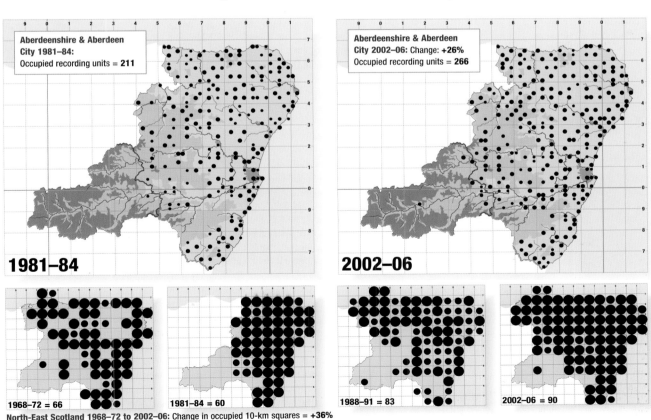

North-East Scotland 1968–72 to 2002–06: Change in occupied 10-km squares = **+36%**

Stock Dove

Columba oenas

Locally common resident. Estimated population in North-East Scotland: **2,000–4,000 pairs** (24% of Scottish population, <1% of UK)

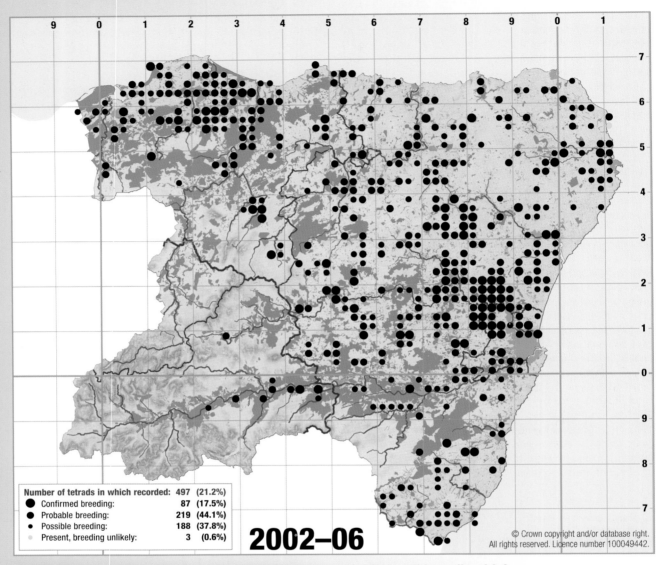

Number of tetrads in which recorded:	497	(21.2%)
● Confirmed breeding:	87	(17.5%)
● Probable breeding:	219	(44.1%)
• Possible breeding:	188	(37.8%)
· Present, breeding unlikely:	3	(0.6%)

2002–06

Stock Dove, Berkshire, January 2011. © *Gavin Bennett*

Habitat and breeding biology

Mature broad-leaved trees with suitable nesting holes, in conjunction with arable farmland for feeding are the predominant breeding habitat requirements for Stock Doves and these exist widely across lowland North-East Scotland. In addition, birds will also use nestboxes such as Tawny Owl boxes, derelict buildings with suitable cavities, and cliff sites such as quarry walls. In the past, birds bred regularly in Rabbit burrows on the Moray coast but this has not been recorded in recent times. The breeding season extends from the end of March until the end of September. Pairs can be solitary or semi-colonial with several pairs close together. Nest sites are often used repeatedly over a number of years.

Scottish distribution and status

Stock Doves are patchily distributed in the Borders, Central Lowlands and North-East Scotland but they are largely absent from the north and west. They colonised Scotland in the second part of the 19th century and increased rapidly in association with the spread of arable farming. There was a big decline in the 1950s and 1960s, coinciding with agricultural intensification, although numbers have since partially recovered. The Scottish population is estimated at 10,000–15,000 pairs (Jardine in *BS3*).

Distribution and status in North-East Scotland

The map shows that Stock Doves are widely but irregularly distributed throughout the lowlands but are largely absent from the high interior. The highest concentrations occur in lower Donside, between Aberdeen and Inverurie, and in lowland Moray. Large gaps appear on the Buchan plain and in Kincardine. This does not support the indication in the 1988–91 BTO Atlas that Buchan is one of the highest density breeding areas in Scotland. They avoid heavily-forested areas which may explain their sparse distribution in Deeside compared to Donside. The Stock Dove is not an obvious species and may be under-recorded by observers not familiar with its song and not confident in separating flying birds from Feral Pigeons. There are no known regular movements of Stock Doves in North-East Scotland and birds probably stay close to their breeding territories all year round, with singing recorded from the start of January until the end of October.

Changes in distribution

Following their colonisation of North-East Scotland in the late 1800s, Stock Doves were at their most numerous in the early part of the 20th century. In common with other parts of Scotland, they became scarce in the 1950s and 1960s but they have recovered well and this range expansion has continued, with 39% more 10-km squares occupied in 2002–06 than in 1968–72. Comparing the smaller recording units in Aberdeenshire/Aberdeen City, the increase between 1981–84 and 2002–06 is revealed more dramatically, the level of occupancy having nearly trebled. This increase is due to infilling of the former range with expansion in all directions except into the uplands, though increased recording effort may have been influential in some areas.

Population and trends

There have been no methodical attempts to estimate the Stock Dove population in North-East Scotland. The Scottish population has recently been estimated at 10,000–15,000 pairs with about a quarter of the range lying within the

Stock Dove, Ballater, April 2008. © *Harry Scott*

boundaries of this current atlas (Jardine in *BS3*) which might suggest a population of between 2,000–4,000 pairs in the North-East. Stock Doves were recorded in 497 tetrads which would give an average density of 4–8 pairs/occupied tetrad but it is possible this could still be an underestimate. Numbers have clearly increased in North-East Scotland over the last 20 years and being predominantly a seedeater the Stock Dove has undoubtedly benefited from set-aside and agri-environmental schemes. Lack of nest sites still causes large gaps in the distribution and it is likely that the species will be sensitive to possible future changes in agricultural practice, so it remains to be seen whether the recent positive trend can be maintained.

Author: *Andrew Stalker*

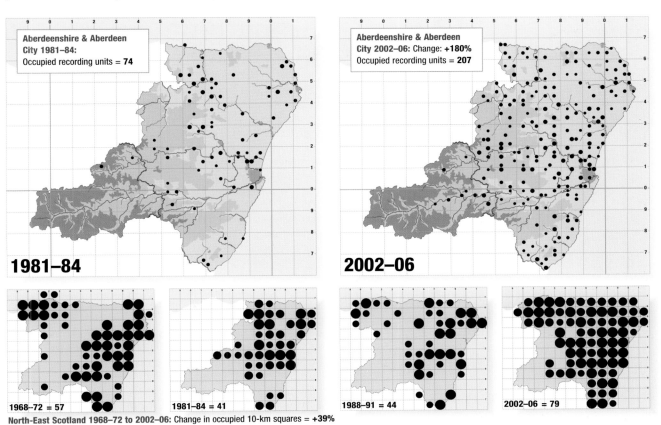

Aberdeenshire & Aberdeen City 1981–84: Occupied recording units = **74**

1981–84

Aberdeenshire & Aberdeen City 2002–06: Change: **+180%** Occupied recording units = **207**

2002–06

1968–72 = 57   1981–84 = 41   1988–91 = 44   2002–06 = 79

North-East Scotland 1968–72 to 2002–06: Change in occupied 10-km squares = +39%

Woodpigeon   *Columba palumbus*

Very common resident and migrant. Estimated population in North-East Scotland: *90,000–110,000 pairs* (18% of Scottish population, 4% of UK)

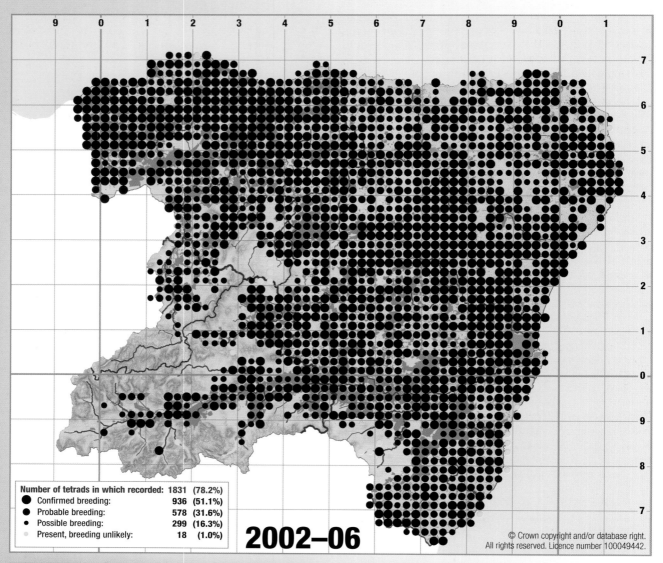

Number of tetrads in which recorded:	1831	(78.2%)
● Confirmed breeding:	936	(51.1%)
● Probable breeding:	578	(31.6%)
● Possible breeding:	299	(16.3%)
● Present, breeding unlikely:	18	(1.0%)

2002–06

Woodpigeon, Aberdeen, April 2007. © *John Chapman*

Habitat and breeding biology

Woodpigeons breed in a wide range of woodlands, as well as parkland, scrub, hedgerows and gardens. In North-East Scotland, dense conifer plantations (especially Sitka Spruce) adjacent to arable land probably support the largest numbers (Colquhoun 1951), although suburban gardens have also become increasingly important. The flimsy, open nest is placed in a wide range of locations wherever dense foliage hides the incubating bird, eggs or chicks. The breeding season extends from April to September, longer in suburban areas; birds were still incubating eggs on 18th October at St Cyrus in 2002 (*NESBR* 2002). Breeding success is probably highest in August–September when the supply of cereal grains is greatest (Murton 1965). This minimises foraging time of adults provisioning chicks, enabling them to spend more time at the nest.

Scottish distribution and status

The Woodpigeon is a widespread breeding species, found wherever arable feeding areas are adjacent to suitable nesting sites. It is most abundant in the south and east of Scotland and is absent from treeless and montane areas of the north and west mainland and the islands (McKay in *BS3*). The Scottish population is estimated to lie within the range 488,000–600,000 pairs (McKay in *BS3*). BBS data show a non-significant decline of 11% in Scotland during 1994–2007 (Risely *et al.* 2008).

Distribution and status in North-East Scotland
Woodpigeons are found throughout middle and low altitudes in North-East Scotland from Aberdeen City and the coast to upland plantations. They are probably most abundant in arable areas with pockets of dense woodland or thickets - such as conifers planted as shelter belts or game cover, and along the edges of extensive conifer plantations. Such areas extend in a broad band from the coastal lowlands to the foothills of the Grampians. They are absent from non-wooded upland and montane areas, and scarce or absent from some treeless parts of the Buchan plain, the Deeside Caledonian pine woodlands (whose open nature provides little nesting cover), and extensive tracts of coniferous plantation where these are distant from arable feeding grounds.

Woodpigeon, Alford, July 2000. © *Ian Francis*

Changes in distribution
There has been no significant change in distribution over the last 40 years. At the 10-km square level, occupancy has remained almost constant at 103–107 squares, and the number of occupied recording units in Aberdeenshire/Aberdeen City has risen only slightly between 1981–84 and 2002–06. These small differences are more likely to be due to variations in observer effort than to any genuine range change.

Population and trends
It is difficult to estimate the Woodpigeon population size as the species is hard to census by standard methods. Small areas of suitable nesting habitat can support high nesting densities: Colquhoun (1951) found 24.7 nests/ha in thicket stage spruce at Loch of Skene, whilst up to 37.4 nests/ha were found in similar habitats in Angus (pers. obs.). An estimated 56 pairs were found in a 1-km square at Keith Hall (Inverurie) in 2004 but in many parts of the North-East densities will be lower. In the absence of local data we can apply densities from other well-populated parts of Scotland. Population estimates for the tetrad atlases in South-East Scotland and Fife assumed a density of 40 pairs/tetrad which, if applied to the 1,813 occupied tetrads in North-East Scotland where breeding was considered at least possible, would give a total population of 72,520 pairs. However, estimates of breeding density in 6 tetrads in an intensively searched study area in Angus during 2007–08 ranged between 45 and 190 pairs/tetrad (average 115) (pers. obs.). This suggests that 40 pairs/tetrad may be a conservative estimate; 50–60 pairs/tetrad may be more realistic, suggesting a total population in the region of 90,000–110,000 pairs.

Author: *Clive McKay*

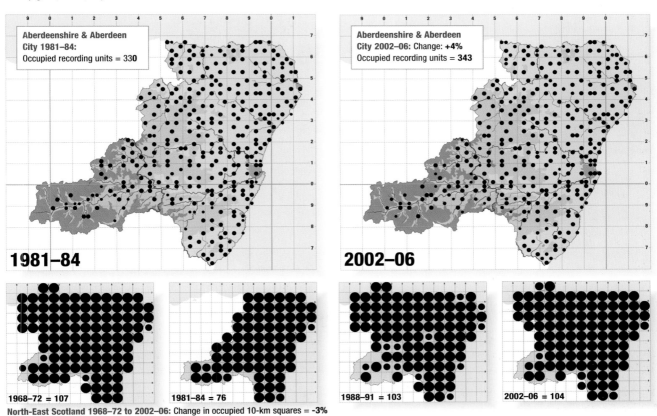

Aberdeenshire & Aberdeen City 1981–84: Occupied recording units = 330

1981–84

Aberdeenshire & Aberdeen City 2002–06: Change: +4% Occupied recording units = 343

2002–06

1968–72 = 107   1981–84 = 76   1988–91 = 103   2002–06 = 104

North-East Scotland 1968–72 to 2002–06: Change in occupied 10-km squares = -3%

Collared Dove

Streptopelia decaocto

Common resident. Estimated population in North-East Scotland: **2,000–3,500 pairs** (28% of Scottish population, <1% of UK)

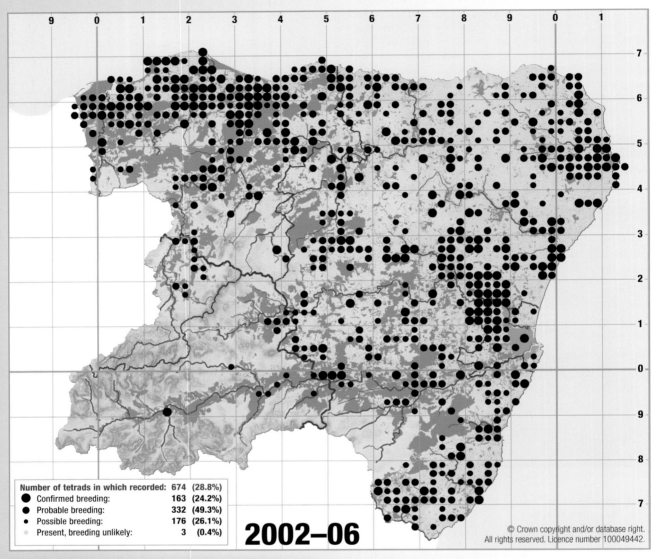

Number of tetrads in which recorded:	674	(28.8%)
● Confirmed breeding:	163	(24.2%)
● Probable breeding:	332	(49.3%)
● Possible breeding:	176	(26.1%)
· Present, breeding unlikely:	3	(0.4%)

2002–06

Collared Dove, Kintore, February 2009. © *Walter Burns*

Habitat and breeding biology

The favoured breeding habitat of Collared Doves is in lowland areas near human habitation with highest numbers near towns, villages, farms and gardens, but avoiding large city centres. They are found mainly at low density in open farmland areas where scattered pairs associate with farm buildings. The main breeding season in Scotland is from February to November and they often produce multiple broods, with an average clutch size of 1.93 (Insley in *BS3*). At the height of the breeding season, females may still be feeding young from a previous brood while incubating the next clutch (*BTO 1st Atlas*). The flimsy nests may be built either in conifers or in deciduous trees as well as, less commonly, on ledges on buildings.

Scottish distribution and status

Collared Doves breed widely throughout much of Scotland but avoid the uplands. Their range includes the Hebrides and the Northern Isles, although Shetland is sparsely populated. They favour the coastal lowlands and are particularly concentrated around the inner Moray Firth, north-east Aberdeenshire, central and south-west Scotland. The Scottish population is currently estimated at 8,000–12,000 pairs (Insley in *BS3*).

Distribution and status in North-East Scotland

The influence of human habitation combined with habitat dictates the breeding distribution of Collared Doves. The coastal plain of Moray with its farms and villages is particularly favoured, along with lower Donside and the area around Peterhead. Heavily forested areas of Moray and south-east Aberdeenshire are largely avoided and they are thinly spread through the arable countryside of Buchan. They penetrate the river valleys where human settlements exist and the highest altitude populations are found at 300–350 m around Braemar, Cabrach and Tomintoul.

Changes in distribution

The first breeding in Scotland took place at Covesea, in Moray, in 1957 and by 1960 Collared Doves had spread to Elgin and Forres. A rapid range expansion followed, and by 1964 the population of the Laich of Moray was estimated at 99–134 pairs (Cook 1992). The first Aberdeen record was in 1960, and a pair was there in 1961, but the first proved breeding records in Aberdeenshire came from Newburgh and Stonehaven in 1963 (MacMillan 1965). By 1968–72, 68 10-km squares throughout the lowlands of North-East Scotland were occupied (*BTO 1st Atlas*). This number increased to 70 in 1988–91 (*BTO 2nd Atlas*) and 90 in 2002–06 during fieldwork for the current Atlas. Comparison of the Aberdeenshire/Aberdeen City 1981–84 and 2002–06 maps shows a general in-filling of the existing range with a 30% increase in occupied recording units. There is a greater distribution of breeding birds in both Deeside and Donside and even in the thinly populated human settlements of Buchan. These changes may be due to continued exploitation of a previously unfilled ecological niche.

Collared Dove, Aboyne, March 2002. © *Harry Scott*

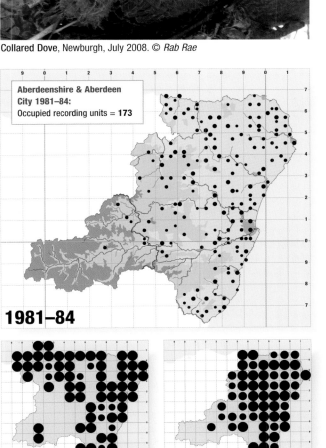

Collared Dove, Newburgh, July 2008. © *Rab Rae*

Population and trends

There have been no local studies of Collared Dove populations and relevant data are sparse. A few tetrads which are centred on rural villages may contain at least ten pairs (pers. obs.) but a range of 3–5 pairs/occupied tetrad is probably more typical. Applying this range to the 673 occupied tetrads found during 2002–06 suggests a North-East Scotland population within the range of 2,000–3,500 pairs. Local BBS data suggest a slight increase in the population during 1994–2006 but the sample size is very small and conflicts with the Scottish figure of a 25% decline over the period 1994–2007 (Risely *et al.* 2008).

Author: *Jenny Cook*

Aberdeenshire & Aberdeen City 1981–84:
Occupied recording units = **173**

1981–84

Aberdeenshire & Aberdeen City 2002–06: Change: +30%
Occupied recording units = **225**

2002–06

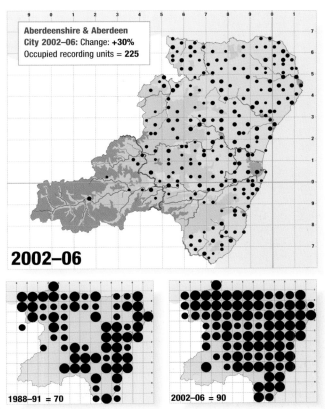

1968–72 = 68   1981–84 = 60   1988–91 = 70   2002–06 = 90

North-East Scotland 1968–72 to 2002–06: Change in occupied 10-km squares = **+32%**

Cuckoo

Cuculus canorus

Scarce summer migrant breeder. Estimated population in North-East Scotland: *350–400 pairs* (12% of Scottish population, 3% of UK)

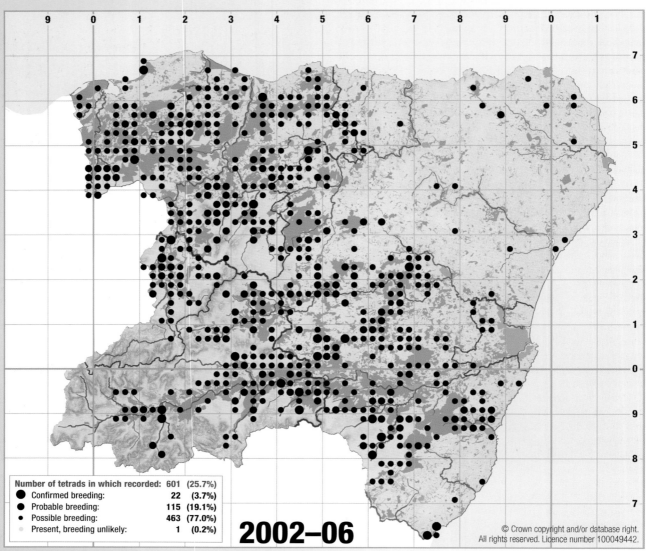

Number of tetrads in which recorded:	601	(25.7%)
● Confirmed breeding:	22	(3.7%)
● Probable breeding:	115	(19.1%)
● Possible breeding:	463	(77.0%)
Present, breeding unlikely:	1	(0.2%)

2002–06

Cuckoo, Dinnet, June 2005. © *Ed Duthie*

Habitat and breeding biology

Cuckoos occupy a wide range of habitats. In North-East Scotland they most favour moorlands, open woodlands and woodland edges which support high densities of potential host species. These are likely to be Meadow Pipits, Tree Pipits (R. Duncan pers. comm.) or Dunnocks in the North-East while at least 10 other passerine species, and even Common Sandpiper, are known to have been parasitized in Scotland (Okill in *BS3*). After their arrival, from mid April, Cuckoos start to locate the nests of their host species and lay a single egg in each. Once it has hatched, the nestling is fed by the host parents and may be dependent on them until late July.

Scottish distribution and status

Cuckoos breed in most parts of Scotland and are particularly numerous in upland areas of the north and west. Highest breeding densities are in middle altitude moorland, a habitat also favoured by Meadow Pipits. A somewhat speculative estimate of the Scottish population in 2007 was 2,100–4,400 pairs (Okill in *BS3*).

Distribution and status in North-East Scotland

In Aberdeenshire, Cuckoos are widespread in mid and upper Deeside and Donside but they are scarce as a breeding species in Buchan, with few occupied tetrads north-east of a line from Aberdeen to Cullen in east Moray. In Moray they are far more widely distributed although again there are few records from the coastal strip. Highest densities are found on moorland and lightly wooded areas up to an altitude of *c*.500 m, with fewer birds in the dense conifer plantations and agricultural areas. Whilst this may be related to the distribution of a favourite host species, the Meadow Pipit, this does not account for the Cuckoo's lack of occupancy of tetrads in areas of Buchan eastwards from Tore of Troup and New Pitsligo where Meadow Pipits breed in reasonable numbers. Perhaps prey availability is a factor in these more intensively farmed areas. First returning birds are usually heard in late April with the majority arriving in early May. During 2002–06, first arrival dates ranged from 20th April to 1st May (*NESBRs*, *MNBRs*).

Changes in distribution

In 1968–72, Cuckoos were found in 100 10-km squares but this number fell substantially to 71 in 1988–91 before recovering to 85 in 2002–06. At a finer level of detail, there were 146 occupied recording units in Aberdeenshire/Aberdeen City in 1981–84 and this increased by 16% to 170 by 2002–06, also suggestive of a recovery since the 1980s. By contrast with a 37% decline in the UK as a whole, Scottish BBS data indicate a 39% population increase during 1994–2007 (Risely *et al.* 2008), giving credence to the likelihood of a range expansion. Within Aberdeenshire, this expansion has been in formerly-populated areas with no evidence of spread into the agricultural lowlands.

Population and trends

Proof of breeding for Cuckoos is very hard to gather and this was only achieved in 22 tetrads out of 601 in which birds were recorded. During 1988–91, the British population was calculated using an estimate of 5–10 pairs/10-km square, with North-East Scotland an area of low abundance (*BTO 2nd Atlas*). If we apply the average figure of 5 pairs/10-km square to the 85 occupied

squares, and make allowances for incomplete squares by deducting an area equivalent to eight 10-km squares, then the population may lie around 350–400 pairs.

Author: *Dominic Funnell*

Cuckoo, Mar Lodge, June 2006. © *Rab Rae*

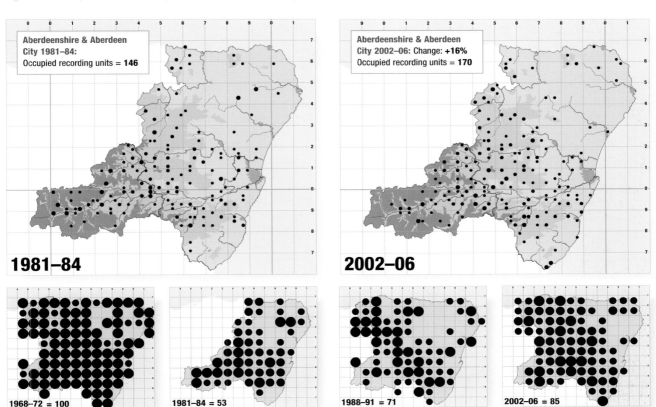

Aberdeenshire & Aberdeen City 1981–84:
Occupied recording units = **146**

1981–84

Aberdeenshire & Aberdeen City 2002–06: Change: +16%
Occupied recording units = **170**

2002–06

1968–72 = 100   1981–84 = 53

1988–91 = 71   2002–06 = 85

North-East Scotland 1968–72 to 2002–06: Change in occupied 10-km squares = **-15%**

Barn Owl

Tyto alba

Scarce resident. Estimated population in North-East Scotland: **200 pairs** (27% of Scottish population, 5% of UK)

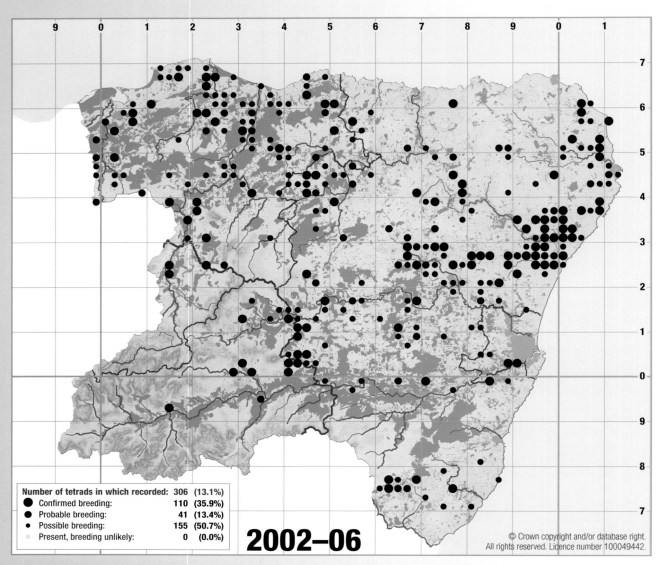

Number of tetrads in which recorded:	306	(13.1%)
● Confirmed breeding:	110	(35.9%)
● Probable breeding:	41	(13.4%)
• Possible breeding:	155	(50.7%)
· Present, breeding unlikely:	0	(0.0%)

2002–06

Habitat and breeding biology

Barn Owls inhabit agricultural areas which offer open grassland over which they can hunt for their small mammal prey. They also hunt along field margins, woodland edges and road verges; the latter accounting for numerous casualties caused by traffic. Their range also extends to the moorland edge where rough grazing and derelict crofts provide breeding opportunities. The majority of pairs nest in older farm buildings although large tree holes are commonly used and even cliff cavities. They also take readily to nest boxes, which has enabled range extensions in some parts of Scotland. The chief prey species, the Field Vole, shows cycles of abundance, typically building to a peak every three years. In the uplands, where there is little alternative prey, this influences the Barn Owls' clutch size, fledged brood size and number of broods. Indeed they may not attempt to breed at all when vole populations are at their lowest. The effect is less marked in lowland areas where a greater range of prey species is available (Shaw in *BS3*).

Scottish distribution and status

Central and southern Scotland holds the majority of the population, especially in Borders, Dumfries & Galloway, Ayrshire and parts of Argyll. To the north, Barn Owls are largely confined to the lowland fringe of Scotland with a concentration around the inner Moray Firth. They have recently extended their range northwards into Caithness but remain absent as breeders in the Outer Hebrides, the Northern Isles and the north-west of the mainland. The Scottish breeding population is currently estimated at 500–1,000 pairs (Shaw in *BS3*).

Distribution and status in North-East Scotland

Barn Owls are widespread but scarce breeders over much of North-East Scotland although they are conspicuously absent from much of the uplands and from extensive tracts of forestry; both habitats usually fail to provide adequate hunting or nesting opportunities. On occasion, however, Barn Owls can do well in upland areas, such as near Braemar and around Gairnshiel and Glen Fenzie where breeding was proved at 300–350 m. Over much of the lowlands the distribution is patchy with an obvious concentration around Ellon, related in part to intensive fieldwork effort here. Other well-populated areas include north and east Moray, around Peterhead, the Garioch between Insch and Oldmeldrum, upper Donside, around Logie Coldstone and north of Fettercairn. There is little apparent reason why Barn Owls should be distributed in this way when similar

The Breeding Birds of North-East Scotland

habitat is a lot more widespread. Barn Owls can be very secretive in the breeding season and a lot less vocal than other nocturnal owl species. It seems very likely therefore that recording effort has had a significant influence on the appearance of the distribution map, and that the range is rather more extensive than is shown.

Barn Owl, Logie Coldstone, May 2008. © *Harry Scott*

Changes in distribution

During the first (1968–72) and second (1988–91) BTO Breeding Bird Atlases, Barn Owls were located in 29 and 14 10-km squares respectively. In the 2002–06 survey, however, 78 10-km squares were found to be occupied. A similar trend of apparent dramatic increase is revealed by the rise from only eight occupied recording units in Aberdeenshire/Aberdeen City in 1981–84 to 127 in 2002–06. British data lends credence to the decline during the 1970s and 1980s (*BTO 2nd Atlas*) but what of the subsequent expansion? Work in the south and west of Scotland has revealed steady growth in the population since the 1980s (Shaw in *BS3*) but even if this is replicated in North-East Scotland it is most unlikely to have caused the degree of range expansion described above. Nonetheless, Barn Owls have been extending their range northwards into Sutherland and Caithness since the 1990s and this genuine spread may augment what is otherwise likely to be an apparent increase in distribution in North-East Scotland, driven to a large degree by improved recording effort.

Population and trends

In view of the factors outlined above, any attempt at a North-East Scotland population estimate is likely to be highly speculative. Atlas fieldwork during 2002–06 confirmed breeding in 110 tetrads. In some instances, records with lower breeding evidence in adjacent tetrads will be due to local movement from nearby breeding territories. The presence of birds in more isolated tetrads in summer is likely, however, to indicate undetected breeding in many instances. It is also very probable that breeding pairs have been missed in tetrads which received only day time visits. A conservative estimate would therefore place the population at 110–200 pairs. However, in view of the fact that systematic work in East Ross during 1995–99 revealed a local density as high as 18 pairs/10-km square (McGhie 2000), the North-East population probably exceeds 200 pairs.

Author: *Martin Cook*

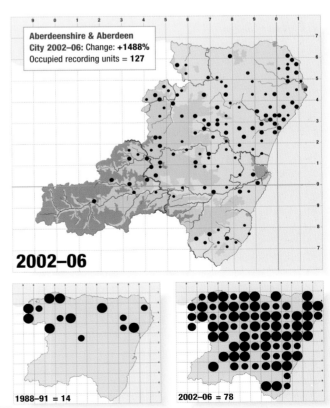

Aberdeenshire & Aberdeen City 1981–84:
Occupied recording units = **8**

1981–84

Aberdeenshire & Aberdeen City 2002–06: Change: **+1488%**
Occupied recording units = **127**

2002–06

1968–72 = 29   1981–84 = 7

1988–91 = 14   2002–06 = 78

North-East Scotland 1968–72 to 2002–06: Change in occupied 10-km squares = **+169%**

Tawny Owl
Strix aluco

Common resident. Estimated population in North-East Scotland: *1,500–2,000 pairs* (29% of Scottish Population, 9% of UK)

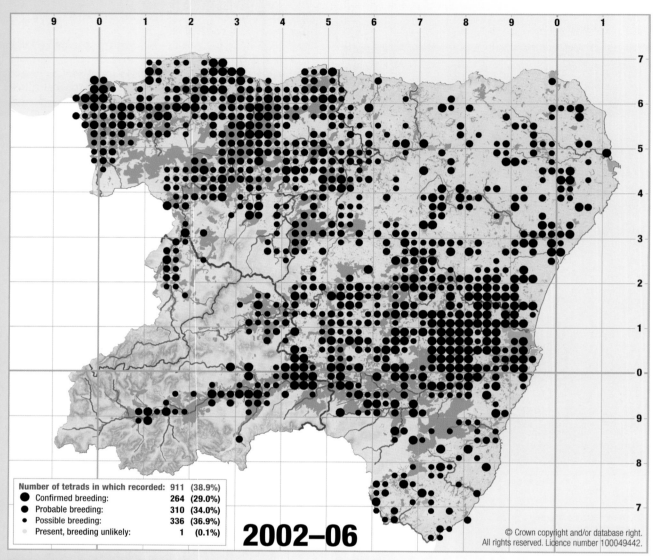

Number of tetrads in which recorded: 911 (38.9%)
- Confirmed breeding: 264 (29.0%)
- Probable breeding: 310 (34.0%)
- Possible breeding: 336 (36.9%)
- Present, breeding unlikely: 1 (0.1%)

2002–06

Habitat and breeding biology
The Tawny Owl is primarily a bird of woodlands but can also be found on farmland and in urban areas with sufficient small woods and trees. Breeding densities are highest in deciduous woodland but it can also be found in mature conifer plantations where the mix of crop ages provides food and shelter. The distinctive song and calls are heard throughout the year, but birds are particularly noisy in late winter and early spring prior to breeding. The favoured nest site is a cavity in a tree, but where these are not available a range of alternative sites can be used including ledges and cavities in crags, buildings and stick nests of other species. They take readily to nest boxes. In the Mar area they sometimes nest on the ground - under roots and in the scree slopes within the forests (R. Rae pers. comm.). The earliest clutches are usually laid in March. In years when their rodent food supply is scarce, many pairs lay reduced clutches or may fail to breed.

Scottish distribution and status
Tawny Owls breed widely across most of mainland Scotland, where suitable habitat is present. They are more common in southern and eastern Scotland, thinning out in upland areas. They are scarce in the west, especially the relatively tree-less uplands of north-west Scotland, and they are absent from the Outer Hebrides and Northern Isles. The most recent Scottish population estimate is about 6,000 pairs (Petty in *BS3*).

Distribution and status in North-East Scotland
Tawny Owls are widespread and relatively common in the North-East, although the density varies across the area. They are absent from the higher uplands of the Cairngorms and the associated moorlands of the foothills which stretch north-east from the upper Deeside area, towards Strathdon, and up to Tomintoul and Glenfiddich. They are also absent from much of the uplands and moorlands in the south, bordering Perth & Kinross and Angus. The greatest density is found in a broad band of well-wooded country between the high uplands and the agricultural lowlands of the north-east. They thin out markedly to the north and east of this band and in the far south where there is much less woodland in the fertile farmland. The lack of birds in the lower hills above Dallas and Kellas and across to the Spey Valley reflects an area of moorland and although there is extensive forestry, this is too young at present to support significant numbers of Tawny Owls. It is likely that birds are under-recorded in many areas such as Fetteresso Forest, south of Banchory, as birds are generally active at night when few people are present,

and observer coverage is limited. They are well recorded in areas with detailed surveys such as north Moray or long-running studies such as around Skene and Dunecht (Massie 2000, Massie & Walker 2007). In the agricultural north-east of Aberdeenshire the absence of woodland with suitable nest sites is the principal reason for the species' scarcity although they are probably under-recorded here also. Their willingness to breed in close proximity to human habitation is well demonstrated by the extent of proved breeding within the central areas of Aberdeen City.

Tawny Owl, Dinnet, May 2005. © *Harry Scott*

Changes in distribution

At the 10-km square level, the current distribution is very similar to that found in 1968–72 (*BTO 1st Atlas*). The apparent temporary reduction in occupied 10-km squares in 1988–91 (*BTO 2nd Atlas*) is due, in part at least, to reduced observer coverage. There is, however, a suggestion of a decline in the 1970s and 1980s due, perhaps, to adverse winter weather and agricultural changes (*NES 1st Atlas*). This possible decline has subsequently been reversed, and comparison of the Aberdeenshire/Aberdeen City maps shows a doubling of occupied recording units since 1981–84. In the southern parts of North-East Scotland the increase has been due to infilling of gaps but from Donside northwards there has been a more general range expansion.

Population and trends

Published breeding densities for Tawny Owls in Scotland range from 1.4–2.2 pairs/km^2 (5.6–8.8 pairs/tetrad) in mature spruce plantations (Petty in *BS3*) to 1.2 pairs/km^2 (4.8 pairs/tetrad) in farmland in Aberdeenshire (Hardey 1992); but these numbers are derived from work in the 1970s–early 1980s. Densities of 4 pairs/tetrad in well-wooded habitat and 1 pair/tetrad in poorer habitat have been applied in South-east Scotland and in Fife (Murray *et al.* 1998, Elkins *et al.* 2003). These east coast areas both show similar patterns of coastal farmland leading onto moorland and uplands which can be broadly compared to North-East Scotland. Approximately one third of the occupied range in the North-East is in relatively well wooded areas so if we apply the higher density of 4 pairs/km^2 to 300 of the 912 occupied tetrads and the lower density of 1 pair/km^2 to the remainder, then we obtain a conservative population estimate of around 1,500–2,000 pairs. Without doubt, however, Tawny Owls are under-recorded and it is quite possible that the North-East population exceeds this, perhaps by a substantial margin.

Author: *Alastair Young*

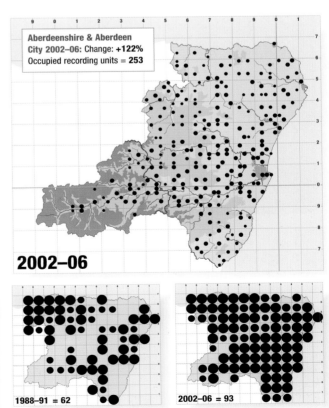

Aberdeenshire & Aberdeen City 1981–84: Occupied recording units = 114

1981–84

Aberdeenshire & Aberdeen City 2002–06: Change: **+122%** Occupied recording units = **253**

2002–06

1968–72 = 96

1981–84 = 52

1988–91 = 62

2002–06 = 93

North-East Scotland 1968–72 to 2002–06: Change in occupied 10-km squares = -3%

Ballochbuie Forest, Balmoral estate

One of Scotland's premier Caledonian pine woodlands, Ballochbuie extends from the River Dee high onto the slopes of Lochnagar. The breeding birds of the forest and adjacent areas include Teal, Goosander, Black Grouse, Sparrowhawk, Buzzard, Merlin, Woodcock, Green Woodpecker, Tree Pipit, Redstart, Jay, Raven and all three Crossbill species. Capercaillie are now very rare in all upper Deeside woodlands such as those in the Ballochbuie area. October 2006 © *Ian Francis*

The Forest of Mar, Mar Lodge estate

This landscape of native woodland and planted pine and broad-leaves holds breeding crossbills (all three species are possible in the Forest of Mar area), Redstart, Tree Pipit, Spotted Flycatcher, Jay, Woodcock, Cuckoo, Long-eared Owl, Green Woodpecker, Black Grouse and Goosander. Capercaillie are now very rare in these upper Deeside woodlands. Crested Tits do not occur in Deeside, except as very rare occasional visitors. Mar Lodge estate is owned by the National Trust for Scotland. July 2010 © *Ian Francis*

Long-eared Owl

Asio otus

Scarce resident. Passage migrant. Estimated population in North-East Scotland: *150–300 pairs* (16% of Scottish population, 7% of UK)

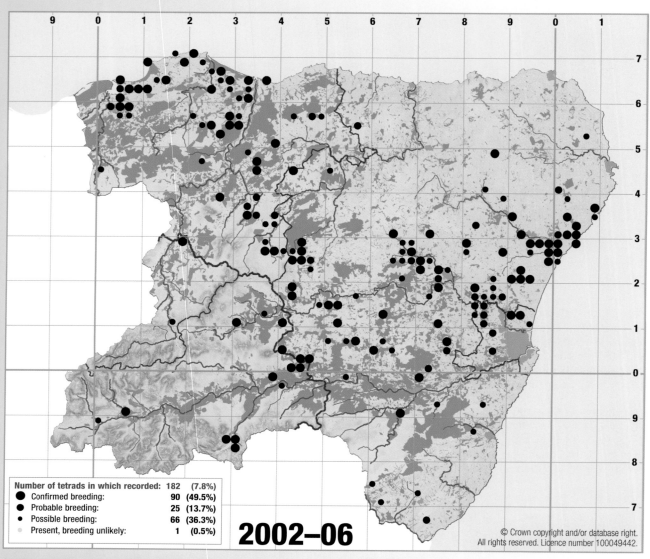

Number of tetrads in which recorded: 182 (7.8%)
- Confirmed breeding: 90 (49.5%)
- Probable breeding: 25 (13.7%)
- Possible breeding: 66 (36.3%)
- Present, breeding unlikely: 1 (0.5%)

2002–06

Habitat and breeding biology

Long-eared Owls are found in woods close to farmland, open grassland or the moorland edge. Pairs typically breed in small coniferous woods or shelter belts but also at the edges of larger forests. Patches of willow scrub on lowland mosses also provide sites. They lay their eggs in the disused stick nests of birds such as crows, Magpies and Sparrowhawks. This enables them to occupy areas where trees are of insufficient size to provide cavities for the hole-nesting Tawny Owls with which they may be at a competitive disadvantage (*BTO 2nd Atlas*). Depending on the abundance of Field Voles, their preferred food, they can lay up to six eggs, usually in mid April (Jardine in *BS3*). Between late May and mid July the young utter persistent begging calls which provide the easiest opportunity to prove breeding for this inconspicuous and strictly nocturnal species.

Scottish distribution and status

Long-eared Owls have a wide breeding distribution in Scotland but their range appears disjoined and patchy. It is not clear to what extent this may be as a result of under-recording of this secretive species. Favoured areas appear to include Argyll, and southern and eastern Scotland as far

north as the north coast of Sutherland and Caithness. Recording difficulties with this species have resulted in uncertainty about the size of the Scottish population; it probably lies somewhere within the wide range of 600–2,200 pairs (Jardine in *BS3*).

Distribution and status in North-East Scotland

The species is sparsely distributed across the lowlands of North-East Scotland but with pockets of greater density in a few areas such as the Moray plain, around Forvie and the lower Ythan, lower Donside, along the River Urie above Inverurie and in the Cabrach/Rhynie area. There are few records in the uplands although breeding was proved near Linn of Dee and in three tetrads near Loch Muick at altitudes of 400–450 m. Extensive forestry blocks are clearly avoided and Long-eared Owls are apparently almost completely absent from the north-east quarter, from the Moray boundary eastwards. However the substantial presence around Ellon and Inverurie suggests that the area just to the north may be better populated than fieldwork during 2002–06 has revealed - though woodland is often scarce here. Visits to small woodlands and shelter belts in Buchan to search for this species would be needed to resolve the issue.

Long-eared Owl, Ythan estuary, August 2002. © *Harry Scott*

Changes in distribution

Surveys since the late 1960s suggest wide fluctuations in distribution. During 1968–72, Long-eared Owls were recorded in 48 10-km squares in our area (*BTO 1st Atlas*) but this number had fallen to 18 10-km squares by 1988–91 (*BTO 2nd Atlas*) before rising again to 61 10-km squares in 2002–06. In Aberdeenshire/Aberdeen City the number of occupied recording units increased three-fold from 28 in 1981–84 (*NES 1st Atlas*) to 88 in 2002–06. Most remarkable of all is the apparent appearance of Long-eared Owls in 30 recording units in 17 10-km squares in the area between Insch, Turriff, Mintlaw and Newburgh where none existed 20 years previously. Clearly our knowledge of changes in Long-eared Owl distribution in North-East Scotland is very incomplete due to differences in recording effort in recent surveys, and all comparisons must be treated very cautiously.

Population and trends

The minimum situation, as revealed during 2002–06, is that Long-eared Owls were confirmed to be breeding in 90 tetrads and may have done so in a further 91. This would suggest a breeding population of 100–200 pairs, although the map is a composite of five years and all occupied tetrads may not have held birds in each of the five years. It also seems inevitable that a substantial number of pairs was missed and therefore a range of 150–300 pairs may be more realistic.

Author: *Martin Cook*

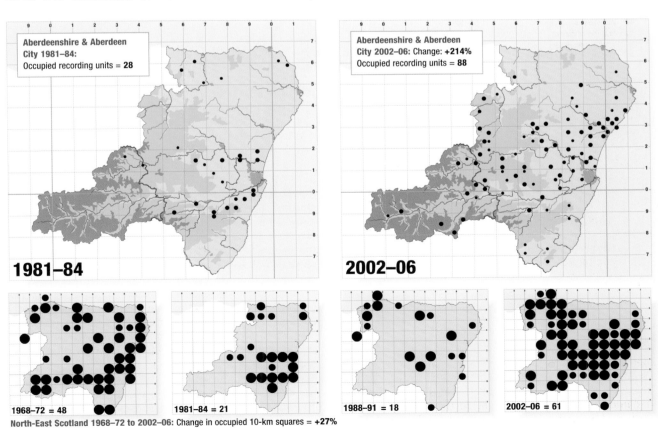

Aberdeenshire & Aberdeen City 1981–84: Occupied recording units = **28**

1981–84

Aberdeenshire & Aberdeen City 2002–06: Change: **+214%** Occupied recording units = **88**

2002–06

1968–72 = 48

1981–84 = 21

1988–91 = 18

2002–06 = 61

North-East Scotland 1968–72 to 2002–06: Change in occupied 10-km squares = **+27%**

Short-eared Owl

Asio flammeus

Rare resident and migrant breeder. Passage migrant and winter visitor. Estimated population in North-East Scotland: **20–70 pairs** (7% of Scottish population, 2% of UK)

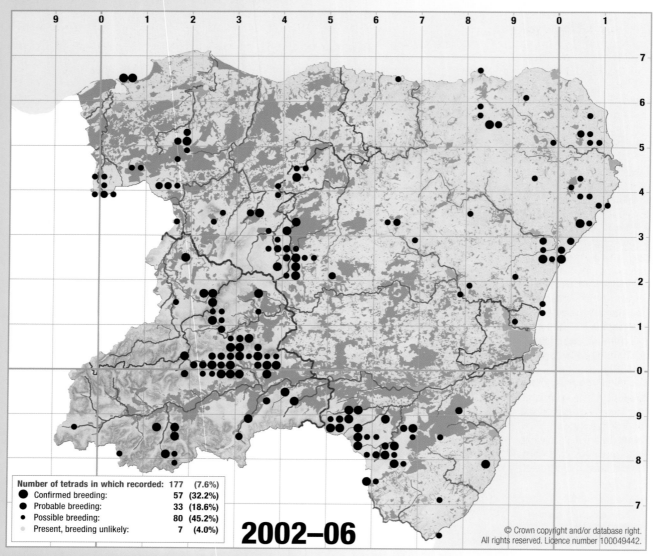

	Number of tetrads in which recorded:	177	(7.6%)
●	Confirmed breeding:	57	(32.2%)
●	Probable breeding:	33	(18.6%)
●	Possible breeding:	80	(45.2%)
●	Present, breeding unlikely:	7	(4.0%)

2002–06

Short-eared Owl, Slug Moor, 1986. © *Graham Rebecca*

Habitat and breeding biology

The breeding habitats most favoured by Short-eared Owls in North-East Scotland in recent years are, in order of importance, Heather moorland, coastal grasslands and inland peat mosses and bogs. Young conifer plantations that were an important nesting habitat during the 1980s (Buckland *et al.* 1990) now appear to be little used, probably because many of these plantations are now too mature. The altitude of breeding territories on moorland can vary from 250–520 m and preferred nest sites are usually in patches of tall Heather on dry slopes or flat ground, depending on the topography. Nests are usually well hidden under the overhanging deep Heather or other rank vegetation and are seldom exposed like those of the Hen Harrier that also nests in tall Heather. There is invariably some grassland within the general area of the nest site. Breeding sites in coastal grassland and inland bogs and marshes are more erratically used. Short-eared Owls establish their breeding territories in March, fledge their young in June and usually depart their breeding grounds by July or August.

Scottish distribution and status

The Short-eared Owl has a wide breeding distribution across the uplands of Scotland. The highest nesting densities are

The Breeding Birds of North-East Scotland

found in the uplands of south, central and eastern areas with significant numbers on some islands including Orkney, the Uists, Islay and Mull. A few pairs still nest near sea level along the coast of North-East Scotland. There have been various estimates of the Scottish population with the most realistic ranging from 125 pairs in a poor vole year to as many as 1,250 pairs in a good year (Knowler in *BS3*).

Distribution and status in North-East Scotland

The Short-eared Owl is often considered to be a nomadic species but within North-East Scotland there are several sites where they are recorded every year, suggesting that although there may be differences in annual productivity, some territories are favoured annually, regardless of vole numbers. The main concentration of breeding Short-eared Owls is on moorlands in the uplands where approximately 85% of breeding attempts in 2002–06 took place. Most breeding attempts during those years were in four main areas: upper Deeside extending northwards from Ballater to Morven then westwards from Morven to the River Gairn catchment; Cairn o' Mount extending north-west through Glen Dye and Forest of Birse to Glen Tanar on Deeside; upper Donside extending north-west across the Lecht to Tomintoul, and the area extending north-west from Lumsden, through the Cabrach to near Glenfiddich in Moray. Elsewhere, for example in the upper Dee catchment south of Braemar and on the fragmented northern Moray moors, breeding pairs were scattered more thinly. After Heather moorland, the next most favoured nesting habitat was in open country near the coast (9%) followed by lowland bogs and mosses (6%).

Changes in distribution

Analysis of the comparative maps shows that the distribution has remained relatively stable in the upland moorland habitat in Aberdeenshire between 1981–84 and 2002–06 with breeding birds still occupying favoured areas. However, there has apparently been a marked increase in breeding range in coastal areas. During 1981–84, breeding was confirmed or probable in only two 10-km squares and possible in a further three. By 2002–06 this had increased to five and seven 10-km squares respectively. This apparent increase in recent years in comparison to the decline noted in 1968–72 (*BTO 1st Atlas*) may have been due to the substantial amount of tree planting that took place in the coastal area in the 1990s and early 2000s. The young plantations with their grassy undergrowth would have created good habitat for hunting and nesting. Set-aside was also plentiful at this time and provided good habitat for prey species. There has been no significant change in range in lowland bogs and mosses. In Moray, by contrast, there has been an apparent contraction of range over the long term. During 1968–72 breeding was confirmed or probable in 15 10-km squares and possible in another 12 (*BTO 1st Atlas*). During 2002–06, breeding was only confirmed or probable in nine 10-km squares and possible in a further six. Moorland fragmentation by afforestation and the subsequent maturation of young plantations have undoubtedly reduced former nesting habitat in Moray. Fragmentation of moorland by afforestation can also lead to a loss of interest in moorland management for grouse on the remaining moorland, leading to an increase in predators such as Foxes that can have a detrimental effect on ground nesting birds like the Short-eared Owl.

Population and trends

Analysis of data from various sources suggests an annual breeding population of 20–70 pairs in North-East Scotland (*MNBR 1999–2006, NESBR 1999–2006, 2002–06 Atlas data*). This may be an underestimate as confirmation of breeding can be difficult for this species. Breeding numbers may vary from year to year as vole numbers fluctuate, and from area to area as habitat changes take place. Population trends are hard to detect in this species that often exhibits dramatic food-linked population swings. Nevertheless, breeding numbers appear to have increased in Aberdeenshire between 1981–84 and 2002–06, and substantially decreased in Moray.

Author: *Jim Craib*

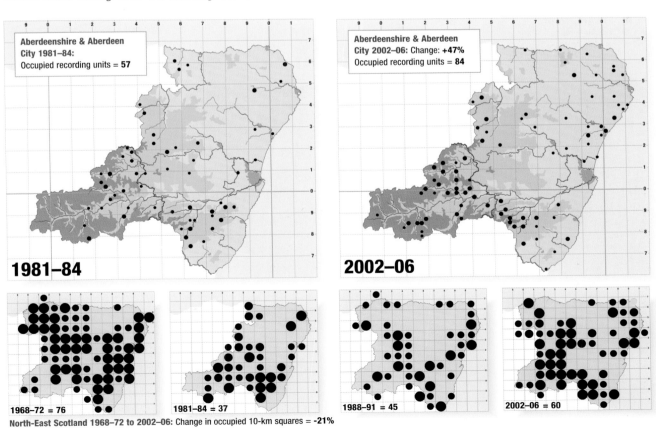

Aberdeenshire & Aberdeen City 1981–84:
Occupied recording units = 57

1981–84

Aberdeenshire & Aberdeen City 2002–06: Change: +47%
Occupied recording units = 84

2002–06

1968–72 = 76   1981–84 = 37   1988–91 = 45   2002–06 = 60

North-East Scotland 1968–72 to 2002–06: Change in occupied 10-km squares = -21%

Nightjar

Caprimulgus europaeus

Occasional summer visitor. Former breeder. Estimated population in North-East Scotland: usually *0 pairs*

Red list; Annex 1; UK and Scottish BAP lists

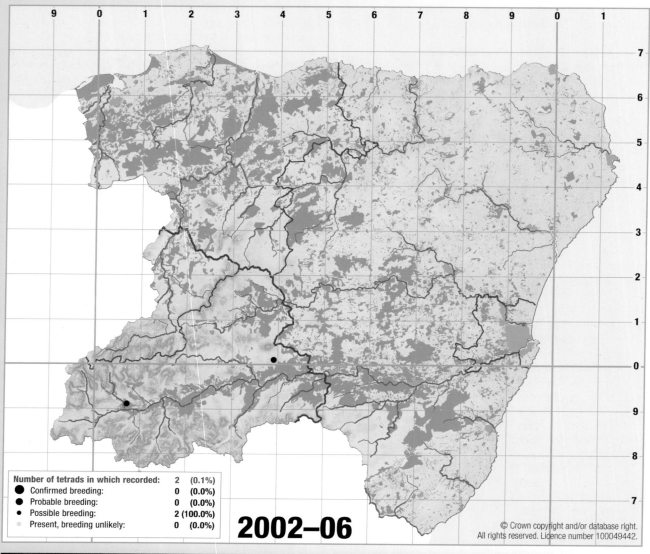

Number of tetrads in which recorded:	2	(0.1%)
● Confirmed breeding:	0	(0.0%)
● Probable breeding:	0	(0.0%)
• Possible breeding:	2	(100.0%)
Present, breeding unlikely:	0	(0.0%)

2002–06

Nightjar, Hampshire, June 2008. © *Martin Bennett*

The Breeding Birds of North-East Scotland

Habitat used by **Nightjar**, Glen Culsten, Deeside, May 2006. © *Ian Francis*

Nightjar, Gloucestershire, June 2008. © *Lewis Thomson*

Habitat and breeding biology

The small Scottish breeding population currently occupies clearings in conifer plantations on well-drained soils below 200 m. Nightjars show particular affinity for clear-felled and replanted areas of forestry where the trees are small and there is plenty of open ground. Territories are occupied during May, sometimes early in the month as indicated by a nest with two eggs on 14th May at Peebles in 1994. Birds may vacate their breeding areas as late as mid September which conceivably leaves time for two broods, as happens in England where spring arrival is earlier (Shaw in *BS3*).

Scottish distribution and status

Historically, Nightjars appear to have been widespread and numerous throughout mainland Scotland but numbers declined during the first half of the 20th century and by 1958 breeding was only taking place intermittently in most regions of the country. In 2007, the whole Scottish population was estimated at only 27 territorial males, with the great majority in Dumfries & Galloway (Shaw in *BS3*).

Distribution and status in North-East Scotland

During 2002–06, there were two records of Nightjars in possible breeding habitat. In 2003, a 'churring' bird was heard in Glen Culsten (north-east of Ballater) and one was seen in open pinewood in Glen Lui on 20th July 2005. Neither bird was relocated.

Changes in distribution

In North-East Scotland, the timing of the decline from a formerly widespread and familiar summer visitor to a very scarce breeder approximately matches that seen elsewhere in Scotland. In the late 1950s, breeding was still taking place at Culbin and near Fochabers (Cook 1992) but by 1968–72 Nightjars were found only at Monaughty, where breeding was proved for the last time in North-East Scotland, and near Fochabers where it may also have occurred (*BTO 1st Atlas*). In the remainder of the 20th century, 'churring' birds were heard near Forres in June 1975 and in inland Aberdeenshire in June 1995, but in neither case was breeding confirmed. There were also records of spring migrants in Aberdeenshire in 1977 and 1996 (Phillips 1997, Cook 1992). As a regular breeder in North-East Scotland the Nightjar has now been lost. Any possible re-colonisation in the future is likely to depend on several factors such as climate change, and the availability of suitable habitat and of appropriate insect prey. With the population in south-west Scotland continuing to decline the chances of re-establishment in the North-East in the near future seem slim.

Author: *Martin Cook*

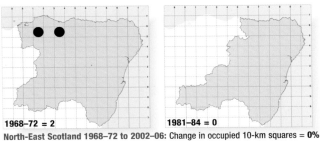

1968–72 = 2

1981–84 = 0

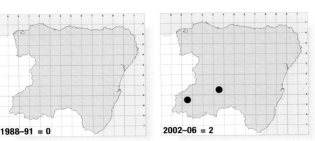

1988–91 = 0

2002–06 = 2

North-East Scotland 1968–72 to 2002–06: Change in occupied 10-km squares = 0%

Swift

Apus apus

Common summer migrant breeder. Estimated population in North-East Scotland: *500–1,500 pairs* (14% of Scottish population, 1% of UK

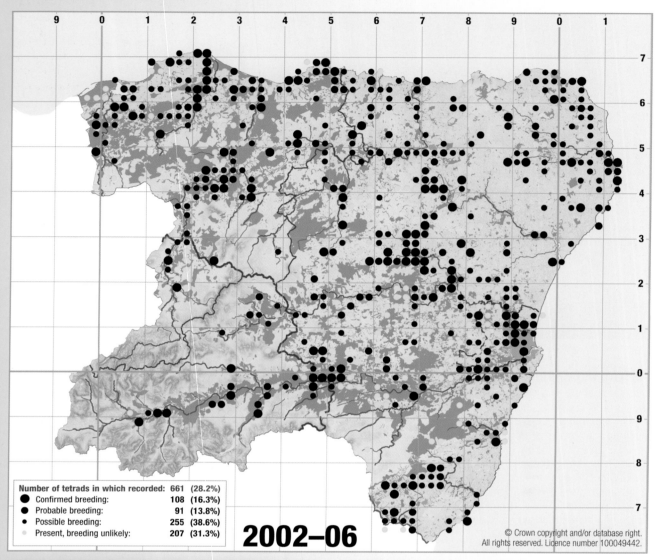

Number of tetrads in which recorded:	661	(28.2%)
● Confirmed breeding:	108	(16.3%)
● Probable breeding:	91	(13.8%)
● Possible breeding:	255	(38.6%)
● Present, breeding unlikely:	207	(31.3%)

2002–06

Swift, Portsoy, July 1988. © *John Edelsten*

Habitat and breeding biology

Swifts are found over a wide variety of habitats when searching for food. Breeding sites, however, are more restricted and nowadays closely associated with buildings, particularly in towns and cities. Nests are generally in older buildings with means of access to suitable sites within. Additionally, nest boxes attached to trees and buildings have been successfully used in the UK and Europe. Natural nest sites include fissures in cliffs (both coastal and inland) and holes in trees, notably in Scots Pine, where holes excavated by Great Spotted Woodpeckers have been used for a number of years at Abernethy Forest (Summers 1999). The usual clutch of two eggs is laid in late May or early June and young fledge by mid July. The length and success of the nestling period is weather dependent as this affects the availability of flying insect food.

Scottish distribution and status

Breeding Swifts are found mainly in the south and east of Scotland with concentrations in the Central Lowlands, especially around large towns and cities. They are largely absent from upland areas in the north and west of Scotland, and from the Northern and Western Isles. A population estimate between 6,000–8,000 pairs in Scotland was suggested in 2007 (Zonfrillo in *BS3*).

Distribution and status in North-East Scotland

Swifts are distributed widely over North-East Scotland, although the breeding range is dictated by the availability of nesting sites. Most sites are below 300 m but breeding was recorded up to 350 m at Tomintoul and Gairnshiel Lodge near Ballater. Clusters of occupied tetrads are sometimes evident, such as around Craigellachie, Aboyne, Garioch and the north of Aberdeen City. Whether such 'hot-spots' are genuine or an artefact generated by intensive surveying effort is uncertain. Swifts forage widely away from their nest sites; a fact that accounts for the high proportion (31%) of records in tetrads where breeding was considered unlikely. Forested areas are largely bereft of breeding Swifts but given their recorded use of Great Spotted Woodpecker holes there may be potential breeding sites in old woodlands in upper Deeside. Most birds arrive in late April and early May, and have left the area by mid August.

Changes in distribution

Little overall change in distribution is apparent at the 10-km square level over the past 40 years but there was a 21% increase in occupied recording units in Aberdeenshire/Aberdeen City between 1981–84 and 2002–06. Most of this increase is due to infilling of the existing range although Swifts do appear more widespread in Deeside, above Aboyne. It is unclear why this apparent increase in range has occurred at a time of substantial population decline, but observer effort may be a factor.

Population and trends

We have little idea of the true population size of the Swift in North-East Scotland. The picture is confused by the presence of non-breeders around colonies, the fact that several pairs may gain access to a site through a single opening and that birds forage far from breeding colonies. Assuming a minimum of one pair per occupied tetrad where breeding was considered at least possible, the population will be at least 454 pairs. Alternatively, judging from the extent of occupied areas, we might estimate the proportion of the Scottish population which inhabits North-East Scotland; this is unlikely to exceed 20% and could be as low as 10%, which suggests between 600–1,600 pairs. A range of 500–1,500 pairs may therefore be a reasonable, but very approximate estimate. Scottish data from the BBS indicate a 53% decline in the Swift population during 1994–2007 (Risely *et al.* 2007). Several factors may have contributed to this, including a reduction in nest sites through demolition or renovation of old buildings, lack of access to nest sites in new buildings, a reduction in food supply, or prolonged poor weather during egg and chick stages.

Author: *Bob Proctor*

Swift, Portsoy, July 1988. © *John Edelsten*

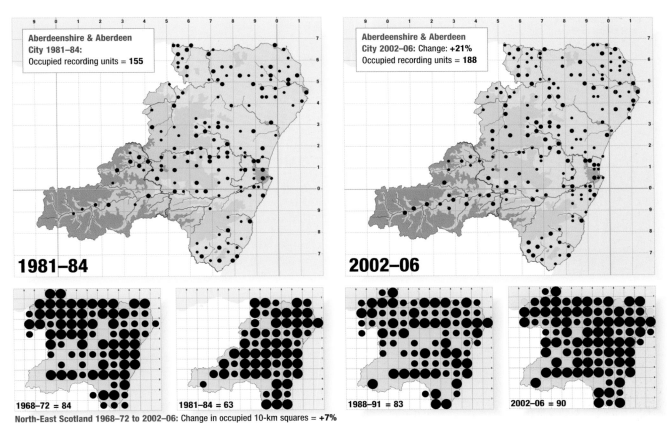

Aberdeenshire & Aberdeen City 1981–84:
Occupied recording units = **155**

1981–84

Aberdeenshire & Aberdeen City 2002–06: Change: **+21%**
Occupied recording units = **188**

2002–06

1968–72 = 84   1981–84 = 63   1988–91 = 83   2002–06 = 90

North-East Scotland 1968–72 to 2002–06: Change in occupied 10-km squares = **+7%**

Kingfisher

Alcedo atthis

Rare resident. Estimated population in North-East Scotland: *40–60 pairs* (13% of Scottish total, 1% of UK)

Amber list; Schedule 1; Annex 1; Scottish BAP list.

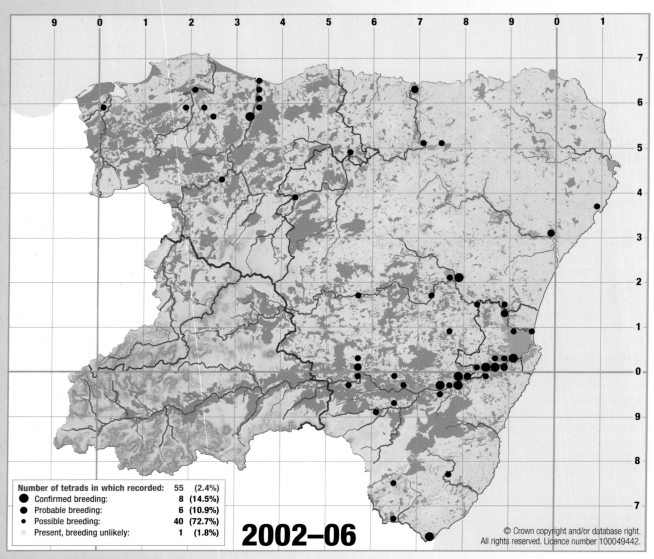

Number of tetrads in which recorded:	55	(2.4%)
● Confirmed breeding:	8	(14.5%)
● Probable breeding:	6	(10.9%)
● Possible breeding:	40	(72.7%)
● Present, breeding unlikely:	1	(1.8%)

2002–06

Habitat and breeding biology

The Kingfisher is found in habitats with abundant small freshwater fish and perches for hunting. Preferred habitat is usually slow flowing streams and rivers with overhanging riparian vegetation and large numbers of fish 35–100 mm in length. Adult Kingfishers are usually resident on territories throughout the year and thus distribution is limited to the mid to lower reaches of rivers, where the river remains free enough of ice to ensure winter survival. Kingfishers are highly territorial and vigorously defend their stretch of water from other Kingfishers. When juveniles are dispersing in summer and autumn they can be found in a wider variety of habitats, especially small ponds and lochs. The Rivers Dee and Don contain most of the breeding pairs in North-East Scotland. Nest burrows are typically situated in vertical or near-vertical banks as close to water as possible. River course management has had an effect on the distribution of nest sites. Erosion of the sides of the river is important for creating suitable nesting banks. Stabilising the banks with large blocks and removing banks for better fishing access is limiting the distribution of nests in some areas. In Scotland, two broods are usually attempted, occasionally even three (Wood in *BS3*), often in different burrows. Eggs can be laid as early as mid March and chicks from the last broods fledge as late as the end of September (Campbell & Ferguson-Lees 1972). Nests occasionally fail due to disturbance, bank collapse or, more regularly, flooding. Brood size is relatively large with 4–7 young usually reared per brood, although there are few brood sizes recorded for North-East Scotland.

Scottish distribution and status

Distribution is dependent on suitable habitat, ice-free water and food availability; therefore most pairs are found in the south and west of Scotland. Breeding has rarely been recorded north of Inverness. Kingfisher numbers vary

Kingfisher, Lower Deeside, 2005. © *Ewan Weston*

widely as relatively large numbers of individuals are produced from each breeding attempt and mortality can be very high in cold winters. Most healthy rivers and larger streams have breeding pairs of Kingfishers in their mid and lower reaches although they are under-recorded. The Scottish breeding population was estimated at 330–450 pairs in 2007 (Wood in *BS3*).

Distribution and status in North-East Scotland

The Kingfisher remains an uncommon species in North-East Scotland with the exception of the River Dee between Banchory and Aberdeen, where breeding was proved in six tetrads and probably, or possibly, took place in a further eight. Breeding was also confirmed in single tetrads on the Rivers Don, Spey and the North Esk. The scatter of occupied tetrads on other rivers may indicate further breeding sites, although fledged young are evicted from their parents' territories from July onwards and this may account for some sightings in non-breeding areas (Wood in *BS3*).

Changes in distribution

Breeding was first confirmed at Stuartfield in 1910, but not again in the region until 1984 (Buckland *et al.* 1990). Since the late 1960s, there has been a large increase in the Kingfisher range in North-East Scotland. In 1968–72 they were found in three 10-km squares with no proof of breeding (*BTO 1st Atlas*), and by 1988–91 this had risen to five occupied squares with breeding confirmed in three (*BTO 2nd Atlas*). The situation in 2002–06, when birds were found in 29 10-km squares, with breeding proved or probable in 11, therefore represents a very substantial extension of the range. In Aberdeenshire/Aberdeen City the number of occupied recording units has expanded even more dramatically, from only one in 1981–84 (*NES 1st Atlas*) to 35 in 2002–06. There is some evidence that the population has expanded out of the traditional areas on the Rivers Dee and Don. Recent records of confirmed breeding on the River Spey near Fochabers are suggestive of a potential for population expansion and growth in Moray.

Kingfisher, Aberdeen, May 2004. © *John Chapman*

Population and trends

There have been no formal surveys of Kingfishers conducted in North-East Scotland and the population size is difficult to estimate because birds are surprisingly inconspicuous and nests are difficult to locate. During 2005, 15 pairs were found on part of the River Dee between Crathes and Aberdeen; of these, 11 pairs were confirmed as breeding (pers. obs.). Based on a rough estimate of the likely numbers breeding on the main rivers in North-East Scotland it seems likely that there are 40–60 pairs. These are mostly on the Dee and its tributaries (20), the Don and its tributaries as far up as Inverurie (10) with the possibility of another five pairs each on the Spey, Ythan and Deveron. Smaller rivers and large burns elsewhere are likely to raise the total by a few more pairs. The actual number of nests is difficult to establish as many may be on tributaries and burns but the range increase has clearly been matched by a substantial increase in the population.

Author: *Ewan Weston*

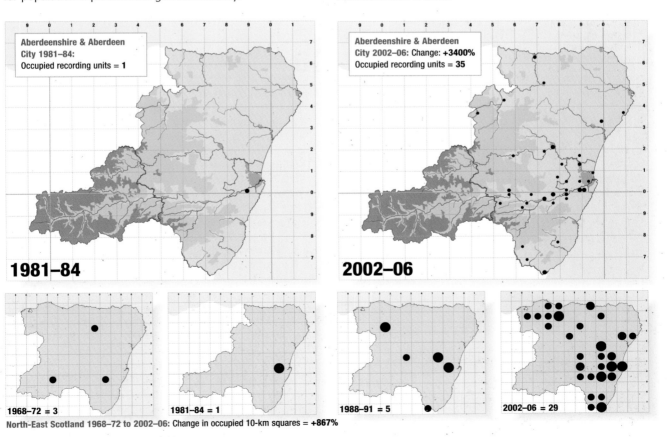

Aberdeenshire & Aberdeen City 1981–84: Occupied recording units = **1**

1981–84

Aberdeenshire & Aberdeen City 2002–06: Change: **+3400%** Occupied recording units = **35**

2002–06

1968–72 = 3

1981–84 = 1

1988–91 = 5

2002–06 = 29

North-East Scotland 1968–72 to 2002–06: Change in occupied 10-km squares = +867%

Wryneck

Jynx torquilla

Occasional in summer, has bred. Passage migrant. Estimated population in North-East Scotland: usually
0 pairs

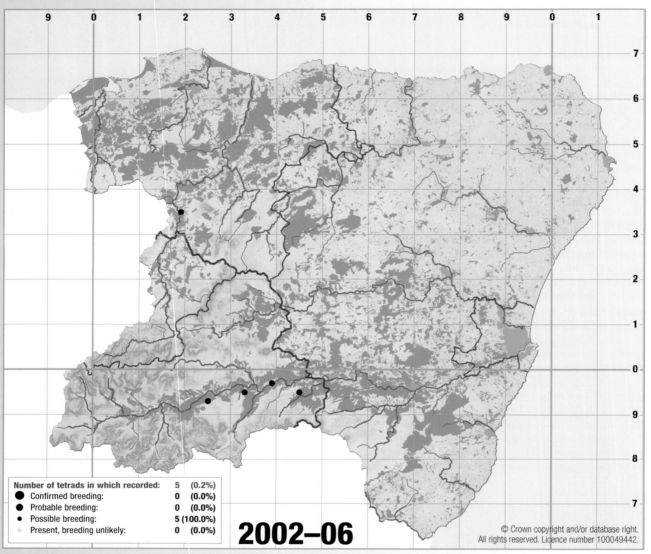

Number of tetrads in which recorded: 5 (0.2%)
- ● Confirmed breeding: 0 (0.0%)
- ● Probable breeding: 0 (0.0%)
- • Possible breeding: 5 (100.0%)
- ○ Present, breeding unlikely: 0 (0.0%)

2002–06

Wryneck, Speyside, July 1986. © *Dave Pullan*

Habitat and breeding biology

The Wryneck is only an occasional breeder in Scotland but
when this has taken place it has been in natural or semi-
natural open Scots Pine forest - either pure or associated
with Juniper and broad-leaf species such as birch or Rowan.
The presence of wood ant nests as a food source also
appears to be important. Records in Deeside during
2002–06 all came from widely spaced mature Scots Pine
plantations or native pine woodland. The Moray record was
of a bird in a mature birch wood, albeit for only a single day.
This habitat is very different from the large gardens,
orchards and parkland which traditionally held Wrynecks
when they were widespread breeders in England in the first
half of the 20th century. Instead it more closely resembles
the habitat occupied in Scandinavia, from where Scottish
colonists may well have originated. Eggs are laid in existing
holes in trees, either natural or excavated by woodpeckers;
nest boxes have also been used.

Scottish distribution and status

Wrynecks are scarce passage migrants in Scotland, chiefly
appearing on the east coast and in the Northern Isles during
migrant falls in spring and autumn. There are marked peaks
of occurrence in May and in late August–mid September

The Breeding Birds of North-East Scotland

(Woodbridge in *BS3*). During the first half of the 20th century, Wrynecks were occasionally found in potential breeding habitat, most notably in Strathspey. It was here, in 1969, that breeding was first proved (Burton *et al.* 1970). Breeding continued in this area in the 1970s and 1980s with up to 14 males located in a season. Since then the population has dwindled although a few birds are found in apparently suitable nesting habitat in most years (Dennis 1995, *Highland Bird Reports*).

Distribution and status in North-East Scotland

Almost all instances of breeding or summer presence of Wrynecks in North-East Scotland have been at sites on Deeside. During 2002–06, single birds were located in potential breeding areas in Deeside in 2002 (1), 2003 (1) and 2005 (2). The only Moray record is of a single bird in birch woodland near Ballindalloch in May 2005.

Wryneck, Johnshaven, April 2008. © *Micky Maher*

Changes in distribution

In upper Deeside, a Wryneck was found in Glen Quoich in July 1968 (*SBR* 1968). There were further Deeside records at one site in 1975, two sites in 1978 and two sites in 1979, one of which held four birds in mid June. In 1980 one pair bred successfully in a nest box and three other sites were briefly occupied. In 1985 five birds were found at one site in summer and in 1988 there were two birds at one site (*NES 1st Atlas*). Breeding was proved again in 1991, in a nest box (*NESBR* 1991), and sporadic records of birds in possible breeding habitat have continued since that time.

Population and trends

Wrynecks are undoubtedly rare breeders in North-East Scotland but they are quiet and difficult to locate once they are paired. It is therefore quite possible that the occasional pair breeds undetected in Deeside and possibly elsewhere, particularly in summers which follow a good fall of spring migrants on the coast.

Author: *Martin Cook*

Wryneck habitat, Deeside, May 2005. © *Ian Francis*

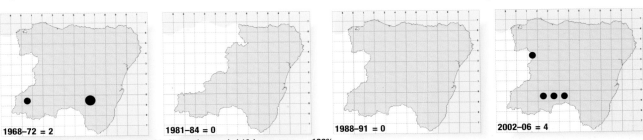

1968–72 = 2   1981–84 = 0   1988–91 = 0   2002–06 = 4

North-East Scotland 1968–72 to 2002–06: Change in occupied 10-km squares = +100%

Green Woodpecker · *Picus viridis*

Rare resident. Estimated population in North-East Scotland: **60–130 pairs** (13% of Scottish population, <1% of UK)

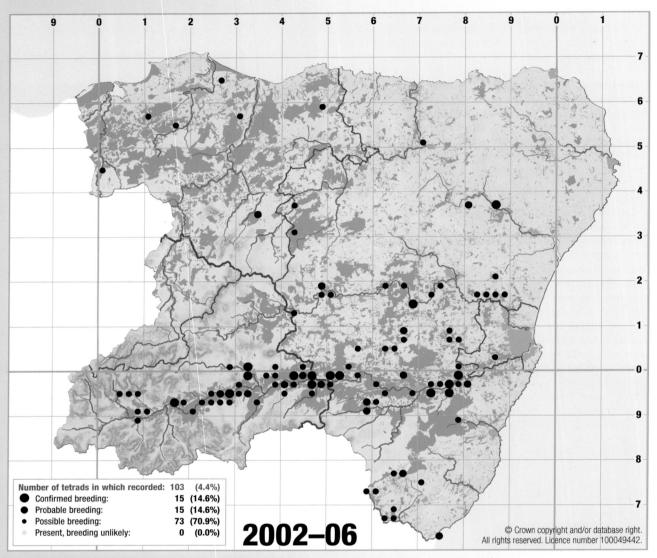

Number of tetrads in which recorded: 103 (4.4%)
- ● Confirmed breeding: 15 (14.6%)
- ● Probable breeding: 15 (14.6%)
- • Possible breeding: 73 (70.9%)
- · Present, breeding unlikely: 0 (0.0%)

2002–06

Green Woodpecker, Fife, March 2008. © *John Anderson*

Habitat and breeding biology

Green Woodpeckers require open woodland close to areas with short vegetation or grazed grassland, where they can forage on the ground for ants, which constitute most of their diet. On Deeside, they usually breed in birch woods where the trees are widely spaced and also in mixed mature woodland with pine. The nest chamber is excavated in a mature tree, often birch in Scotland, at a height of 2–6 m. Although the species is single-brooded, the onset of breeding may occur over a protracted period from early April until late June (Storie in *BS3, BTO 2nd Atlas*). A clutch of 5–6 eggs is normally laid which takes about 18 days to hatch, followed by a 23–27 day fledging period.

Scottish distribution and status

The recorded colonisation of Scotland by Green Woodpeckers took place during the second half of the 20th century. Between the early 1950s and late 1970s their range in the east expanded northwards from the Borders to the Moray Firth (Storie in *BS3*). By 1998, Argyll and much of Highland was also colonised, but since that time there has been a range retraction from northern and western parts of Scotland. Currently, Green Woodpeckers can be found in the south and east of the country from Dumfries & Galloway

The Breeding Birds of North-East Scotland

to North-east Scotland, with the largest numbers in Borders, Lothian, Fife, Perth & Kinross, Angus & Dundee and Dumfries & Galloway. The Scottish population is estimated at 600–900 pairs (Storie in *BS3*).

Distribution and status in North-East Scotland

Deeside is the stronghold of the Green Woodpecker in North-East Scotland. Here they occupy woods from Durris to Braemar and up into the glens beyond. In 2002–06, birds were found in the woods of Glen Derry and Glen Quoich at altitudes of 450–500 m, although breeding was not proved. Several tetrads were also occupied on Donside, from the Aberdeen City boundary as far west as Glenkindie. Outwith land bordered by Deeside and Donside there were nine occupied tetrads in and around the Mearns, but otherwise Green Woodpeckers were very thinly spread. To the north of Donside just 12 tetrads were occupied, with breeding confirmed only near Methlick.

Changes in distribution

Green Woodpeckers were first recorded in North-East Scotland in 1968–72, when they were found in seven 10-km squares in Deeside and south Kincardine - but not to the north of Aberdeen (*NES 1st Atlas, BTO 1st Atlas*). By 1981–84, the range had extended considerably with 26 occupied 10-km squares in Aberdeenshire/Aberdeen City - with six of them to the north of Donside (*NES 1st Atlas*). In 1988–91, birds were found in 28 10-km squares in the whole North-East of which 11 were now to the north of Donside, including eight in Moray. Green Woodpeckers were recorded in Moray in 1974 and annually from 1977 although breeding was not proved until 1985. By 2002–06 the number of occupied 10-km squares in the North-East had increased further, to 38, but only ten were north of Donside. Although there were still seven occupied squares in Moray, this is a five-year composite picture that masks the almost total collapse of the Moray population since the mid 1990s. The number of localities

Green Woodpecker, Dinnet, May 2005. © *Harry Scott*

providing breeding season records fell from 10–15 in the mid 1990s to 1–2 in the years after 2000.

Population and trends

During 2002–06, Green Woodpeckers were recorded in 103 tetrads but breeding was considered no more than possible in 71% of these. It seems safe to assume that the 30 tetrads where breeding was probable or confirmed each held 1–2 pairs. It is however impossible to say how many of the other 73 tetrads held isolated pairs or perhaps only single calling birds. If we assume that half, perhaps even all, of these contain one breeding pair then there may be 60–130 pairs in the North-East in total.

Author: *Martin Cook*

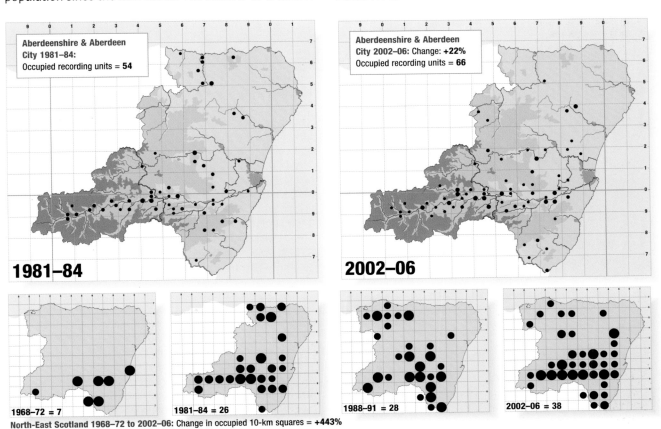

Aberdeenshire & Aberdeen City 1981–84: Occupied recording units = 54

1981–84

Aberdeenshire & Aberdeen City 2002–06: Change: +22% Occupied recording units = 66

2002–06

1968–72 = 7   1981–84 = 26   1988–91 = 28   2002–06 = 38

North-East Scotland 1968–72 to 2002–06: Change in occupied 10-km squares = **+443%**

Great Spotted Woodpecker   *Dendrocopos major*

Common resident. Estimated population in North-East Scotland: *750–1500 pairs* (16% of Scottish population, 3% of UK)

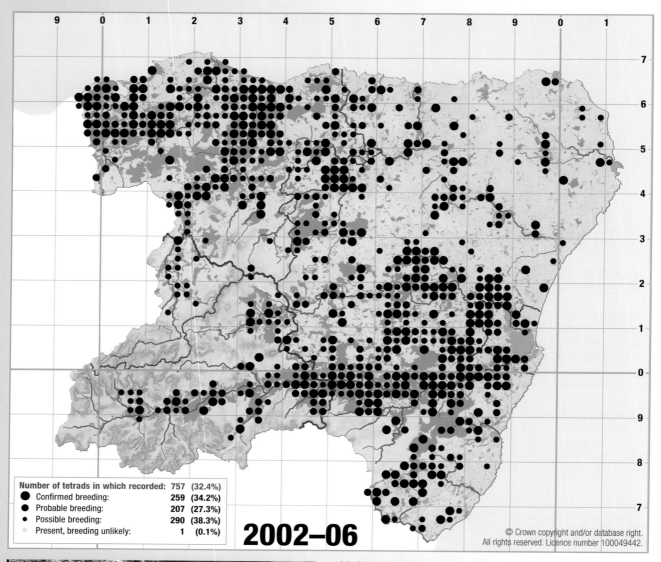

Number of tetrads in which recorded: 757 (32.4%)
- Confirmed breeding: 259 (34.2%)
- Probable breeding: 207 (27.3%)
- Possible breeding: 290 (38.3%)
- Present, breeding unlikely: 1 (0.1%)

2002–06

Great Spotted Woodpecker, Angus, March 2007. © *John Anderson*

Habitat and breeding biology

Great Spotted Woodpeckers occupy a wide variety of woodland habitats where these contain dead and dying timber that harbours their invertebrate food. Broad-leaf and coniferous woodlands are occupied, with mature birch woods holding good populations. Conifer plantations only prove suitable for breeding if they contain dead trees of sufficient diameter to accommodate nest chambers. The presence of native tree species with associated higher populations of wood-boring insects may also be important. The breeding season begins as early as January when territorial drumming can be heard, but eggs are usually not laid until early or mid May with most young fledging in late June or early July.

Scottish distribution and status

Great Spotted Woodpeckers are widely distributed in forested areas but are absent or scarce in the north-west Highlands and the Northern and Western Isles. Over the rest of the mainland, treeless hills and open moorland lack woodpeckers and predominantly agricultural zones contain few pairs. There is much uncertainty about the size of the Scottish breeding population but it is believed to lie within the range 4,000–10,000 pairs (McGowan in *BS3*).

The Breeding Birds of North-East Scotland

Great Spotted Woodpecker, Stonehaven, June 2003. © Sam Alexander

Distribution and status in North-East Scotland

There are two densely-populated areas in North-East Scotland. In Moray and neighbouring north-west Aberdeenshire there are high densities in the western forests of Culbin, Darnaway and Altyre, as well as the more easterly woods of lower Speyside and the Bin Forest near Huntly. Many tetrads are occupied in the mixed riverside woodlands of mid Speyside and Strathavon but much of the extensive afforestation on the Moray moors is not sufficiently mature to hold breeding woodpeckers. The second concentration in North-East Scotland is in the forests of Deeside and Donside, and the woods between these catchments. The agricultural Buchan plain has only scattered pairs, where suitable woodland exists. Similarly, the upland distribution is limited by the absence of

sufficiently extensive woodland but where this exists birds penetrate up the glens to at least 500 m above sea level as in Glen Derry and Glen Quoich.

Changes in distribution

Although once probably widely distributed in Scotland, by the mid 19th century the species was all but extinct. Suggested reasons include forest clearance, intensive woodland management, competition with Starlings for nest sites, and predation by Red Squirrels (McGowan in *BS3*). In Moray, breeding had resumed at Pluscarden and Altyre by 1924 (Cook 1992) and within a few years the species was once again widespread in the North-East. In 1968–72 Great Spotted Woodpeckers were found in 72 10-km squares in North-East Scotland (*BTO 1st Atlas*) but by 1988–91 this had fallen to 47 10-km squares (*BTO 2nd Atlas*) with most of the reduction in Aberdeenshire, where fieldwork for the first local atlas had also noted a substantial decline in 1981–84 (*NES 1st Atlas*). Encouragingly, however, the comparative maps for Aberdeenshire/Aberdeen City indicate an increase in range and density over the last 20 years. This is borne out by the increase in birds detected by the BBS. It seems likely that this expansion is due to the progressive maturity of the extensive forestry in the area.

Population and trends

In the absence of local data we need to look elsewhere for measures of abundance of Great Spotted Woodpeckers. In Scotland as a whole, measured densities have ranged from 0.5–1.0 pairs/km^2 in coniferous woodland with, locally in the south, much higher densities in broad-leaves (McGowan in *BS3*). Bearing in mind that often only a part of a tetrad contains suitable habitat, the lower end of the range is more appropriate and we can apply the density of 1–2 pairs/tetrad in the 758 occupied tetrads, giving an estimated North-East Scotland population of 750–1,500 pairs.

Author: *Martin Cook*

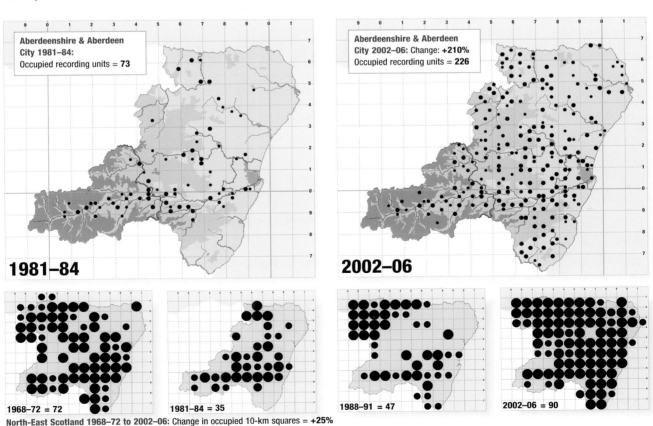

Aberdeenshire & Aberdeen City 1981–84: Occupied recording units = **73**

Aberdeenshire & Aberdeen City 2002–06: Change: **+210%** Occupied recording units = **226**

1981–84

2002–06

1968–72 = 72   1981–84 = 35   1988–91 = 47   2002–06 = 90

North-East Scotland 1968–72 to 2002–06: Change in occupied 10-km squares = +25%

Red-backed Shrike

Lanius collurio

Occasional possible, and former, summer migrant breeder. Passage migrant. Estimated population in North-East Scotland: **0 pairs**

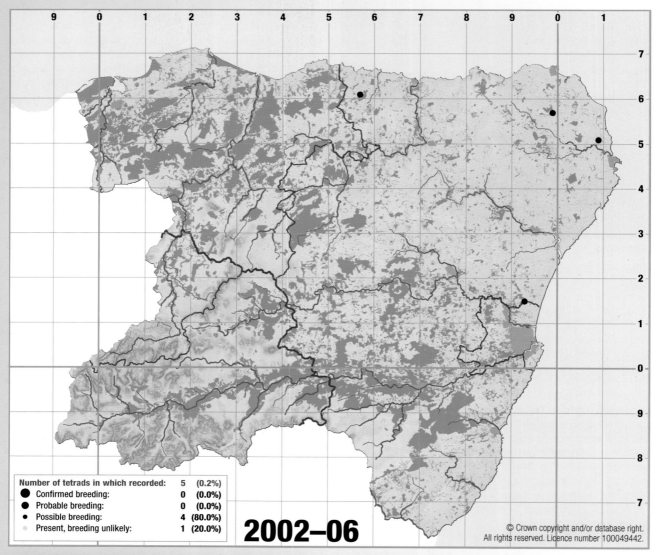

Number of tetrads in which recorded:	5	(0.2%)
● Confirmed breeding:	0	(0.0%)
● Probable breeding:	0	(0.0%)
● Possible breeding:	4	(80.0%)
● Present, breeding unlikely:	1	(20.0%)

2002–06

Red-backed Shrike, St Cyrus, September 2006. © *Harry Scott*

Habitat and breeding biology

Breeding Red-backed Shrikes require sunny, sheltered habitats with an open scatter of shrubs or low trees to provide look-out perches for spotting prey. Prior to their extinction as breeders in England, they favoured dry, bushy heaths with a mixture of Gorse, Heather and small trees (*BTO 1st Atlas*). This English population typically laid clutches of 5–6 eggs in late May–early June in a bramble clump, thicket or overgrown hedge (Witherby *et al.* 1940). In North-East Scotland, the 1977 nest at Invercauld was *c.*1.7 m above ground in a 2 m cypress hedge at the edge of a conifer nursery, while the 1979 Inverey nest, at the edge of a garden bordering open country, was *c.*0.9 m off the ground in a bushy spruce *c.*1.2 m high (A. Knox pers. comm.).

Scottish distribution and status

Red-backed Shrikes are primarily passage migrants to Scotland. During the period 1968–2004 the average annual spring total for the whole of Scotland was 77 birds while the average autumn produced only 26 birds. Annual totals are however highly variable. In both seasons there is a distinct easterly and northerly bias, with the Northern Isles especially favoured. The first confirmed breeding in Scotland was in 1977 and there had been 13 further attempts by 2004. Breeding has taken place in Perth & Kinross, North-East Scotland, Highland, Caithness and Shetland (Thorpe in *BS3*).

Distribution and status in North-East Scotland

Breeding has been confirmed in North-East Scotland on four occasions and there are four other probable, and three possible, instances:

Confirmed
1977 nest with two eggs at Invercauld found 26th June, deserted with four eggs on 18th July (A. Knox pers. comm.)

male carrying food on 25th June at another site (*NES 1st Atlas*)

1979 pair nested near Inverey, and fledged three young by 13th July (A. Knox pers. comm.)

1981 pair raised three young in a cottage garden at Braemar (Dickson 1997, A. Thorpe pers. comm.)

Probable
1977 pairs present at two additional sites in mid-late June (*NES 1st Atlas*)

1987 pair on Ythanside mid June (*NES 1st Atlas*)

1998 pair near Huntly 29th July–6th August (I. Francis pers. comm.)

Possible
1979 males at two additional sites during the second week in June (*NES 1st Atlas*)

1987 one male on Deeside 21st July (*NES 1st Atlas*)

As migrants, Red-backed Shrikes in North-East Scotland follow the Scottish pattern. They are most frequent in spring, peaking in May, at east coast localities. The smaller autumn passage peaks in September (Phillips 1997). The average annual total during the ten-year period 1997–2006 has been around seven birds but with wide variation from only one in 1999 to as many as 17 in 1998 and 2004. The five records during 2002–06 were all of single birds within 10 km of the coast in May or June; there is no reason to believe that any of these were other than migrants. One of five to six presumed migrants in 2007 was a female near New Pitsligo on 4th May and it, or another female, was at the same site on 28th June (*NESBR* 2007). There is no evidence of any increase in migrants from which potential North-East Scottish breeding birds might be drawn. It therefore seems unlikely that Red-backed Shrikes will be anything more than very occasional breeders for the foreseeable future.

Author: *Martin Cook*

Habitat used by Red-backed Shrike, Inverey, July 1979. © *Alan Knox*

Red-backed Shrike nest site, Inverey, July 1979. © *Alan Knox*

Red-backed Shrike nest, Inverey, July 1979. © *Alan Knox*

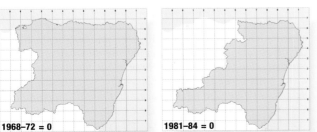
1968–72 = 0　　**1981–84 = 0**　　**1988–91 = 0**　　**2002–06 = 4**

North-East Scotland 1968–72 to 2002–06: Change in occupied 10-km squares = 0%

Magpie

Pica pica

Common resident. Estimated population in North-East Scotland: *1,750–3,500 pairs* (17% of Scottish population, <1% of UK)

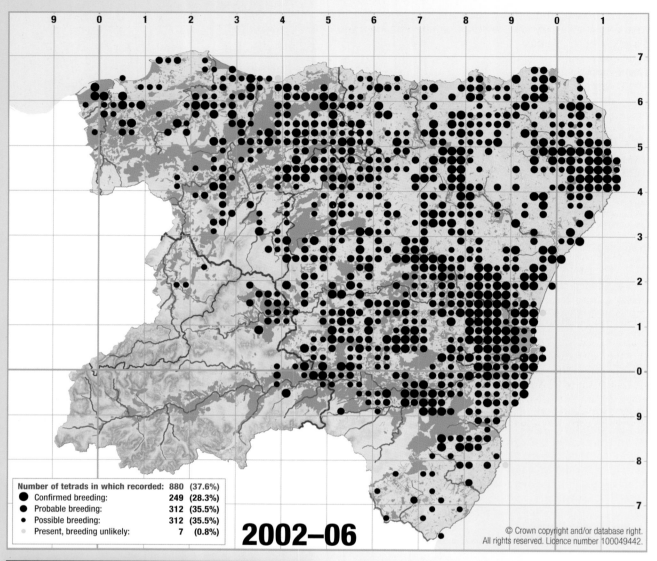

Number of tetrads in which recorded:	880	(37.6%)
● Confirmed breeding:	249	(28.3%)
● Probable breeding:	312	(35.5%)
● Possible breeding:	312	(35.5%)
Present, breeding unlikely:	7	(0.8%)

2002–06

Magpie, Brotherfield, 1985. © *John Young*

Habitat and breeding biology

Magpies favour a mixture of grassland and small woodlands or scrub; they occupy a range of habitats from mixed farmland to suburban and urban areas where they breed in parks and gardens. They are absent from treeless hill country and larger forestry plantations where feeding opportunities are limited. Territories are occupied all year and the conspicuous, usually dome-shaped, stick nests are built before the leaves emerge in April. Studies in open agricultural land between Newburgh and Cruden Bay (Love & Summers 1973) found that most pairs built their nests at heights of 2–8 m (average 4.5 m) in small clumps of trees around farms. The clutch, averaging 6.7 eggs, was laid in late April or early May.

Scottish distribution and status

The Magpie is a familiar species throughout much of the central lowlands of Scotland, as well as Ayrshire and Dumfries & Galloway. Further north, it occurs widely in North-east Scotland and Moray, with smaller numbers around the inner Moray Firth. The Scottish population was estimated at 14,000–17,000 pairs in 2007 (Young in *BS3*).

Distribution and status in North-East Scotland

Magpies are widespread breeders but their distribution is uneven, with some parts of the North-East, such as the Peterhead, Aberdeen and Keith/Huntly areas, more densely populated than others. They are rather scarce across much of Moray, parts of the Buchan plain and in south-east Aberdeenshire. They are absent only from the larger expanses of coniferous plantation and from upland and moorland areas. This reflects their preference for a mixture of short grassland and suitable small woods and shelter belts to provide nest sites. A few pairs penetrate to the margins of the uplands where suitable habitat exists, for example around Cabrach where birds inhabit the farmland areas but are absent from the adjacent plantations on the moorland edge. In the agricultural Buchan plain where they are more thinly distributed, this is partly due to a relative scarcity of woodland, but also perhaps to the higher proportion of arable ground with limited open grassland. On most upland shooting estates, and in some lowland areas, many Magpies are killed by gamekeepers and farmers, which is also a strong influence on their breeding distribution

Changes in distribution

Over the last 40 years, Magpies have steadily consolidated and expanded their range across North-East Scotland. In 1968–72 they were found in 66 10-km squares (*BTO 1st Atlas*); by 1988–91 this had increased to 78 (*BTO 2nd Atlas*) and by 2002–06 to 83 10-km squares. This increase has mainly been caused by infilling of the existing range together with expansion southwards from Stonehaven into the Mearns. Similarly, the 20% increase in occupied recording units in Aberdeenshire/Aberdeen City between 1981–84 and 2002–06 is attributable to infilling and southward expansion but also with a hint of westward spread in Strathdon and the Ballater area.

Magpie, Banchory Devenick, April 1998. © *Ed Duthie*

Population and trends

There is little information on breeding densities in the area, although 0.22 pairs/km^2 was recorded in 50 km^2 of farmland in the 1970s (Love & Summers 1973) when numbers were lower. In recent years, four tetrads in an agricultural landscape with small woodlands at Clochan (Moray) have held around ten pairs, at a density of 2.5 pairs/tetrad (M. Cook pers. comm.). While this may not be optimal habitat, it suggests that a range of two to four pairs in the 876 tetrads where Magpies were present in 2002–06 is a reasonable estimate and, from this, a population of 1,750–3,500 pairs can be extrapolated for North-East Scotland. It is likely that the Magpie will continue to consolidate and slowly increase its range in line with the overall Scottish population, which has increased by 14% during the period 1994–2007 (Risely *et al.* 2008).

Author: *Alastair Young*

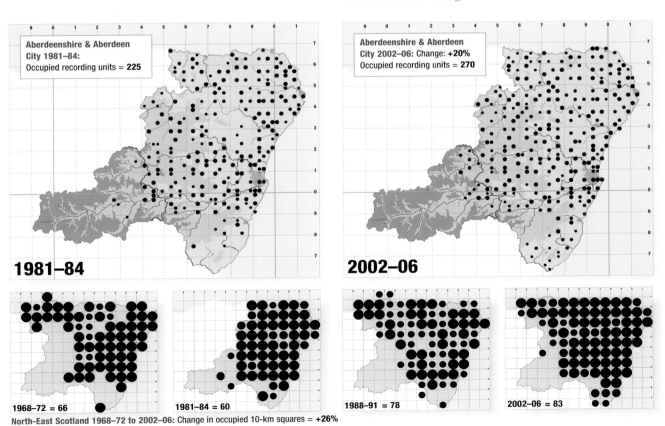

Aberdeenshire & Aberdeen City 1981–84: Occupied recording units = **225**

1981–84

Aberdeenshire & Aberdeen City 2002–06: Change: **+20%** Occupied recording units = **270**

2002–06

1968–72 = 66

1981–84 = 60

1988–91 = 78

2002–06 = 83

North-East Scotland 1968–72 to 2002–06: Change in occupied 10-km squares = **+26%**

Jay

Garrulus glandarius

Scarce resident. Estimated population in North-East Scotland: *415–1,245 pairs* (10% of Scottish population, <1% of UK)

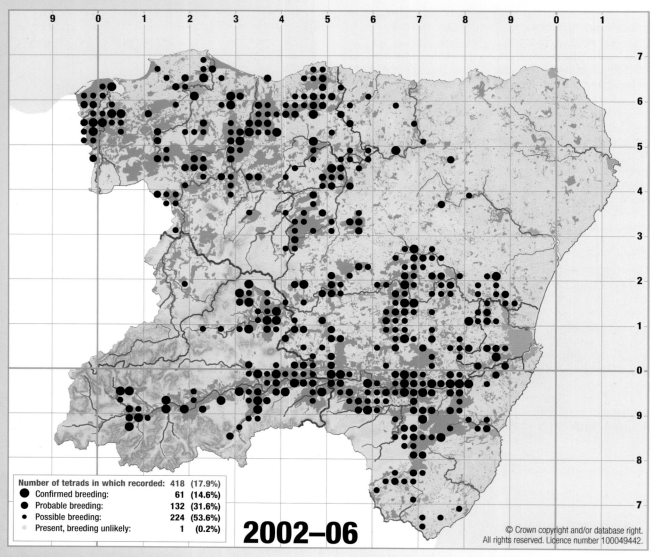

Number of tetrads in which recorded: 418 (17.9%)
- Confirmed breeding: 61 (14.6%)
- Probable breeding: 132 (31.6%)
- Possible breeding: 224 (53.6%)
- Present, breeding unlikely: 1 (0.2%)

2002–06

Habitat and breeding biology

Within Scotland, the Jay is a woodland species, found mainly in larger areas of mixed woodland and conifer plantations. In the North-East it has a strong association with larger conifer plantations such as those found in the Dee and lower Spey valleys. It is a relatively secretive species, more often heard than seen, and confirmation of breeding generally relies on the presence of family parties in late summer. Nests are often built in thicket-stage woodland and adults can be seen carrying food for nestlings in June and July - Large Black Slugs often feature in the diet at this time (McNee in *BS3*).

Scottish distribution and status

Jays are widely but locally distributed across Scotland to the south and east of the Great Glen. The main concentrations are found in the southern Highlands from Perthshire & Kinross across to north Clyde and central Argyll. The Scottish population was estimated at 6,000–10,000 pairs in 2007 (McNee in *BS3*).

Distribution and status in North-East Scotland

The Jay is a widespread breeding bird in the wooded areas of North-East Scotland, but is absent from the treeless uplands

and from the agricultural Buchan plain where the extent of woodland is very limited. Its distribution clearly follows that of mature conifer plantations, in a broad band below the Cairngorms and down onto the coastal plains of Moray. They are well established in the Dee and Don valleys where the range extends furthest inland into plantations as far as upper Strathdon and beyond Braemar. Here they can be found breeding in Scots Pine woods up to 500 m in Glen Derry and Glen Quoich. Jays are more sparsely distributed in Moray. This generally reflects the more recent colonisation of this part of North-East Scotland although in some areas, such as around Dallas, the young age of the plantations is doubtless a contributory factor.

Changes in distribution

Comparison of the number of occupied 10-km squares in the two BTO Atlases and the current map reveals an increase from ten in 1968–72 to 18 in 1988–91 and 71 by 2002–06; a seven-fold increase in 35 years. The distribution in the early 1970s was confined to the south-east of Aberdeenshire but by the end of the 1980s, Deeside and Donside were extensively occupied and the range had extended towards Moray. Here, there were only five breeding season records during the 20th century prior to the 1990s when a rapid spread took place, from only four occupied localities in 1993 to 39 ten years later (Cook 1992, *MNBR*s). In Aberdeenshire/Aberdeen City there was a 202% increase in occupied recording units over the 20 years between 1981–84 and 2002–06.

Population and trends

Jays were found in 418 tetrads during 2002–06 but there has been no attempt to assess population density in North-East Scotland. It is likely that densities in Deeside woods are higher than those in Moray where the species is a compar-

atively recent colonist. On the assumption that most occupied tetrads hold 1–3 pairs then the suggested population would be in the range 415–1,245 pairs, but there is much uncertainty. Jays are likely to continue to expand their range, especially within Moray where extensive areas of woodland appear to be unpopulated and Jays may move in as younger plantations mature. The species may, however, experience difficulty in becoming well established in heavily-keepered estates.

Author: *Alastair Young*

Jay, Drum, May 1983. © *John Massie*

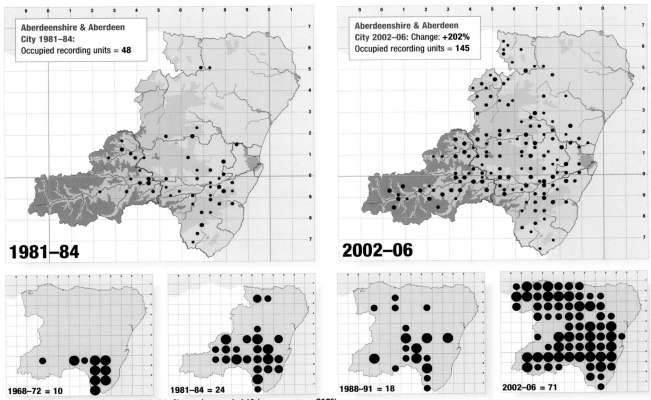

North-East Scotland 1968–72 to 2002–06: Change in occupied 10-km squares = +610%

Jackdaw

Corvus monedula

Very common resident. Estimated population in North-East Scotland: **16,000–24,000 pairs** (20% of Scottish population, 4% of UK)

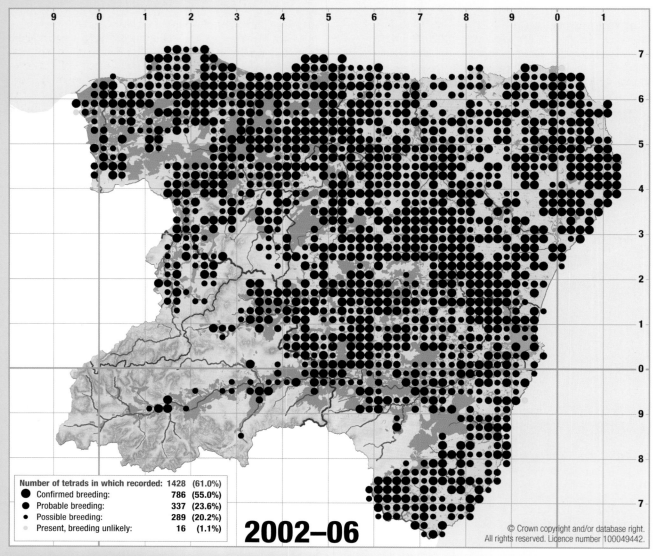

Number of tetrads in which recorded: 1428 (61.0%)
- ● Confirmed breeding: 786 (55.0%)
- ● Probable breeding: 337 (23.6%)
- ● Possible breeding: 289 (20.2%)
- · Present, breeding unlikely: 16 (1.1%)

2002–06

Jackdaw, Dinnet, April 2007. © *Harry Scott*

Habitat and breeding biology

The Jackdaw has adapted to a range of habitats, often nesting where there is a combination of grazed or mown grassland for feeding, and suitable nest sites. Its favoured habitats therefore include farmland, towns, quarries and coastal cliffs. It is absent only from large areas of commercial plantation, upland moorland and mountain areas, and where farmland becomes extensively arable with few trees. Jackdaws breed individually or colonially with groups of displaying birds a familiar site in many villages in spring. They usually nest in cavities in trees, cliffs or man-made structures, notably chimneys and ruined buildings. The clutch, most commonly of 4–5 eggs, is laid in late April or early May, with the young fledging in early June. Jackdaws are single-brooded.

Scottish distribution and status

Jackdaws are widespread breeding birds in central, southern and eastern Scotland. They are absent from large upland areas in the north and west of the country. They breed very locally in the Outer Hebrides, widely in Orkney but not at all (since 1972) in Shetland. The Scottish population is estimated to fluctuate within the range 80,000–120,000 pairs (Thomas in *BS3*).

Distribution and status in North-East Scotland

Jackdaws are widespread across the low ground below *c.*350 m but above this altitude farmland gives way to open moorland where feeding is poor and nest sites less frequent. A few birds do occur higher up the valleys where conditions are suitable, up to 400 m in Glen Muick although breeding was not confirmed here. At lower altitudes they are absent from large conifer plantations such as Fetteresso, Clashindarroch, Dallas and the extensive plantations in the middle to lower Dee valley. This is presumably a consequence of limited feeding areas, with few older trees to provide suitable nest sites. Jackdaws are also more thinly distributed in the extensive arable areas along the coast to the south of Aberdeen and, especially, parts of the Buchan plain. Feeding might be expected to be good in such areas so the availability of nest sites is presumably the limiting factor.

Changes in distribution

There has been very little change in the 10-km square distribution since 1968–72 (*BTO 1st Atlas*) although there is some evidence of a retraction from the upland edge of the range in south-west Aberdeenshire. This is also apparent from examination of the Aberdeenshire/Aberdeen City maps where, although the total number of occupied recording units has remained unchanged over the period 1981–84 to 2002–06, there is a reduced distribution in the vicinity of Braemar. Reasons for this are uncertain but perhaps relate to land-use changes, as the Jackdaw population in the North-East as a whole is rising (Francis 2006).

Population and trends

Throughout the occupied range in North-East Scotland, population density will vary considerably with some tetrads containing a single farm, with 3–4 pairs in its chimneys, while other tetrads may embrace a small village with 30 or more pairs. This makes the calculation of a reliable estimate of the whole population problematic. The map of relative abundance in *BTO 2nd Atlas* suggests that the North-East might contain around 20% of the Scottish total, *i.e.* 16,000–24,000 pairs. Alternatively we can adopt the Fife densities of 2.24 pairs/km^2 in farmland and 4.86 pairs/km^2 in woodland (Elkins *et al.* 2003) and make an approximation, based on limited observation in Moray, of 25 pairs/km^2 in suburban and rural housing areas. Applying these densities to relevant land cover areas in North-East Scotland reveals a total of 19,504 pairs, around the mid-point of the range suggested above.

Author: *Alastair Young*

Jackdaw, Ballater, May 2009. © *Harry Scott*

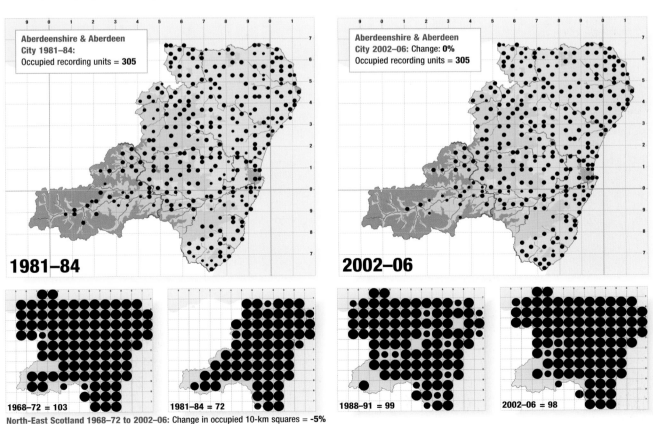

Aberdeenshire & Aberdeen City 1981–84:
Occupied recording units = **305**

1981–84

Aberdeenshire & Aberdeen City 2002–06: Change: **0%**
Occupied recording units = **305**

2002–06

1968–72 = 103

1981–84 = 72

1988–91 = 99

2002–06 = 98

North-East Scotland 1968–72 to 2002–06: Change in occupied 10-km squares = **-5%**

Rook

Corvus frugilegus

Very common resident. Estimated population in North-East Scotland: *82,000–90,000 pairs* (22% of Scottish population, 7% of UK)

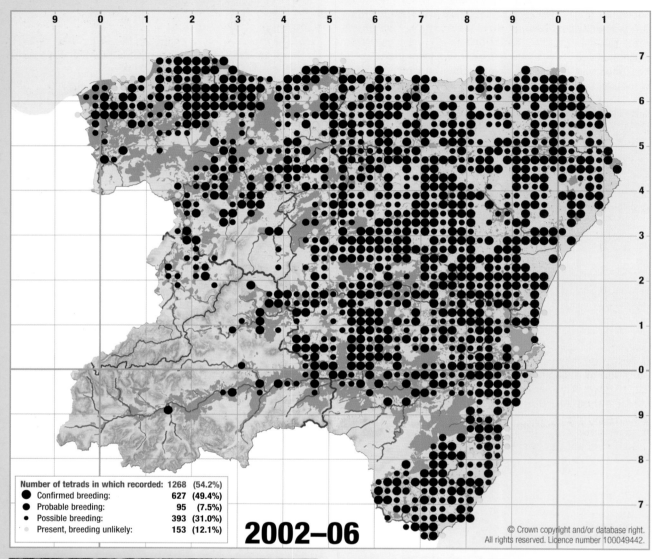

Number of tetrads in which recorded:	1268	(54.2%)
● Confirmed breeding:	627	(49.4%)
● Probable breeding:	95	(7.5%)
● Possible breeding:	393	(31.0%)
○ Present, breeding unlikely:	153	(12.1%)

2002–06

Rook, Ballater, April 1987. © *Ed Duthie*

Habitat and breeding biology

The Rook is a gregarious nesting species, preferring a mixture of small woodlands within farmland with areas of both pasture and cereals. Birds usually forage in flocks, feeding on pasture all year with the cereal fields being important during the winter. They nest colonially in both coniferous and deciduous woodlands although tall Scots Pines are preferred in Scotland. Rookeries range from a few pairs to huge colonies containing 2,000–3,000 nests (Gimona in *BS3*). Rooks breed early in the North-East; nest building starts in February, and the clutch of 2–6 eggs is laid in early April with young fledging from mid May. This ensures that the young are in the nest at a time of maximum availability of their soil invertebrate food supply.

Scottish distribution and status

Rooks are common birds of lowland farmland across the south and east of Scotland but they are scarce in the west and north. The Outer Hebrides and Shetland each hold a single rookery. Areas of greatest abundance include Dumfries & Galloway, parts of the Central Lowlands, Fife, North-east Scotland, Moray & Nairn and north-east Caithness. The Scottish population was estimated at 300,000–500,000 pairs in 2007 (Gimona in *BS3*).

The Breeding Birds of North-East Scotland

Distribution and status in North-East Scotland

Rooks breed widely across the lowlands of North-East Scotland but are notably absent from extensive blocks of coniferous plantation. Distribution in the Buchan plain is restricted by the limited number of suitable nesting woodlands in the intensively farmed landscape. Most Rooks nest below 300 m although there are rookeries at c.350 m in the Braes of Glenlivet, Glen Buchat and at Braemar. The absence above this height reflects farming practices with little improved pasture or cereal grown outside the river valleys. In the past, and again in recent years, two small rookeries have existed in the centre of Aberdeen, but they were not recorded during 2002–06. On winter nights, Rooks gather in huge communal roosts; in the late 1960s up to 65,000 roosted at Hatton Castle (Watson 1967), in the early 1970s 25,000–30,000 roosted at Carron (Munro 1975) and in 1994–95 14,000 roosted near Alford (Francis 1998).

Rook, Oldmeldrum, March 2003. © *Sam Alexander*

Rook is at the edge of its range, this could be attributable to a change in farming practice such as a reduction in arable stubbles which are important for winter feeding.

Table 1. The 1975 census of rookeries in the former counties now comprising North-East Scotland (Castle 1977).

County	Rookeries	Nests	Average nests per rookery
Moray	77	7,389	96
Banff	103	14,117	137
Aberdeen	359	49,650	138
Kincardine	65	3,707	57
Total	594	74,780	125

Changes in distribution

In terms of occupancy of 10-km squares, there is no indication of a significant change in distribution over the last 40 years. The number of occupied recording units in Aberdeenshire/Aberdeen City has declined by 5% since 1981–84 but this difference could relate to local changes or observer coverage. The only area that shows any notable pattern of change is in the vicinity of the upper Dee valley where the number of occupied recording units above Ballater decreased from 14 to four. In this area, where the

Population and trends

There has been no detailed census of the Rook population of North-East Scotland since 1975 (Castle 1977). This is unfortunate as our area contains the highest population densities and largest rookeries in Britain, and probably in the whole of Europe (Gimona in *BS3*). The largest single rookery, at Arnage Castle, contained 2,087 nests (Castle 1977) while the Hatton Castle complex held over 2,600 nests in 16 groups (Thom 1986). This however is notably lower than 1957, when the Hatton Castle complex held 6,697 nests (Watson 1967). The area was well covered in 1975 and the population estimate at that time was considered to be good. A current estimate must therefore take into account trends in the population since 1975. During the 1940s–1970s the British Rook population declined but the Scottish population has shown a partial recovery since the 1970s (Gimona in *BS3*) although Scottish BBS results indicate a non-significant reduction of 12% during the period 1994–2007 (Risely *et al.* 2008). Using the total number of nests found in the 1975 census (74,780) and applying 10% and 20% increases gives a current population range of the order of 82,000–90,000 pairs of Rooks in North-East Scotland.

Author: *Alastair Young*

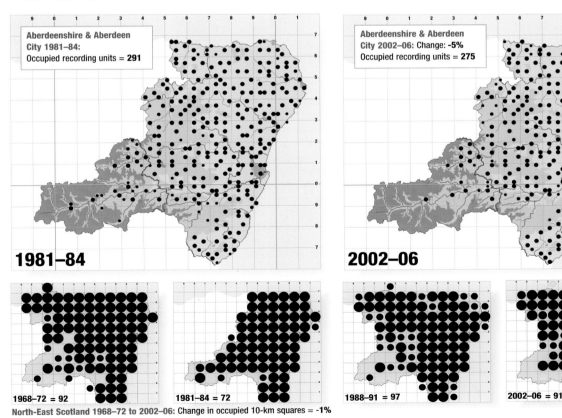

Aberdeenshire & Aberdeen City 1981–84:
Occupied recording units = 291

1981–84

Aberdeenshire & Aberdeen City 2002–06: Change: -5%
Occupied recording units = 275

2002–06

1968–72 = 92

1981–84 = 72

1988–91 = 97

2002–06 = 91

North-East Scotland 1968–72 to 2002–06: Change in occupied 10-km squares = -1%

Carrion Crow

Corvus corone

Very common resident. Estimated population in North-East Scotland: **15,600–20,400 pairs** (12% of Scottish population, 2% of UK)

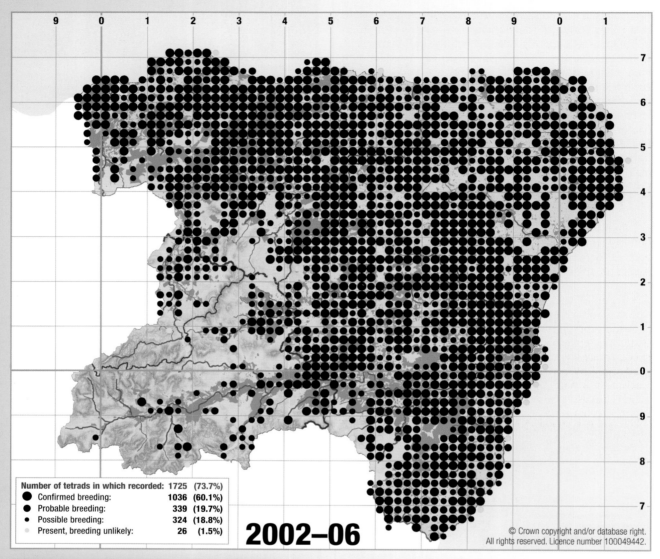

Number of tetrads in which recorded:	1725	(73.7%)
● Confirmed breeding:	1036	(60.1%)
● Probable breeding:	339	(19.7%)
● Possible breeding:	324	(18.8%)
● Present, breeding unlikely:	26	(1.5%)

2002–06

Carrion Crow, Newburgh, May 2009. © *Rab Rae*

Habitat and breeding biology

Breeding Carrion Crows are found across almost all habitats, absent only from the high uplands and extensive treeless moorland. They are particularly common in mixed farmland and suburban areas, but tend to avoid dense conifer plantations. Birds remain paired throughout the year and start to build nests in March. The clutch, usually 3–5 eggs, is laid in late April or early May. Incubation takes around 20 days and the young fledge about 32 days later (Young in *BS3*).

Scottish distribution and status

Carrion Crows are widespread and most abundant across the south and east of Scotland as far north as North-east Scotland and Moray. Around the rest of the Moray Firth and up to Caithness they are present in smaller numbers. They are absent in the west and north-west, including the Hebrides and Northern Isles, where they are replaced by Hooded Crows. Where the two species meet they interbreed and a hybridisation zone occurs. Currently this zone extends from Kintyre in Argyll, north and east to the Cairngorms and then north to Inverness and along the north-east coast to Sutherland and Caithness. The hybridisation zone has been documented moving north and west in North-East Scotland over the last century as Carrion Crows have replaced Hooded Crows.

The Breeding Birds of North-East Scotland

Distribution and status in North-East Scotland

Carrion Crows breed widely across North-East Scotland, being absent primarily from moorland and mountain areas. The distribution shows a limit at about 300 m, which stretches around the Cairngorms to Tomintoul, past Glenfiddich and on to Strathdon, then across to Ballater and southwards. Above this altitude, Carrion Crows have presumably reached the edge of suitable nesting habitat where woodland and improved grassland are replaced by moorland. In addition to this, many of the moorland areas are managed for game, and predator control removes any birds present or moving in. The patchy distribution in some lowland areas is also likely to be the result of predator control. This is most obvious along the Dee valley between Ballater and Braemar, and south of Forres. Elsewhere, they have a patchy distribution through parts of the Buchan plain and, here again, predator control, coupled with a predominance of arable farming, may be restrictive factors. Throughout North-East Scotland there is a substantial non-breeding population which can often be found in flocks or counted at summer roost sites. Of 41 flocks recorded in 2007, 14 contained more than 20 birds, the largest being 45 and 52 (pers. obs.). Summer roosts included 70 birds at Alves and 48 near Craigellachie in April 2008.

Changes in distribution

The Carrion Crow has spread north and west across Scotland since around the middle of the 19th century, gradually replacing the Hooded Crow. Where the two species meet, mixed pairs may be formed and hybrid young produced. The centre of this hybridisation zone has spread westwards across North-East Scotland since the 1920s. (This is discussed in more detail under 'Hooded Crow'). The proportion of Carrion Crows has steadily increased over this time, and today more than 96% of the crows in the North-East are Carrion. Over the last 40 years there has been very little change in the range of Carrion Crows in the North-East although the number of Aberdeenshire recording units

Carrion Crow, Portsoy, 1980s. © *John Edelsten*

which were occupied to the west of Braemar has reduced from 11 to four since 1981–84.

Population and trends

During 1966–69 a study of crows was undertaken in 7 km^2 of woods and farmland adjacent to Heather moorland at Kerloch, at that time in the hybridisation zone. This revealed densities of 2.3–3.0 pairs/km^2, or 9.2–12.0 pairs/tetrad (Picozzi 1975). There is no evidence of substantial population changes since the 1960s. While some tetrads may have higher densities others, due to factors including nest site availability and shooting, will have less, so it may be reasonable to apply this density to the 1,701 tetrads in the North-East where breeding was considered to be at least possible in 2002–06. This suggests a North-East Scotland breeding population of 15,600–20,400 pairs. The non-breeding population has been variously estimated at 20–35% of all birds (Young in *BS3*) so if we adopt the figure of 25% then there are likely to be around 12,000 non-breeding Carrion Crows in summer in the North-East.

Author: *Alastair Young*

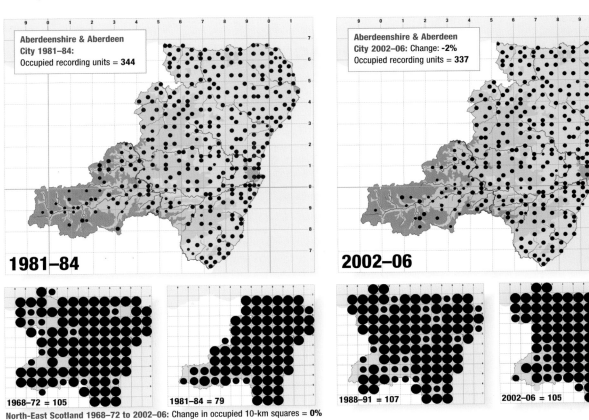

Aberdeenshire & Aberdeen City 1981–84: Occupied recording units = 344

1981–84

Aberdeenshire & Aberdeen City 2002–06: Change: -2% Occupied recording units = 337

2002–06

1968–72 = 105

1981–84 = 79

1988–91 = 107

2002–06 = 105

North-East Scotland 1968–72 to 2002–06: Change in occupied 10-km squares = **0%**

Hooded Crow including hybrids *C. cornix* x *C. corone*   *Corvus cornix*

Rare resident. Carrion x Hooded hybrids are scarce residents. Estimated population in North-East Scotland: **50–100 breeding individual Hooded Crows** (<1% of Scottish and UK populations) and **1,000–1,500 breeding hybrids**

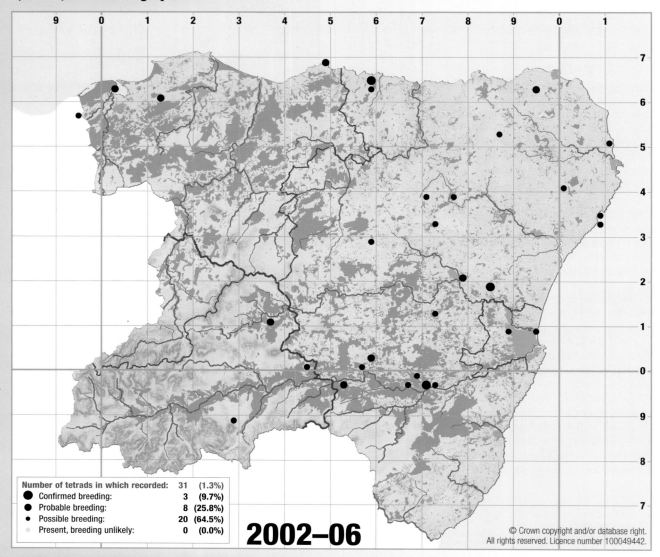

Number of tetrads in which recorded:	31	(1.3%)
● Confirmed breeding:	3	(9.7%)
● Probable breeding:	8	(25.8%)
• Possible breeding:	20	(64.5%)
Present, breeding unlikely:	0	(0.0%)

2002–06

Hooded Crow, Skye, August 2008. © *Dave Pullan*

Habitat and breeding biology
Hooded Crows and their hybrids are found in almost all habitats, absent only from the high uplands. They favour mixed farmland, where there are many small woods, and suburban areas. They are scarce in large conifer plantations and on moorlands. They occupy similar habitats to Carrion Crows and, where both are present, they freely inter-breed to produce hybrid offspring (Picozzi 1976). Where this occurs, Carrion Crows replace Hooded Crows over time, although hybrids may be found for many years. Where birds are widespread, non breeding birds gather into flocks and roost together.

Scottish distribution and status
Within Scotland, the main distribution of Hooded Crows is to the north and west of a line from the Clyde Islands and Argyll, to Inverness. Along this line, where Hooded and Carrion Crows meet, lies a zone of hybridisation. Hooded Crows do occur in small numbers to the east of this line but they are often paired with Carrion Crows or hybrids.

Distribution and status in North-East Scotland
The distribution of Hooded Crows is difficult to assess, primarily because of the difficulty of separating pure Hooded Crows from 'Hooded type' hybrids. In 2002–06 the Hooded Crow was found to be a rare bird in North-East Scotland with only 31 occupied tetrads, distributed across much of the area. However, hybrids, and records which failed to distinguish between Hooded Crows and hybrids,

The Breeding Birds of North-East Scotland

Hooded Crow, Sutherland, April 1986. © *Ed Duthie*

Changes in distribution

The zone of hybridisation between Hooded and Carrion Crows moved steadily west across North-East Scotland during the 20th century (Cook 1975) and by 1968–72 Hooded Crows were proved to breed in just six 10-km squares in the North-east Scotland recording area, although they remained widespread in Moray where they bred in 16 10-km squares (*BTO 1st Atlas*). By 1988–91, breeding was confirmed in only three 10-km squares in the whole North-East (*BTO 2nd Atlas*) - and this was the same in 2002–06. The situation in terms of occupied recording units in Aberdeenshire/Aberdeen City appears contrary to this trend and it is possible that, at different times, different criteria for the separation of Hooded Crows and hybrids were applied. This explanation is supported by the fact that the number of occupied recording units for Hooded Crow fell substantially between 1981–84 and 2002–06, during which period the units occupied by hybrids increased.

Population and trends

Hooded Crows were recorded in 31 tetrads and most of these birds were isolated individuals paired with Carrion Crows or hybrids, and some are likely to be mis-identified hybrids. Taking this into consideration, and allowing for the few birds which were not recorded, the total population is likely to be in the range of 50–100 birds. It is much more difficult to estimate the number of hybrids. However, the survey in 2007 gave a total of 3.6% of all crows being hybrids, and with an estimated population of *c.*36,000 breeding adult crows in the North-East, this suggests a population of about 1,000–1,500 hybrids. It is clear that there is a slow trend towards the disappearance of the Hooded Crow as a breeding species from the North-East and the proportion of hybrids is therefore also likely to dwindle.

Author: *Alastair Young*

were widespread across the area (see map overleaf). Moray is well populated, as is the area between Donside and Huntly, and country to the west of Aberdeen. They are widely but thinly distributed through Buchan, especially just to the south of Turriff. They are absent from the higher mountains and moorlands in the south-west, and few are found south of the River Dee. In 2007, a survey was carried out across the whole of the North-East, to determine the proportion of Carrion, Hooded and hybrid crows in the breeding population. Of 1,090 pairs checked in 87 10-km squares, 96.1% were Carrion, 3.6% were hybrid and 0.3% were pure Hooded Crows. Considered in 10 km wide bands from south (Laurencekirk) to north (Moray Firth coast), the proportion of Hooded Crows increased from 0% to 0.6%, and of hybrids from 0% to 6.5%. Moving from east (North Sea coast) to west (Nairn to the Braemar area), the proportion of Hooded Crows increased from 0.2% to 1.9%, and of hybrids from 4.2% to 16.7%. This shows a clear increase in the proportion of Hooded Crows and hybrids from south-east to north-west. With the exception of a single bird near Huntly, all the pure Hooded Crows were within a few miles of the coast (pers. obs.).

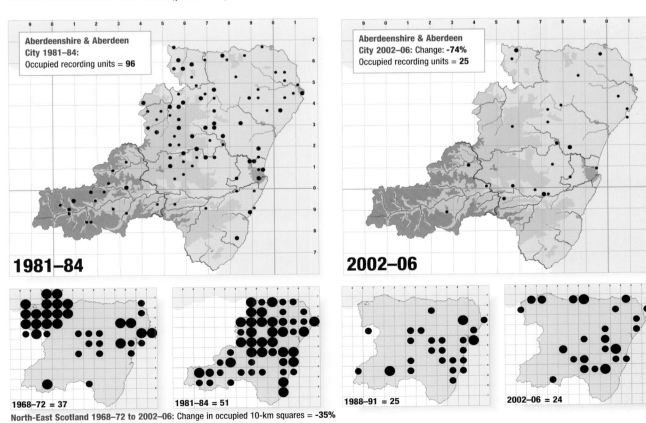

Aberdeenshire & Aberdeen City 1981–84:
Occupied recording units = 96

1981–84

Aberdeenshire & Aberdeen City 2002–06: Change: -74%
Occupied recording units = 25

2002–06

1968–72 = 37

1981–84 = 51

1988–91 = 25

2002–06 = 24

North-East Scotland 1968–72 to 2002–06: Change in occupied 10-km squares = -35%

Hooded x Carrion Crow, Fife, July 2009. © *John Anderson*

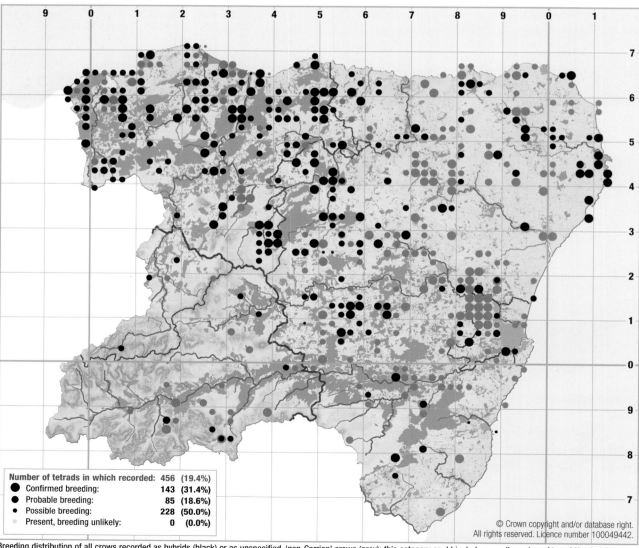

Number of tetrads in which recorded:	456	(19.4%)
● Confirmed breeding:	143	(31.4%)
● Probable breeding:	85	(18.6%)
• Possible breeding:	228	(50.0%)
Present, breeding unlikely:	0	(0.0%)

Breeding distribution of all crows recorded as hybrids (black) or as unspecified, 'non-Carrion' crows (grey); this category could include a small number of 'pure' Hooded Crows.

The Breeding Birds of North-East Scotland

Portknockie cliffs

The cliffs around the Bow Fiddle Rock and Tronach Head, 2 km to the west, hold a large proportion of the breeding Black Guillemots in the North-East. Razorbills have recently started to breed, joining Fulmars, Kittiwakes and an expanding Shag colony. Rock Pipits and a few pairs of House Martins nest on the cliffs and Eiders raise broods around the rocks. A pair of Ravens breeds near Tronach Head. The cliff-top Gorse holds Stonechats, Linnets and Yellowhammers, while Corn Buntings sing nearby. August 2010 © *Martin Cook*

Raven

Corvus corax

Rare resident. Estimated population in North-East Scotland: 15 pairs (<1% of Scottish and UK populations)

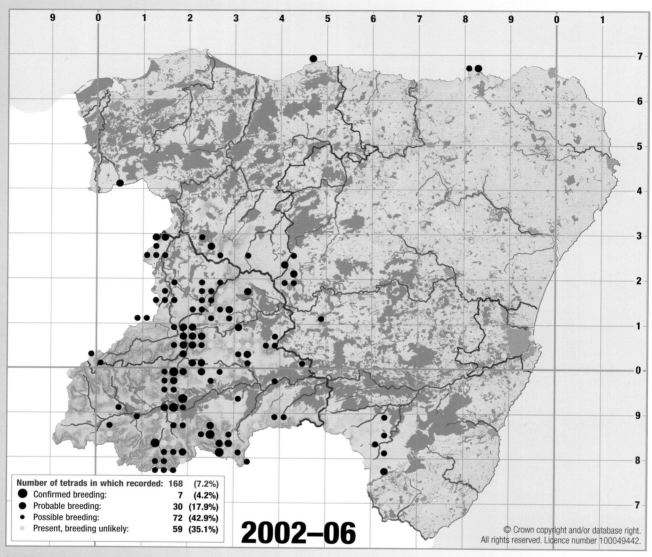

Number of tetrads in which recorded: 168 (7.2%)

● Confirmed breeding: 7 (4.2%)
● Probable breeding: 30 (17.9%)
● Possible breeding: 72 (42.9%)
● Present, breeding unlikely: 59 (35.1%)

2002–06

Habitat and breeding ecology

Ravens are wide-ranging generalist scavengers that, in Scotland, occupy the most open of landscapes in the uplands and on the coast (Mearns in *BS3*). They feed on a range of foods, primarily the carcasses of large mammals such as sheep and deer, but also smaller carcasses from the roadside or coastal strandlines. During the breeding season, they feed opportunistically on a variety of smaller items; invertebrates, birds' eggs, nestlings and small mammals (Marquiss & Booth 1986, Ewins *et al*. 1986). Young Ravens, in flocks or non-breeding pairs, aggregate to roost and to feed on animal remains such as deer grallochs and sheep carcasses, or to scavenge among garbage at landfill sites. Breeding adults are less mobile, foraging in pairs within commuting distance of the nesting territory. They nest on coastal cliffs, inland crags and in trees, laying eggs in March. Young are reared during April and most fledge in May (Ratcliffe 1997).

Scottish distribution and status

Ravens occur throughout Scotland but the highest breeding densities are in the north and west, and in particular on those islands where hill sheep numbers are high and mammalian scavengers absent. Breeding densities are lowest in eastern Scotland, dominated by deer forest and grouse moor

(Ratcliffe 1997). Ravens were formerly ubiquitous but became scarce due to persecution by the 19th century. In the 20th century, away from game areas their numbers increased, but fell again wherever sheepwalks were afforested across the uplands (Marquiss *et al*. 1978). Most recently, an increase in sheep densities and a reduction in the use of poison resulted in increased numbers of Ravens in flocks and the re-establishment of breeding, albeit at low density, on lowland farms. It was thought that in 2004 there were roughly 2,500 to 6,000 pairs (Mearns in *BS3*).

Distribution and status in North-East Scotland

Ravens commonly visit the North-East in autumn when Red Deer grallochs offer seasonal food abundance. Many of these birds overwinter and there are also a few resident breeders. In 2002–06, Ravens were found mainly at intermediate elevations between 300–750 m, particularly on those moors with sheep. Elsewhere, Ravens were almost absent. The high Cairngorms have far fewer large mammal carcasses since reductions in deer density, and the lowlands are dominated by forestry and mixed farming, again offering little in the way of carrion. Two headlands on the north coast each held single pairs. The pattern of distribution of occupied tetrads includes many records away

The Breeding Birds of North-East Scotland

from breeding sites. Ravens travel widely, often heard calling as they fly high overhead; non-breeders in March and April and family parties from May onwards. Thus, although there were records from 168 tetrads, this reflects the distribution of foraging birds rather than their numbers.

Changes in distribution

The change in records between atlases was pronounced. In 1968–72, Ravens were still widely recorded across the uplands, but by the 1980s there were few. In the 2002–06 atlas period, birds were observed in almost five times the number of recording units in Aberdeenshire and more of such observations showed evidence of breeding. The recent increase has also been accompanied by a widening distribution with more records on the fringes of the Cairngorms and the Mounth, occasional records in the lowlands and the colonisation of two headlands on the north coast. The current distribution is as expected from the known habitat use by Ravens elsewhere. If, as in other parts of Scotland, Ravens continue to increase then we can expect more on coastal cliffs, and if they start to nest in trees we can anticipate substantially more breeding at lower elevations.

Population and trends

Ravens have long been scarce breeders in the North-East. In the mid 20th century there were about a dozen traditional breeding sites inland and three or four on the coast. During the 1960s, poisoning substantially reduced the population in the Grampians (Weir 1978) with only three or four pairs left in the North-East by 1971, and a single pair at most in subsequent years. In the last decade of the century, the introduction of intensive crow trapping was accompanied by a reduction in the use of poisoned meat baits and colonising Ravens became more frequent. Pairs then re-established and some now attempt to breed annually. In the atlas years 2002–06, the numbers of tetrads with 'confirmed breeding' could be taken to indicate the minimum population, whereas tetrads with 'probable breeding' were undoubtedly far in excess of the number of breeding pairs. The actual population probably involved pairs at about 15 territories, most of which would have had at least one breeding attempt by 2006.

Author: *Mick Marquiss*

Raven, Iceland, June 2007. © *Sam Alexander*

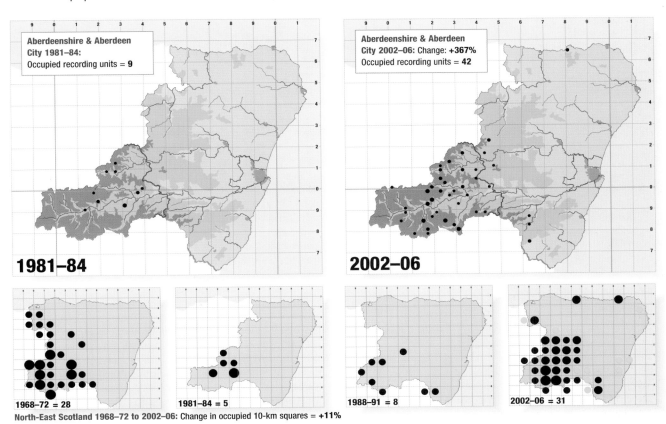

Aberdeenshire & Aberdeen City 1981–84: Occupied recording units = **9**

1981–84

Aberdeenshire & Aberdeen City 2002–06: Change: +367% Occupied recording units = **42**

2002–06

1968–72 = 28   1981–84 = 5   1988–91 = 8   2002–06 = 31

North-East Scotland 1968–72 to 2002–06: Change in occupied 10-km squares = +11%

Goldcrest

Regulus regulus

Very common resident. Passage migrant and winter visitor. Estimated population in North-East Scotland:
40,000–90,000 pairs (12% of Scottish population, 8% of UK)

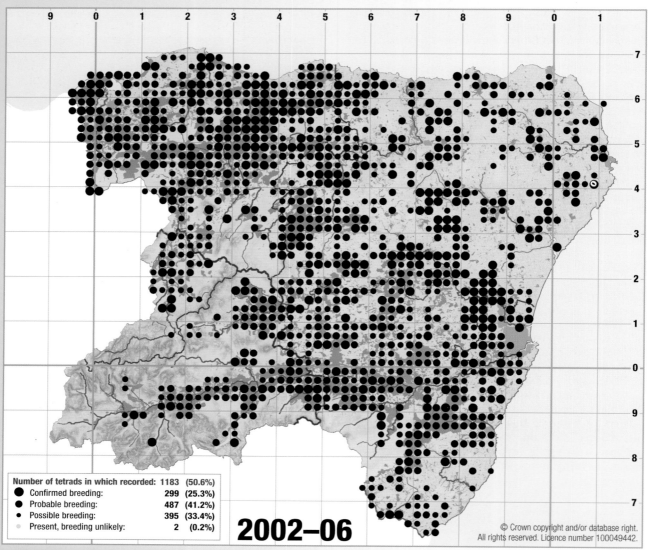

Number of tetrads in which recorded:	1183	(50.6%)
● Confirmed breeding:	299	(25.3%)
● Probable breeding:	487	(41.2%)
● Possible breeding:	395	(33.4%)
● Present, breeding unlikely:	2	(0.2%)

2002–06

Goldcrest, Dunecht, May 1986. © *John Massie*

Habitat and breeding biology

The primary habitat for Goldcrests is conifer woodland with a preference for spruce. The species is also found in broad-leaved woodland where conifers are present. Males sing as early as February and breeding frequently starts early. The nest is generally suspended in twigs at the end of a conifer branch and the clutch size is in the range 9–11 eggs. Incubation by the female takes around 16 days, the young fledge after 17–22 days and become independent two weeks later (*BWP*). Springtails are an especially important element of the diet of newly hatched young (Thaler & Thaler 1982). The population is significantly affected by severe winter weather with high levels of mortality (Hilden 1982).

Scottish distribution and status

Goldcrests are common resident breeders across the whole country with the exception of treeless uplands and moorland. There are small numbers in the Outer Hebrides and the Northern Isles with breeding first recorded in Shetland in 1972. BBS data for 1994–2007 indicate a population increase of 86% in Scotland (Risely *et al.* 2008), perhaps reflecting the expansion in available habitat. The Scottish population may fall in the range of 300,000–750,000 pairs (Insley in *BS3*).

The Breeding Birds of North-East Scotland

Distribution and status in North-East Scotland

Goldcrest distribution in North-East Scotland is closely associated with the distribution of the species' core breeding habitat of conifer woodland, especially spruce. Although distributed across the region the main concentrations are in Deeside, Donside and Moray with good populations in Blackhall Forest near Banchory and up the Dee valley as far as Braemar. They are also widespread in Clashindarroch and other large forests such as those in lower Speyside. They are conspicuously absent from the treeless uplands but the more scattered occurrence in Buchan and the Mearns reflects the patchy distribution of mature conifer plantations, restocking and developing riparian woodlands. Populations are present in small estate woodlands such as Fetternear and within the limits of Aberdeen City. The planting of farm woodlands has resulted in a wider distribution near places such as Marykirk, in the Mearns, and Peterhead and Mintlaw in Buchan.

Goldcrest, Kilminning, Fife, October 2010. © *John Anderson*

Changes in distribution

The distribution in North-East Scotland has changed substantially since 1984. The increase in conifers, particularly spruce and larch, across the region has resulted in an increased presence on lowland farmland. During 1968–72 Goldcrests were recorded in 94 10-km squares (*BTO 1st Atlas*) and this has risen to 101 in 2002–06, indicating only a small increase in distribution. However, there has been a 42% increase in the number of occupied recording units in Aberdeenshire/Aberdeen City between 1981–84 and 2002–06, perhaps reflecting greater habitat availability.

Population and trends

There has been a 300% increase in conifer woodlands between the 1940s and the 1990s with approximately 18% of North-East Scotland now covered by woodland. There are likely to be future increases with demands for biomass plantings and further woodland planting schemes, associated with a revival in spruce planting. The increase in available habitat within the existing Goldcrest range in North-East Scotland should ensure a continued increase in the local breeding population particularly as trees planted in the last 20 years are not yet able to support the highest densities (Moss 1978, Moss *et al.* 1979). Goldcrest breeding densities vary considerably, depending on forest age and type, ranging from 29.7 to 201.1 pairs/km^2 in spruce woodland (Moss 1978, Moss *et al.* 1979), to 0.3–28 territories/ km^2 in various woodland types in Deeside (Jenkins & Watson 1999) and 17 pairs/km^2 in deciduous woodland (Bibby *et al.* 1989). The increase in occupied recording units suggests an increased North-East Scotland population. Risely *et al.* (2008) estimated that the Scottish population had increased by 86% between 1994–2007 and, using the density figures calculated by Moss *et al.* (1979), it is likely that the North-East Scotland population is in the range 40,000–90,000 pairs.

Author: *Martin Auld*

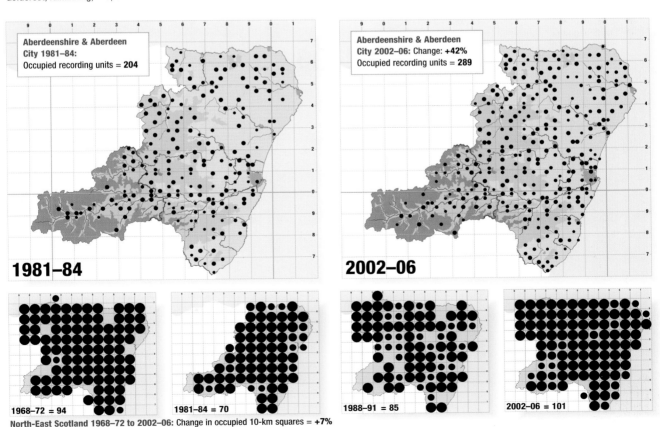

Aberdeenshire & Aberdeen City 1981–84:
Occupied recording units = **204**

1981–84

1968–72 = 94

1981–84 = 70

Aberdeenshire & Aberdeen City 2002–06: Change: +42%
Occupied recording units = **289**

2002–06

1988–91 = 85

2002–06 = 101

North-East Scotland 1968–72 to 2002–06: Change in occupied 10-km squares = +7%

Blue Tit
Cyanistes caeruleus

Very common resident. Estimated population in North-East Scotland: *70,000–90,000 pairs* (12% of Scottish population, 2% of UK)

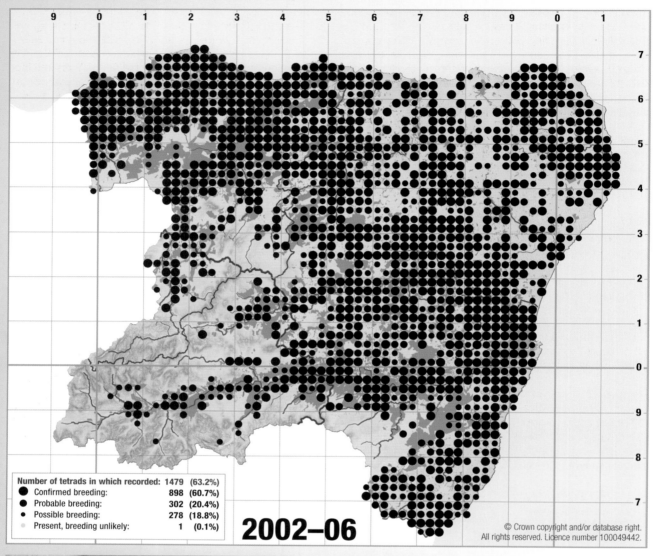

Number of tetrads in which recorded: 1479 (63.2%)

● Confirmed breeding:	898	(60.7%)
● Probable breeding:	302	(20.4%)
• Possible breeding:	278	(18.8%)
· Present, breeding unlikely:	1	(0.1%)

2002–06

Blue Tit, Aboyne, May 2004. © *Harry Scott*

Habitat and breeding biology

The preferred breeding habitat of Blue Tits is broad-leaved woodland although they nest at lower densities in conifer plantations where nest sites are available. They are, however, highly adaptable and will readily breed in gardens including those close to the centre of large towns. Most pairs build their nests in natural holes and cracks in trees but a wide variety of artificial sites is used, such as holes in walls and, especially, nest boxes. Song can usually be heard from February onwards and eggs are laid in late April or early May. Near the Moray coast during 2002–06, the mean size of 66 clutches in mixed broad-leaved woodland at Loch Spynie was 8.2 while 61 clutches in nearby Lossie Forest, a mixed conifer plantation, averaged 7.7 (*MNBRs*). In common, however, with many other lowland plantations, Lossie Forest contains small patches of birch and willow where Blue Tits often feed and close to which they tend to nest.

Scottish distribution and status

Although Blue Tits have a very wide breeding distribution in Scotland, they are absent from the Northern Isles and very scarce in the Outer Hebrides. Similarly, densities are very low north-west of the Great Glen and in the central Highlands. They are most abundant in the lowlands of south and east Scotland where densities as high as 200 pairs/km² have been reported. The most recent estimate, in 2007, suggested a Scottish breeding population in the range 600,000–750,000 pairs (McCulloch in *BS3*).

Distribution and status in North-East Scotland

Confirmation of breeding is easy to obtain for Blue Tits, both when adults are feeding young and when noisy broods are newly on the wing, and breeding was proved in 61% of occupied tetrads. Blue Tits are widespread in North-East Scotland but are more thinly distributed in much of the Buchan plain where suitable woodland is more patchy. Although the woodlands of Deeside are well populated, younger plantations around Fetteresso and Hill of Fare, as well as Dallas Moor and Elchies in Moray, yielded few records. Blue Tit densities are low in small woods in the uplands and here the proportion of confirmed breeding records was not so high. Nonetheless, birds penetrate well up some of the glens of upper Deeside such as Glens Clunie, Derry, Muick and Quoich; some as high as 400 m above sea level.

Changes in distribution

There is no evidence to suggest any substantial change in distribution over the last 40 years since the first BTO Atlas. Comparison of the Aberdeenshire/Aberdeen City maps for 1981–84 and 2002–06 shows a 10.2% increase in occupied recording units but this is largely the result of infilling rather than expansion of the range. On a more local scale, the maturing of forests in areas where none previously existed will of course extend the range. Local retraction will also occur when felling takes place.

Population and trends

Most measured densities for Blue Tits in different habitats in North-East Scotland are either out of date or relate to areas with extensive nest box provision. In the latter category are damp, deciduous woodlands around Loch Spynie where the density can reach 88 pairs/km². 1–29 territories/km² were recorded in a range of woodland types in Deeside (Jenkins & Watson 1999). Data from various sources (*BS3*, *NES 1st Atlas*, Murray *et al.* 1998) indicate that average densities of 45 pairs/km² in broad-leaved woodland, 22 pairs/km² in coniferous woodland and 10 pairs/km² in farmland and suburban gardens may be applicable to North-East Scotland. Applying these densities to the area of relevant land cover types (LC 2000 data) suggests a total of about 83,000 pairs in the North-East. However, Blue Tit populations are prone to large annual fluctuations and it is therefore only possible to estimate a range of 70,000–90,000 pairs. Scottish BBS data indicate a 16% increase in the Blue Tit population during 1994–2007 (Risely *et al.* 2008).

Author: *Martin Cook*

Blue Tit, Inverness, June 2008. © *Derek McGinn*

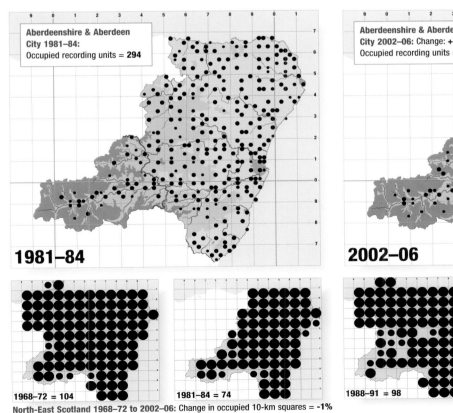

Aberdeenshire & Aberdeen City 1981–84:
Occupied recording units = **294**

1981–84

1968–72 = 104

1981–84 = 74

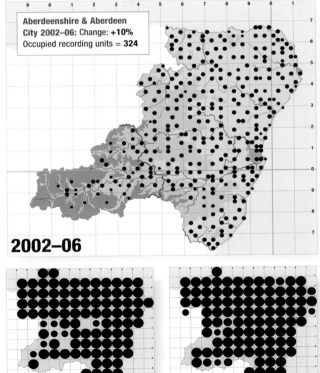

Aberdeenshire & Aberdeen City 2002–06: Change: **+10%**
Occupied recording units = **324**

2002–06

1988–91 = 98

2002–06 = 103

North-East Scotland 1968–72 to 2002–06: Change in occupied 10-km squares = **-1%**

Great Tit

Parus major

Very common resident. Estimated population in North-East Scotland: *35,000–45,000 pairs* (11% of Scottish population, 2% of UK)

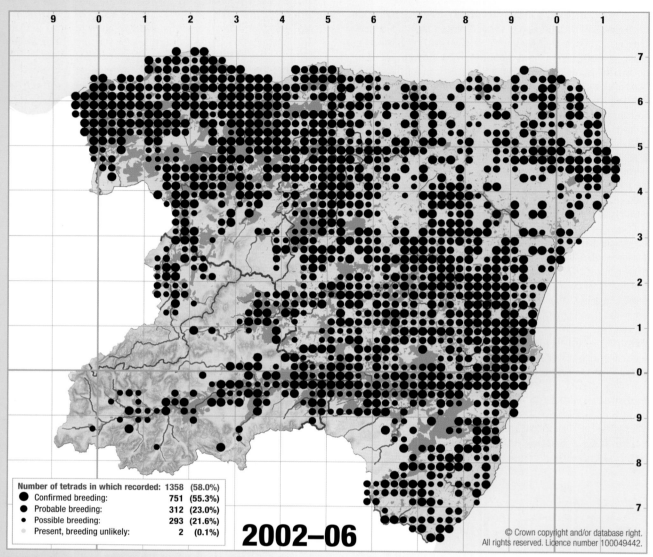

Number of tetrads in which recorded: 1358 (58.0%)
- ● Confirmed breeding: 751 (55.3%)
- ● Probable breeding: 312 (23.0%)
- ● Possible breeding: 293 (21.6%)
- ● Present, breeding unlikely: 2 (0.1%)

2002–06

Habitat and breeding biology

The preferred breeding habitat of the Great Tit in Scotland is open deciduous or mixed woodland; they also populate mature plantations, usually where some deciduous trees are present, but at lower density. Other favoured habitats include farmland with scattered trees, rural gardens, and gardens and parks in towns and cities where these contain suitable nest sites. Nests are built in holes in trees, walls and a range of other man-made structures including nest boxes which are readily adopted. The nest is constructed largely of moss and lined with hair or fur, but seldom feathers. The start of egg-laying varies between late April and early May, depending on prevailing weather conditions. Incubation takes around two weeks and fledging a further three.

Scottish distribution and status

Great Tits breed throughout mainland Scotland with the exception of the higher, treeless uplands. They can be found on many of the Inner Hebrides but are absent from the Outer Hebrides and the Northern Isles. Highest densities are found in Dumfries & Galloway, Borders, the central lowlands, Fife, lowland Perth & Kinross and Angus & Dundee, as well as parts of North-East Scotland and around the inner Moray Firth. The Scottish breeding population in 2007 was estimated to fall within the range of 300,000–450,000 pairs (Wilson in *BS3*).

Distribution and status in North-East Scotland

Great Tits are widespread and common breeders in North-East Scotland, conspicuously absent only from treeless uplands and moors. Even here, a small and remote patch of woodland may provide nesting habitat, as at Glas-allt-Shiel

Great Tit, Aboyne, May 2004. © *Harry Scott*

on the shores of Loch Muick at about 400 m altitude. In the agricultural north-east of the area, the occupied range becomes more patchy due, presumably, to a lack of trees to provide nest sites. It is likely, however, that over much of this farmland Great Tits are breeding, but at a density so low that their detection is difficult. Another habitat often bereft of Great Tits is extensive young conifer plantations, as is apparent on Dallas Moor in Moray and Fetteresso Forest near Stonehaven. Provision of nest boxes in mature plantations quickly leads to the establishment of substantial Great Tit populations, for example in Lossie Forest; further evidence that nest site availability is an important limiting factor in parts of North-East Scotland.

Changes in distribution

The two comparative maps indicate an increase in occupied recording units in Aberdeenshire/Aberdeen City of 21% between 1981–84 and 2002–06. This is apparently caused by infilling of the former range rather than extension into new areas. This infilling appears particularly marked in the area of Buchan bordered by the Rivers Ythan and Deveron. Here the increase in occupied recording units has been 48%. The increase in this area may partly be attributed to observer effort but a population increase in Scotland between 1994–2007 of 87% (Risely *et al.* 2008) may, if repeated in North-East Scotland, have provided the stock for a spread into more marginal areas.

Population and trends

Deriving a population estimate is difficult as there is little detailed local information and the population is likely to fluctuate markedly from year to year depending, in particular, on the survival rate of the previous year's juveniles. In lowland Moray, breeding densities have been measured at 8.2 pairs/km^2 in coniferous plantation in Lossie Forest and as high as 60 pairs/km^2 in damp deciduous woodland around Loch Spynie; but in both cases the provision of nest boxes has probably inflated the natural

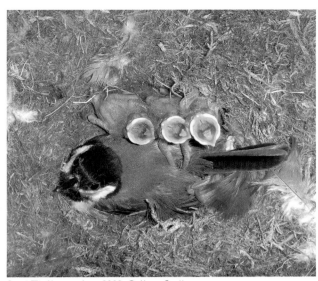

Great Tit, Aboyne, June 2008. © *Harry Scott*

density. 0–31 territories/ km^2 were recorded in a range of woodland types in Deeside (Jenkins & Watson 1999). Data from various sources (*BS3*, *NES 1st Atlas*, Murray *et al.* 1998) indicate that average densities of 30 pairs/km^2 in broad-leaf woodland and 5 pairs/km^2 in other occupied habitats may be appropriate for the North-East. Applying these densities to the area of relevant land cover types (LC 2000 data) suggests a Great Tit population of about 40,000 pairs in North-East Scotland. Clearly this is a highly speculative number and a cautious approach might be to place the breeding population between 35,000–45,000 pairs, or around 11% of the Scottish total. BBS results in Scotland indicate an 87% increase over the period 1994–2007 (Risely *et al.* 2008) and local BBS data provide supporting evidence for a marked population increase.

Author: *Martin Cook*

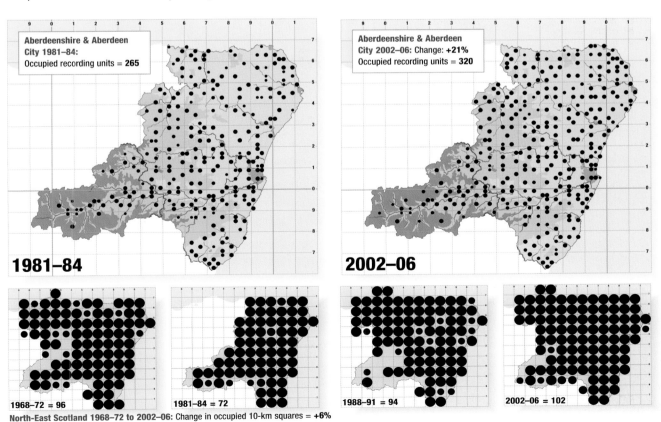

Aberdeenshire & Aberdeen City 1981–84:
Occupied recording units = 265

1981–84

Aberdeenshire & Aberdeen City 2002–06: Change: +21%
Occupied recording units = 320

2002–06

1968–72 = 96   1981–84 = 72   1988–91 = 94   2002–06 = 102

North-East Scotland 1968–72 to 2002–06: Change in occupied 10-km squares = +6%

Crested Tit

Lophophanes cristatus

Scarce resident. Estimated population in North-East Scotland: ***300–450 pairs*** (25% of Scottish and UK population)

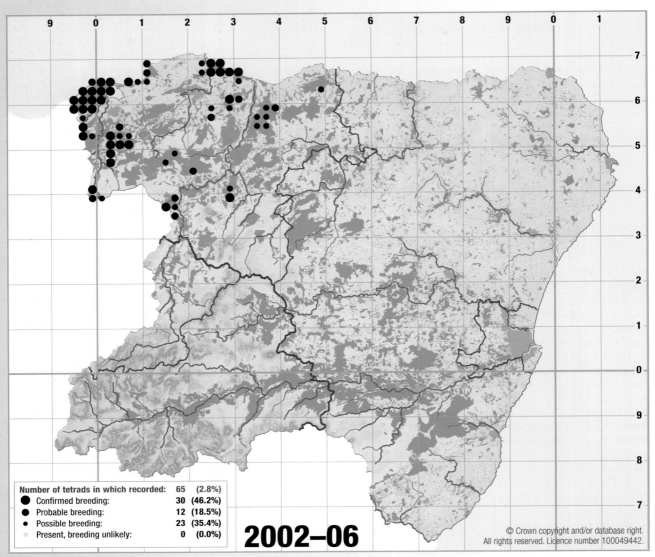

Number of tetrads in which recorded: 65 (2.8%)

● Confirmed breeding:	30	(46.2%)
● Probable breeding:	12	(18.5%)
• Possible breeding:	23	(35.4%)
Present, breeding unlikely:	0	(0.0%)

2002–06

Habitat and breeding biology

Crested Tits in Scotland are primarily birds of Scots Pine woodland, inhabiting ancient native pinewoods and, as is the case in North-East Scotland, plantations. In mixed woodland they can, infrequently, be found among other conifers, such as Lodgepole Pine, and even deciduous broad-leaved species such as birch and Rowan (Summers *et al.* 1999). Heather is also an important feature of the habitat as this provides winter foraging opportunities. In late summer, post-breeding dispersal of young birds accounts for their occasional presence in atypical habitats such as willow scrub and agricultural land. The birds excavate their own nest holes into the sapwood of pine stumps and dead pines, requiring a minimum diameter of at least 20 cm to accommodate the nest chamber. They will use nest boxes, more readily when deep boxes filled with wood shavings are available. First eggs may be laid as early as the first week in April but more commonly in mid April, and occasionally laying may be delayed until early May. Mean clutch size of 51 clutches in Lossie Forest during 1989–2003 was 5.7 eggs (pers. obs.).

Scottish distribution and status

The breeding range, of the Scottish endemic subspecies *L. c. scoticus*, extends from the ancient pinewoods of upper Strathspey to the plantations of lower Strathspey and the coastal plains around the inner Moray Firth from Moray to south-east Sutherland. They can also be found in the forests of the west Highland glens, including Strath Bran, Strathconon, Strathfarrar, Glen Affric, Glen Moriston and Glen Garry. The number of winter social groups has been estimated at 2,300–3,300, comprising 5,600–7,900 individuals (Summers *et al.* 1999). By early spring this number will be substantially reduced and the breeding population may fluctuate within the range 1,000–2,000 pairs (Cook in *BS3*).

Distribution and status in North-East Scotland

The entire North-East Scottish population of Crested Tits is found in Moray. Along the coast, Culbin, Roseisle and Lossie Forests all hold substantial numbers and they are widely, but more thinly, distributed in the Darnaway, Altyre and Newtyle Forests south of Forres. Even small pinewoods as far up country as Dava hold a few birds. A similar low density is typical in the Whiteash Hill and Ordiequish woods near Fochabers, and up the Spey valley. Other extensive tracts of forestry such as Dallas moor, Monaughty and Aultmore appear uninhabited or, at best, hold birds at such low density that they were not detected during Atlas fieldwork. Some of these woods

Crested Tit, Glengarry Forest, June 2008. © *David Whitaker*

contain rather little Scots Pine while other blocks may be insufficiently mature. Although Crested Tits do not breed there, they have reached Aberdeenshire in nine years during the period 1968–2004 (Cook in *BS3*). Although most of these occurrences have been during autumn or winter, single birds were seen in apparently suitable breeding habitat in May 1977 (*NESBR* 1977) and one bird was at Linn of Dee during April and May 1999 (*NESBR* 1999). The reason for the absence of breeding Crested Tits from the apparently suitable ancient Scots Pinewoods of upper Deeside is unclear.

Changes in distribution

The lowland and coastal plantations of Moray were gradually colonised, presumably from upper Speyside, during 1860–1940. First records came from the Fochabers area in the 1860s and by the end of the century they were well established there. By 1910 they had spread to the Forres area and the lower Findhorn valley (Cook 1982, 1992). As more plantations matured along the coast the population was consolidated. There is little evidence of further range changes in more recent times - the increase in occupied 10-km squares since the early 1970s is probably a consequence of further spread into mature plantations within the existing range. Natural colonisation of Deeside seems unlikely in the near future as the Cairngorms present a barrier to any substantial eastward movement from Strathspey and the predominantly Sitka Spruce plantations of lower Banffshire and Donside would appear to provide little opportunity for immigration from the north.

Crested Tit, Culbin Forest, July 1980. © *Martin Cook*

Population and trends

Crested Tits were recorded during 2002–06 in 65 tetrads. Even where it was not proved, the sedentary nature of Crested Tits during the breeding season suggests that breeding probably occurred in most of these tetrads. Taking into account the area of each tetrad that contains suitable habitat reveals about 120 km^2 of such habitat, of which 39 km^2 is in the coastal forests. Assuming that the approximate density of 4–5 pairs/km^2 in Lossie Forest (pers. obs.) is typical of the coastal forests, and that the density elsewhere is lower at, perhaps, 2–3 pairs/km^2 then a population range between 300–450 pairs would be likely in a typical year. Although this fits reasonably alongside the Scottish estimate of 1,000–2,000 pairs, a more reliable estimate of numbers in the North-East will depend on density measurements from a wider range of woodlands.

Author: *Martin Cook*

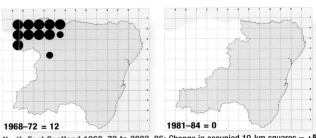

1968–72 = 12

1981–84 = 0

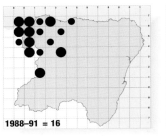

1988–91 = 16

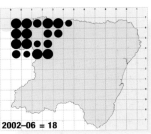

2002–06 = 18

North-East Scotland 1968–72 to 2002–06: Change in occupied 10-km squares = +50%

Coal Tit

Periparus ater

Very common resident. Estimated population in NE Scotland: **40,000–80,000 pairs** (20% of Scottish population, 9% of UK)

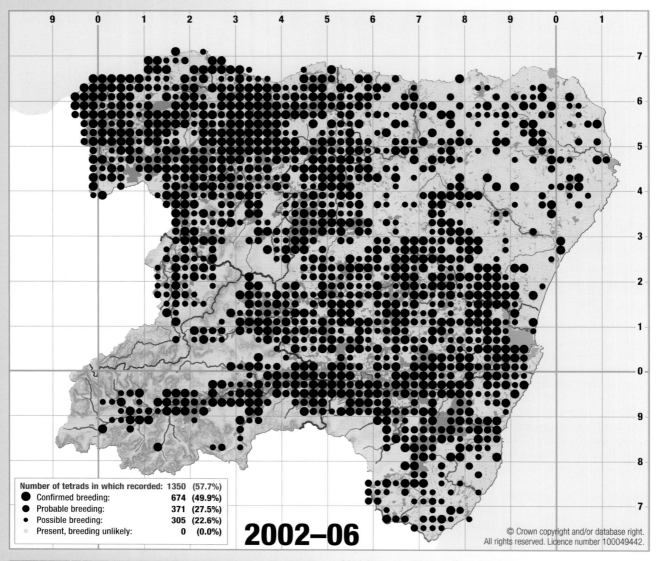

Number of tetrads in which recorded:	1350	(57.7%)
● Confirmed breeding:	674	(49.9%)
● Probable breeding:	371	(27.5%)
• Possible breeding:	305	(22.6%)
· Present, breeding unlikely:	0	(0.0%)

2002–06

Coal Tit, Ballater, May 2004. © *Harry Scott*

Habitat and breeding biology

Coal Tits are the characteristic tit species of coniferous woodland but they are by no means confined to this habitat. They occur at high density in natural and semi-natural Scots Pine forests and all types of conifer plantation. Even a few conifers in farmland or large gardens may be sufficient to attract a pair to breed. Coal Tits are also present, usually at lower densities, in mixed and deciduous woods, including upland birch woods. They penetrate wooded glens to higher altitudes than other tit species. Nests are built in existing tree cavities, usually with small entrance holes and often close to ground level. Indeed, they frequently nest among tree roots or in the holes and runs made by small mammals. Holes in dry stone dykes may also be used. They commence breeding earlier than Blue and Great Tits, with the onset of egg-laying in Lossie Forest varying between mid April in some years and early May in others.

Scottish distribution and status

Coal Tits have a wide breeding distribution throughout much of Scotland with the exception of the highest ground. They occur more sparsely in the north-west and are absent from much of the Outer Hebrides and, as breeders, all of the Northern Isles. Densities are highest in areas of the country

Coal Tit, Ballater, May 2004. © *Harry Scott*

most extensively planted with conifers. The most recent Scottish population estimate lies between 200,000–400,000 pairs (Sellers in *BS3*).

Distribution and status in North-East Scotland

Coal Tits have an extensive range in North-East Scotland with the most densely occupied area in a broad band from the Moray coast in the north to the coast between Aberdeen and Stonehaven in the south. To the north-east of this zone lies the Buchan plain where the range is more restricted due, primarily, to the relative scarcity of woodland. The same applies to the Mearns area, south from Stonehaven. To the south-west lies the high ground and open moorland where upper Deeside and Donside, as well as glens such as Glen Muick and Glen Avon, provide suitable

habitat in the otherwise-hostile uplands. Even well-isolated woodlands such as at Baddoch in upper Glen Clunie, the Glas-allt-Shiel woodland at the head of Loch Muick, and Inchrory in Glen Avon are often populated. Here, Coal Tits attain their maximum breeding altitude in North-East Scotland of around 400–450 m.

Changes in distribution

At the 10-km square level, the number of occupied squares has remained very similar over the period 1968–72 (*BTO 1st Atlas*), 1988–91 (*BTO 2nd Atlas*) and 2002–06. Comparison of the Aberdeenshire/Aberdeen City maps between 1981–84 and 2002–06 shows a small increase of 9% in occupied recording units. North-east of a line from the mouth of the Deveron to the mouth of the Ythan however, the increase is 33% which suggests a real range extension in the Buchan area, perhaps as a result of the increased availability of conifer plantations.

Population and trends

Problems with providing a population estimate for this species are compounded by the range of habitats which are occupied and the range of breeding densities which occur there. In the early 1980s, densities in mid Deeside ranged from 15–65 pairs/km^2 in pinewood to 5–100 pairs/km^2 in birchwood (*NES 1st Atlas*). More recent densities in a range of woodland types in a Deeside glen ranged from 8–25 territories/km^2 (Jenkins & Watson 1999). An alternative approach is therefore required. North-East Scotland occupies approximately 15% of the Scottish breeding distribution of Coal Tits, but the local population density is higher than in many other areas of the country (Sellers in *BS3*) so it is possible that the North-East holds 20% of the population. Applying this figure to the Scottish population estimate suggests a North-East Scotland population in the range 40,000–80,000 pairs.

Author: *Martin Cook*

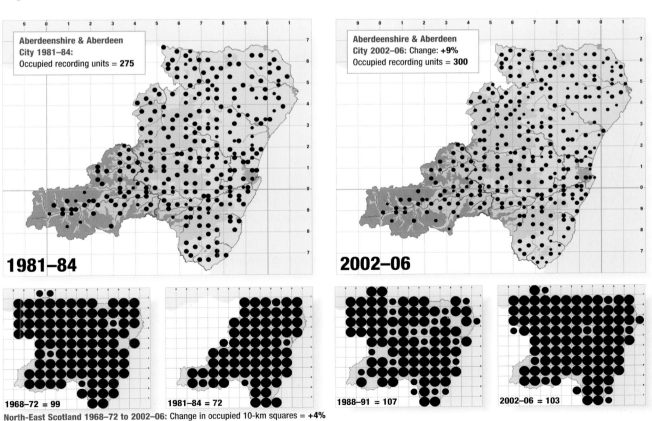

Aberdeenshire & Aberdeen City 1981–84: Occupied recording units = **275**

1981–84

Aberdeenshire & Aberdeen City 2002–06: Change: +9% Occupied recording units = **300**

2002–06

1968–72 = 99   1981–84 = 72   1988–91 = 107   2002–06 = 103

North-East Scotland 1968–72 to 2002–06: Change in occupied 10-km squares = **+4%**

Bearded Tit

Panurus biarmicus

Very rare resident. Estimated population in North-East Scotland: Up to **5 pairs** (2% of Scottish population, <1% of UK)

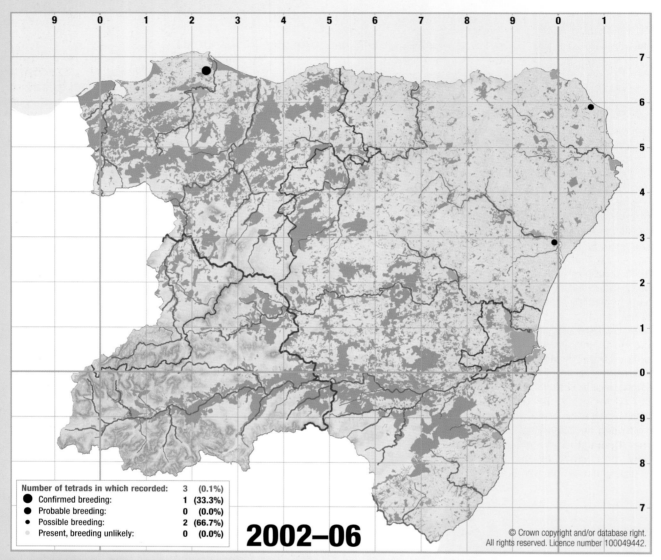

Number of tetrads in which recorded:	3	(0.1%)
● Confirmed breeding:	1	(33.3%)
● Probable breeding:	0	(0.0%)
• Possible breeding:	2	(66.7%)
Present, breeding unlikely:	0	(0.0%)

2002–06

Bearded Tit, Tay reedbeds, April 2007. © *John Anderson*

Habitat and breeding biology

As breeders, Bearded Tits are confined to reedbeds, in freshwater in Moray but also those in brackish and saltwater elsewhere in Britain. These are usually extensive but the largest reedbed in North-East Scotland, at Loch Spynie, only occupies approximately 24 hectares and this is the one confirmed breeding site. No nests have been found at Loch Spynie but proof of breeding has been obtained from adults carrying food and faecal sacs, and from newly fledged parties of juveniles. If the breeding cycle matches that in the Tay reedbeds then first clutches, usually of 4–8 eggs, will be laid in early April with the first juveniles on the wing from the end of April (Moyes in *BS3*).

Scottish distribution and status

In Scotland, Bearded Tits breed only at Loch Spynie and in the Tay reedbeds. They were not seen at the Tay until August 1991. Since that time they have increased rapidly and in 2004 the population was estimated at over 250 pairs, perhaps 30% of the British total (Moyes in *BS3*). Numbers fluctuate here, and crashed especially badly during the 2004–05 winter (A. Leitch, H. Morton pers. comm.). Recovery is usually rapid due, presumably, to prolific breeding output.

Distribution and status in North-East Scotland

The first Bearded Tits recorded in North-East Scotland were three birds which were seen at Loch of Strathbeg on 5th November 1972, two of which remained until the following March. The next record, and the first spring/summer occurrence, was also at Loch of Strathbeg, on 12th April 1976 (*NES 1st Atlas*). There were no further records there until three males and a female were found on 4th March 1997. In 1998, a single female was present on two dates in June and again in September, but in October there were six birds; smaller numbers remained until mid November when the last was seen. A female was present at the loch throughout 1999, and a male was there in January and August. In 2000, one or two birds were present in January and March but there were no further records until a juvenile or female on 18th June 2005 and a male in late March 2006. Elsewhere in Aberdeenshire, a male and female were in reeds by Logie Buchan bridge on the Ythan estuary in June–July 2006. Bearded Tits were first found at Loch Spynie in 1998 when three birds remained in a small area of the reedbed for two weeks in late May and later, in September, a party of eight was seen. Since that time, birds have been seen at the loch annually with the exception of 2002. Breeding was proved in 2003 (one pair of adults with up to seven juveniles), 2004 (adults carrying food in July), 2005 (adult carrying a faecal sac in June), 2006 (adults carrying food in late May) and 2007 (adult carrying food in June). In September 2007 a party of 18 birds was seen, the largest gathering yet reported. (Although mentioned in the text, the breeding at Loch Spynie has been omitted from the distribution map in *BS3*).

Changes in distribution

Only three sites in North-East Scotland have held Bearded Tits in the breeding season, starting with Loch of Strathbeg in 1976, followed by Loch Spynie in 1998 and the Ythan estuary in 2006. Permanent presence has only been at Loch Spynie and indeed it is only here that breeding has been confirmed.

Bearded Tit, Loch Spynie, July 2003. © *Martin Cook*

Population and trends

Estimating the size of a small population of an elusive passerine, in a habitat to which access is limited, is fraught with problems. Numbers at Loch Spynie are undoubtedly small; 18 is the largest group seen at the end of the breeding season and may well have represented the entire population in 2007. It is unlikely that more than five pairs have bred at the loch in any one year and the absence of any records in 2009 raises questions over the survival of Bearded Tits at Loch Spynie.

Author: *Martin Cook*

Bearded Tit habitat, Loch Spynie, May 2010. © *Martin Cook*

Skylark   *Alauda arvensis*

Very common resident and migrant breeder. Passage migrant. Estimated population in North-East Scotland: *50,000 pairs* (12% of Scottish population, 3% of UK)   Red list; UK and Scottish BAP lists

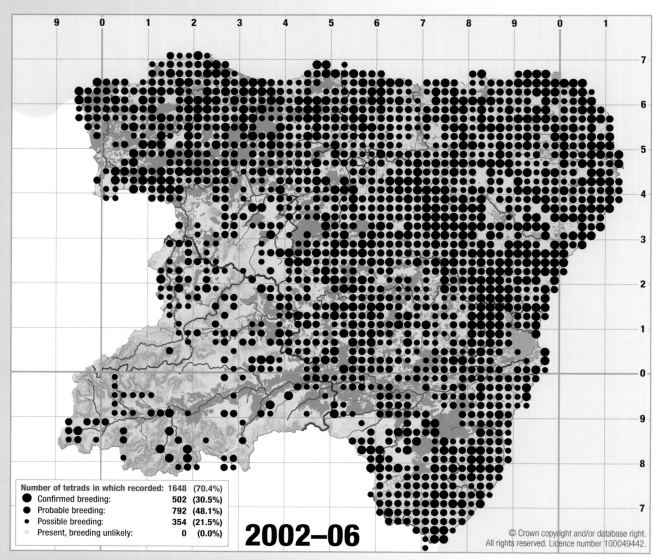

Number of tetrads in which recorded: 1648   (70.4%)
- ● Confirmed breeding: 502   (30.5%)
- ● Probable breeding: 792   (48.1%)
- ● Possible breeding: 354   (21.5%)
- · Present, breeding unlikely: 0   (0.0%)

2002–06

Skylark, Auchenblae, June 2009. © *Sam Alexander*

Habitat and breeding biology

With its familiar song, the Skylark is one of the most characteristic species of open countryside in North-East Scotland. It is primarily a lowland species, breeding on farmland, rough grassland and dunes and avoiding the close proximity of trees and woodland. On farmland it particularly favours areas where there is a high proportion of set-aside or spring sown cereals, although the diversity of habitats available (including autumn sown crops and grassland) also appears to be important (pers. obs.). In the uplands, Skylarks are usually restricted to grass-dominated habitats and avoid Heather moorland, although large areas of burnt Heather can temporarily attract breeding pairs. A few pairs can even be found on the tops of the highest mountains. The nest is a shallow depression on the ground and two or three nesting attempts are made between April and July.

Scottish distribution and status

The Skylark is a common and widespread breeding bird throughout Scotland with an estimated breeding population of 290,000–557,000 pairs (Dougall in *BS3*). In contrast to the much publicised decline in England since the rise of autumn sown crops in the 1970s, there is little

Skylark, Fisherbriggs, 2007. © *Hywel Maggs*

evidence of a corresponding population decline in Scotland (Risely *et al.* 2008).

Distribution and status in North-East Scotland

Skylarks are extremely widespread below the 200 m contour, with obvious gaps in distribution around the forests of Moray and Deeside and the centre of Aberdeen. Smaller gaps are evident around wooded lowland estates such as Dunecht, Haddo House, Forglen and Auchmacoy. In the uplands, the Skylark is more sparsely distributed, probably as a result of the dominance of Heather moorland. Obvious clusters are present along some upper Deeside glens, around Morven and on the hills around Glen Callater and upper Glen Dye. These are all areas where grazing or the underlying geology have resulted in grass dominated vegetation. Skylarks generally move out of the uplands between August and March, but are present year-round in the lowlands.

Changes in distribution

There has been no obvious change in Skylark distribution since 1981–84, with a negligible 1.5% increase in the number of recording units occupied in Aberdeenshire/Aberdeen City - even this may not be a real increase, given a higher level of observer coverage.

Population and trends

In lowland arable areas, 50 pairs/km^2 can be found on some sites, but 14 pairs/km^2 is more typical (pers. obs.). Densities are much lower in the uplands and information from atlas fieldwork and the BBS suggests that 8 pairs/km^2 is probably a reasonable estimate for the 1,651 occupied tetrads across the region as a whole, implying a total population of about 50,000 pairs. There has been a decline in peak counts in those BBS squares that have been regularly surveyed since 1994 (Francis 2008) but peak counts across all BBS squares in the region have been stable over the same period, suggesting that any population changes may be highly localised. As the only significant arable area in Britain where more crops are sown in spring than autumn (National Statistics 2007, 2008), it is unlikely that there has been a widespread population decline in North-East Scotland, although the impact of the loss of compulsory set-aside in 2007 remains to be seen.

Author: *Paul Chapman*

Skylark, Blackhill of Slains, June 2008. © *Hywel Maggs*

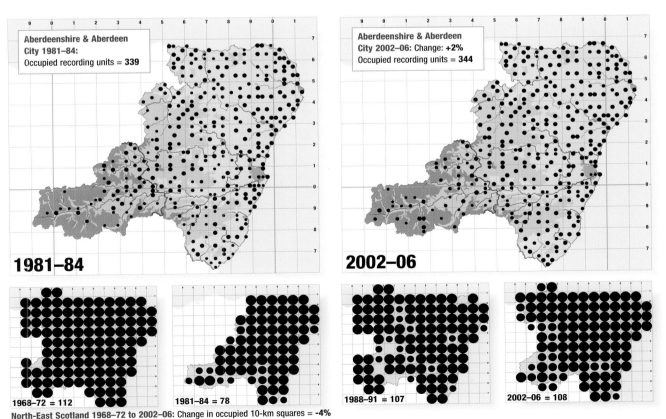

Aberdeenshire & Aberdeen City 1981–84:
Occupied recording units = 339

1981–84

Aberdeenshire & Aberdeen City 2002–06: Change: +2%
Occupied recording units = 344

2002–06

1968–72 = 112

1981–84 = 78

1988–91 = 107

2002–06 = 108

North-East Scotland 1968–72 to 2002–06: Change in occupied 10-km squares = -4%

Shore Lark

Eremophila alpestris

Occasional in breeding habitat. Passage migrant and winter visitor. Estimated population in North-East Scotland: **0 pairs**

Number of tetrads in which recorded:	1	(0.0%)
● Confirmed breeding:	0	(0.0%)
● Probable breeding:	0	(0.0%)
• Possible breeding:	1	(100.0%)
· Present, breeding unlikely:	0	(0.0%)

Shore Lark, Canada, June 1992. © *Ed Duthie*

Habitat and breeding biology

In northern Europe, Shore Larks breed in arctic or sub-arctic tundra and in montane habitats in Norway and Sweden (*BWP*). In Scotland, they have bred only in the alpine zone of the Cairngorms massif. The only nest to be found here, in 1977, contained three eggs on 25th June. It was built on the ground in an area of gravel and boulders with patches of short rushes and moss (Ellis 1990).

Scottish distribution and status

The Shore Lark is primarily a rare but regular passage migrant and winter visitor to the coast of eastern Scotland. It is also a very rare breeding species, apparently confined to the Cairngorms within the Highland boundary. The first summer record there was in 1972, and breeding almost certainly took place in 1973, when the evidence suggested that there were at least two fledged chicks (Watson 1973). A male was seen in 1976 (Sharrock *et al*. 1978) and breeding was confirmed in 1977 when a nest containing three eggs was found (Ellis 1990). There were no further records until 1997 when a pair was seen (Ogilvie *et al*. 1999). Between 1999 and 2002, at least one bird was seen annually and breeding was again confirmed in 2003 (Holling *et al*. 2007). A pair was present the following year (Holling *et al*. 2007) and a single bird in 2005 (Holling *et al*. 2008).

Distribution and status in North-East Scotland

In view of the breeding activity in Highland it is likely that Shore Larks are occasionally present in summer in those parts of the Cairngorms that fall within North-East Scotland. In 1977, an independent fully grown juvenile was

Shore Lark, Norway, June 1990. © *Ed Duthie*

seen within this area (A. Watson pers. comm.) and it is likely that this bird fledged from the Highland nest described above. The only record during 2002–06 was of a single singing bird in this area in 2005. One was also seen on the high tops of the North-East in June 1975 but the habitat was considered unsuitable for nesting (*NES 1st Atlas*, Ferguson-Lees *et al*. 1977).

Author: *Martin Cook*

Ladder Hills

Lapwing, Curlew, Snipe and Redshank breed in the marshes and rough grazing land while Dunlin and Golden Plover nest among the wet bogs and pools of the higher ground. Burns hold Dipper, Grey Wagtail and Common Sandpiper. Moorland breeding raptors include Merlin, and Hen Harrier when they are undisturbed, while Kestrels and, occasionally, Barn Owls utilise barns and ruined croft buildings, along with Swallows and Pied Wagtails. May 2006 © *Martin Cook*

Sand Martin

Riparia riparia

Common summer migrant breeder. Passage migrant. Estimated population in North-East Scotland: **6,000–8,000 pairs** (17% of Scottish population, 4% of UK)

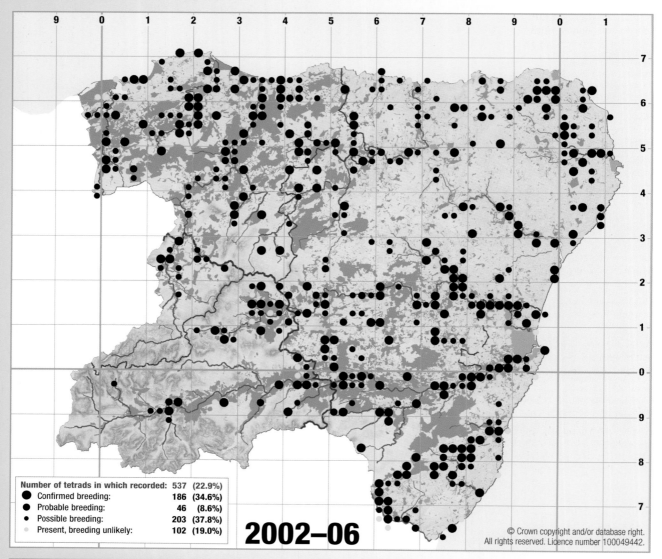

Number of tetrads in which recorded:	537	(22.9%)
● Confirmed breeding:	186	(34.6%)
● Probable breeding:	46	(8.6%)
● Possible breeding:	203	(37.8%)
● Present, breeding unlikely:	102	(19.0%)

2002–06

Sand Martin, Newburgh, July 2009. © *Ed Duthie*

Habitat and breeding biology

Sand Martin colonies are established in riverbanks and sand or gravel quarries, usually close to water. Less commonly used sites include road cuttings and eroded coastal dunes where suitable sandy faces provide opportunity for the excavation of nesting burrows. Smaller colonies, in particular, may be occupied for a few years until excessive erosion or invasion by vegetation causes the birds to move. Winter erosion often requires the digging of new burrows each year; for example, virtually all traces of a large colony in a bank of glacial deposits beside the River Spey near Fochabers disappear each winter. Clutches are laid from mid May and chicks fledge from late June onwards.

Scottish distribution and status

Sand Martins are widely distributed on the Scottish mainland, especially in the south and east. Very few are found in the uplands and moorlands of the west and they are absent as regular breeders in the Outer Hebrides and Northern Isles. Recent estimates of the Scottish breeding population range from 20,000–65,000 pairs (Turner in *BS3*).

Distribution and status in North-East Scotland

The distribution map clearly illustrates the species' use of sandy cliffs along waterways, with many colonies sited along river systems such as the Lossie, Spey, Ythan, Don and Dee. Between river systems the distribution is patchy, reflecting the presence of sand pits and other, often temporary, banks. Although scarce in the uplands, small colonies can be found along the banks of rivers to altitudes of 400 m in upper Donside. Within coastal areas, small colonies exist in sand dunes, even along the foreshore such as at Covesea and Findhorn. Sand Martins are absent from many habitats where suitable breeding sites are not present; these include large stretches of coast, farmland, continuous forestry, and much of the upland and mountainous areas within the region. As can be seen from the map, birds are present in many tetrads in which they are not breeding, indicating their willingness to forage widely away from their colonies. Sand Martins are usually one of the first summer migrants to arrive, generally in the last days of March. They often gather in large numbers over open water prior to the start of breeding. Most birds depart by mid September.

Sand Martin, Fochabers, June 2007. © *Martin Cook*

Changes in distribution

The number of occupied 10-km squares fell by 28% from 92 in 1968–72 (*1st BTO Atlas*) to 66 in 1988–91 (*2nd BTO Atlas*), but recovered to 94 by 2002–06. In addition, the number of occupied recording units in Aberdeenshire/Aberdeen City more than doubled between 1981–84 and 2002–06 with notable increases along Deeside and Donside, in southern areas around Stonehaven and St. Cyrus, and in coastal lowland areas around Banff, Turriff and Fraserburgh.

Population and trends

Although numerous colonies have been counted in recent years, it is likely that such counts are biased towards larger colonies; smaller groups of burrows are less likely to be located. During 2002–06, the largest colony reported, at Glen Rinnes sandpit, contained about 250 apparently occupied

nest burrows, but the mean size of 31 other colonies was 32 burrows. Applying this figure to the 186 tetrads where breeding was confirmed, and assuming only one colony in each tetrad, yields 5,952 pairs. Sand Martins were considered to be probably breeding in a further 46 tetrads and assuming a smaller colony size of 10 pairs in these, adds another 460 pairs. Possible breeding was recorded in 203 tetrads which therefore contain an additional, unknown, number of pairs. The best that can be said is therefore that the population probably lies in the range of 6,000–8,000 pairs. Sharp population fluctuations have taken place in Scotland over the last 40 years (Turner in *BS3*). If these trends are applicable to North-East Scotland then numbers have increased substantially since the population crashes of the late 1960s and early 1980s which were associated with drought in the African Sahel wintering grounds.

Author: *Bob Proctor*

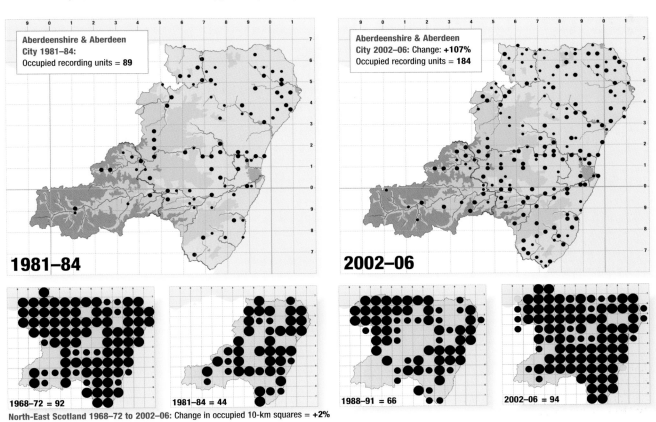

Aberdeenshire & Aberdeen City 1981–84: Occupied recording units = **89**

1981–84

Aberdeenshire & Aberdeen City 2002–06: Change: **+107%** Occupied recording units = **184**

2002–06

1968–72 = 92

1981–84 = 44

1988–91 = 66

2002–06 = 94

North-East Scotland 1968–72 to 2002–06: Change in occupied 10-km squares = +2%

Swallow

Common summer migrant breeder. Passage migrant. Estimated population in North-East Scotland: **6,500–10,000 pairs** (8% of Scottish population, 1% of UK)

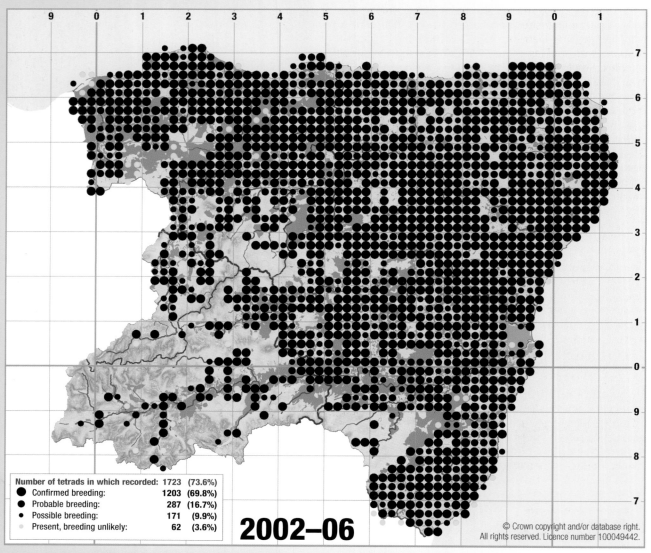

Number of tetrads in which recorded: 1723	(73.6%)
● Confirmed breeding: 1203	(69.8%)
● Probable breeding: 287	(16.7%)
● Possible breeding: 171	(9.9%)
● Present, breeding unlikely: 62	(3.6%)

2002–06

Swallow, Skene, May 2005. © *John Young*

Habitat and breeding biology

Feeding birds frequent open areas where insects are found, such as fields, meadows, over water and along woodland edges. During the breeding season the preference is for lowland areas, especially around farms with livestock, particularly cattle (Turner in *BS3*). Nest sites are usually in open outbuildings or barns, though a wide variety of other sites may be used including sheds, garages, porches, and bridges. Once pairs have formed and nests either newly built or repaired, eggs are laid from mid May to mid June, followed by second clutches from late June to late July. Late broods, therefore, may not fledge until late September or early October. Breeding success can be dependent on weather conditions, with low productivity during periods of prolonged rain or hot dry weather.

Scottish distribution and status

The Swallow is a widely distributed breeding species over most of Scotland, including the Outer Hebrides, Orkney and Shetland. Highest densities are in the south and east of the country and they are scarce or absent in moorland or mountainous areas. A realistic population estimate in 2007 suggests a range of 80,000–120,000 pairs in Scotland (Turner in *BS3*).

Distribution and status in North-East Scotland

Swallows are very widespread in North-East Scotland breeding wherever suitable feeding habitat with nest sites occurs. They are absent from large towns, including most of Aberdeen, areas of continuous forestry and, particularly, upland and mountain habitats. Nevertheless, breeding at upland sites was confirmed at 400–500 m in Glens Clunie, Dee, Derry and Muick, at 500 m and 600 m in Glen Avon and as high as 650 m at the Lecht ski complex. Swallows usually arrive in the region in early to mid April. In Moray, at least, there has been a four day shift towards earlier arrival over the period 1985–2002. Most depart by late September, although stragglers occasionally linger into November or even December.

Changes in distribution

There was only an insignificant 3% increase in occupied recording units in Aberdeenshire/Aberdeen City between 1981–84 and 2002–06. No shift in range was discernable.

Swallow, Loch Kinord, June 2007. © *Harry Scott*

Swallow, Glen Tanar, August 2004. © *Harry Scott*

Population and trends

Studies of Swallows in arable countryside near Buckie in the early 1970s found a density of 0.66 pairs/km², or 2.64 pairs/tetrad (McGinn 1979). Similar values have been reported in Lothian but up to 4.4 pairs/km², or 17.6 pairs/tetrad, in agricultural land around Stirling (Turner in *BS3*). It is unlikely that the latter density is frequently reached in North-East Scotland, and in some upland tetrads there may be only one pair. Adopting an average of 4–6 pairs/tetrad and applying this to the 1,661 tetrads where breeding was at least possible during 2002–06, suggests a population in the range 6,500–10,000 pairs. BBS data suggest a 5% increase in Swallow numbers over the period 1994–2007 (Risely *et al.* 2008).

Author: *Bob Proctor*

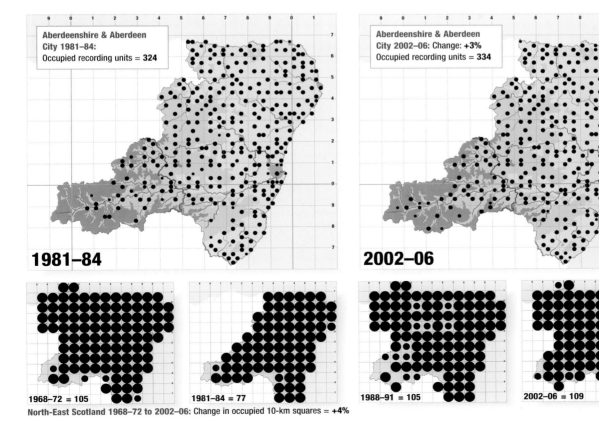

Aberdeenshire & Aberdeen City 1981–84:
Occupied recording units = 324

1981–84

Aberdeenshire & Aberdeen City 2002–06: Change: **+3%**
Occupied recording units = 334

2002–06

1968–72 = 105   1981–84 = 77   1988–91 = 105   2002–06 = 109

North-East Scotland 1968–72 to 2002–06: Change in occupied 10-km squares = **+4%**

House Martin

Delichon urbicum

Common summer migrant breeder. Passage migrant. Estimated population in North-East Scotland: **3,300–6,700 pairs** (9% of Scottish population, 1% of UK)

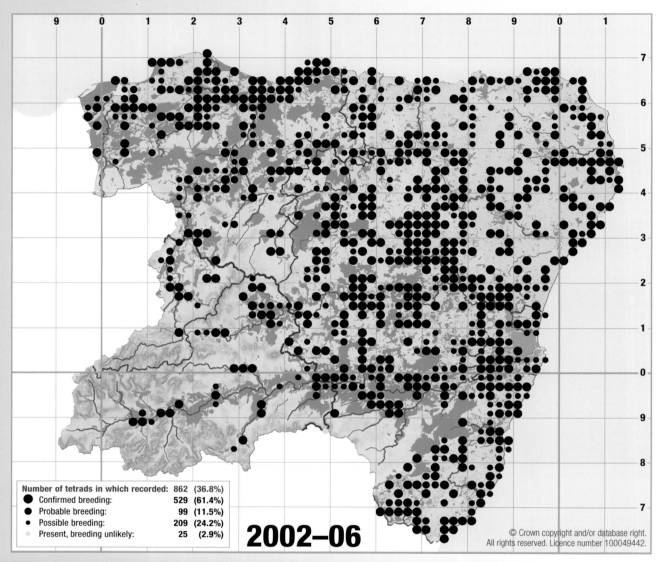

Number of tetrads in which recorded:	862	(36.8%)
● Confirmed breeding:	529	(61.4%)
● Probable breeding:	99	(11.5%)
● Possible breeding:	209	(24.2%)
· Present, breeding unlikely:	25	(2.9%)

2002–06

House Martin, Fife, June 2007. © *John Anderson*

Habitat and breeding biology

Feeding House Martins can be seen over a range of habitats where insect food is found, including grassy areas, lochs, ponds, rivers and coastal marshes. They nest colonially and the majority of breeding sites are associated with buildings, although traditional coastal cliff colonies still exist. In country villages, new houses with suitable eaves may be colonised rapidly, suggesting that nest site availability is a limiting factor in some areas. The mud-pellet nests are built and lined in 11–22 days and eggs are laid from mid May to late June. Many pairs may attempt a second brood, though this appears to be dependent on food supplies in June and July (Riley 1992, cited in Turner in *BS3*). Unfledged young still in nests in October may be the result of a third brood.

Scottish distribution and status

House Martins are widely distributed throughout much of mainland Scotland although they are scarce or absent in the north-west, the Outer Hebrides and Shetland, as well as upland areas elsewhere. The Scottish population is estimated to be in the region of 38,000–74,000 pairs (Turner in *BS3*).

Distribution and status in North-East Scotland

In North-East Scotland, the House Martin is a widespread breeding species but has a patchy distribution in many lowland agricultural areas and is absent from upland and mountain habitats as well as densely forested areas. They exploit new housing developments quickly, where good nest sites under the eaves of houses and ample supplies of mud for nest building are often available. In upland areas, breeding associated with buildings was confirmed at Inverey, Braemar, Crathie, Glen Gairn, Tomintoul and, at a maximum altitude of c.400 m, at Spittal of Glenmuick, Corgarff and Inchrory. Several coastal cliff colonies exist, the largest being at St. Cyrus (108 nests in 2004) and Inverbervie (60 nests in 2004),

but most, such as those at Portknockie, Collieston, Pennan, Forvie, Muchalls, Catterline, Johnshaven, New Aberdour and Stonehaven, contain less than 30 nests. House Martins begin to return to North-East Scotland in mid to late April and depart in late August and early September. However in most years there are late individuals in October and November, with a very few records in December.

Changes in distribution

At the 10-km square level there was an apparent decrease in range between 1968–72 (*BTO 1st Atlas*) and 1988–91 (*BTO 2nd Atlas*) from 102 occupied squares to 89. The 2002–06 survey indicates a return to the former level of 102. Further evidence of recent improvement in the species' fortunes is provided by the number of occupied recording units in Aberdeenshire/Aberdeen City which has increased by 36% between 1981–84 and 2002–06. Most of this increase has been in lowland areas, possibly reflecting an increase in housing developments, with little change evident in the uplands.

Population and trends

In the absence of any systematic colony counts in North-East Scotland it is necessary to estimate an average number of pairs/tetrad. A few large colonies may lead to tetrad populations of 100 pairs or more but the great majority of colonies are small and published densities from elsewhere in Scotland of 1–2 pairs/km^2 (Turner in *BS3*) seem appropriate for North-East Scotland. Applying this range of 4–8 pairs/tetrad to the 840 tetrads where birds were at least possibly breeding in 2002–06 indicates a House Martin breeding population in the range 3,300–6,700 pairs. BBS data indicate a Scottish population increase of as much as 152% over the period 1994–2007 (Risely *et al.* 2008). Although the North-East Scotland increase may be less extreme, this would at least partly explain the range expansion since 1981–84.

Author: *Bob Proctor*

House Martin, St Cyrus, June 2003. © *Harry Scott*

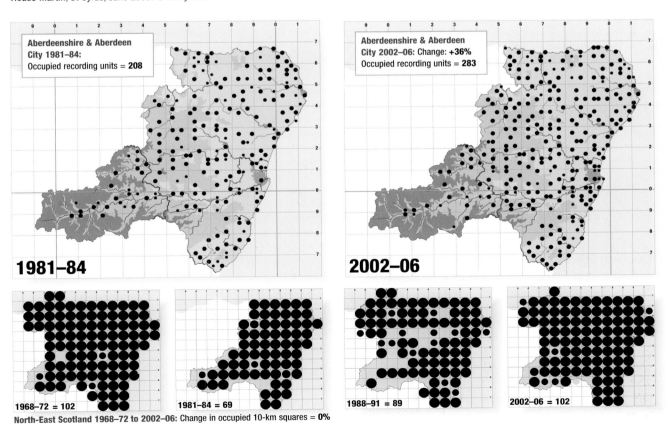

Aberdeenshire & Aberdeen City 1981–84:
Occupied recording units = **208**

1981–84

Aberdeenshire & Aberdeen City 2002–06: Change: +36%
Occupied recording units = **283**

2002–06

1968–72 = 102   1981–84 = 69   1988–91 = 89   2002–06 = 102

North-East Scotland 1968–72 to 2002–06: Change in occupied 10-km squares = 0%

Long-tailed Tit

Aegithalos caudatus

Common resident. Estimated population in North-East Scotland: *5,000–6,000 territories* (15% of Scottish population, 2% of UK)

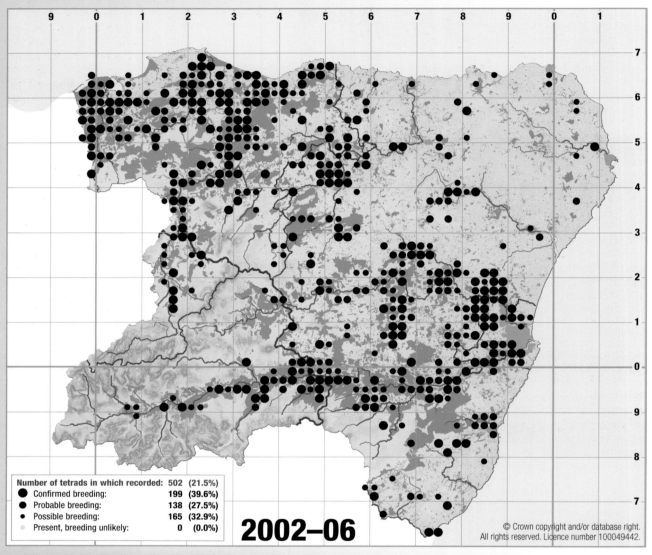

Number of tetrads in which recorded:	502	(21.5%)
● Confirmed breeding:	199	(39.6%)
● Probable breeding:	138	(27.5%)
● Possible breeding:	165	(32.9%)
· Present, breeding unlikely:	0	(0.0%)

2002–06

© Crown copyright and/or database right.
All rights reserved. Licence number 100049442.

Long-tailed Tit, Cults, May 2002. © *Ed Duthie*

Habitat and breeding biology

In the breeding season, Long-tailed Tits favour open mixed and broad-leaf woodlands especially those containing birch. They can also be found in mixed thickets of large bushes, shrubs and small trees. Plantations of pure conifers are avoided. Winter flocks break up in February and pairs establish territories within the range of the winter flock. During March they construct the elaborate domed nest of moss and cobwebs, lined with feathers and covered with lichens. This may be placed in the dense cover of a bush, or much higher and openly in the fork of a tree. Long-tailed Tits are single brooded but may, if their nesting attempt fails, help at the nest of a relative.

Scottish distribution and status

Long-tailed Tits are resident breeders throughout mainland Scotland wherever suitable habitat exists. They are absent from treeless uplands and moors but penetrate far into the hills along glens and river valleys where these contain a good growth of birch, Juniper or other scrub. The Scottish population in 2007 was estimated at 30,000–45,000 pairs (Storie in *BS3*).

■ 312 *The Breeding Birds of North-East Scotland*

Long-tailed Tit, Drum, 1978. © *Graham Rebecca*

Distribution and status in North-East Scotland

The influence of habitat preference is clear to see in the distribution map. Two regions of North-East Scotland stand out as being well-populated. One is Moray and parts of Aberdeenshire that border its eastern boundary. The second area is centred on lower and mid Donside, and Deeside. Penetration of birds into the highlands can be seen in Glen Avon, south of Tomintoul, and also along the Dee beyond Braemar to altitudes of at least 350 m in both areas. They are absent from the treeless uplands and extremely thinly spread over predominantly agricultural areas such as the Laich of Moray, the Mearns and, especially, large swathes of north-east Aberdeenshire. They are also conspicuously sparse through large areas of forestry plantation. The more open and birch-mixed pine woods of Deeside appear favourable to Long-tailed Tits, in contrast to the dense blocks of alien conifers found elsewhere.

Changes in distribution

Comparison of the Aberdeenshire/Aberdeen City maps reveals infilling of the 1981–84 range to a greater density but also an apparent large-scale expansion into previously unoccupied areas to the west and north of Alford along the Moray boundary north to the coast. Occupied recording units in this area have increased ten-fold from three in 1981–84 to 32 in 2002–06. It seems unlikely that change of this magnitude is explicable in terms solely of observer effort. Reasons may lie with changes from agricultural to forestry land use into which a proportion of broad-leaf trees are now incorporated. Clear-felled areas of forestry are often colonised by birch scrub which may also provide suitable habitat.

Population and trends

There is little locally-generated data to assist with producing a North-East Scotland population estimate; 0–4 territories/km^2 were recorded in various woodland types in Deeside (Jenkins & Watson 1999). Using this, and other density estimates cited in BS3, it is probably reasonable to adopt North-East densities of 6 territories/km^2 in broad-leaf woodland, 1 territory/km^2 in coniferous woodland and 0.5 territories/km^2 in other occupied habitats. Applying these densities to the area of land cover types in North-East Scotland (LC 2000 data) indicates a population within the range 5,000–6,000 territories. Local BBS data indicate a slight population increase during 1994–2006 that supports the national trend of an 8% UK increase in 1994–2007 (Risely et al. 2008), although the local data set is small. Nonetheless if the apparent range extension is genuine then there are likely to be substantially more Long-tailed Tits in North-East Scotland at present than in 1981–84.

Author: *Martin Cook*

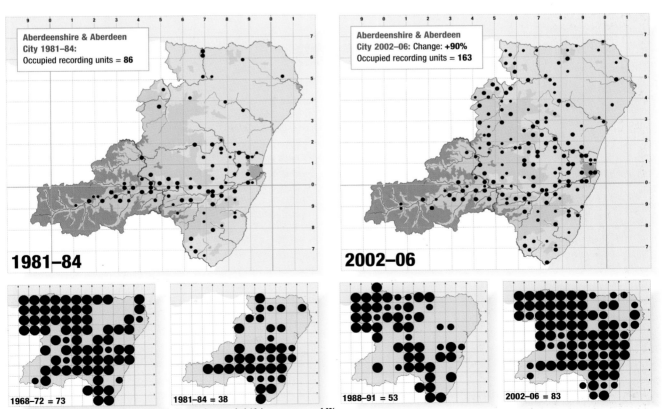

Aberdeenshire & Aberdeen City 1981–84:
Occupied recording units = **86**

Aberdeenshire & Aberdeen City 2002–06: Change: **+90%**
Occupied recording units = **163**

1981–84

2002–06

1968–72 = 73

1981–84 = 38

1988–91 = 53

2002–06 = 83

North-East Scotland 1968–72 to 2002–06: Change in occupied 10-km squares = +14%

Wood Warbler
Phylloscopus sibilatrix

Rare summer migrant breeder. Passage migrant. Estimated population in North-East Scotland: **20–40 territories** (<1% of Scottish and UK populations)

Red list; UK and Scottish BAP lists

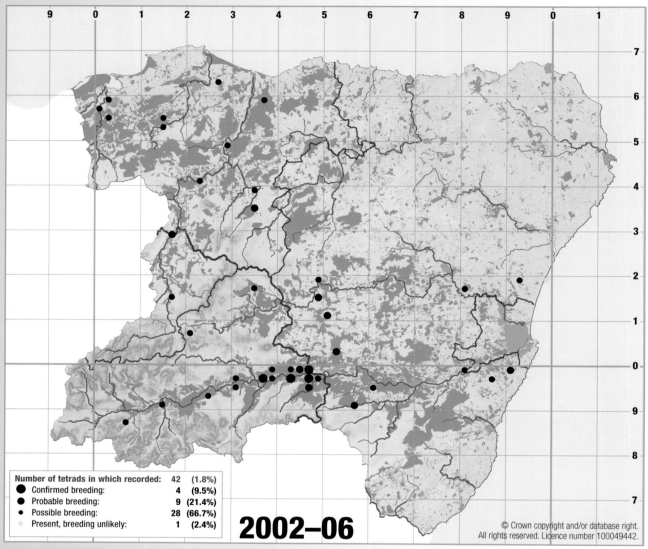

Number of tetrads in which recorded:	42	(1.8%)
● Confirmed breeding:	4	(9.5%)
● Probable breeding:	9	(21.4%)
● Possible breeding:	28	(66.7%)
Present, breeding unlikely:	1	(2.4%)

2002–06

Wood Warbler, Ballater, June 2009. © *Harry Scott*

Habitat and breeding biology

Wood Warblers breed almost exclusively within mature deciduous woodland containing oak or birch, where they sing strongly and persistently prior to pair formation. A dense understory such as Bracken provides the cover they require when nesting on the ground. The males generally return to the breeding grounds during the first days of May, followed shortly afterwards by the females. The domed nest contains a clutch of between 5–7 eggs which generally hatch around the end of May, with young fledging in late June or early July. Most males are monogamous but in some areas polygyny is not uncommon (da Prato in *BS3*). It is not known whether this occurs in North-East Scotland although the population may be too low to permit it.

Scottish distribution and status

Wood Warblers have a central and westerly breeding distribution in Scotland with highest densities in Lochaber, up the Great Glen, in parts of Argyll, around Loch Lomond and near Dumfries. In most other regions of Scotland they are locally distributed at low densities, and they do not breed in the Outer Hebrides or the Northern Isles (da Prato in *BS3*). The BTO estimated a Scottish breeding population of 2,900–3,300 pairs in 2000.

Distribution and status in North-East Scotland

Wood Warblers were found in 42 tetrads during 2002–06 but were mostly concentrated in the Aboyne to Ballater section of the Dee valley where the birds particularly favour oak woodland sites near Ballater and Dinnet. In Moray, Kellas oak wood is the only reliable site for this species although there is sporadic presence of singing males in other woods.

Changes in distribution

There was a small increase in the number of occupied recording units in Aberdeenshire/Aberdeen City between 1981–84 and 2002–06 from 15 to 21, but the general distri-

Wood Warbler, Ballater, June 2009. © *Harry Scott*

bution has remained similar and the regular sites for this species have remained fairly constant over the past few decades. In Moray, occupied 10-km squares have increased slightly from six during 1968–72 (*BTO 1st Atlas*) and five in 1988–91 (*BTO 2nd Atlas*) to eight in 2002–06. However, Wood Warblers were confirmed breeding in the lower Deveron area near Turriff during 1968–72 (*BTO 1st Atlas*), where they now appear to be absent.

Population and trends

During the last decade, the average number of singing males recorded annually has been seven in Aberdeenshire and three in Moray. 2004 was the best year with singing birds in at least seven sites in Moray, while there were ten singing birds at four sites in Aberdeenshire. Dinnet oak wood is an important site - six birds sang there in 2004 and seven in 2005 (*NESBRs*). Of the 17 records of singing birds in 2004, just two confirmed breeding attempts were recorded, with two broods of young seen at one site. It therefore appears that relatively few of the singing males pair and breed successfully each year. Wood Warblers are prone to breeding at varying locations from year to year and therefore observer effort focussing on the region's three or four top sites cannot accurately reflect the total numbers attempting to breed in North-East Scotland. The 41 tetrads where breeding was considered to be at least possible represent a composite picture over five years; on the other hand the species may be under-recorded as many remote birch woods are seldom visited. For these reasons it is not possible to present a precise population estimate, other than to say that it seems likely that the number of singing males in most years is within the range of 20–40. There has been a 67% decline in the UK Wood Warbler population over the period 1994–2007 (Risely *et al.* 2008) and there is evidence of a similar reduction across Scotland (da Prato in *BS3*).

Author: *Harry Scott*

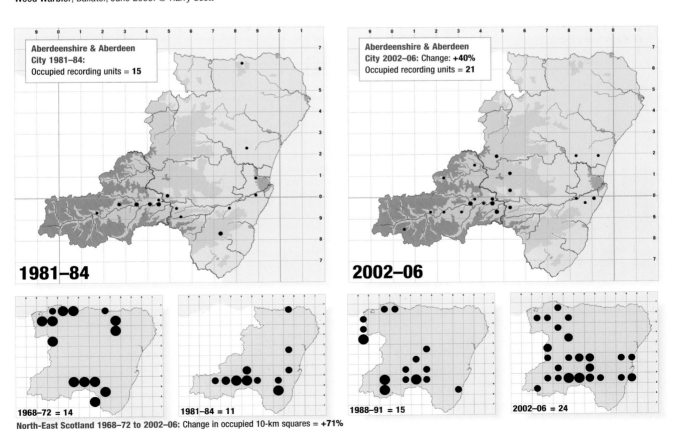

Aberdeenshire & Aberdeen City 1981–84:
Occupied recording units = **15**

1981–84

Aberdeenshire & Aberdeen City 2002–06: Change: **+40%**
Occupied recording units = **21**

2002–06

1968–72 = 14

1981–84 = 11

1988–91 = 15

2002–06 = 24

North-East Scotland 1968–72 to 2002–06: Change in occupied 10-km squares = +71%

Chiffchaff

Phylloscopus collybita

Common summer migrant breeder. Passage migrant, few in winter. Estimated population in North-East Scotland: *960–1,090 territories* (2% of Scottish population, <1% of UK)

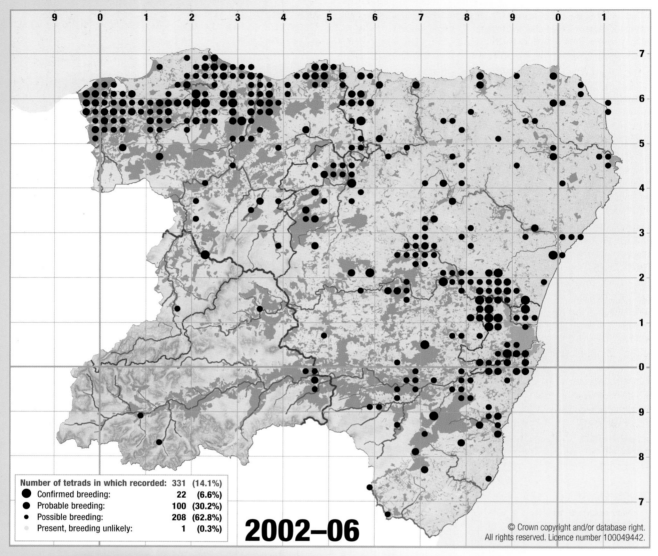

Number of tetrads in which recorded: 331 (14.1%)
- ● Confirmed breeding: 22 (6.6%)
- ● Probable breeding: 100 (30.2%)
- • Possible breeding: 208 (62.8%)
- Present, breeding unlikely: 1 (0.3%)

2002–06

Chiffchaff, Lincolnshire, April 2011. © *Trevor Gunby*

Habitat and breeding biology

Chiffchaffs have a strong preference for tall deciduous trees. Mature policy woodlands with dense Rhododendron are particularly favoured but parks, large gardens and other woodlands are also used, occasionally including conifer plantations. Chiffchaffs are single brooded and the nest is concealed in vegetation on or close to the ground. The duration of song becomes less once pairing has occurred and it is believed that some males that sing throughout the day may be unmated (da Prato in *BS3*).

Scottish distribution and status

The Chiffchaff is a widespread summer visitor to low altitude woodland throughout Scotland, although the breeding population of about 50,000 pairs is mostly concentrated in the south and west, especially Dumfries & Galloway, Ayrshire and Arran (da Prato in *BS3*). The northern half of the country was only colonised from the 1950s onwards and the population continues to increase with ongoing consolidation of the range throughout Scotland.

Distribution and status in North-East Scotland

Chiffchaffs are well established as a breeding species in the Laich of Moray and east towards Cullen, as well as in the lower valleys of the Don (below Inverurie) and the Dee (below Drumoak). There are also clusters of breeding records along the Urie between Pitcaple and Old Rayne and along the Deveron north of Huntly. Elsewhere, they are widespread but scarce. They are rarely found in upland areas although breeding was proved at c.270 m near Tomnavoulin and singing birds were heard at 380–400 m near Inverey and in Glen Clunie. Many records of singing birds may relate to unpaired males. Chiffchaffs are occasionally heard singing in mid March, but typically they start to return to their breeding areas during the last week of March, at least a week earlier than was the case during 1981–84 (NES 1st Atlas). Departure from breeding areas is thought to take place in late August and September.

Changes in distribution

There has been a significant increase in distribution since 1981–84, when the Chiffchaff was considered to be a sporadic breeder with most records relating to unpaired males (NES 1st Atlas). The development of well-established populations in parts of our region reflects the national population increase and range expansion. The number of occupied 10-km squares in North-East Scotland increased from 19 in 1968–72 (BTO 1st Atlas) to 38 in 1988–91 (BTO 2nd Atlas) and 78 in 2002–06. There is some suggestion that most of the original colonisation was in the coastal lowlands, with subsequent expansion of the range into inland areas. Since 1981–84 the number of occupied recording units in Aberdeenshire/Aberdeen City has increased nearly three-fold by an infilling of the original sparse distribution.

Population and trends

Clusters of singing males spaced approximately 300 m apart have been recorded in Moray (pers. obs.), corresponding to a density of about 11 territories/km². However, such densities are not sustained across large areas and information from Bird Reports and atlas field work suggests that occupied tetrads in the Laich of Moray hold about four

Chiffchaff, Cults, June 1988. © Ed Duthie

singing males on average. Applying this figure to the areas where the species is well established, and assuming that most other records relate to 1–2 territories/tetrad, suggests a total of 960–1,090 territories in North-East Scotland, with more than half in Moray. The Scottish BBS index over the period 1994–2007 shows an increase of 217% in Chiffchaff numbers (Risely et al. 2008) so it is very likely that the population in the North-East will continue to grow.

Author: *Paul Chapman*

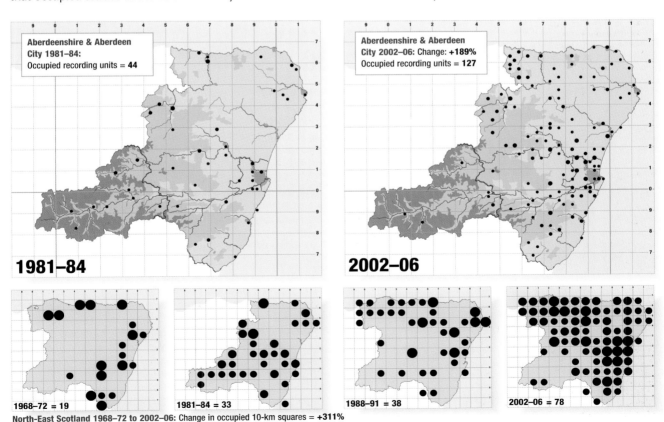

Aberdeenshire & Aberdeen City 1981–84: Occupied recording units = 44

1981–84

Aberdeenshire & Aberdeen City 2002–06: Change: +189% Occupied recording units = 127

2002–06

1968–72 = 19

1981–84 = 33

1988–91 = 38

2002–06 = 78

North-East Scotland 1968–72 to 2002–06: Change in occupied 10-km squares = +311%

Willow Warbler
Phylloscopus trochilus

Very common summer migrant breeder. Passage migrant. Estimated population in North-East Scotland: **70,000–100,000 pairs** (15% of Scottish population, 4% of UK)

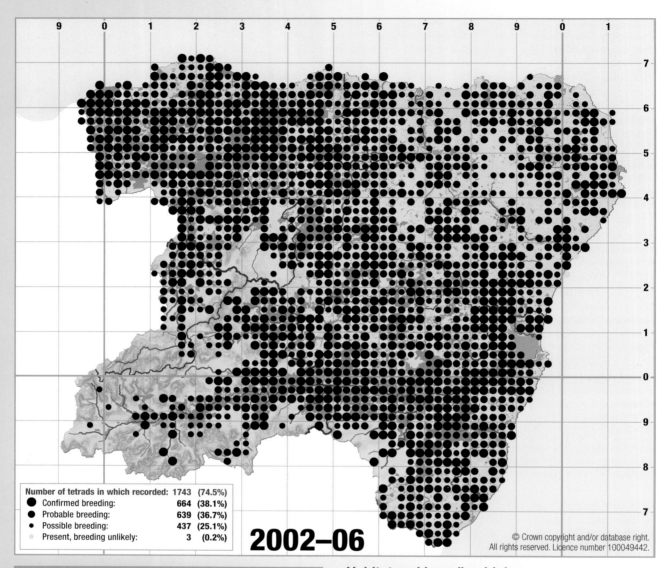

Number of tetrads in which recorded: 1743		(74.5%)
● Confirmed breeding:	664	(38.1%)
● Probable breeding:	639	(36.7%)
● Possible breeding:	437	(25.1%)
○ Present, breeding unlikely:	3	(0.2%)

2002–06

Willow Warbler, Newburgh, May 2009. © *Ed Duthie*

Habitat and breeding biology

Willow Warblers are found wherever there are trees and tall shrubs that do not form a closed canopy. Open birch woodland and young plantations (both coniferous and broad-leaved) are particularly favoured but all types of woodland are used including small patches of trees and tall scrub in otherwise open habitats such as farmland and moorland. In mature plantations with a closed canopy the species is usually found near the woodland edge, along rides or around clearings. Most pairs are single-brooded with eggs usually laid in late May or early June in a nest placed on or close to the ground.

Scottish distribution and status

The Willow Warbler is an abundant and widespread summer visitor across much of Scotland, with a breeding population of 540,000–590,000 pairs (Cobb in *BS3*). Between 1994–2007, the Scottish population showed a significant 31% increase, in contrast to a significant 27% decline in England (Risely *et al.* 2008), although there is some evidence of localised declines in parts of eastern Scotland.

Willow Warbler, Dinnet, May 2010. © *Harry Scott*

Distribution and status in North-East Scotland

This is one of the most widespread breeding birds in North-East Scotland and was recorded in 75% of tetrads in the region. The only substantial areas from which they are absent are the treeless uplands and the urban centre of Aberdeen. However, the population seems to be more thinly distributed in parts of Formartine and Buchan, where suitable habitat is scarce. Willow Warblers have, exceptionally, been recorded in North-East Scotland at the end of March (in 1974, 1988 and 2003) but the first birds normally return during April, with the main influx towards the end of the month and into early May. Willow Warblers depart from their breeding areas during August and September.

Changes in distribution

There have been no significant changes in distribution since 1981–84, although there has been a small increase in the number of occupied recording units, mostly on the upland fringes of Deeside, possibly as a result of woodland regeneration in these areas.

Population and trends

Very high densities, equivalent to 300 territories/km^2, can be found in pockets of ideal habitat, even in the more thinly populated coastal plain (pers. obs.); 22–115 territories/km^2 were found in various scrub and woodland habitats in a Deeside glen (Jenkins & Watson 1999). However, such densities are not usually sustained across large areas and 10–15 pairs/km^2 is probably a realistic average across the region as a whole. This is in line with the densities used to calculate the national population estimate and suggests a population of 70,000–100,000 pairs in North-East Scotland. BBS data suggest that there has been a clear population increase in the region since 1994, in line with the Scottish trend (Francis 2008), although unpaired singing males may confuse the issue (Cobb in *BS3*).

Author: *Paul Chapman*

Willow Warbler, Dinnet, June 2010. © *Harry Scott*

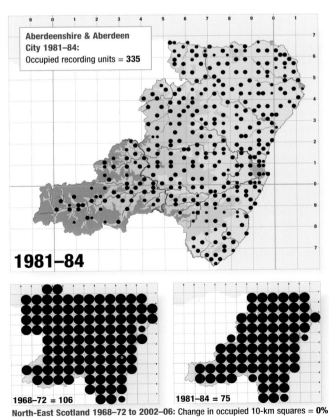

Aberdeenshire & Aberdeen City 1981–84:
Occupied recording units = **335**

1981–84

1968–72 = 106

1981–84 = 75

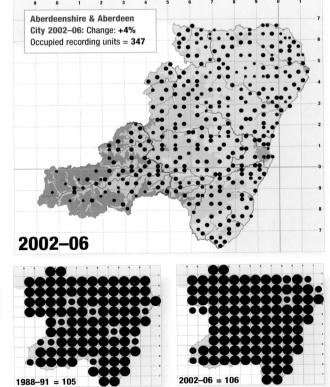

Aberdeenshire & Aberdeen City 2002–06: Change: +4%
Occupied recording units = **347**

2002–06

1988–91 = 105

2002–06 = 106

North-East Scotland 1968–72 to 2002–06: Change in occupied 10-km squares = **0%**

Blackcap

Sylvia atricapilla

Common summer migrant breeder. Passage migrant and winter visitor. Estimated population in North-East Scotland: *2,100–4,300 pairs* (6% of Scottish population, <1% of UK)

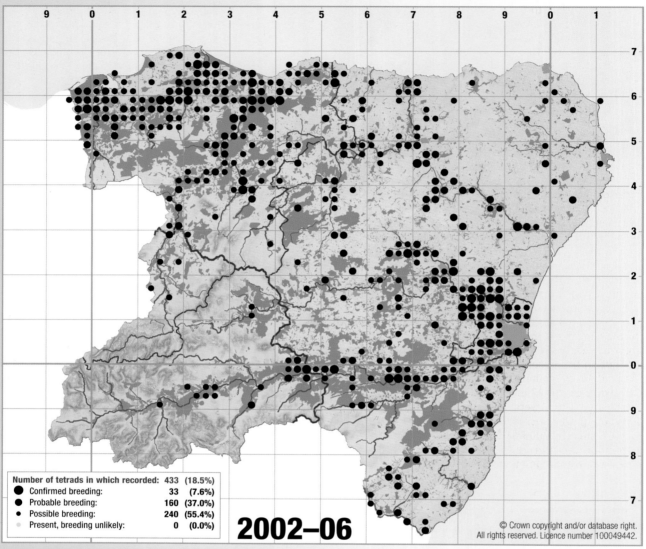

Number of tetrads in which recorded:	433	(18.5%)
● Confirmed breeding:	33	(7.6%)
● Probable breeding:	160	(37.0%)
● Possible breeding:	240	(55.4%)
· Present, breeding unlikely:	0	(0.0%)

2002–06

Blackcap, Inverurie, June 2009. © *Chris Jones*

Habitat and breeding biology

Blackcaps usually breed in mature deciduous and policy woodland, often with an under-storey of shrubs and other vegetation. Most breeding sites occur in the lowlands, typically below 300 m, in areas of thick Bramble, Hawthorn or Nettle scrub, usually up to 2 m above ground level. The first birds arrive on breeding territories in North-East Scotland from mid April onwards, and there are records of fledged young in Scotland from early June. Blackcaps usually raise a single brood during the season, and birds depart from early August.

Scottish distribution and status

Blackcaps occur throughout much of the central, southern and north-eastern lowlands of Scotland. There are scattered populations along low-lying areas of the Great Glen and Inner Hebrides, but breeding birds are largely absent from upland areas and much of the far north. However, breeding was confirmed in Orkney for the first time in 2001, and up to six birds on territory have been recorded recently in Shetland (da Prato in *BS3*). There has been a marked increase in the Scottish population, particularly since the 1980s, with a 146% increase in the numbers of Blackcap recorded in Scotland between 1994–2007 (Risely *et al.*

2008). The Scottish population is currently estimated at around 56,000 pairs (da Prato in *BS3*).

Distribution and status in North-East Scotland

Blackcaps are widespread throughout suitable habitat in lowland areas of North-East Scotland, with concentrations in deciduous woodland areas associated with the main rivers of the region, including lower and mid Donside, the Deveron and Ythan, and the Dee as far west as Braemar. Blackcaps range widely through lowland Moray and up Speyside and Avonside as far as the Tomintoul area. They are largely absent from upland areas, and have a rather thin and scattered population in the Buchan plain. Blackcaps which have arrived in spring tend to begin singing on territory in mid-late April, but the arrival dates are confused by the presence of wintering birds. This is a relatively recent (mid 1970s) phenomenon in North-East Scotland, and small numbers of birds are now reported regularly during the winter months, often visiting gardens and bird tables in suburban areas into late March and early April. Ringing studies suggest that most British and Irish wintering Blackcaps breed in central Europe (Langslow 1979, Berthold & Terrill 1988).

Changes in distribution

Comparison with *NES 1st Atlas* reveals 160 occupied recording units in the present study compared with 42 in 1981–84, reflecting a very significant expansion into areas of suitable habitat, especially into deciduous woodland associated with the mid and lower regions of the Dee, Don, Ythan and Deveron valleys. A considerable expansion in distribution has occurred in Moray where the number of occupied 10-km squares has risen from four in 1968–72 (*BTO 1st Atlas*), to 17 in 1988–91 (*BTO 2nd Atlas*) and 27 in 2002–06. There were 19 singing males in 15 sites in 1989, and this had increased to 129 singing birds recorded from 65 sites in 2005 (*MNBR* 2005). These changes in distribution are mirrored in the rest of Scotland, where there have been large increases particularly in the central

Blackcap, Cults, June 1988. © *Ed Duthie*

and southern lowlands (da Prato in *BS3*). It is tempting to speculate that recent expansions in breeding distribution may be linked with climate change. There may be improved winter survival due to more birds over-wintering north of the Sahara (*BTO 2nd Atlas*).

Population and trends

Estimating the size of the North-East Scotland breeding population is not easy due to great variation between the number of pairs in different tetrads, the steadily increasing range and the fact that measured densities from elsewhere in Scotland, which might apply here, are at least 20 years old (*BTO 2nd Atlas*). In recent years, tetrad densities in North-East Scotland have occasionally been recorded at over 20 singing males, as along the lower River Findhorn, but are usually much lower - typically 1–5 with 10–20 where good habitat exists. Assuming a mean density of 5–10 pairs/tetrad, and applying this number to the 430 tetrads in which Blackcaps were found in 2002–06, gives a speculative estimate of 2,150–4,300 pairs. This represents 4–8% of the Scottish population. Despite the difficulties in producing accurate population estimates, it is clear that Blackcaps have become more common and widespread in the region since the early 1980s.

Author: *Ian Broadbent*

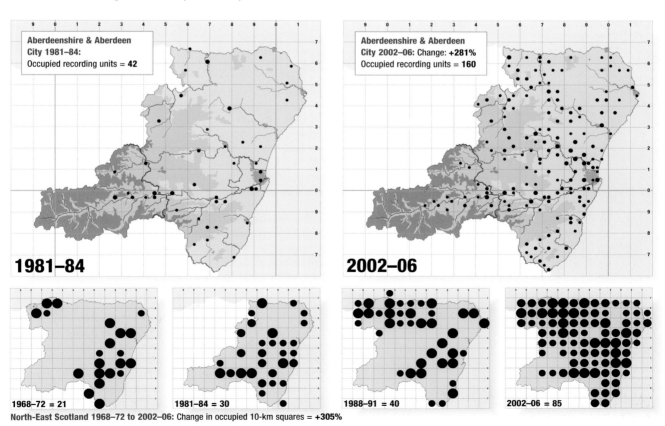

Aberdeenshire & Aberdeen City 1981–84:
Occupied recording units = **42**

1981–84

Aberdeenshire & Aberdeen City 2002–06: Change: **+281%**
Occupied recording units = **160**

2002–06

1968–72 = 21

1981–84 = 30

1988–91 = 40

2002–06 = 85

North-East Scotland 1968–72 to 2002–06: Change in occupied 10-km squares = **+305%**

Garden Warbler

Sylvia borin

Scarce summer migrant breeder. Passage migrant. Estimated population in North-East Scotland: **200–300 pairs** (2% of Scottish population, <1% of UK)

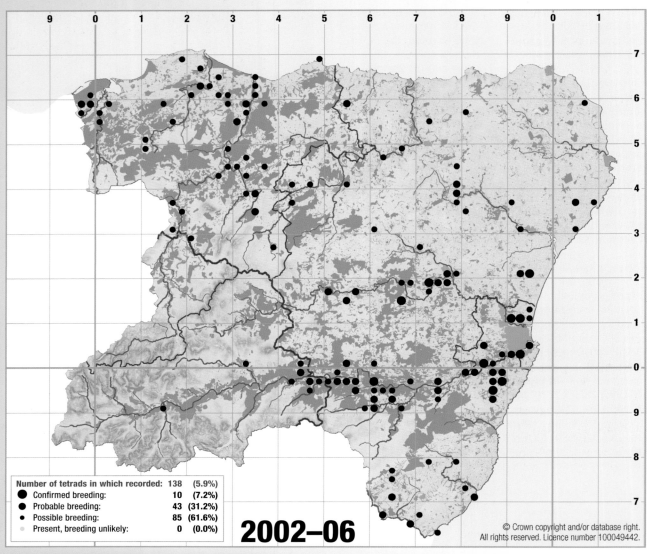

Number of tetrads in which recorded:	138	(5.9%)
● Confirmed breeding:	10	(7.2%)
● Probable breeding:	43	(31.2%)
● Possible breeding:	85	(61.6%)
Present, breeding unlikely:	0	(0.0%)

2002–06

Garden Warbler, Cults, June 1988. © *Ed Duthie*

Habitat and breeding biology

Garden Warblers typically breed in areas of mature woodland with an understory of dense scrub. The strongholds of the species are associated with deciduous woodlands along river valleys. Their habitats are similar to those of the Blackcap although they are less dependent on mature woodland, and Garden Warblers are also found in conifer plantations, provided that areas of dense ground scrub (typically Bramble or Rhododendron) are present. They mostly occur at lower altitudes, between 100–200 m, but can be found up to 400 m, whereas Blackcaps are scarcer above 300 m (*NES 1st Atlas*, da Prato in *BS3*). Breeding takes place quite late in the season, with the typical clutch of 4–5 eggs often not laid until late May or June.

Scottish distribution and status

The main strongholds of the Garden Warbler in Scotland are the southern and central lowland regions, with areas of higher density in Dumfries & Galloway, the Borders (*e.g.* the Hirsel) and in woodlands surrounding Loch Lomond. Smaller numbers are found further north in Ross & Cromarty, along the Great Glen and south to some of the Inner Hebrides (Mull, Colonsay and Eigg). They are absent from much of northern Scotland, the Highlands and the

Northern Isles, but there have been very occasional scattered records of singing birds from Skye and Lewis. The Scottish breeding population has been estimated recently as 10,500–18,000 pairs, having increased generally as numbers in southern Britain have declined (da Prato in *BS3*, K. Mustin pers. comm., Amar *et al.* 2006).

Distribution and status in North-East Scotland

Most of the breeding sites of Garden Warblers in North-East Scotland are associated with woodlands along the main river valleys of the region, with the greatest concentrations being along mid and lower Deeside from Aberdeen to Aboyne, mid Donside and the Spey, typically at altitudes between 200–400 m. Breeding is more sporadic elsewhere in the region, with scattered records in the south-east towards Stonehaven and Laurencekirk, and from the far north-east around Fraserburgh and Peterhead, although they are generally scarce in Buchan. Singing birds arrive on territory during late April to mid May, typically slightly later than Blackcaps, which often out-compete Garden Warblers for suitable nest sites (Garcia 1983). Birds leave from late July onwards, with migrant birds being reported at coastal sites typically from August until mid October, and rarely into November.

Changes in distribution

During the period 1981–84 to 2002–06 there was an increase in occupied recording units in Aberdeenshire/Aberdeen City from 33 to 69, with several new occupied units along the mid and lower Dee, and mid Donside around Inverurie (*NES 1st Atlas*). In Moray, the number of occupied 10-km squares was 17 in 2002–06, compared with three in 1968–72 (*BTO 1st Atlas*) and seven in 1988–91 (*BTO 2nd Atlas*). The results of the current study reveal a continuing trend of range expansion in North-East Scotland since breeding was first confirmed in the region in the late 1960s (*BTO 1st Atlas*), mirroring at a smaller scale the expansion seen in the distribution of Blackcaps in the region.

Population and trends

Breeding was possible, probable or confirmed in 138 tetrads surveyed during the current study. Although Garden Warblers are scarce, it is not uncommon for sites to hold more than one pair (*e.g. NESBR* 2006) which leads to an estimated population range of 200–300 pairs in the region. Data from BBS fieldwork suggest a stable population in the UK as a whole over the period 1994–2007 (Risely *et al.* 2008) but it seems likely that, in view of the considerable range expansion, the North-East Scotland population has risen substantially over recent years.

Author: *Ian Broadbent*

Garden Warbler, Norwood, May 1982. © *John Young*

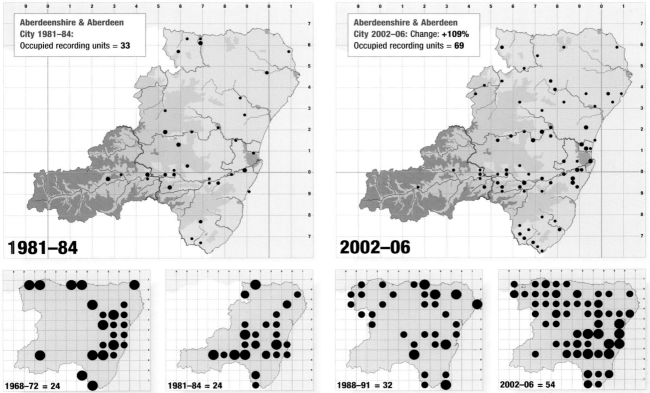

Aberdeenshire & Aberdeen City 1981–84: Occupied recording units = 33

1981–84

Aberdeenshire & Aberdeen City 2002–06: Change: **+109%** Occupied recording units = **69**

2002–06

1968–72 = 24

1981–84 = 24

1988–91 = 32

2002–06 = 54

North-East Scotland 1968–72 to 2002–06: Change in occupied 10-km squares = **+125%**

Lesser Whitethroat

Sylvia curruca

Occasional summer migrant breeder. Passage migrant. Estimated population in North-East Scotland: **0–5 pairs** (<1% of Scottish and UK populations)

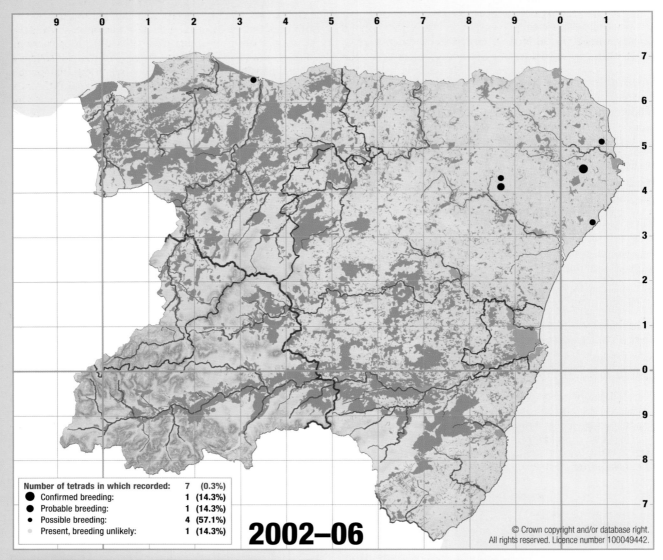

Number of tetrads in which recorded: 7 (0.3%)
- Confirmed breeding: 1 (14.3%)
- Probable breeding: 1 (14.3%)
- Possible breeding: 4 (57.1%)
- Present, breeding unlikely: 1 (14.3%)

2002–06

Lesser Whitethroat, Cults, July 1982. © *Ed Duthie*

Habitat and breeding biology

Lesser Whitethroats breed in areas of Hawthorn, Blackthorn, or Sea Buckthorn scrub, with a dense understory of Bramble, Gorse or Dog-rose. Breeding typically occurs below 200 m (Byars *et al.* 1991). There are few nesting records from North-East Scotland, but breeding elsewhere in Scotland often occurs in old hedgerows, along railway embankments, quarries or mineral workings, and coastal areas where such patches of dense scrub are likely to be found.

Scottish distribution and status

Since the mid 1970s, there has been a marked expansion of the range of the Lesser Whitethroat into southern Scotland, where it now breeds locally in several areas. The main populations are concentrated in Lothian and Borders, but scattered populations occur in Clyde, Dumfries & Galloway, Ayrshire and Fife. Breeding records north of the central belt are irregular, but single pairs have been noted as far north as Orkney and Shetland (Byars in *BS3*).

Distribution and status in North-East Scotland

The Lesser Whitethroat is by far the scarcest breeding *Sylvia* warbler in the region, and nesting was only confirmed for the first time in 1977 (*NES 1st Atlas*). Breeding occurs sporadically in scattered locations, with little evidence of any preferred areas, although singing birds were recorded in the same area at Kingston (Moray) in five of the years from 1991–2002, suggesting that the habitat in the area is favourable (*MNBR* 2002). During 1977–2002, the majority of breeding records occurred in lower Deeside and near Aberdeen, but interestingly no birds were recorded in these areas during 2002–06. Indeed, only one record of confirmed breeding was received during this period, near Kinmundy,

with breeding thought to be probable near Methlick, and possible at a further four sites. Spring migrants typically arrive in North-East Scotland during early-mid May, with autumn occurrences between mid August and early November. Numbers vary considerably between years, with only four records in the North-East during 2003, but over 35 in 2004, although only three of these were in spring. Indeed, between 2002–05, the number of recorded spring migrants was very low (1–3 birds per year), which is perhaps reflected in the paucity of breeding records during this period. Despite the low numbers of spring migrants in 2002 (three records), six of the seven breeding season records during 2002–06 occurred in this year. A little surprisingly, only one possible breeding record was noted in 2006, a year in which the number of spring migrants in the region (nine records) was the highest during the Atlas period.

Changes in distribution

There is no clear evidence of any major changes in the breeding distribution since 1981–84, although perhaps surprisingly, there were no records from Aberdeen or lower Deeside during 2002–06, in areas where birds bred at one site in 1984 and at three sites in 1986 (*NES 1st Atlas*).

Population and trends

The single confirmed breeding record during the current study is almost certainly an underestimate of the breeding population, due to the rather inconspicuous habits of the species and its preference for impenetrable nest locations. Similarly, in 1981–84, breeding was only confirmed at one site, with possible or probable breeding at a further four sites (*NES 1st Atlas*). During the 2002–06 fieldwork, all but one of the records came from 2002, suggesting strong annual variations in the numbers of breeding birds in the region. It seems likely that the breeding population may reach five pairs in some years while there are none in others.

Author: *Ian Broadbent*

Lesser Whitethroat, Seaton Park, July 1977. © *Ed Duthie*

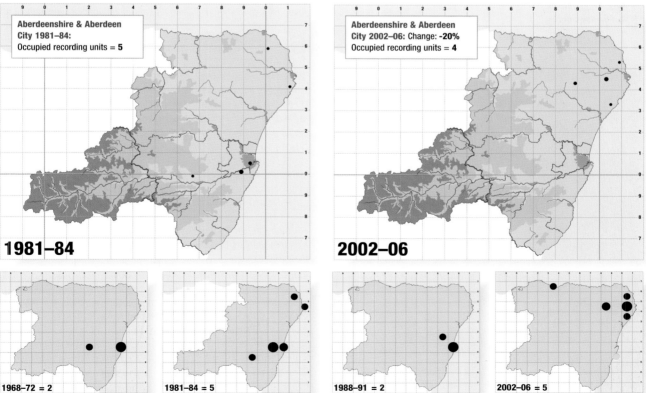

Aberdeenshire & Aberdeen City 1981–84:
Occupied recording units = **5**

1981–84

Aberdeenshire & Aberdeen City 2002–06: Change: **-20%**
Occupied recording units = **4**

2002–06

1968–72 = 2

1981–84 = 5

1988–91 = 2

2002–06 = 5

North-East Scotland 1968–72 to 2002–06: Change in occupied 10-km squares = **+150%**

Whitethroat

Sylvia communis

Common summer migrant breeder. Passage migrant. Estimated population in North-East Scotland:
7,500 pairs (8% of Scottish population, <1% of UK)

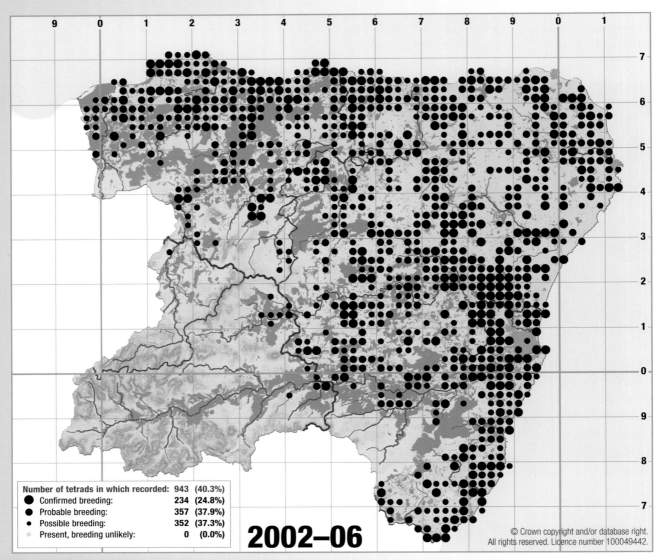

Number of tetrads in which recorded:	943	(40.3%)
● Confirmed breeding:	234	(24.8%)
● Probable breeding:	357	(37.9%)
● Possible breeding:	352	(37.3%)
● Present, breeding unlikely:	0	(0.0%)

2002–06

Whitethroat, St Cyrus, June 2005. © *Harry Scott*

Habitat and breeding biology

Whitethroats are usually found around hedgerows, young trees and scrub in otherwise open landscapes such as farmland. They have a particular preference for Hawthorn and Gorse, from which they sing or launch their song-flights. Nests are usually placed close to the ground in tall grass, Brambles or Nettles, so a mixture of scrub and lower, herbaceous vegetation is ideal. Where scrub or hedgerows are found along arable field boundaries, nests can sometimes be placed in the adjoining crop, particularly when this is Oil-seed Rape. Most pairs lay eggs in late May or early June and while a single brood is usual, second broods are not uncommon (da Prato in *BS3*).

Scottish distribution and status

A common summer visitor to lowland areas of southern and eastern Scotland, the Whitethroat has a breeding population of 70,000–133,000 pairs (da Prato in *BS3*). The population crashed in the late 1960s and early 1970s due to drought in its West African wintering grounds but there has been a significant 85% population increase between 1994–2007 (Risely *et al.* 2008).

The Breeding Birds of North-East Scotland

Distribution and status in North-East Scotland

The Whitethroat is widely distributed throughout the region but is largely absent from areas over 250 m above sea level and from areas with extensive forest cover. The distribution closely matches that of arable farmland in the region, although the species appears to be thinly distributed in the more intensively farmed areas of Formartine and the Mearns. Whitethroats start to return to their breeding areas in the last few days of April or the first few days of May. Departure from breeding areas usually takes place during August although a few birds may remain into September.

Changes in distribution

The general pattern of distribution in North-East Scotland has not changed greatly since 1981–84, but there has been a 30% increase in the number of recording units occupied in Aberdeenshire/Aberdeen City. This has largely resulted from the infilling of gaps within the previous, sparse range.

Population and trends

Whitethroat breeding populations can fluctuate considerably from year to year, but recent surveys over 15 km^2 of farmland in lowland Aberdeenshire found an average of 1.7 territories per km^2 (pers. obs.). Locally higher densities are likely to occur in more extensive areas of scrub, but such habitats do not occupy a significant proportion of the overall range. An average of 2 pairs/km^2 across the 943 occupied tetrads is probably a realistic estimate and is in line with the figure of 2–3 pairs/km^2 for open farmland that was used to calculate the national population estimate (da Prato in *BS3*). This suggests a population of about 7,500 pairs in North-East Scotland. Local BBS results have shown a clear upward population trend between 1994 and 2006 (Francis 2008), which is in line with the national increase and is supported by the increase in occupied recording units since 1981–84.

Author: *Paul Chapman*

Whitethroat, Whitecairns, June 2007. © *Rab Rae*

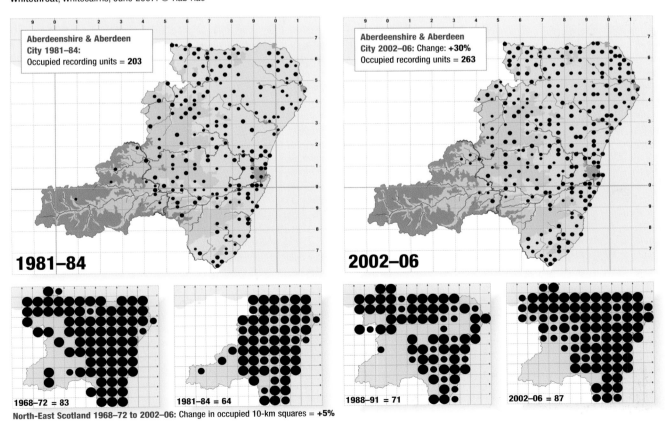

Aberdeenshire & Aberdeen City 1981–84:
Occupied recording units = 203

1981–84

Aberdeenshire & Aberdeen City 2002–06: Change: +30%
Occupied recording units = 263

2002–06

1968–72 = 83

1981–84 = 64

1988–91 = 71

2002–06 = 87

North-East Scotland 1968–72 to 2002–06: Change in occupied 10-km squares = +5%

Grasshopper Warbler
Locustella naevia

Scarce summer migrant breeder. Passage migrant. Estimated population in North-East Scotland: **200–300 pairs** (11% of Scottish population, 2% of UK)

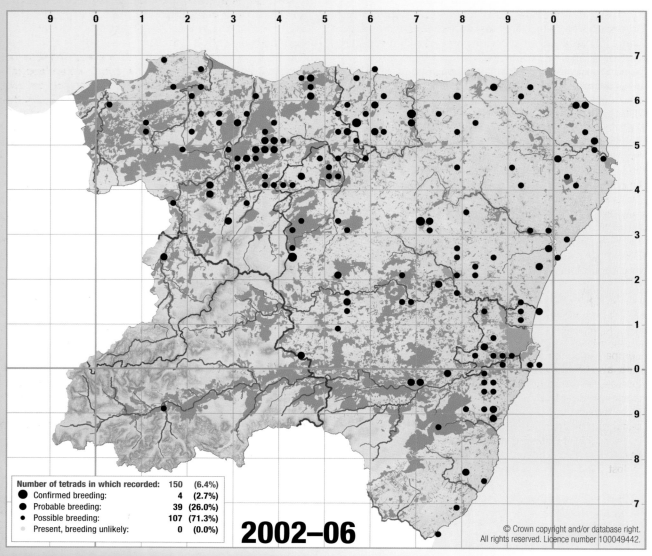

Number of tetrads in which recorded:	150	(6.4%)
● Confirmed breeding:	4	(2.7%)
● Probable breeding:	39	(26.0%)
● Possible breeding:	107	(71.3%)
● Present, breeding unlikely:	0	(0.0%)

2002–06

Grasshopper Warbler, Logie Buchan, June 2007. © *Rab Rae*

Habitat and breeding biology

Grasshopper Warblers are found in a range of damp to dry habitats, including marsh, heath, low scrub and young forestry plantations, where there is a dense ground layer in which they can nest. This often includes rushes, but mature tussocks of Tufted Hair-grass were identified as the key feature of territories at a regular Banffshire site (Leverton 2002). Here, all territories were between 150 and 190 m altitude, above primarily agricultural land, and this may be typical of many inland sites in the region, whereas it has been reported that the majority of Scottish sites are below 150 m (Donald in *BS3*). Although it is uncertain whether Scottish breeders have two broods (Donald in *BS3*), Leverton (2002) considered that a second period of territorial song in late June indicated that this was the case in Banffshire.

Scottish distribution and status

The species is widely, but thinly distributed across most of the lower-lying areas of Scotland, but largely absent from the outer island groups. It is commonest in the south-west, notably Dumfries & Galloway, Ayrshire and Argyll (including Islay). Numbers vary considerably between years, perhaps partly relating to spring drift of continental birds. There is considerable disparity between population estimates at a regional level and those based on UK-wide data, leading to a broad Scottish population estimate of 900–3,700 pairs (Donald in *BS3*).

Distribution and status in North-East Scotland

The species has a scattered distribution across the lowland parts of the region, particularly along river valleys in the foothills. It is commonest in the north and east, and appears to be almost absent from mid and upper Deeside. Favoured areas include lower Deeside, and the gentle hill country dividing the Rivers Isla and Spey, west of Keith. Some coastal records may be of short-staying, singing migrants. There were very few confirmed breeding records, but the species is notoriously skulking. The patchy distribution of records may, to some extent, reflect observer effort, as males mainly sing between dusk and dawn, and often stop entirely once paired, when they become extremely difficult to detect. The species frequently displays a clustered distribution, perhaps due to new arrivals being attracted by the song of an already established bird (Leverton 2002). The first males are generally heard in the last week of April, with the earliest arrival date during 2002–06 being 19th April. Birds may linger, and sing, into August, but few are detected after mid-month.

Changes in distribution

At the 10-km square level, the number of occupied squares has approximately doubled between the two BTO Atlases (1968–72 and 1988–91) and the present survey in 2002–06. Comparison with the Aberdeenshire/Aberdeen City 1981–84 data also shows a dramatic expansion, with a three-fold increase in the number of occupied recording units. This expansion is particularly evident on the Buchan plain, where there were no breeding records during 1981–84. Conversely, two former hotspots, at Muir of Dinnet and in the south-east of the region, produced few records in 2002–06. The species may vacate areas as plantations mature and the under-storey is lost, and is also susceptible to habitat loss through drainage; it is possible the fewer records from the Muir of Dinnet may be due to maturing of the colonising birch woodland. The species may also colonise new plantations. The general range expansion in the region between the two local atlases is most likely to be due largely to a genuine population increase.

Population and trends

Gibbons *et al.* (1993) suggested a density of ten pairs per occupied 10-km square in Britain, which would lead to a population estimate of 600 pairs for the region. However, this density is considered optimistic, and many of the occupied 10-km squares in the region contained only one or two occupied tetrads. As an alternative, a lower density of 0.34 pairs/km^2 found in Lothian farmland (da Prato 1985) translates to 1.36 pairs/tetrad, and therefore around 200 pairs in the 149 occupied tetrads in North-East Scotland. However, BBS data for the UK as a whole indicate a 68% increase during the period 1994–2007 (Risely 2008) and, although there is insufficient data to confirm that such a trend applies in Scotland, it is reasonable to assume that population densities will have increased, in addition to range expansion. It is also likely that the species is generally under-recorded, particularly in many of the remoter parts of the region, and that this was also the case during the atlas fieldwork. It may be realistic, therefore, to say that the North-East Scotland population lies in the range 200–300 pairs. As with Scotland as a whole, numbers appear to be very variable; bird report data for the region indicate that singing birds were reported at between nine and 24 sites in any single year between 1999 and 2006, although the influence of observer effort on these figures is unknown. The reasons for an increase are unclear, but could be related to decreased mortality on wintering grounds or during migration, rather than to improved breeding success in the region.

Author: *Hugh Addlesee*

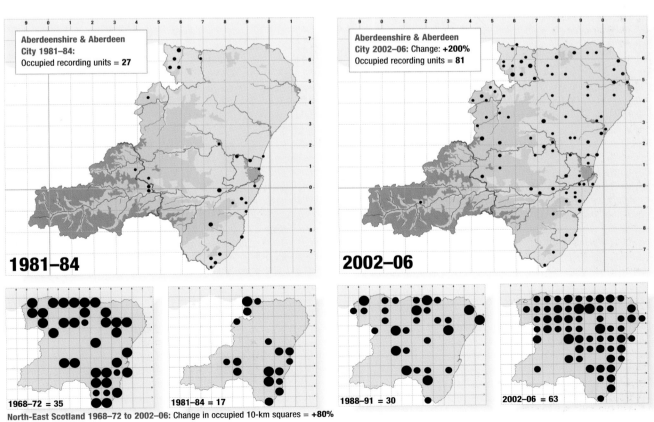

North-East Scotland 1968–72 to 2002–06: Change in occupied 10-km squares = **+80%**

Sedge Warbler   *Acrocephalus schoenobaenus*

Common summer migrant breeder. Passage migrant. Estimated population in North-East Scotland: **3,350–6,700 pairs** (6% of Scottish population, 2% of UK)

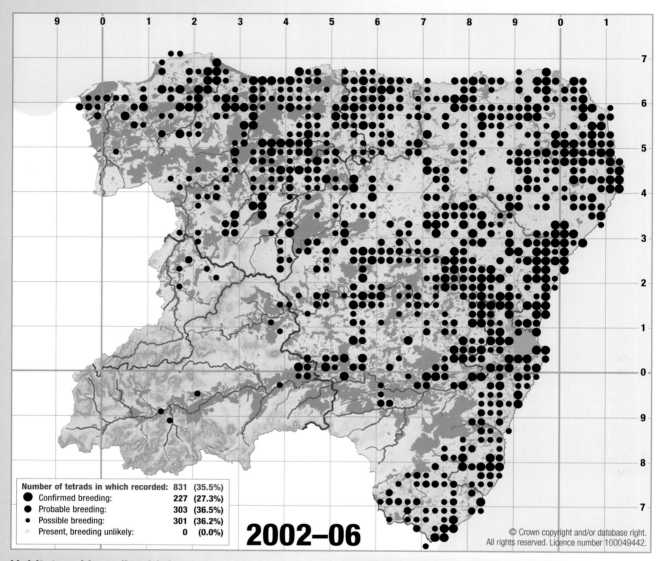

Number of tetrads in which recorded:	831	(35.5%)
● Confirmed breeding:	227	(27.3%)
● Probable breeding:	303	(36.5%)
• Possible breeding:	301	(36.2%)
Present, breeding unlikely:	0	(0.0%)

2002–06

Habitat and breeding biology

Sedge Warblers are found in a variety of lowland habitats, including marshes, rank vegetation along waterways, scrub, young conifer plantations and arable fields containing crops such as Oil-seed Rape. Breeding territories are usually small, of the order of 0.1–0.2 ha. Egg-laying begins in mid to late May, with usually 4–6 eggs laid, though clutch sizes can range between 3–8 eggs. Chicks begin to fledge in late June and July. Two nesting attempts often take place in territories at Logie Buchan, even when the first has been successful. Second nests can be late, and birds can still be feeding chicks into late August (H. Maggs pers. comm.). There is, however, no evidence of second broods at Loch Spynie (pers. obs.).

Scottish distribution and status

The breeding distribution follows much of the lowland habitat around mainland Scotland and the main island groups with the exception of Shetland, where there have been only three recent breeding attempts (Hatton in *BS3*, Pennington *et al.* 2004). The higher concentrations in east and south-west Scotland are attributed to the abundance of suitable habitat, particularly eutrophic wetlands and waterways. It has been suggested that Scotland holds 28%

Sedge Warbler, Newburgh, August 2008. © *Ed Duthie*

Sedge Warbler, Bridge of Don, June 2009. © *Chris Jones*

of the UK population, giving an estimated Scottish population of 90,000 pairs (Hatton in *BS3*).

Distribution and status in North-East Scotland

The Sedge Warbler is a widespread breeding species across the lowland areas of North-East Scotland, occurring in wetlands, low scrub and certain arable crops but avoiding mature forest and the majority of upland areas. Particularly richly populated areas are the east coast lowlands, mid and lower Donside and the Moray/Aberdeenshire border area as far inland as Huntly and Craigellachie. Although not proved to be breeding, a few birds were found in marshes in river valleys on the moorland edge such as around Braemar and Tomintoul at around 300 m. Higher still were birds at around 350 m in the Braes of Glenlivet, Glen Fiddich and Strathdon. Large agricultural areas such as coastal Moray and inland parts of the Buchan plain have only scattered populations suggesting a lack of suitable farmland breeding habitat. However, some agri-environment scheme options have benefited this species and Aberdeenshire farms that manage water margins often have breeding Sedge Warblers (H. Maggs pers. comm.). Sedge Warblers arrive back in breeding areas from late April and remain until late August or early September.

Changes in distribution

The number of occupied recording units in Aberdeenshire/ Aberdeen City increased from 211 in 1981–84 to 257 in 2002–06. This increase was evenly distributed over the area although the presence of a few birds in upper Deeside is notable. This restores part of the range occupied in 1968–72 (*BTO 1st Atlas*). Some of the increase may be attributed to the species' use of Oil-seed Rape fields for nesting and to improvement of water margin habitats.

Population and trends

Sedge Warblers were recorded in 831 (36%) of tetrads surveyed during 2002–06 with breeding confirmed in 227 of these. Population density can be very high, as at Loch of Strathbeg where 260 singing birds were estimated in May 1981 (*NESBR* 1981). However, local fieldwork suggests 4–8 pairs per tetrad may be a realistic density over most of the range. This suggests a total population of 3,350–6,700 pairs. Despite a 28% increase in the Scottish population over the period 1994–2007 (Risely *et al.* 2008), the local BBS data suggest no recent change in the population and there was a decline during the fieldwork period of the Atlas. This decline was also recorded at Loch Spynie, where ringing at the Constant Effort Site revealed a sharp drop in adult numbers between 2002–03. Nationally, populations fluctuate, with crashes linked to drought conditions in the wintering grounds. A correlation has been established between rainfall in the floodplains of the River Niger and River Senegal in west Africa, and the numbers of adult Sedge Warblers returning to Britain. In years with drought conditions dramatic declines have been recorded (Hatton in *BS3*).

Author: *Bob Proctor*

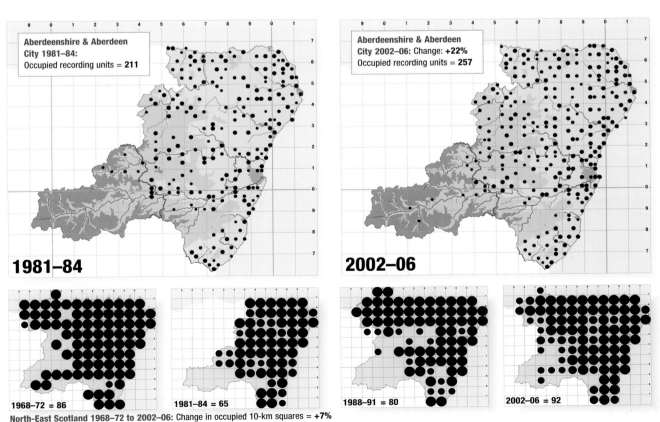

Aberdeenshire & Aberdeen City 1981–84:
Occupied recording units = **211**

1981–84

Aberdeenshire & Aberdeen City 2002–06: Change: **+22%**
Occupied recording units = **257**

2002–06

1968–72 = 86

1981–84 = 65

1988–91 = 80

2002–06 = 92

North-East Scotland 1968–72 to 2002–06: Change in occupied 10-km squares = **+7%**

Treecreeper

Certhia familiaris

Common resident. Estimated population in North-East Scotland: *7,000–10,000 pairs* (16% of Scottish population, 4% of UK)

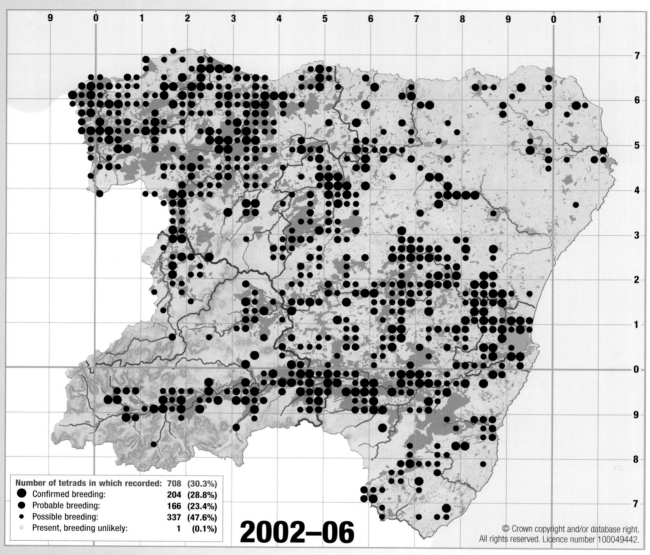

Number of tetrads in which recorded:	708	(30.3%)
● Confirmed breeding:	204	(28.8%)
● Probable breeding:	166	(23.4%)
● Possible breeding:	337	(47.6%)
● Present, breeding unlikely:	1	(0.1%)

2002–06

Habitat and breeding biology

Treecreepers are common in mature woodland habitats, where they can find nest sites behind loose bark or in crevices in damaged or decaying trunks. They occur in a wide range of woodland types, from coastal conifer plantations to upland birchwoods, but are generally scarce or absent from younger woodland, where few suitable nest sites are available. They will, however, use nest boxes, as for example in the Culbin and Lossie Forests. First broods in the region typically fledge in late May or early June, with second broods fledging in July. They are vulnerable to cold and wet winters, and may not easily re-colonise woods in fragmented landscapes due to their sedentary nature.

Scottish distribution and status

Treecreepers occur in woodland across mainland Scotland, and also on a few offshore islands. Due to their habitat requirements they are absent from many upland areas, and are scarcest in the far north and west. The Scottish population has recently been estimated at 40,000–70,000 pairs (Robinson in *BS3*), while BBS data indicate that the population rose by 60% during the period 1994–2007 (Risely *et al.* 2008). In part, this is likely to be a result of expansion into plantations as they have matured, while the dearth of cold winters during that period has probably aided this spread.

Distribution and status in North-East Scotland

Treecreepers are well distributed across the wooded parts of the region, with particular concentrations along the valleys of the Rivers Dee and Don, around Huntly, and in much of Moray. They are present around the River Deveron and the

Treecreeper, Lossie Forest, May 1981. © *Martin Cook*

upper Ythan, but largely absent from the Buchan plain, other than scattered populations, such as in the Forest of Deer. This reflects the lack of old woodland across this part of the region. The species is notably scarce in the large forests of Durris, Fetteresso, Dallas moor and Drumtochty, which are probably still too young to provide plentiful nest sites. In 1980–83, average densities at mid Deeside study sites were found to be highest in oakwoods and lowest in pinewoods, with birchwoods intermediate (*NES 1st Atlas*).

Changes in distribution

The number of occupied 10-km squares in North-East Scotland has remained virtually unchanged between 1968–72 (*BTO 1st Atlas*) and 2002–06. Closer scrutiny, however, reveals a 23% increase in occupied recording units in Aberdeenshire/Aberdeen City between 1981–84 and 2002–06. This expansion is most apparent in the north-west of Aberdeenshire, particularly around Huntly, for example in the Bin and Clashindarroch Forests. Forests in this area are largely 20th century conifer plantations, often at relatively high altitude, which are perhaps only now able to support reasonable Treecreeper populations due to increasing maturity and aided by recent mild winters.

Population and trends

As with Scotland as a whole, where Risely et al. (2008) reveal an increase of 60% over the period 1994–2007, BBS data for North-East Scotland suggest an increasing Treecreeper population, which supports the distribution data presented here. Densities of 0–19 territories/km^2 were recorded in various woodland types in Deeside (Jenkins & Watson 1999). Using the areas of different woodland types in the region (Forestry Commission 1997) and average densities of 10 pairs/km^2 for Scots Pine and broad-leaved woodlands and 5 pairs/km^2 for other conifers (Robinson in *BS3*), an estimate of approximately 10,000 pairs can be derived. However, the conifer densities frequently apply to mature spruce plantations and a substantial proportion of

our plantations have yet to attain the maturity required to support a high density of Treecreepers. It is impossible, therefore, to be more precise than to say that the population in the North-East is likely to fall within the range 7,000–10,000 pairs, or 16% of the Scottish population - but there is much uncertainty. Altered forestry management practices and increasing maturity of plantations are likely to continue to benefit Treecreepers in the region.

Author: *Hugh Addlesee*

Treecreeper, Ballater, May 2002. © *Ed Duthie*

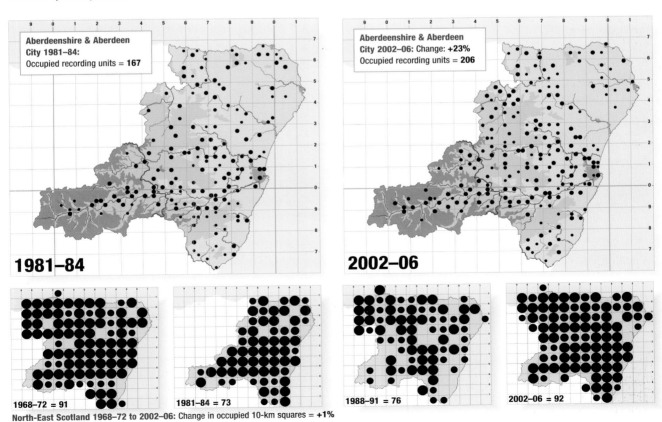

Aberdeenshire & Aberdeen City 1981–84: Occupied recording units = 167

1981–84

Aberdeenshire & Aberdeen City 2002–06: Change: +23% Occupied recording units = 206

2002–06

1968–72 = 91   1981–84 = 73   1988–91 = 76   2002–06 = 92

North-East Scotland 1968–72 to 2002–06: Change in occupied 10-km squares = +1%

River Findhorn

Within Moray, the River Findhorn runs through a series of rocky gorges and well-wooded valleys as it flows from Relugas down to Findhorn Bay. The lower reaches of the river regularly hold good numbers of Red-breasted Merganser – one of only two sites in the North-East to do so. Other typical birds of the fast-flowing river are Common Sandpiper, Dipper, and Grey and Pied Wagtails. The riverside woodlands hold many Willow Warblers and smaller numbers of Chiffchaff and Blackcap as well the locally scarce Garden Warbler and, occasionally, Wood Warbler. Tree Pipits and Spotted Flycatchers are numerous and in the coniferous woods there are Siskins, Jays and crossbills. June 2009 © *Martin Cook*

Cloddach Quarry

This patchwork of active and disused gravel workings, south of Elgin, provides habitat for breeding Mute Swan, Mallard, Tufted Duck, Coot, Moorhen and Little Grebe. The water-side vegetation holds Sedge Warblers and Reed Buntings, while Yellowhammers and Linnets nest in the thickets of Gorse. Sand Martins burrow into sandbanks, and gravel areas hold nesting Ringed Plover and Oystercatcher; Common Sandpipers have occasionally bred. Breeding species in small woods and shelter belts nearby include Buzzard, Sparrowhawk, Blackcap and Chiffchaff. June 2009 © *Martin Cook*

Wren

Troglodytes troglodytes

Very common resident. Estimated population in North-East Scotland: *200,000–300,000 territories* (16% of Scottish population, 3% of UK)

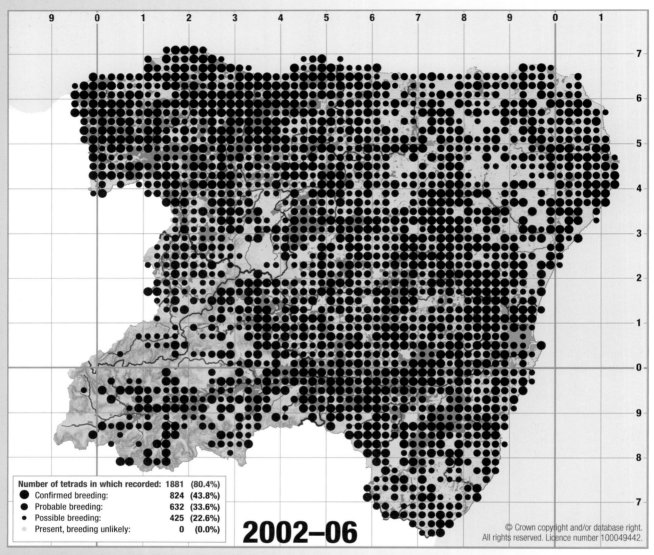

Number of tetrads in which recorded: 1881 (80.4%)		
● Confirmed breeding:	824	(43.8%)
● Probable breeding:	632	(33.6%)
● Possible breeding:	425	(22.6%)
· Present, breeding unlikely:	0	(0.0%)

2002–06

Wren, Loch Kinord, May 2008. © *Harry Scott*

Habitat and breeding biology

Wrens are present in a range of habitats from sea cliffs to moorland edges. They are very adaptable, nesting from near sea level up to 750 m, in habitats ranging from boulder beaches and upland scree slopes to gardens, scrub and woodland. Nest building starts in early April in holes in walls and trees, in dense vegetation on vertical surfaces and occasionally in buildings. Plantations can be used in early growth stages and also dense mature Heather although this is sub-optimal habitat. Wrens feed on invertebrates, especially beetles and spiders. Males often build several nests, the female choosing one and lining it with feathers. Clutch sizes are in the range 4–8 eggs and incubation, by the female, takes 14–15 days with fledging taking 16–17 days. Although many males are monogamous, large numbers are polygynous resulting in significantly increased breeding success (Garson 1980, Sweeney 1998).

Scottish distribution and status

In Scotland, Wrens are common birds across the whole country although densities are lower in upland areas. There are four endemic subspecies, in the Outer Hebrides, St Kilda, Shetland and Fair Isle. They are highly sedentary with birds rarely moving more than a few kilometres from their natal area. It is estimated that there are 1.4–1.8 million occupied territories of the mainland subspecies *indigenus* in Scotland with a summer population of probably 4–5 million adult birds. There are a further 13,000 pairs of the four island subspecies combined. Between 1994–2007 there was an increase in the Scottish breeding population of 88% (Risely *et al.* 2008).

Wren, Drum, 1975. © *Graham Rebecca*

Distribution and status in North-East Scotland

Wrens are widespread in North-East Scotland, occurring in more tetrads than any other species except Chaffinch. They are found in almost all habitats except moorlands above 750 m. On higher ground in the Cairngorms they prefer taller Heather in which they feed near small lochs and streams. Although present in good numbers up Deeside and Donside they are apparently absent from large parts of the Ladder Hills and in some areas of Buchan and the Mearns. This is most likely to be due to the lack of suitable nesting habitats although there may also be an issue with low observer coverage, especially in parts of Buchan. They are well distributed around the suburbs of Aberdeen but occur less widely near the city centre.

Changes in distribution

The distribution in North-East Scotland has changed little since 1968–1972 when Wrens were recorded in 113 10-km squares (*BTO 1st Atlas*); there were 111 occupied squares in 2002–06. However, there has been an 18% increase in the number of occupied recording units in Aberdeenshire/Aberdeen City between 1981–84 (312) and 2002–06 (369), perhaps indicating an increase in the amount of available nesting and feeding habitat in the current range. The expansion into sub-optimal habitat in the higher areas of the Cairngorms is perhaps a reflection of increasing population and full occupation of optimal habitats in the valleys coupled with increasing woodland planting at higher levels.

Population and trends

Wren breeding densities vary greatly depending on habitat, which makes the estimation of population size problematic. Densities in woodland range from 9 pairs/km^2 in Scots Pine with no under-storey to 302 pairs/km^2 in some deciduous woodlands (Williamson 1974, Moss 1978). Farmland densities are lower, ranging from 4 pairs/km^2 in mainly arable areas to 127 pairs/km^2 where there is a mix of arable and shelter belts (da Prato 1985). There have, however, been few density measurements in Scotland since the 1970s and 1980s, since when population levels have changed significantly; without doubt, populations can still be high, such as 13–131 territories/km^2 in various scrub and woodland habitats in Deeside (Jenkins & Watson 1999) and 53 singing males in 1 km^2 in farmland near Inverurie in 2000. An approach to deriving a population estimate for North-East Scotland involves using the total area of eight major habitat types, and applying a range of possible breeding densities for each one. This calculation results in an estimated range of 212,921–297,534 occupied territories and suggests that 200,000–300,000 territories may be a good approximation of the range within which the North-East's Wren population fluctuates. Projected future increases in woodland, and possible scenarios relating to climate change (Huntley *et al.* 2007), may ensure a continued increase in the local breeding population.

Author: *Martin Auld*

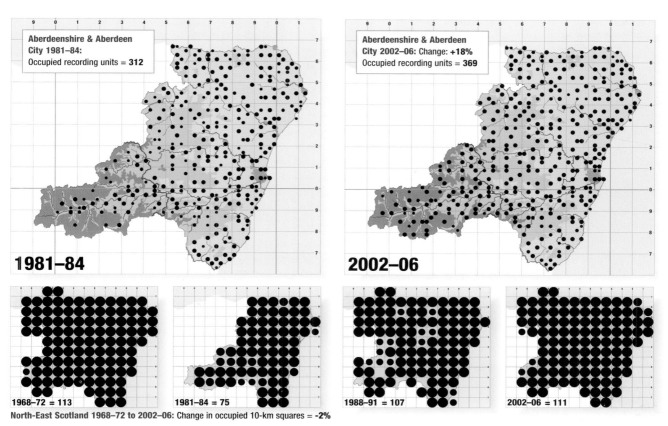

Aberdeenshire & Aberdeen City 1981–84: Occupied recording units = 312

1981–84

Aberdeenshire & Aberdeen City 2002–06: Change: +18% Occupied recording units = 369

2002–06

1968–72 = 113   1981–84 = 75   1988–91 = 107   2002–06 = 111

North-East Scotland 1968–72 to 2002–06: Change in occupied 10-km squares = -2%

Starling

Sturnus vulgaris

Very common resident. Winter visitor and passage migrant. Estimated population in North-East Scotland:
40,000–50,000 pairs (19% of Scottish population, 6% of UK)

Red list; UK BAP list

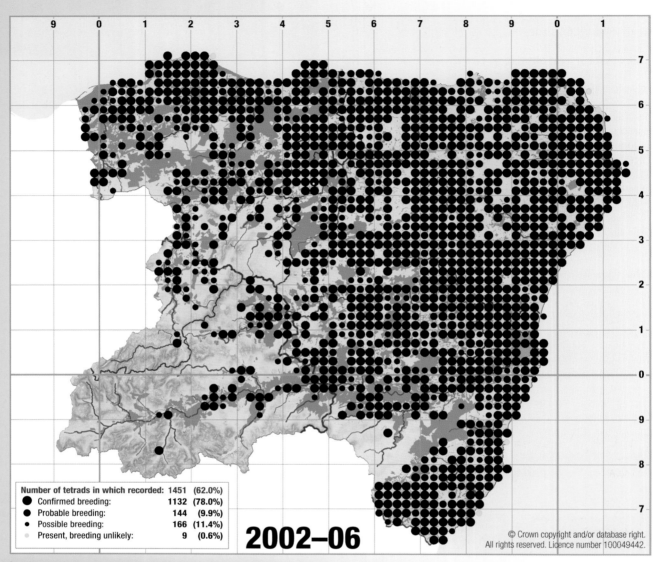

	Number of tetrads in which recorded:	1451	(62.0%)
●	Confirmed breeding:	1132	(78.0%)
●	Probable breeding:	144	(9.9%)
●	Possible breeding:	166	(11.4%)
●	Present, breeding unlikely:	9	(0.6%)

2002–06

Starling, Newburgh, May 2009. © *Rab Rae*

Habitat and breeding biology

Starlings occur in a wide variety of habitats in North-East Scotland, excluding mountainous areas and dense forest, but particularly favouring farmland and gardens, where they feed on invertebrates in short grassland and lawns. Nests are typically in natural tree holes and other cavities such as inside dry stone dykes and under the guttering of buildings. Starlings take readily to nest boxes, and around 50 of these at Aberdeen University's Culterty Field Station in Newburgh have seen a high rate of occupancy each year since the 1950s. At Culterty, in the 1950s, most clutches, usually of 4–5 eggs, were started between 13th–25th April and 74–84% of eggs produced fledged young (Anderson 1961). Second clutches are often laid but the proportion of pairs that do this varies considerably from year to year (Clark in *BS3*).

Scottish distribution and status

Starlings are widespread in Scotland, except in the mountainous areas of the Central Highlands and western Scotland. Strongholds are in south-western, central and eastern Scotland, as well as in the Northern Isles and the Outer Hebrides. The endemic subspecies *zetlandicus* inhabits Shetland. Elsewhere, the Scottish breeding population of nominate subspecies *vulgaris* was estimated at 170,000–300,000 pairs in 2007 (Clark in *BS3*).

Distribution and status in North-East Scotland

Starlings are distributed widely throughout the agricultural lowlands of North-East Scotland, including villages, towns and Aberdeen city. They are, however, notably absent from extensive tracts of forestry and from much of the uplands above 300 m. Their absence from these habitats is likely to be due to a lack of suitable nest sites; indeed, the presence of large post-breeding flocks on upland pasture suggests that food availability is not a limiting factor. When isolated patches of habitat provide suitable nest sites then Starlings may colonise, as at Inchrory in Glen Avon and in Glen Clunie. The resident breeding population is supplemented each autumn by birds arriving from the continent, mostly from Scandinavia, to spend the winter in North-East Scotland. Large flocks commonly associate with winter flocks of Lapwing and Golden Plover on grass fields in the north-east of the region.

Starling, Aboyne Loch, May 2007. © *Harry Scott*

Changes in distribution

In the mid 18th century, Starlings were common in mainland Scotland but by around 1800 they had almost disappeared, perhaps due to climatic conditions. They subsequently re-colonised from England during the 19th century (Clark in *BS3*). Overall, in North-East Scotland, the occupancy of 10-km squares has declined only slightly between 1968–72 (*BTO 1st Atlas*) and 2002–06, but close examination reveals that this change has been centred on upland areas of Aberdeenshire where nine out of ten 10-km squares in the extreme south-west were occupied by Starlings in 1968–72 but this reduced to seven in 1981–84 (*NES 1st Atlas*), three in 1988–91 (*BTO 2nd Atlas*) and five in 2002–06.

Population and trends

Relative abundance data presented in the *BTO 2nd Atlas* indicate high values for the North-East within Scotland and it is possible that our area contains *c.* 15–20% of the Scottish total, *i.e.* 35,000–47,000 pairs. Abundance in the North-East appears comparable to that in South-east Scotland (*BTO 2nd Atlas*) where, using national data and local studies, Murray et al. (1998) calculated a density of 10–12 pairs/km². Applying this figure in the North-East would generate a higher estimate of 58,000–69,000 pairs, but this is probably excessive. In the absence of any local studies, all that can be said is that the population in our area may lie within the range 40,000–50,000 pairs, or possibly a little higher. Contrary to the UK as a whole, where Starling numbers fell by 26% during 1994–2007, there was a 1% increase in Scotland (Risely *et al.* 2008). The UK decline has been attributed to a reduction in invertebrate abundance as a result of more intensive management of lowland grassland (Vickery *et al.* 2001). In general, breeding productivity has increased nationally while survival, particularly of juveniles, has decreased (Crick *et al.* 2002).

Author: *Paul Doyle*

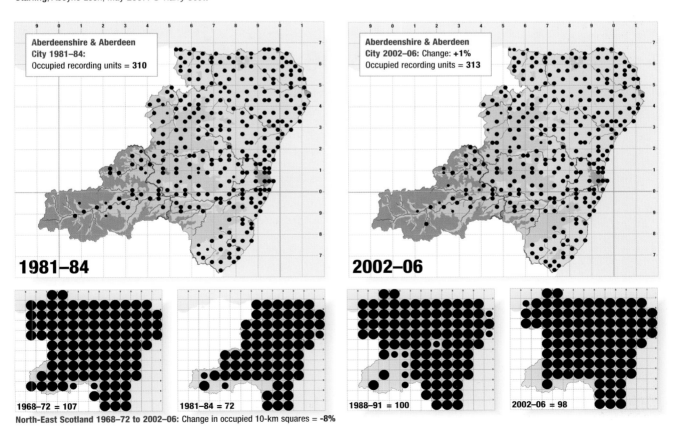

Aberdeenshire & Aberdeen City 1981–84:
Occupied recording units = 310

1981–84

Aberdeenshire & Aberdeen City 2002–06: Change: +1%
Occupied recording units = 313

2002–06

1968–72 = 107   1981–84 = 72

1988–91 = 100   2002–06 = 98

North-East Scotland 1968–72 to 2002–06: Change in occupied 10-km squares = -8%

Dipper

Cinclus cinclus

Scarce resident. Estimated population in North-East Scotland: **500–700 pairs** (5% of Scottish population, <5% of UK)

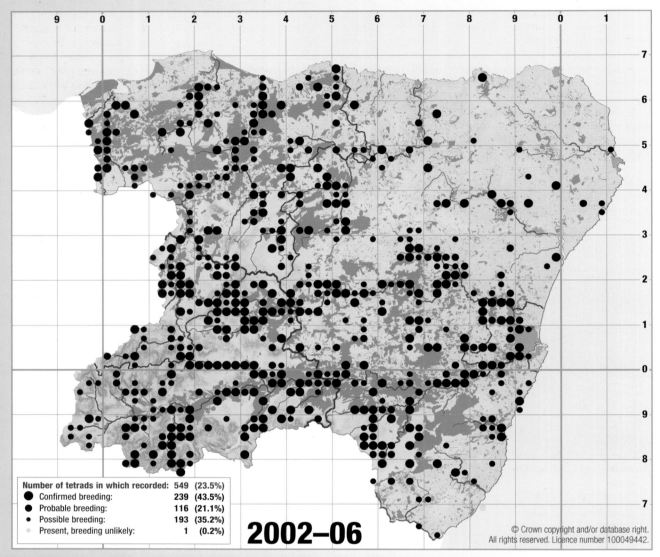

Number of tetrads in which recorded:	549	(23.5%)
● Confirmed breeding:	239	(43.5%)
● Probable breeding:	116	(21.1%)
● Possible breeding:	193	(35.2%)
Present, breeding unlikely:	1	(0.2%)

2002–06

Dipper, Findhorn valley, April 2009. © *Derek McGinn*

Habitat and breeding biology

Dippers are resident in Scotland and breed wherever fast-moving water occurs. This can take the form of large rivers or small streams; slow-moving deep water is generally avoided as are areas with few breeding sites. Sections of rocky river with fast-flowing water are especially favoured as these give good perches for foraging in aerated water with good invertebrate prey. Nest sites are varied but most are on man-made structures such as bridges or walls. Natural sites probably account for less than 5% of the total, with cliffs or eroded banks most commonly used. Less frequently, the domed nests can be placed on top of low tree branches overhanging water or sometimes built into the detritus left by high flood water levels. Birds on the River Don breed earlier on the lower section of the river (in particular around the paper mills) than on the upper stretches around Strathdon. Dippers in the upper reaches of the Don breed up to two weeks earlier than the birds on the upper reaches of the Dee despite these being less than 15 km apart. These differences are probably related to water temperature and the subsequent increase in invertebrate activity associated with this (pers. obs.). Dippers breed early in the year with nest building starting as early as February. Eggs are generally laid in March and

The Breeding Birds of North-East Scotland

hatch 14–16 days later, with chicks fledging when 14–16 days old. One third of pairs were double-brooded in one study in North-East Scotland (Hardey *et al.* 1978).

Scottish distribution and status
The British subspecies of Dipper, *C. c. gularis*, is widespread in Scotland away from the Hebrides (Wilson in *BS3*). It is common wherever suitable habitat occurs but breeding densities are higher in inland and upland areas, and especially in the Borders. The Scottish breeding population is thought to be around 10,000–15,000 pairs (Wilson in *BS3*).

Distribution and status in North-East Scotland
Dippers are familiar breeding birds of the North-East in suitable habitat. They breed from the tidal waters of both the Dee (where they nest on the railway bridge at Torry) and the Don (where they nest by the Brig o' Balgownie), to the upper reaches of the Dee at heights of 650 m in the Cairngorms and 450 m on the Don at Delnadamph. Nest sites are almost always over water though occasionally nests can be several metres away from water, such as one inside an abandoned mine building near Tomintoul. Absence from the River Ugie and parts of the River Ythan is probably explained by unsuitable conditions.

Dipper nest, Glen Tanar, April 2008. © *Harry Scott*

Changes in distribution
There has been little or no real change to the distribution of Dippers in North-East Scotland in recent decades, with a similar number of occupied 10-km squares in 1968–72 and in 2002–06. A small increase in occupied recording areas in the Aberdeenshire/Aberdeen City atlas maps between 1981–84 and 2002–06 may be due to increased observer effort. In the past, Dippers were persecuted on the salmon rivers of the region, especially in the upper reaches, where the bird was suspected of eating salmon eggs and smolts. This practice has now largely ceased although there is still occasional evidence of nest destruction. The lack of persecution on the upper stretches of the Dee and the Don may be one factor that has allowed more birds to breed where few occurred 30 years ago.

Population and trends
Dippers are not considered to be threatened anywhere and their population is regarded as varying around a generally stable level (Wilson in *BS3*). The North-East population has shown no indication of fluctuation although there is little published information. Numbers within a small group of breeding birds on the Dee and Don were stable between 2004 and 2005 (pers. obs.). In one area, the population on *c.*8 km of the Dess burn at Kincardine O'Neil crashed from eight to two pairs in the 1990s, most likely as a result of drainage improvements which resulted in the burn becoming heavily silted up. This population had still not recovered to its former numbers by 2008. Hard winter weather may also affect numbers but there is little local information. There are no reliable figures on overall population densities in North-East Scotland, but using some average estimates per tetrad and taking account of local studies and variation in river type, a figure of 500–700 pairs seems reasonable.

Author: *Robert Rae*

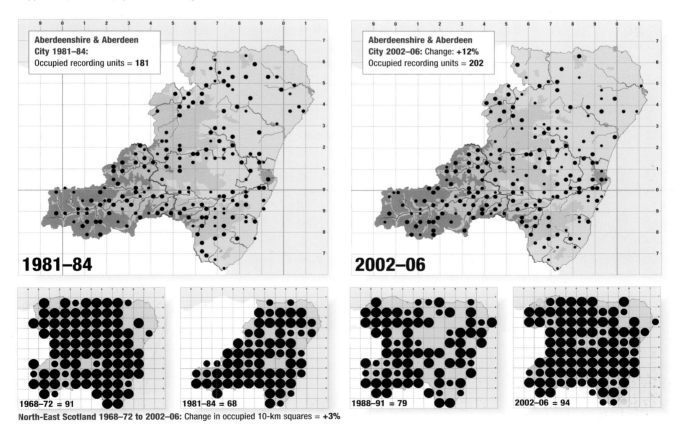

Aberdeenshire & Aberdeen City 1981–84: Occupied recording units = 181

1981–84

Aberdeenshire & Aberdeen City 2002–06: Change: +12% Occupied recording units = 202

2002–06

1968–72 = 91   1981–84 = 68   1988–91 = 79   2002–06 = 94

North-East Scotland 1968–72 to 2002–06: Change in occupied 10-km squares = +3%

Ring Ouzel

Turdus torquatus

Scarce summer migrant breeder. Passage migrant. Estimated population in North-East Scotland: *300–400 pairs* (7% of Scottish population, 5% of UK)

Red list; UK and Scottish BAP lists

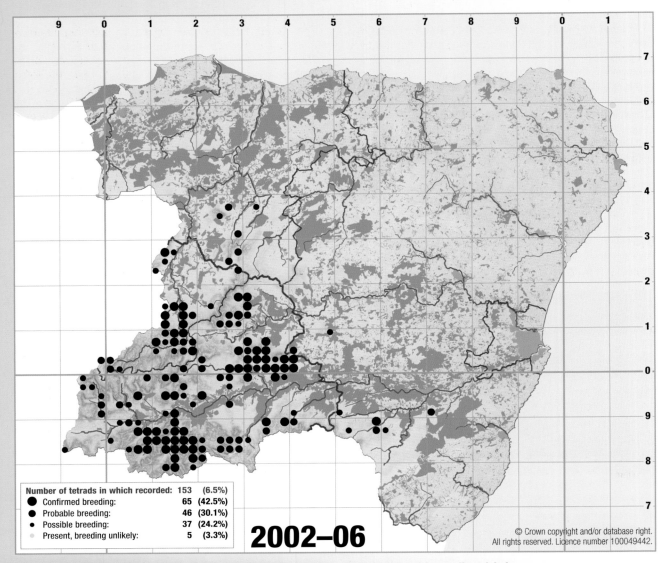

Number of tetrads in which recorded:	153	(6.5%)
● Confirmed breeding:	65	(42.5%)
● Probable breeding:	46	(30.1%)
● Possible breeding:	37	(24.2%)
● Present, breeding unlikely:	5	(3.3%)

2002–06

Ring Ouzel, Glen Clunie, May 2006. © *Andy Hay*

Habitat and breeding biology

In North-East Scotland, Ring Ouzels frequent upland moorland and montane areas, often associating with crags, gullies and scree. Breeding areas usually hold grass or mixed grass-Heather patches where adults often forage. They normally avoid dense woodland, but can utilise open Scots Pine forest and mature Juniper scrub. They usually nest on the ground, often at the base of a rock sheltered by Heather or on a heathery crag. A few pairs nest in Juniper bushes but tree nesting is rare in North-East Scotland and the rest of Britain, as opposed to nest sites in Scandinavia and central Europe. They return to breeding areas in late March to mid April with the males' territorial song carrying for at least 800 m. Most first clutches are started by early May, and many pairs are double brooded. Incubation lasts two weeks; young fledge in 13–14 days, and are independent at five weeks of age. By mid July adults, juveniles and recently fledged young form small flocks. Their diet then changes, from invertebrates such as earthworms, beetles and leatherjackets (Burfield 2002), to include berries such as Blaeberry and Crowberry.

The Breeding Birds of North-East Scotland

Scottish distribution and status

Ring Ouzel declines were widely reported throughout Scotland during the 20th century. Despite this, they still breed in most upland areas of the mainland, with strongholds in the north-east, and the central and north-west highlands (Rollie in *BS3*). In 1999, the Scottish population was estimated at 4,341–5,503 breeding pairs after a partial survey and calculated extrapolation (Wotton *et al.* 2002). Habitat changes, such as the conifer afforestation of moorland (Buchanan *et al.* 2003) and loss of Heather cover (Sim *et al.* 2007) have been implicated in declines throughout Scotland and in the south-east particularly. Additionally, climatic influences, such as warmer summers in breeding areas, and berry crop unreliability at wintering areas in Morocco, have been tentatively linked to declines in Britain (Beale *et al.* 2006).

Distribution and status in North-East Scotland

Ring Ouzels are largely confined to the upland south-west of the region with three concentrations evident in 2002–06. These were to the south of Braemar (encompassing Glens Muick, Callater, Clunie and Ey), the lower Glen Gairn, Glen Fenzie and Morven areas, and to the south of Tomintoul around Glens Loin, Avon and Builg. The main habitats at these areas comprise of various mosaics of Heathers and grasses with much rock and scree, and occasional limestone outcrops with species-rich flushes. The latter two zones also hold extensive Juniper stands.

Changes in distribution

There was a decrease in 10-km square distribution since 1968–72 (*BTO 1st Atlas*), of 22% and 19% by 1988–91 (*BTO 2nd Atlas*) and 2002–06 respectively. The main losses were in the south-east and north-east of the range in Aberdeenshire and in south Moray, areas where extensive conifer afforestation has dramatically changed the previously open moorland habitat since the 1950s–1980s. The effects of this land-use change, directly through habitat loss and indirectly through, for example, increased predation risk, have probably contributed to the declines in a similar manner to that in other areas of Scotland (Buchanan *et al.* 2003).

Population and trends

There has been no previous estimate of breeding numbers for Aberdeenshire or Moray. A maximum of 59 pairs was located in Glens Clunie and Callater in 1998, where numbers had been relatively stable since 1991 (Rebecca 2001). A breeding study then developed in Glen Clunie, but numbers in the core study area declined by 62%, from 39 pairs in 1998 to 15 in 2006. Since then the decline may have levelled out (Sim *et al.* 2010). A similar decline of 63% was reported from Glens Avon and Builg in Moray between 1989 and 2004. One-day surveys of the same areas in June 1989, May 2000 and May 2004 recorded 16, eight and six pairs or singing males respectively (M. Cook pers. comm.). Some high-density tetrads were found in Glen Clunie (five, nine and 11 pairs in 2002) and Glen Callater (6–8 pairs in 2003) and 2–3 pairs were found in tetrads further afield. High-density areas are not thought to be widespread in North-East Scotland (*e.g.* Rebecca 2001) and many tetrads may only hold 1–3 pairs. Assuming that half of the confirmed tetrads may be high-density (average of 5–7 pairs) and half low-density (average of 1–3 pairs) and that the probable and possible tetrads each held at least one pair, a range of 280–410 pairs can be deduced, and an estimate of 300–400 pairs may have been appropriate for North-East Scotland in 2002–06. The range loss and declines in Glens Clunie, Avon and Builg cause concern, particularly as they mirror events occurring throughout Britain (Sim *et al.* 2010). Continued monitoring of the Glen Clunie population is important in regional and national terms as few Ring Ouzel studies in Britain have such continuity (Sim *et al.* 2010).

Authors: *Graham Rebecca & Innes Sim*

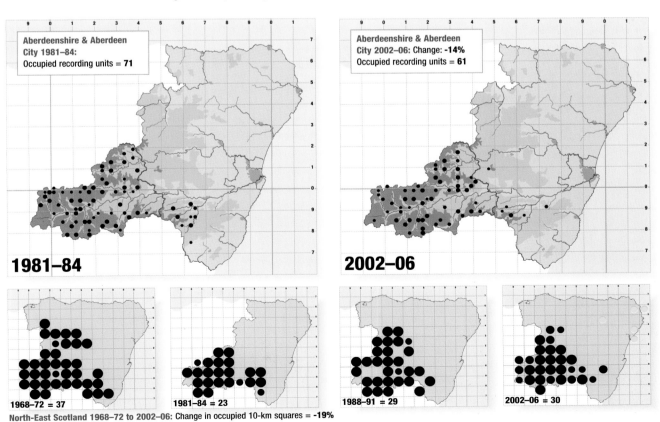

Aberdeenshire & Aberdeen City 1981–84:
Occupied recording units = 71

1981–84

Aberdeenshire & Aberdeen City 2002–06: Change: -14%
Occupied recording units = 61

2002–06

1968–72 = 37   1981–84 = 23   1988–91 = 29   2002–06 = 30

North-East Scotland 1968–72 to 2002–06: Change in occupied 10-km squares = -19%

Blackbird

Turdus merula

Very common resident. Winter visitor and passage migrant. Estimated population in North-East Scotland: *90,000–120,000 pairs* (13% of Scottish population, 2% of UK)

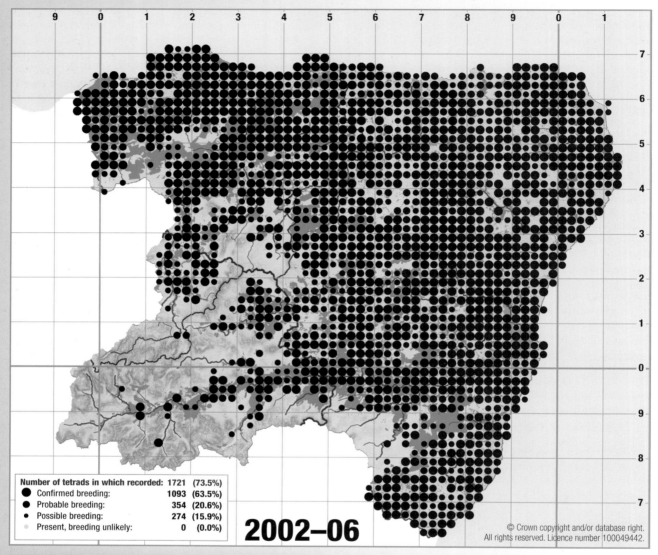

Number of tetrads in which recorded:	1721	(73.5%)
● Confirmed breeding:	1093	(63.5%)
● Probable breeding:	354	(20.6%)
● Possible breeding:	274	(15.9%)
● Present, breeding unlikely:	0	(0.0%)

2002–06

Blackbird, Aboyne, June 2004. © *Harry Scott*

Habitat and breeding biology

Blackbirds are found in a wide variety of habitats, including urban areas, parks, suburban gardens, scrub, farmland, and woodland edges adjacent to moorland. They are generally absent from dense, tall forest such as established coniferous plantations, and from open moorland. Nests are usually in shrubs, bushes or hedges which provide good cover, but may be in trees or even in farm outbuildings or garden sheds. Breeding normally begins in April, rather than March as in more southerly parts of the UK, and most young are fledged by July. However, unseasonably mild weather may result in breeding behaviour even in mid winter; a dead fledgling was found at Torry (Aberdeen) on 24th February 2005.

Scottish distribution and status

In Scotland, Blackbirds are very widely distributed, including the Western Isles, Orkney and Shetland, the last having been colonised during the 20th century (*BTO 1st Atlas*). The only significant gaps in distribution correspond to the mountainous areas of the Cairngorm Mountains and of the western and northern Scottish Highlands. The Scottish population is estimated at 600,000–1,000,000 pairs (Jardine & Clugston in *BS3*) and has increased by 25% over the period 1994–2007 (Risely *et al.* 2008).

The Breeding Birds of North-East Scotland

Blackbird, Aboyne, June 2005. © *Harry Scott*

Distribution and status in North-East Scotland

Blackbirds are widespread in North-East Scotland with the exception of its southern margin (where high ground separates the region from Angus and Perthshire) and the south-west of the region which is occupied by the Cairngorm and Grampian Mountains and their outliers. The breeding range penetrates even these mountainous regions along the valleys of the Rivers Dee, Don and Avon, albeit the distribution is relatively sparse in upper Deeside around Braemar. The almost ubiquitous distribution elsewhere reflects the wide range of habitats in which Blackbirds are found. This includes the city of Aberdeen and the towns of the region - the Blackbird is always one of the most widespread species in the winter RSPB Big Garden Birdwatch, being found in the vast majority of gardens surveyed.

Changes in distribution

There is little evidence of significant change in the Blackbird's range. There were 330 occupied recording units in Aberdeenshire/Aberdeen City in 2002–06 compared to 333 in 1981–84, and it has been consistently recorded in around 70–75% of the BBS squares in North-East Scotland between 1999 and 2006.

Population and trends

Measurements from various sources (*BS3*, *NES 1st Atlas*, Jenkins & Watson 1999, Murray *et al.* 1998, Elkins *et al.* 2003) indicate that average densities of 24 pairs/km^2 in broad-leaved woodland, 13 pairs/km^2 in coniferous woodland, 17 pairs/km^2 in farmland and up to 100 pairs/km^2 in suburban and country gardens may be applicable in the North-East. If these values are applied to relevant land cover areas (LC 2000 data) then a Blackbird population of around 105,000 pairs can be estimated. However, because few of the densities have been measured in our area, and Scottish BBS data reveal a 25% population increase during 1994–2007 (Risely et al. 2008), it is necessary to widen the current estimate to a range of 90,000–120,000 pairs.

Author: *James Piggins*

Blackbird, Glen Tanar, May 2005. © *Harry Scott*

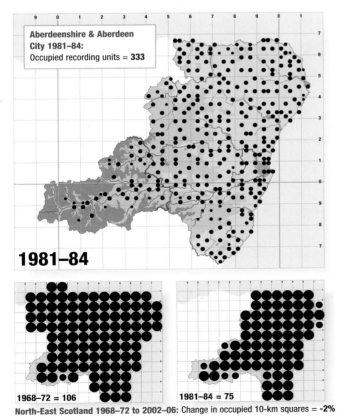

Aberdeenshire & Aberdeen City 1981–84:
Occupied recording units = **333**

1981–84

1968–72 = 106   1981–84 = 75

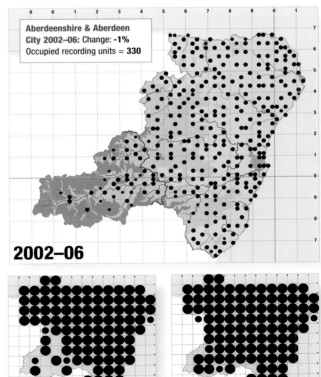

Aberdeenshire & Aberdeen City 2002–06: Change: **-1%**
Occupied recording units = **330**

2002–06

1988–91 = 100   2002–06 = 104

North-East Scotland 1968–72 to 2002–06: Change in occupied 10-km squares = **-2%**

Fieldfare

Turdus pilaris

Occasional breeder. Winter visitor and passage migrant. Estimated population in North-East Scotland: **0–2 pairs** (33% of Scottish population, 33% of UK)

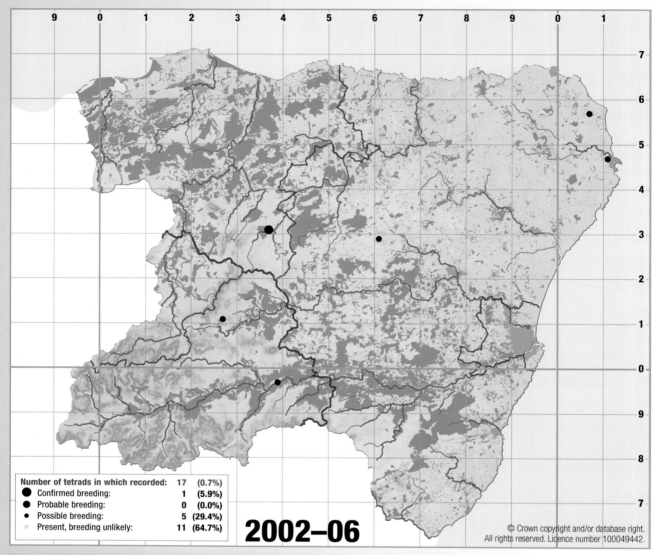

Number of tetrads in which recorded:	17	(0.7%)
● Confirmed breeding:	1	(5.9%)
● Probable breeding:	0	(0.0%)
• Possible breeding:	5	(29.4%)
Present, breeding unlikely:	11	(64.7%)

2002–06

Fieldfare, Norway, June 1989. © *Ed Duthie*

Habitat and breeding biology

Fieldfares are very scarce breeders in Britain. In Scandinavia they breed colonially in a wide range of habitats but the isolated pairs found in northern Britain, including in North-East Scotland, have mostly nested in moorland valleys, hillside birch woods or shelter belts and the edges of plantations (*BTO 2nd Atlas*). Scottish nests have been found at heights of up to eight metres in the branches of oak, Sycamore and conifers but also down to ground level, such as a heathery stream bank (*BTO 1st Atlas*). The timing of breeding in North-East Scotland would appear to be variable as adults have been seen carrying food to young on a spread of dates from 11th May to 29th July.

Scottish distribution and status

Breeding was first proved in Scotland, in Orkney, in 1967. During the period 1967–2004, breeding was confirmed in the Northern Isles, Highland, North-east Scotland, Moray & Nairn, Sutherland, Perth & Kinross, Fife and the Borders; 46–48 records in total with up to 19 of these in Orkney and Shetland. While the number of records during the 1970s and 1980s gave hope of a more widespread colonisation of Scotland this has failed to materialise and recently there have been fewer breeding attempts (Patterson in *BS3*).

Distribution and status in North-East Scotland

Fieldfares have been proved to breed in North-East Scotland on 12 occasions, four in Moray and the remainder in Aberdeenshire. There have been other instances of single birds, or occasionally pairs, in apparently suitable breeding habitat in summer.

The first nesting was in 1972 when four pairs were located, in Glen Avon, Strathdon, near Banchory and between Rhynie and Alford (*BTO 1st Atlas*). There were three more records during the 1970s (*NES 1st Atlas*, Cook 1992) but nothing further until 1987, when a pair was found feeding young at Deskry (Strathdon) on 18th June (RSPB), and 1988 when an adult was seen carrying food in Glen Fiddich on 25th June (Cook 1992). Two subsequent instances of proved breeding, in 1990 and 1991 (when an adult with two juveniles was found in June) were atypical in being close to the north coast of Aberdeenshire (as presently constituted), in the 10-km squares NJ56 and NJ65 (*BTO 2nd Atlas*). The two most recent records were of a bird carrying food on Deeside in late June 2001 and an adult feeding young near Cabrach in May 2002 - the only breeding record falling within the period 2002–06. The few other reports of birds in possible breeding habitat during 2002–06 probably relate to late migrants or conceivably unpaired summering individuals.

Changes in distribution

Of the 12 instances of proved breeding in North-East Scotland, seven took place in the 1970s and only a further five during the subsequent 28 years.

Population and trends

Not all remote birch woodlands or conifer plantations are visited by birders on a regular basis and it is perfectly possible that occasional pairs of Fieldfares breed unnoticed. However most of these areas were visited during the 2002–06 fieldwork period for this Atlas and the fact that only one breeding pair was found indicates that the 'population' is exceedingly small; probably one or two pairs per year at most. The promise of the 1970s has not been fulfilled.

Author: *Martin Cook*

Fieldfare, Finnmark, June 2005. © *Harry Scott*

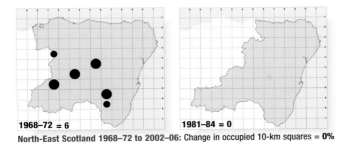

1968–72 = 6

1981–84 = 0

North-East Scotland 1968–72 to 2002–06: Change in occupied 10-km squares = **0%**

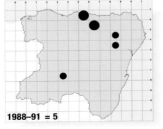

1988–91 = 5

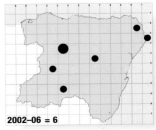

2002–06 = 6

Song Thrush

Turdus philomelos

Very common summer migrant breeder. Passage migrant, few in winter. Estimated population in North-East Scotland: *15,000–20,000 pairs* (7% of Scottish population, 2% of UK) Red list; UK and Scottish BAP lists

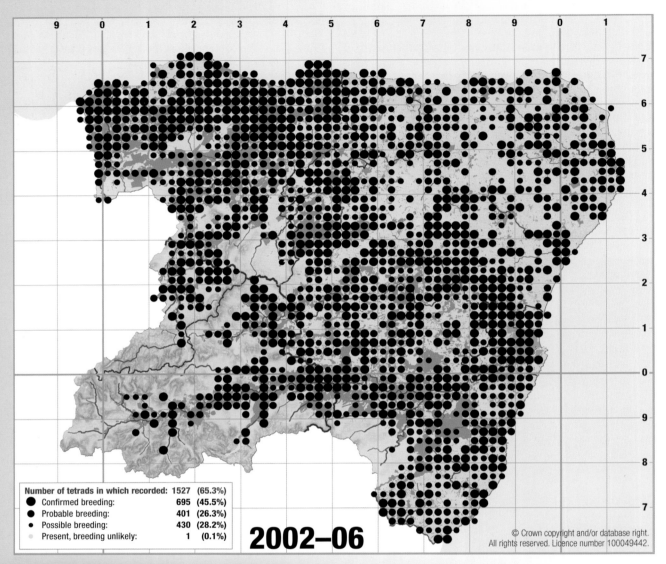

	Number of tetrads in which recorded:	1527	(65.3%)
●	Confirmed breeding:	695	(45.5%)
●	Probable breeding:	401	(26.3%)
●	Possible breeding:	430	(28.2%)
·	Present, breeding unlikely:	1	(0.1%)

2002–06

Song Thrush, Inverness, June 2010. © *Ian Francis*

Habitat and breeding biology

Song Thrushes usually nest about 2–3 m above the ground in dense cover such as hedges, bushes, dense conifers or Ivy, while taller trees and shrubs are used as song posts. Unlike Mistle Thrushes, they rarely feed far from cover and so nearby areas of grassland, leaf litter or similar ground layer vegetation are necessary to provide earthworms, molluscs and other invertebrate prey. These requirements are met in a wide range of woodland types in North-East Scotland, as well as in scrub and gardens. The first fledglings can appear in late April but are more frequently seen in early May. Two broods are normally raised each year but newly fledged third broods can sometimes be seen in early August.

Scottish distribution and status

The Song Thrush is a widespread and common breeding species throughout mainland Scotland with the exception of some mountain and moorland areas in the Highlands. It is most common in parts of Argyll, Dumfries & Galloway, Borders, Lothian, Fife, Angus, lowland Moray & Nairn and around the inner Moray Firth as far north as Sutherland. An endemic subspecies (*hebridensis*) occurs in the Outer Hebrides. The total breeding population is estimated to be around 260,000 pairs (Insley in *BS3*) and although there

The Breeding Birds of North-East Scotland

was a substantial population decline in Britain during the 1970s and 1980s, there has since been a population increase of 12% in Scotland between 1994–2007 (Risely *et al.* 2008).

Distribution and status in North-East Scotland

The Song Thrush is a widespread breeding bird in North-East Scotland and was recorded in 65% of tetrads in the region. They are absent from open hills and moorland but can be found up to 450 m in the higher glens if suitable habitat is present. At lower altitudes the species is ubiquitous in the well-wooded lowlands of Moray and central and southern Aberdeenshire. It is much more sparsely distributed in Buchan and Formartine, most probably due to the relative scarcity of woodland and scrub in this area. It is also possible that the effects of intensive agriculture on food supplies could be an issue in this area, although the species remains widespread in other intensive agricultural areas such as the Mearns and the Moray coastal plain. Song Thrushes leave most inland areas of North-East Scotland in the late summer or autumn, but small numbers over-winter near the coast. Usually they start to return to their breeding territories in late February.

Song Thrush, Glen Gairn, May 2004. © *Harry Scott*

Changes in distribution

There have been no significant changes in distribution since 1981–84. Although there has been a small (4%) increase in the number of occupied Aberdeen/Aberdeenshire recording units, there is no obvious pattern associated with this and, indeed, observer effort maybe a factor.

Population and trends

A proportional share of the Scottish population estimate based on the area covered by North-East Scotland implies a population of around 30,000 pairs in our area. However, this may be an overestimate as population densities may be higher in southern Scotland. Applying habitat-specific densities derived from the BBS (Newson *et al.* 2005) to broad regional habitat data suggests that a population of 15,000–20,000 pairs is more likely. BBS data has revealed an upward population trend in the North-East between 1994 and 2006 (Francis 2008), in line with the national trend, although it is not clear if this may simply be a reversal of a previous decline.

Author: *Paul Chapman*

Song Thrush, Glen Gairn, May 2004. © *Harry Scott*

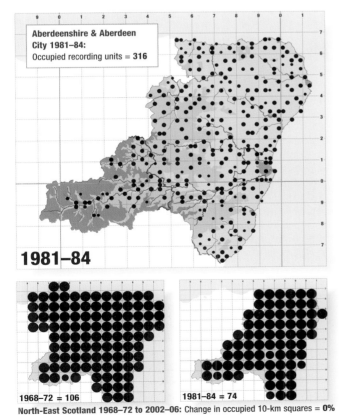

Aberdeenshire & Aberdeen City 1981–84: Occupied recording units = **316**

1981–84

1968–72 = 106   1981–84 = 74

North-East Scotland 1968–72 to 2002–06: Change in occupied 10-km squares = **0%**

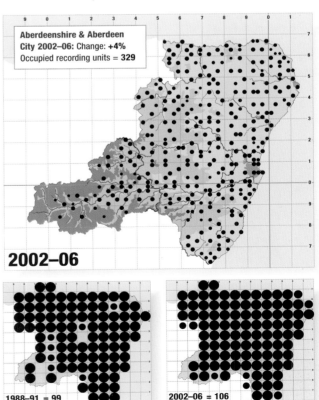

Aberdeenshire & Aberdeen City 2002–06: Change: +4% Occupied recording units = **329**

2002–06

1988–91 = 99   2002–06 = 106

Redwing

Turdus iliacus

Occasional breeder. Winter visitor and passage migrant. Estimated population in North-East Scotland: **0–2 pairs** (2% of Scottish population, 2% of UK)

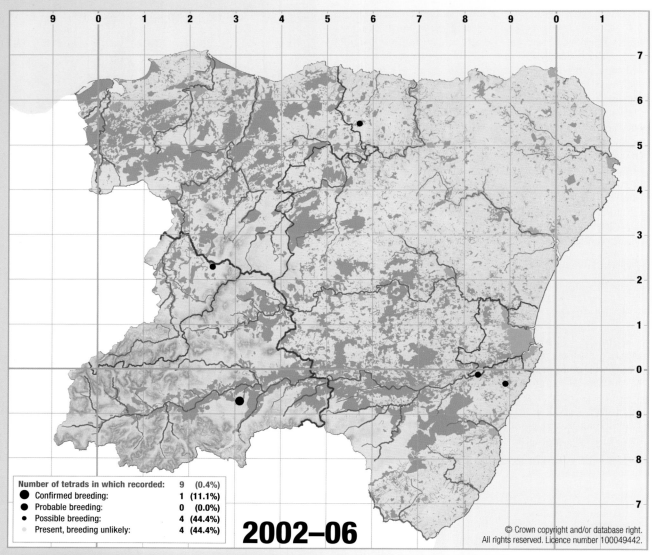

Number of tetrads in which recorded: 9 (0.4%)
- Confirmed breeding: 1 (11.1%)
- Probable breeding: 0 (0.0%)
- Possible breeding: 4 (44.4%)
- Present, breeding unlikely: 4 (44.4%)

2002–06

Redwing, Glen Girnock, June 1975. © *Mike Reid*

Habitat and breeding biology

The small Scottish breeding population of Redwings occupies a range of habitats typically including tall trees with a scrubby understorey and close to short, damp grassland for foraging. These conditions may be met in the mature mixed woodland with Rhododendrons around the lodges and estate houses of the western highlands. Other breeding pairs have been found in hillside birchwoods and Sitka Spruce plantations. Song can be heard from mid April and full clutches have been found by 7th May with fledged young on the wing by the end of May. Redwings are commonly double-brooded (Storie in *BS3*).

Scottish distribution and status

The main Scottish breeding range is on the mainland to the north-west of the Great Glen, and in Badenoch & Strathspey. Breeding was first recorded in the 1930s. By the late 1960s Redwings were well established, with 20 pairs in Wester Ross alone in 1968. Peak numbers were nesting in the 1970s and 1980s when a possible maximum of 77 pairs was located in Scotland in 1984 (Spencer 1986) and it is likely that many other pairs were undiscovered. The population in 1972 was estimated at 300 pairs (*BTO 1st Atlas*). Since that time there has been a marked decline and by 2007 the total Scottish population was placed in the range of 40–80 pairs (Storie in *BS3*).

Distribution and status in North-East Scotland

Redwings are abundant autumn migrants in North-East Scotland and variable numbers remain in the area through the winter. Spring return passage is much lighter and extends through April and early May, when late migrants are a source of confusion in establishing the presence of potential breeders. During 2002–06 there was only a single record of confirmed breeding; a family party of fledged young was found in Glen Girnock near Ballater on 3rd July 2005. In 2003, single birds were seen in lower Deeside at Blairs on 9th June and Tilbouries on 2nd July, but there was no evidence of breeding (*NESBR* 2003). A singing bird at Ordiquhill on 14th April 2002 was likely to have been a lingering migrant, as was another in a plantation in Glenlivet on 23rd April 2005.

Changes in distribution

Redwings have always been rare breeders in North-East Scotland; indeed there were only five confirmed breeding records prior to that in 2005. In May 1969, a pair was found with a nest and eggs at Milltown near Elgin and on 16th May 1971 there was a nest containing four young near Tomintoul (Cook 1992). In 1975, breeding took place at two sites in upper Deeside with three young fledged at one site while, at the other, young disappeared from the nest prior to fledging (*NESBR* 1975). In June 1980, an adult was watched carrying food in Moray (*SBR* 1980). More recently, a bird was gathering nesting material at Inverugie in mid April 1990 but there was no further evidence of breeding (*NESBR* 1990). In 2008, a pair with three recently fledged chicks was found in Deeside in early June, and another singing male was at the same site (*NESBR* 2008). There have been a few other reports of singing or summering birds in suitable habitat, mostly during the 1970s and 1980s.

Population and trends

In view of the small number of confirmed breeding records since 1975 it seems that Redwings are at best only sporadic breeders in North-East Scotland. Occasional pairs may breed undetected but it is unlikely that the annual population normally exceeds one or two pairs, and in many years there may be none. The Scottish peak of the 1970s–1980s is now long past and an upturn of the local population in the short term is not anticipated.

Author: *Martin Cook*

Redwing, Finnmark, June 2008. © *Harry Scott*

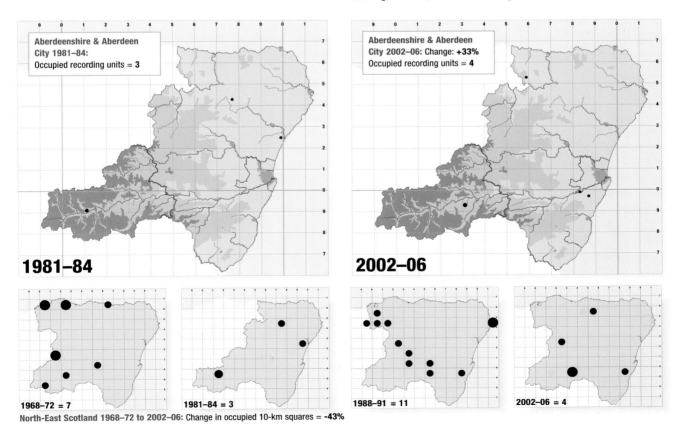

Aberdeenshire & Aberdeen City 1981–84:
Occupied recording units = 3

1981–84

1968–72 = 7

1981–84 = 3

Aberdeenshire & Aberdeen City 2002–06: Change: +33%
Occupied recording units = 4

2002–06

1988–91 = 11

2002–06 = 4

North-East Scotland 1968–72 to 2002–06: Change in occupied 10-km squares = -43%

Mistle Thrush

Turdus viscivorus

Common resident and migrant breeder. Estimated population in North-East Scotland: *7,000–8,000 pairs* (17% of Scottish population, 3% of UK)

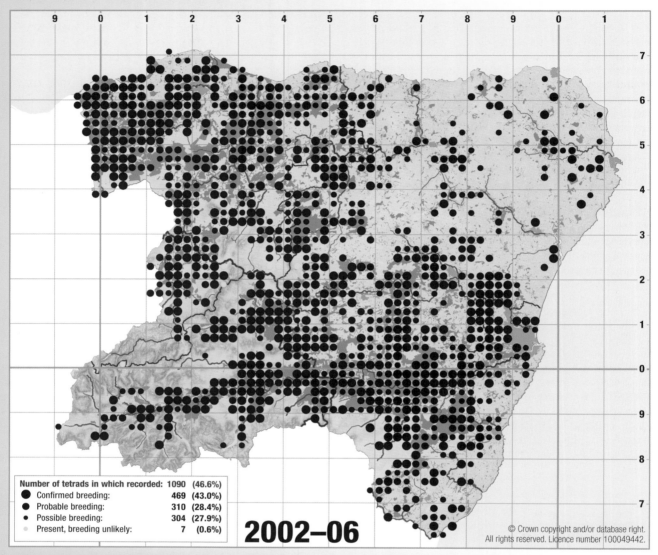

Number of tetrads in which recorded:	1090	(46.6%)
● Confirmed breeding:	469	(43.0%)
● Probable breeding:	310	(28.4%)
● Possible breeding:	304	(27.9%)
● Present, breeding unlikely:	7	(0.6%)

2002–06

Mistle Thrush, Gairnshiel Lodge, May 2009. © *Chris Jones*

Habitat and breeding biology

The Mistle Thrush is predominantly a tree-nesting species which breeds in open woodlands, woodland edges and in parks and gardens. In agricultural areas they may make use of small woods and shelter belts. Peak egg laying takes place in early April although, even in Scotland, nests with young have been found in January. Incubation and fledging each take 12–15 days with the young becoming independent after a further two weeks. The species is, at least sometimes, double-brooded in Scotland but this can be difficult to detect because nesting is initiated over a long period from March to June. They are scarce in upland areas during the mid winter period when they may move to lower lying areas or even out of North-East Scotland, in a southerly direction (Insley in *BS3*).

Scottish distribution and status

Mistle Thrushes are widespread at low densities throughout mainland Scotland and the Inner Hebrides, with the Scottish breeding population estimated at 40,000–50,000 pairs. They are absent as a breeding species from the Western and Northern Isles and densities are low in the north-west Highlands. In late summer and early autumn they often aggregate into flocks of 50–60 birds with occasional records of flocks in excess of 100 individuals. These often occur in the straths around upland areas in the Highlands and southern Scotland from which many birds appear to withdraw during the winter period when larger numbers occur in lowland and coastal areas (Insley in *BS3*).

Distribution and status in North-East Scotland

Mistle Thrushes are still relatively scarce in the agricultural areas of the Buchan plain, breeding only in areas where there are trees. They are also absent from the treeless high ground above 300 m to the west of Fettercairn, in the Cairngorms north and south of Deeside and in upper Donside. Although they are common in the parks and large gardens in suburban areas of Aberdeenshire and Moray, the highest densities appear to be in the well-wooded straths

Mistle Thrush, Cambus o' May, May 1982. © *Ed Duthie*

leading into the Cairngorm massif. Where there are scattered trees or plantations, Mistle Thrushes can breed at higher levels and, until they were recently felled, there were always several pairs in the woods at Well of the Lecht at about 450 m. In common with most of the Highlands, many Mistle Thrushes withdraw from the highest inland areas in the mid winter months of December and January, although breeding pairs appear back from early February.

Changes in distribution

The number of occupied 10-km squares in 2002–06 is closely similar to that found in 1968–72 (*BTO 1st Atlas*). It is uncertain to what extent observer effort contributed to an apparent decline in 1988–91 (*BTO 2nd Atlas*) but it undoubtedly played a part. The number of occupied recording units in Aberdeenshire/Aberdeen City has increased by 26% between 1981–84 and 2002–06 with the most noticeable increase being on the low ground south of a line from Huntly to Aberdeen. Changes in the amount of woodland planted in this area during this period have been insufficient by themselves to account for this increase, which mirrors the strong upward BBS population trend for Scotland (Risely *et al.* 2008).

Population and trends

Published densities from various sources (Jenkins & Watson 1999, Murray *et al.* 1998, *BS3*, *NES 1st Atlas*) indicate that averages of 7 pairs/km^2 in broad-leaved woodland, 3 pairs/km^2 in coniferous woodland and 0.5 pairs/km^2 in farmland might be appropriate in North-East Scotland. When applied to the relevant land cover areas (LC 2000 data) an estimate for the total population of 7,000–8,000 pairs can be derived. Scottish BBS work has revealed a 39% population increase during 1994–2007 (Risely *et al.* 2008), but there is inadequate information from the North-East to confirm this trend in our area.

Author: *Hugh Insley*

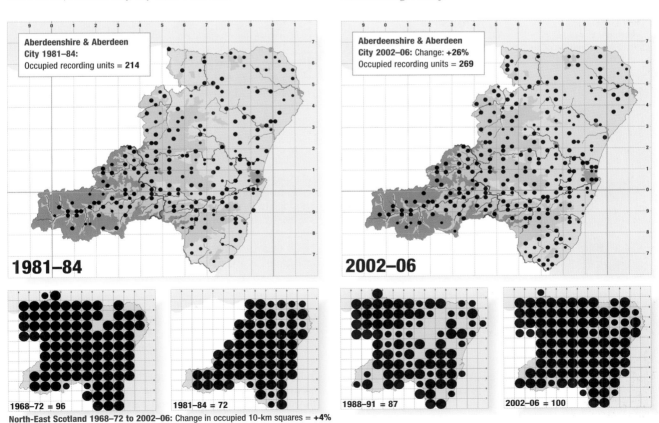

Aberdeenshire & Aberdeen City 1981–84:
Occupied recording units = 214

1981–84

Aberdeenshire & Aberdeen City 2002–06: Change: +26%
Occupied recording units = 269

2002–06

1968–72 = 96

1981–84 = 72

1988–91 = 87

2002–06 = 100

North-East Scotland 1968–72 to 2002–06: Change in occupied 10-km squares = +4%

Spotted Flycatcher   *Muscicapa striata*

Common summer migrant breeder. Passage migrant. Estimated population in North-East Scotland: *2,000–2,500 pairs* (15% of Scottish population, 4% of UK)   Red list; UK and Scottish BAP lists

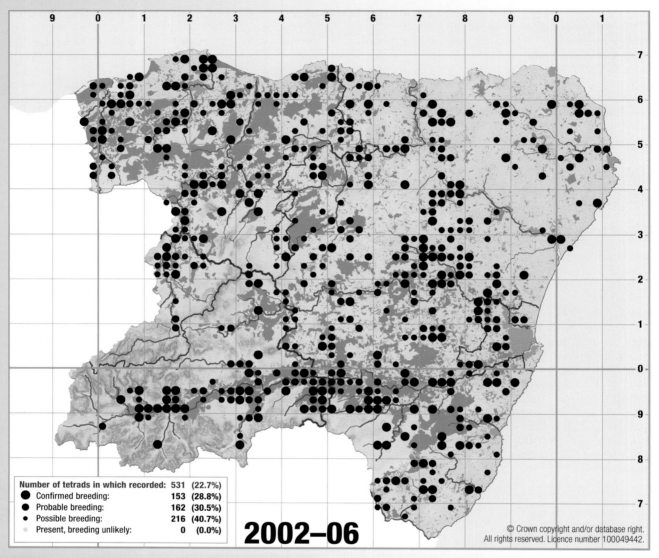

Number of tetrads in which recorded:	531	(22.7%)
● Confirmed breeding:	153	(28.8%)
● Probable breeding:	162	(30.5%)
● Possible breeding:	216	(40.7%)
● Present, breeding unlikely:	0	(0.0%)

2002–06

Spotted Flycatcher, Drum, 1979. © *Graham Rebecca*

Habitat and breeding biology

Spotted Flycatchers are summer visitors to Scotland from May to August, when they can be found in a variety of woodland habitats from native pinewoods to small copses in farmland. Mature deciduous woodland is generally the preferred habitat, but in Deeside fairly high densities have been recorded in mature pine plantations (*NESBR* 2002). It is important that the habitat provides open areas with perches to hunt from, an abundance of insect food and sheltered nest sites. Farmyards and gardens may be occupied, with climbing plants on garden walls and nest boxes providing nest sites. In Scotland, Spotted Flycatchers are single brooded, with a mean clutch size of 4.4 eggs (Baker in *BS3*).

Scottish distribution and status

The species is found commonly across much of Scotland, although usually absent as a breeding bird from the Northern Isles, the Outer Hebrides and higher upland areas of the mainland. Large differences in density between habitats, along with a major decline in numbers in recent years, have made it difficult to assess the total population but the most recent Scottish estimate is within the range of 10,000–20,000 pairs (Baker in *BS3*).

Spotted Flycatcher, Sutherland, June 1988. © *Ed Duthie*

Distribution and status in North-East Scotland

Spotted Flycatchers breed widely across North-East Scotland but, despite being recorded in most 10-km squares, the distribution is patchy with greater concentrations in favoured areas. The distribution map indicates concentrations in Moray, lower Donside and Deeside, where they prefer mature deciduous and mixed woodlands. Over much of the North-East, the map indicates absence from extensive coniferous plantations, especially in their younger stages. The species is also missing from the treeless moorlands although they can be found in birch woods along the upland glens. They are also only sparsely scattered across areas in the south-east of the region and on the Buchan plain. These areas contain extensive arable farmland and the scarcity of Spotted Flycatchers here may be as a result of a lack of suitable areas of woodland, appropriate invertebrate prey and nesting sites.

Changes in distribution

Despite population declines across the UK in recent years, Spotted Flycatchers have not shown a substantial decrease in range in North-East Scotland, with the number of occupied 10-km squares declining only slightly between 1968–72 (*BTO 1st Atlas*) and 1988–91 (*BTO 2nd Atlas*) but with these apparent losses being restored by 2002–06. The more detailed comparative maps for Aberdeenshire/Aberdeen City between 1981–84 and 2002–06 show a very similar picture although there is some evidence of a retraction from parts of the Buchan plain. As studies to discover the reasons for national declines continue, this change cannot be readily explained; the loss of invertebrates on agricultural land that has affected several other farmland birds may be partially responsible. At a local level, the influence of observer effort cannot be discounted.

Population and changes

Tetrad populations were estimated in five tetrads during 2002–06, at an average density of 0.85 pairs/km^2. Extrapolating to the 531 occupied tetrads in the North-East indicates a total population of 1,805 pairs. However, Jenkins & Watson (1999) found higher densities, up to 15 pairs/km^2, in some small woodland areas in Deeside, but it is not known how generally these higher densities apply. A conservative estimate is therefore 2,000–2,500 pairs but there is much uncertainty. No BBS trends can be calculated for Spotted Flycatchers in Scotland so it is not known to what extent the UK decline of 59% during 1994–2007 (Risely *et al.* 2008) has been replicated locally, but there is likely to have been a fall in numbers. The failure of rains in the Sahel region of Africa between 1983 and 1984 may well have been responsible for range, and presumably population, declines in the region between 1981–84 and 1988–91, when several 10-km squares lost their breeding birds (*BTO 2nd Atlas*).

Author: *David Parnaby*

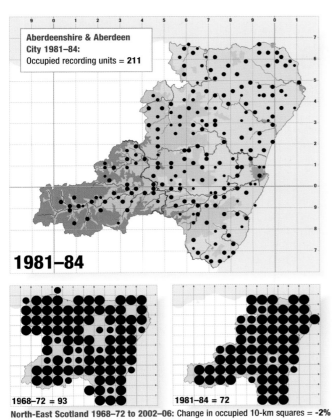

Aberdeenshire & Aberdeen City 1981–84:
Occupied recording units = 211

1981–84

1968–72 = 93   1981–84 = 72

North-East Scotland 1968–72 to 2002–06: Change in occupied 10-km squares = -2%

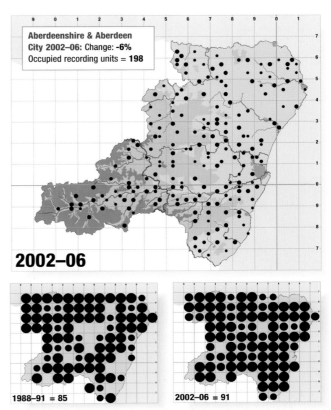

Aberdeenshire & Aberdeen City 2002–06: Change: **-6%**
Occupied recording units = **198**

2002–06

1988–91 = 85   2002–06 = 91

Robin
Erithacus rubecula

Very common resident and migrant breeder. Passage migrant. Estimated population in North-East Scotland: *100,000–130,000 pairs* (11% of Scottish population, 2% of UK)   Scottish BAP list

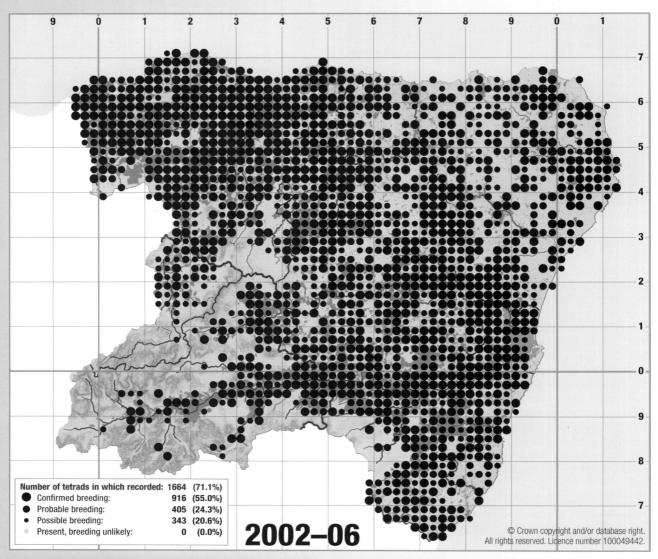

Number of tetrads in which recorded:	1664	(71.1%)
● Confirmed breeding:	916	(55.0%)
● Probable breeding:	405	(24.3%)
● Possible breeding:	343	(20.6%)
Present, breeding unlikely:	0	(0.0%)

2002–06

Habitat and breeding biology

Robins are found in a wide range of woodlands including broad-leaved and coniferous forests as well as copses and shelter belts. They also breed in farmland with hedgerows and in parks and gardens. Adults are territorial at all times of year and can be heard singing in most months except during the July–August moulting period when they become more secretive. In March and early April, females leave their winter territories and join males on their breeding territories. Nests are built on or near the ground, suburban birds often using man-made structures. The clutch of 4–6 eggs is usually laid in April and, in Fife at least, many pairs produce two, or even three, broods in a year (Cobb in *BS3*).

Scottish status and distribution

Robins are widespread and common throughout much of lowland Scotland but numbers decrease with altitude due to the lack of suitable vegetation cover. Densities are highest in south, central and eastern Scotland, and around the Moray Firth. The Scottish breeding population is currently estimated to fall within the range 900,000–1.25 million pairs (Cobb in *BS3*).

Robin, Sutherland, June 1992. © *Ed Duthie*

Status and distribution in North-East Scotland

As would be expected for this very common species, it was reported from most of lowland North-East Scotland with numbers thinning out between 400–500 m and absent from treeless moorland above this altitude. Although not found in some of the upper glens and straths of Deeside and Donside, where Heather moorland predominates, Robins were well recorded in the lower glens where birch woodland and scrub cover provide suitable habitat. In the Buchan plain of north-east Aberdeenshire, where open farmland predominates, there is a more patchy distribution with fewer reports of confirmed breeding. This reflects the lack of woodland and also, perhaps, difficulty in accessing suitable patches of habitat during fieldwork in arable areas. Distribution is also restricted in the extensive sand dunes of the eastern coastal fringe.

Changes in distribution

There is no evidence to suggest any major change in distribution since 1968–72. During that period, and also in 1988–91 and 2002–06, the number of occupied 10-km squares remained between 101–106 (*BTO 1st* and *2nd Atlases*). The number of occupied recording units in Aberdeenshire/Aberdeen City increased by 5% between 1981–84 and 2002–06 but this is as likely to reflect observer effort as any genuine increase in range.

Population and trends

The only measured density of Robin territories in North-East Scotland during 2002–06 was 57 in 5 km^2 around Harlaw, north-west of Inverurie. A few years earlier, 9–123 territories/km^2 were recorded in various scrub and woodland habitats in Deeside (Jenkins & Watson 1999). Woodland densities measured elsewhere in Scotland ranged from 10 pairs/km^2 in Scots Pine to as high as 170 pairs/km^2 in oakwoods, and there were 39 pairs/km^2 in conifer plantations in Northumberland (sources cited by Cobb in *BS3*). Applying averages from these numbers to relevant

Robin, Aboyne, June 2004. © *Harry Scott*

land cover types in the North-East (LC 2000 data) suggests a total population in the range 100,000–130,000 pairs. The BBS in Scotland revealed a 7% increase in the Robin population between 1994 and 2007 (Risely *et al.* 2008).

Author: *Rob Fuchs*

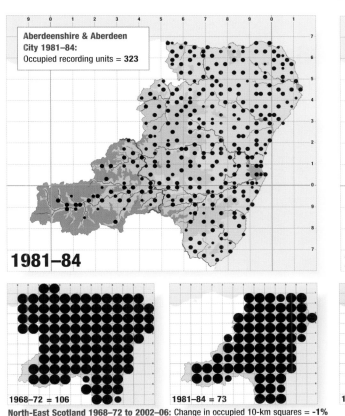

Aberdeenshire & Aberdeen City 1981–84:
Occupied recording units = 323

1981–84

1968–72 = 106

1981–84 = 73

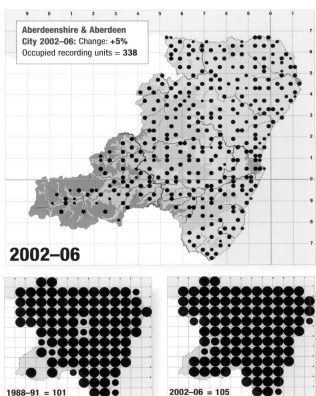

Aberdeenshire & Aberdeen City 2002–06: Change: +5%
Occupied recording units = 338

2002–06

1988–91 = 101

2002–06 = 105

North-East Scotland 1968–72 to 2002–06: Change in occupied 10-km squares = -1%

Bluethroat

Luscinia svecica

Probable breeder on one occasion. Passage migrant. Estimated population in North-East Scotland: usually 0 pairs

Schedule 1

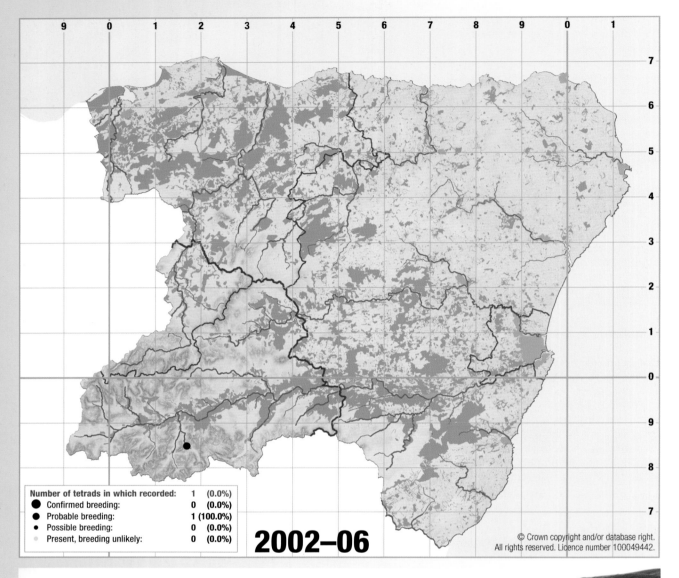

Number of tetrads in which recorded:	1	(0.0%)
● Confirmed breeding:	0	(0.0%)
● Probable breeding:	1	(100.0%)
• Possible breeding:	0	(0.0%)
Present, breeding unlikely:	0	(0.0%)

2002–06

Bluethroat habitat, Lochcallater Lodge, May 2009. © *Graham Rebecca*

Bluethroat, Finnmark, June 2009. © *Harry Scott*

Habitat and breeding biology
Confirmed breeding records in Scotland have been in wetlands with dense vegetation or in open Heather moorland with patches of Juniper (Harvey in *BS3*). The one record of probable breeding in North-East Scotland during the atlas period was in Glen Callater, an upland area with acid grassland, moorland and scattered scrub.

Scottish distribution and status
There have been only three records of confirmed breeding in Scotland: at Insh Marshes in Strathspey in 1968 and 1985 and near Inverness in 1995. Around 22 other possible or probable breeding records occurred between 1968 and 2004, with a tendency for single territorial males and breeding attempts to follow above average spring influxes (Harvey in *BS3*). Otherwise, the Bluethroat is a scarce annual passage migrant (usually fewer than 100 birds), mainly in spring in eastern parts of the country.

Distribution and status in North-East Scotland
The only record during the atlas period was of probable breeding - a male carrying foliage in its beak in early June 2003 near Lochcallater Lodge, south of Braemar (Harvey in *BS3*). This apparent breeding attempt followed a spring with no records of migrants in North-East Scotland. The only other possible breeding record in North-East Scotland was of a singing male in Glen Feardar, Upper Deeside on 31st

May 1985, which did follow a spring with a large influx of migrants (*NES 1st Atlas*). Generally, almost all records are of coastal migrants, mainly in the spring, and mostly of the Red-spotted Bluethroat subspecies *L. s. svecica*; the White-spotted Bluethroat *L. s. cyanecula* has occurred only three times in North-East Scotland. There have been only eight Bluethroat records in Moray, including a white-spotted bird at Orton on the early date of 20th March 1975. The remains of one red-spotted bird were found on 23rd May 1987 on the Cairn Gorm plateau (Cook 1992).

Changes in distribution
There have been insufficient breeding records to exhibit any possible changes, and there is no evidence of any change in the almost exclusively coastal location of migrants.

Population and trends
In Scotland, there is some evidence of an increase in the number of annual records of migrants, possibly linked to expansion of the Scandinavian breeding range (Harvey in *BS3*). This increase has been shared over the long term in North-east Scotland (Phillips 1997), but less so in the last ten years, where annual records of migrants have become extremely variable.

Author: *Ian Francis*

Redstart

Phoenicurus phoenicurus

Scarce summer migrant breeder. Passage migrant. Estimated population in North-East Scotland: 300–1,000 pairs (3% of Scottish population, <1% of UK

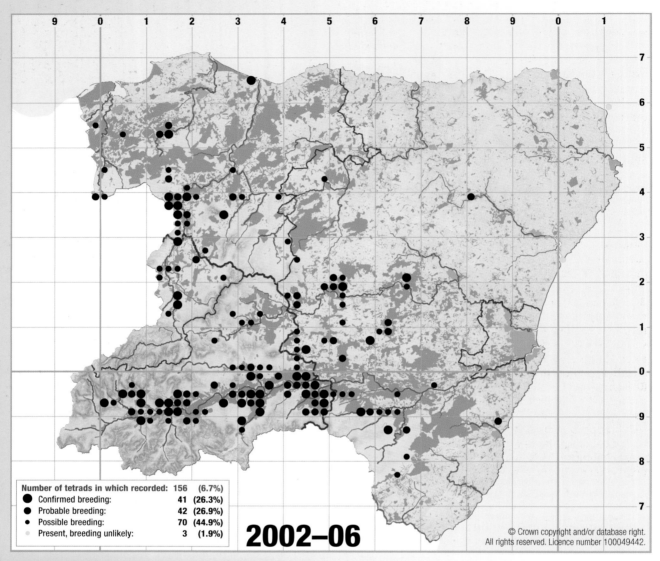

Number of tetrads in which recorded:	156	(6.7%)
● Confirmed breeding:	41	(26.3%)
● Probable breeding:	42	(26.9%)
● Possible breeding:	70	(44.9%)
· Present, breeding unlikely:	3	(1.9%)

2002–06

Redstart, Ballater, June 2002. © *John Chapman*

Habitat and breeding biology

Redstarts are associated with mature woodland, generally oak or pine, at middle altitude between 200–450 m in North-East Scotland. Preferred breeding woods have large trees and an open structure with little or no shrub layer, which allows better visibility and accessibility to insect prey (Lack & Venables 1939). They nest in natural tree holes, and also use nest boxes, which has boosted populations in some parts of Scotland. The clutch, usually of 5–7 eggs, is laid in May, followed by 12–14 days of incubation and a further 14–15 day fledging period. It is likely that some pairs raise second broods, which fledge in August (Wilson & Murray in *BS3*).

Scottish distribution and status

Redstarts are widely but sparsely distributed in mainland Scotland, avoiding the higher uplands and arable lowlands, where little suitable habitat exists. They are found at lower altitudes and in larger numbers in the west than in the east. Highest densities occur in Strathspey, the Great Glen, Argyll, the Trossachs, around Loch Lomond and along the upper Tweed. The Scottish population was estimated at 20,000–30,000 pairs in 2007 (Wilson & Murray in *BS3*). During 1994–2007, the UK population increased by 23% (Risely *et al.* 2008) although data specifically for Scotland are not available.

Distribution and status in North-East Scotland

The main concentrations of breeding Redstarts are in mid and upper Deeside, Strathspey and Strath Avon, with smaller numbers in lower Deeside and Donside. They occur very sparsely elsewhere. They are most widespread along Deeside from Aboyne to the Linn of Dee, where breeding was confirmed or probable in 46 tetrads compared with 37 in the rest of North-East Scotland. Most occupied habitat is at middle altitudes where cultivation is impossible and mature woodland survives. This has permitted pairs to occupy woods far up the glens beyond Braemar, up to 450 m altitude in Glens Luibeg, Derry and Quoich. Coastal breeding is exceptional in North-East Scotland; during 2002–06 this was confirmed only at Kingston, near the mouth of the Spey, and also probably took place near Stonehaven. Returning birds are back on territory, singing, from the middle of April onwards. Singing declines during nest-building, and as the breeding season progresses; Redstarts can then be surprisingly elusive which makes it difficult to survey their populations.

Changes in distribution

Although the number of occupied 10-km squares has remained broadly similar between 1968–72 (*BTO 1st Atlas*) and 2002–06 (with a dip in 1988–91 shown in the *BTO 2nd Atlas* likely to be due to reduced observer coverage), examination of the Aberdeenshire/Aberdeen City maps reveals a substantial expansion in range over the last 20 years. Deeside has remained the core area but the range has extended northwards and eastwards. In 1981–84 only one recording unit north of the latitude of Aberdeen contained Redstarts - in 2002–06 there were 23. The reasons for this change are uncertain, although variable observer effort may have had an impact. The availability of nest holes and suitably open forest habitats probably constrains the distribution but there may have been changes in grazing or forest management which have permitted an increased population to expand into sub-optimal habitats.

Redstart, Logie Coldstone, May 2005. © *Harry Scott*

Population and trends

During the early 1980s, densities in occupied mid Deeside woods ranged from 10–30 pairs/km^2 in pine and 10–25 pairs/km^2 in oak to 5–15 pairs/km^2 in birch (Buckland *et al.* 1990). Sites where Redstarts certainly, or probably, bred covered around 50 km^2 at that time, but a population estimate depends on the proportion of suitable habitat present in that area. If we assume 10–20 pairs/km^2 as an average density overall and that 10–25% of each recording unit was suitable, then the population of Aberdeenshire will have been between 50–250 pairs. Although UK BBS data indicate a significant increase in the Redstart population between 1994–2007 (Risely *et al.* 2008) there is inadequate Scottish information to reveal local trends. Assuming, therefore, that the density of Redstarts within the same types of habitat has not changed markedly between 1981–84 and 2002–06, then with breeding confirmed or probable in 83 tetrads (332 km^2) in North-East Scotland and 10–25% of this area having suitable habitat, a population of 332–1,660 pairs can be estimated. Given that tetrads are not habitat based, which the 1981–84 recording units were, the proportion of suitable habitat in tetrads, on which this population estimate is based, is likely is to be lower. A reasonable estimate therefore probably lies in the range 300–1,000 pairs.

Author: *Paul Doyle*

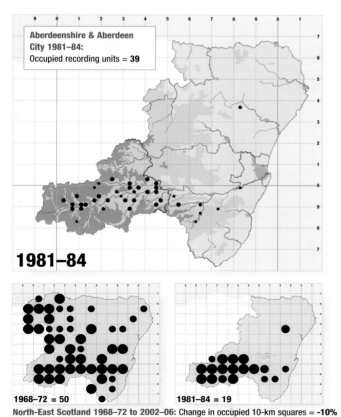

1981–84

1968–72 = 50   1981–84 = 19

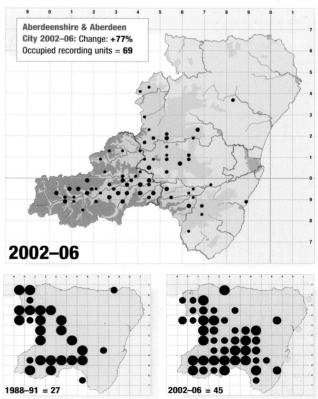

2002–06

1988–91 = 27   2002–06 = 45

Aberdeenshire & Aberdeen City 1981–84:
Occupied recording units = **39**

Aberdeenshire & Aberdeen City 2002–06: Change: **+77%**
Occupied recording units = **69**

North-East Scotland 1968–72 to 2002–06: Change in occupied 10-km squares = -10%

Whinchat

Saxicola rubetra

Scarce summer migrant breeder. Passage migrant. Estimated population in North-East Scotland: **130–200 pairs** (<1% of Scottish and UK populations)

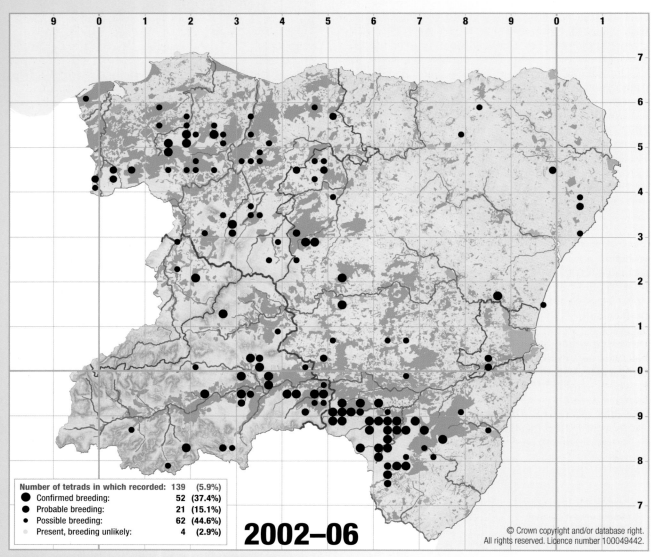

Number of tetrads in which recorded:	139	(5.9%)
● Confirmed breeding:	52	(37.4%)
● Probable breeding:	21	(15.1%)
● Possible breeding:	62	(44.6%)
Present, breeding unlikely:	4	(2.9%)

2002–06

Whinchat, Durris, June 1983. © *Rab Rae*

Habitat and breeding biology

The Whinchat is a summer visitor to open-ground habitats. Singing posts are an important component of its home range so Bracken, Gorse, Heather, small trees and fence lines are characteristic. The ground cover of a typical mid Deeside breeding area was made up of 70% Heather and 30% Bracken, with well-scattered small Scots Pines and Rowans. There were two fence lines and some Juniper on the fringes of the site, which was shared with Stonechats (pers. obs.). Young conifer plantations can be important habitats, especially in the uplands, although such areas lose their attractiveness when the forest reaches the thicket stage. Whinchats avoid intensely farmed areas. They generally return to their breeding areas during the last week in April and the first in May. Nests are usually built in patches of low scrub, with 5.8 eggs being the average clutch size in a study in Ayrshire (Gray 1974).

Scottish distribution and status

Whinchats are most numerous in the south and west of Scotland, with strongholds in the Borders, Argyll and especially Dumfries & Galloway. They have declined markedly in eastern counties with the intensification of lowland agriculture. The most recent Scottish population estimate is 15,000–20,000 pairs (Shaw in *BS3*).

The Breeding Birds of North-East Scotland

Distribution and status in North-East Scotland

The Whinchat's stronghold in North-East Scotland is mid Deeside and the moors to the south such as around Glen Dye. Here, there are large open areas with the required song posts and habitat mix that the species prefers in northern Britain. Less intensively managed grouse moors, and areas where birch and Scots Pine have started to regenerate, often provide this mix, albeit temporarily (Shaw 2009). They are well-scattered over the Moray moors and there are small numbers between Huntly and Keith, and around the Cabrach/Rhynie area. Elsewhere, there are very few Whinchats and they are virtually absent from the agricultural plain of central and north-east Aberdeenshire.

Changes in distribution

This species was found in exactly the same number of recording units in Aberdeenshire/Aberdeen City in 1981–84 and in 2002–06 although breeding was confirmed at more sites in 1981–84 (*NES 1st Atlas*). This trend is confirmed by examining data at the 10-km square level where the number of occupied squares remained at 49–50 in 1968–72 (*BTO 1st Atlas*), 1988–91 (*BTO 2nd Atlas*) and 2002–06, but the number of squares where breeding was confirmed fell by around one third in 2002–06 compared to the earlier surveys. There have been considerable declines in upper Deeside over the last 20 years due, perhaps, to conifer plantations reaching the thicket stage and to extensive burning of Heather. There has also been a substantial range reduction in areas close to the Moray border, perhaps for similar reasons. However, these factors do not explain the possible increase in mid Deeside. This may be a consequence of improved coverage or may be due to an increase in areas of birch and pine regeneration.

Population and trends

Although Whinchats are reasonably easy to detect, they have a patchy distribution and this makes for difficulty in estimating the population. In 1988–91 the population density was estimated at 0.4–0.8 pairs/tetrad (*BTO 2nd Atlas*). A higher density of 5 pairs/tetrad was applied in South-east Scotland in 1988–94 (Murray *et al*. 1998) but this is certainly too high for most of the current North-East Scotland range. There are no published BBS data for the Whinchat in Scotland alone, but in the UK as a whole a decline of 26% has been detected over the period 1994–2007 (Risely *et al*. 2008). It might be reasonable to adopt a population density of 1 pair/tetrad where breeding during 2002–06 was possible or probable, and 1–2 pairs/tetrad where breeding was confirmed. This suggests a total somewhere within the range of 130–200 pairs in North-East Scotland.

Author: *Ken Shaw*

Whinchat, Glen Finglas, July 2008. © *Gina Prior*

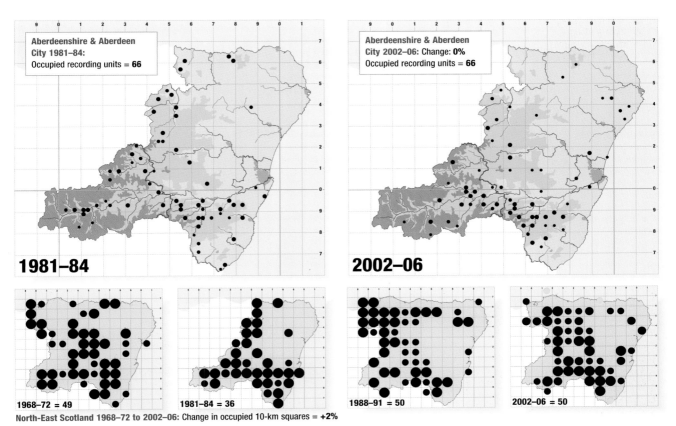

1981–84

Aberdeenshire & Aberdeen City 1981–84:
Occupied recording units = **66**

2002–06

Aberdeenshire & Aberdeen City 2002–06: Change: **0%**
Occupied recording units = **66**

1968–72 = 49   1981–84 = 36   1988–91 = 50   2002–06 = 50

North-East Scotland 1968–72 to 2002–06: Change in occupied 10-km squares = **+2%**

Stonechat

Saxicola torquatus

Scarce resident and migrant breeder. Estimated population in North-East Scotland: **450–1,000** pairs (4% of Scottish population, <4% of UK)

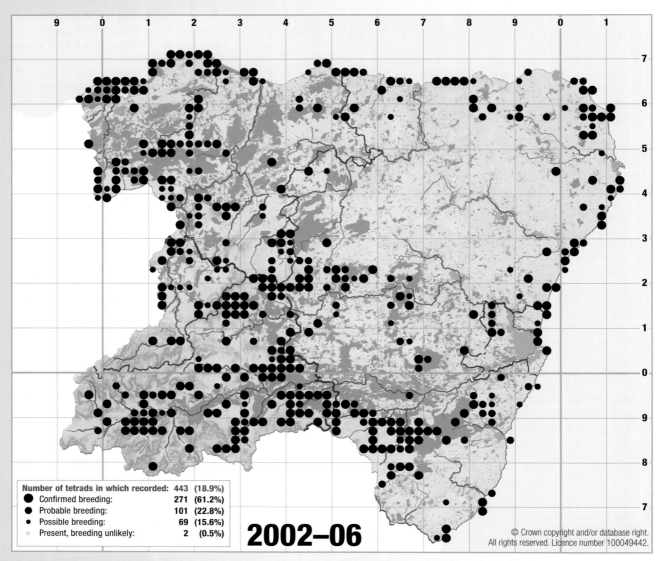

Number of tetrads in which recorded: 443 (18.9%)
- ● Confirmed breeding: 271 (61.2%)
- ● Probable breeding: 101 (22.8%)
- • Possible breeding: 69 (15.6%)
- ∘ Present, breeding unlikely: 2 (0.5%)

2002–06

Habitat and breeding biology

Stonechats breed in thick cover, typically in Gorse, Heather and in young plantations with dense undergrowth. At coastal sites, they often frequent golf courses where the short grass sward combined with the 'rough' is ideal foraging and nesting habitat. They often use prominent perches such as fence posts or phone wires from which to sing, display and seek insect prey. The breeding season may be protracted with triple brooding noted on several occasions (pers. obs.). In the 1990s, egg laying was recorded in mid-late March at the Forest of Birse, where snow cover can often occur at this time (pers. obs.), and breeding may continue until July (Thorpe in *BS3*).

Scottish distribution and status

Stonechats breed over most of Scotland but are scarce in the agricultural eastern lowlands and in Shetland. They are most numerous in southern and western coastal areas including the Outer Hebrides. Populations can crash and recover in response to winter severity, hence the wide limits of the most recent Scottish population estimate: 11,600–29,700 pairs in 2000 (Thorpe in *BS3*). BBS data indicate a 254% increase during the period 1994–2007 (Risely *et al*. 2008) which reflects the response of a prolific breeder in the absence of recent prolonged cold winters, prior to 2009–10.

Distribution and status in North-East Scotland

During 2002–06, Stonechats were widely distributed at both coastal and inland sites across North-East Scotland. They are, however, almost absent from intensively farmed areas such as the Buchan plain due, almost exclusively, to the lack of suitable breeding habitat. For similar reasons they are absent from extensive tracts of mature forestry. However, clear-felled areas within such forests are readily

Stonechat, Inverness, July 2006. © *Derek McGinn*

The Breeding Birds of North-East Scotland

Stonechat, Birse, May 2005. © *John Chapman*

colonised by Stonechats; a situation observed in the sandy coastal forests of Moray, such as Culbin, Roseisle and Lossie (M. Cook pers. comm.). The distribution map reflects areas where Gorse, Heather and young plantations are to be found, and this largely determines the Stonechat's range. On the moors they only occupy the lower ground where patches of scrub are frequent. They do, however, populate suitable riverside habitat along the glens and in this way penetrate far into the uplands such as along Glens Avon, Derry and Geusachan to altitudes of over 500 m. Ringing has shown that, at the end of the breeding season, some birds disperse to the coast (Thorpe in *BS3*).

Changes in distribution

Between 1968–72 and 1981–84 there was a considerable decrease in the breeding range in the North-East. This was primarily related to a series of hard winters which had virtually eliminated the coastal breeding population (*NES 1st Atlas*, Cook 1992). The situation was virtually unchanged in 1988–91 when breeding was proved in only 14 10-km squares, of which ten were in Moray (*BTO 2nd Atlas*). By 2002–06, there was a substantial expansion in the breeding range of Stonechats. The most significant gains have been at inland sites in Donside and in the upland range west of Ballater. In 1981–84, no breeding was recorded west of Ballater whereas in 2002–06, following a series of relatively mild winters, there were 48 recording units in this area which contained at least one pair. The coastal population is also now well re-established from the 'crash' of the early 1980s, with 30 recording units occupied in Aberdeenshire/Aberdeen City compared to only nine in 1981–84.

Population and trends

Stonechat populations can be dramatically affected by a succession of severe winters (Thorpe in *BS3*). Attempts to estimate current populations or trends are consequently very difficult, often resulting in a wide range being given. In the North-East, the substantial range expansion since the 1980s is indicative, also, of a recovery in breeding numbers. A series of relatively mild winters in the late 1990s and early 2000s was a major contributory factor. Breeding at inland sites has probably also increased because birds have been able to remain on territory throughout the winter, due to milder conditions, and therefore commence breeding earlier. Given the species' ability to raise two, or even three, broods in a season, the breeding population has the capacity to expand relatively quickly. In North-East Scotland just before, and during, the 2000–06 atlas period the population was possibly as large as it has ever been, with *MNBR* 2000 reporting "an excellent season with 51 pairs located, the best on record". During 2002–06, Stonechats were proved to breed in 272 tetrads, and may have done so in a further 172. If we assume one pair in each tetrad in the latter category and 1–3 where breeding was confirmed then a population of 450–1,000 pairs is likely.

Author: *Andrew Thorpe*

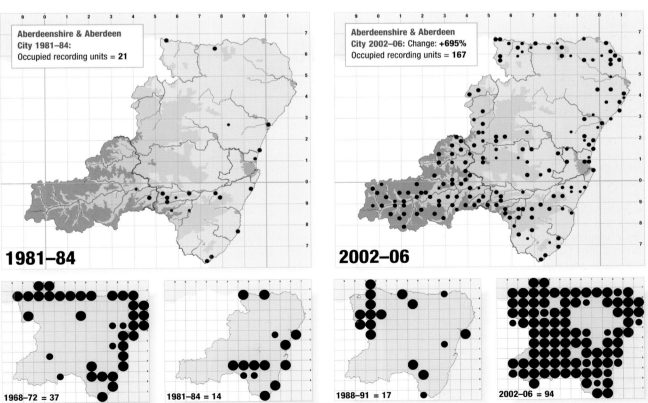

Aberdeenshire & Aberdeen City 1981–84:
Occupied recording units = 21

1981–84

Aberdeenshire & Aberdeen City 2002–06: Change: +695%
Occupied recording units = 167

2002–06

1968–72 = 37

1981–84 = 14

1988–91 = 17

2002–06 = 94

North-East Scotland 1968–72 to 2002–06: Change in occupied 10-km squares = +154%

Wheatear

Oenanthe oenanthe

Common summer migrant breeder. Passage migrant. Estimated population in North-East Scotland:
2,000–3,000 pairs (4% of Scottish population, <4% of UK)

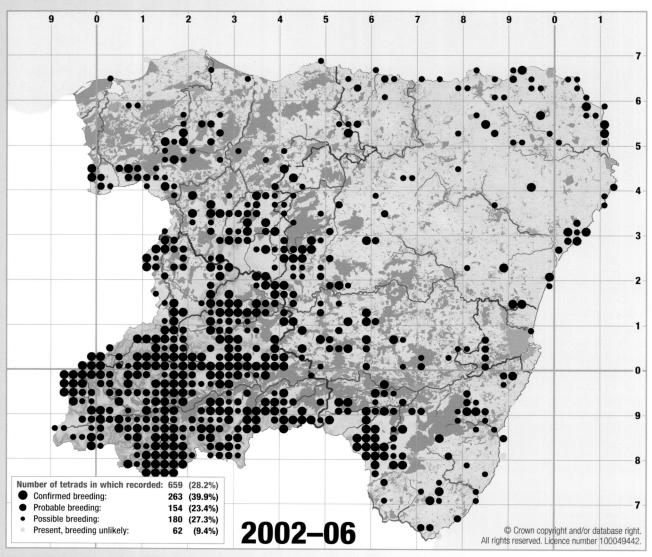

Number of tetrads in which recorded: 659 (28.2%)
- ● Confirmed breeding: 263 (39.9%)
- ● Probable breeding: 154 (23.4%)
- • Possible breeding: 180 (27.3%)
- · Present, breeding unlikely: 62 (9.4%)

2002–06

Habitat and breeding biology

Wheatears require open country where land management is of low intensity. They need areas of short turf for feeding, often in the form of short-cropped vegetation grazed by Rabbits and sheep. For nest sites they use crevices amongst boulders, stones, mountain scree and stone walls, or they can use holes in the ground such as Rabbit burrows. In Scotland, Wheatears are site faithful, returning to sites close to the previous year's nest (Shaw in *BS3*). Song and display begin when they arrive on the breeding grounds in early April. The usual clutch of 5–6 eggs is not laid until May, with young fledging by mid June or later (*NES 1st Atlas*). Scottish Wheatears, which belong to subspecies *O. o. oenanthe*, are single-brooded. Juveniles can appear at non-breeding areas on the coast by early or mid July (*MNBR* 1990, 2003).

Scottish distribution and status

Wheatears are widely distributed throughout most of mainland and island Scotland. Breeding birds reach St Kilda in the west and Unst in the north of Shetland, but they are absent from large portions of the Borders, the Central Lowlands and a broad eastern coastal strip stretching from the Firth of Forth to the Moray Firth. The

most recent estimate for the Scottish population is in the range of 35,000–95,000 pairs (Shaw in *BS3*).

Distribution and status in North-East Scotland

The Wheatear is a common migrant breeder with the first spring arrivals usually appearing in the last week of March or the first week of April. Birds are still widespread in inland breeding areas in late July, while migrants can be seen inland as well as on the coast in August, September and October. During 2002–06, Wheatears were proved to breed in 263 tetrads, with probable breeding in 154 tetrads and possible breeding in a further 180. Breeding pairs were found from sea-level to the high ground of the Cairngorms. Only a thin scattering of pairs are located around the coastal fringe, such as at Loch of Strathbeg and the Forvie area, with the main population between 300–1,200 m above sea level, concentrated in the south-western uplands of North-East Scotland. Although this distribution mirrors the main areas of high ground in the Grampian Mountains it also reflects an avoidance of intensively-managed ground such as agriculture and forestry.

Wheatear, Glen Clunie, May 2009. © *Ed Duthie*

Changes in distribution

In terms of occupied 10-km squares there has been little change between 1968–72 (*BTO 1st Atlas*) and 2002–06 but there has been a very marked decline in coastal breeding in Moray. In 1968–72 this was proved in all nine coastal squares in Moray, but this had fallen to only two by 1988–91. In fact no breeding has taken place along the Moray coast since 1990 and 1991, when a single pair bred at Strathlene (Buckie). The reasons for this are unclear; there has apparently been no overall reduction in the Wheatear population as the number of occupied recording units in Aberdeenshire/Aberdeen City has increased by over 50% during 1981–84 to 2002–06. Furthermore, coastal breeding in Aberdeenshire has increased over this period.

Population and trends

There has been no recent local survey work upon which to base a North-East Scotland population estimate. Assuming that the density in our area is similar to that in Lothian and Borders we could adopt their density of 2 pairs/km^2 (Murray *et al.* 1998) which translates to 8 pairs/tetrad. This suggests a total of 2,128 pairs in the 266 tetrads where breeding was confirmed. If we further assume that half of the tetrads reported as possibly containing breeding Wheatears did in fact contain one pair, and that all 'probable' tetrads contained a single pair, then the total rises to 2,348 pairs, realistically within the range 2,000–3,000 pairs. In view of the fact that Wheatears breed at relatively low density over much of their North-East Scotland range, a suggestion of 4% of the Scottish population may not be unreasonable. Scottish BBS data over the period 1991–2007 indicate a 24% population increase (Risely *et al.* 2008), but there is inadequate information to confirm this trend in the North-East.

Author: *Dave Pullan*

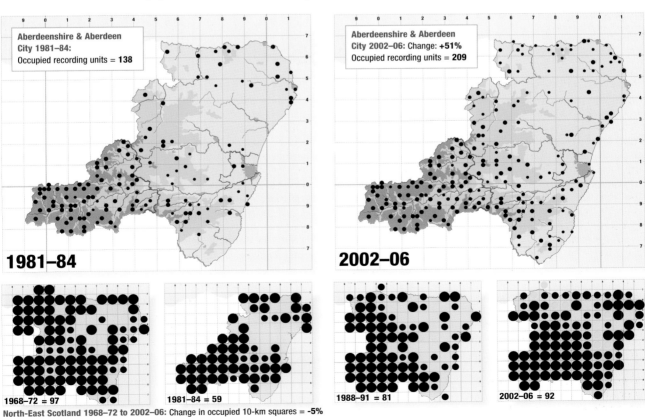

Aberdeenshire & Aberdeen City 1981–84:
Occupied recording units = **138**

1981–84

Aberdeenshire & Aberdeen City 2002–06: Change: +51%
Occupied recording units = **209**

2002–06

1968–72 = 97   1981–84 = 59   1988–91 = 81   2002–06 = 92

North-East Scotland 1968–72 to 2002–06: Change in occupied 10-km squares = **-5%**

Pied Flycatcher

Ficedula hypoleuca

Very rare summer migrant breeder. Passage migrant. Estimated population in North-East Scotland: *1–2 pairs* (<1% of Scottish and UK populations)

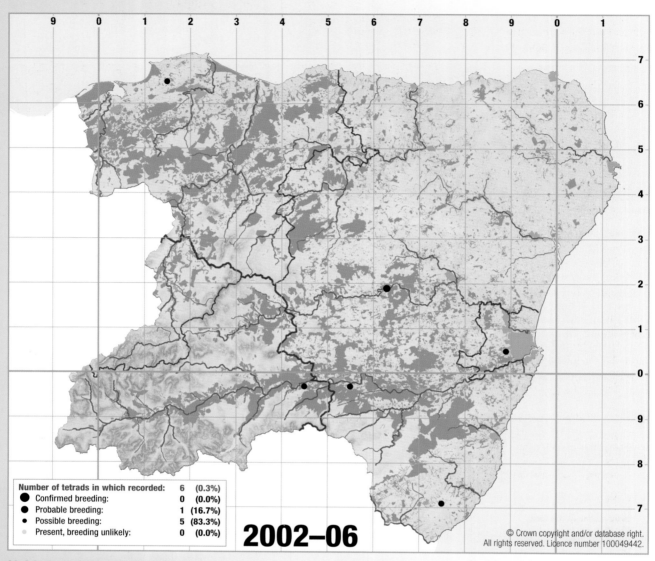

Number of tetrads in which recorded: 6   (0.3%)
- ● Confirmed breeding: 0   (0.0%)
- ● Probable breeding: 1   (16.7%)
- • Possible breeding: 5   (83.3%)
- · Present, breeding unlikely: 0   (0.0%)

2002–06

Habitat and breeding biology

In Scotland, Pied Flycatchers breed in mature broad-leaved woodlands, typically oakwoods but sometimes in birch-dominated woodland. Males arrive in breeding areas in late April and the first half of May, females a little later. Natural tree cavities or disused woodpecker holes are used for nesting, and they take readily to nest boxes. Clutches usually contain 5–8 eggs and are started in the second or third week in May. Incubation and fledging periods both average about two weeks and most chicks have left the nest by the end of June (Metcalfe in *BS3*).

Scottish distribution and status

Pied Flycatchers were first recorded breeding in Scotland in 1864 and slowly extended their range over the next hundred years. In most parts of the country, however, they continue to be only occasional breeders. In recent years the main concentrations have been in Dumfries & Galloway, Ayrshire, Perth & Kinross and west central Scotland. The total Scottish population is around 300–400 pairs (Metcalfe in *BS3*).

Distribution and status in North-East Scotland

The first recorded breeding took place near Aberlour (Moray) where single pairs nested in 1968 and 1969 (Cook 1992). There were no further records until 1981 when the first breeding took place on Deeside. The nest was in a natural hole in an Alder along the River Dee between Dinnet and Ballater. In 1985 a mate-less female laid infertile eggs in a nest box in an oak wood at Ballater and in 1986 a pair bred successfully at the same site. In 1988, three pairs used boxes in the Ballater oakwood. In 1996 one pair bred at Inverey near Braemar and in 1997 pairs did so at Ballater and Inverey. In 1998 one pair bred at Inverey and there were two pairs in the nest boxes at Ballater. There was one pair at Ballater in 2000 but there was no further proof of breeding in North-East Scotland during the period 1999 to 2009 (R. Duncan pers. comm., Metcalfe in *BS3*). During 2002–06, single birds were found in possible breeding habitat in six tetrads; the bird near Keig (Alford) showed signs of anxiety but otherwise there was no suggestion of breeding. In subsequent years, one pair almost certainly bred at Ballater in 2007 and a single male was present there in 2008 (R. Duncan pers. comm.). Also in 2008, a single bird was near Elgin in late May. Drifted migrants on passage to and from Scandinavia make landfall on the coast in small numbers in spring and autumn. Some of these birds may penetrate inland and account for the not-infrequent appearance of apparently unmated birds in suitable breeding habitat.

Population and trends

Pied Flycatchers are clearly rare breeders in North-East Scotland but they are relatively inconspicuous and it is quite possible that a few pairs go undetected. There may be an annual breeding population of one or two pairs. A high proportion of the Scottish population now uses nest boxes and their past use on Deeside suggests that the most likely way to attract a more permanent breeding population might be more extensive provision of nest boxes in oakwoods.

Author: *Martin Cook*

Pied Flycatcher, Oulu, Finland, June 2007. © *Allan Perkins*

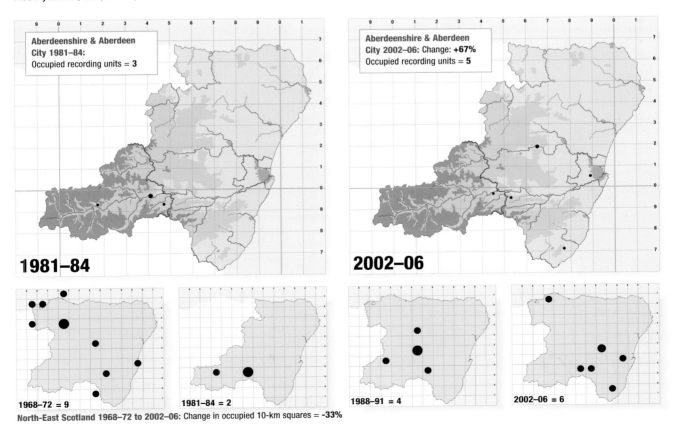

Aberdeenshire & Aberdeen City 1981–84:
Occupied recording units = **3**

1981–84

Aberdeenshire & Aberdeen City 2002–06: Change: **+67%**
Occupied recording units = **5**

2002–06

1968–72 = 9

1981–84 = 2

1988–91 = 4

2002–06 = 6

North-East Scotland 1968–72 to 2002–06: Change in occupied 10-km squares = -33%

Dunnock

Prunella modularis

Very common resident. Estimated population in North-East Scotland: ***50,000–80,000 territories*** (18% of Scottish population, 3% of UK)

UK BAP list

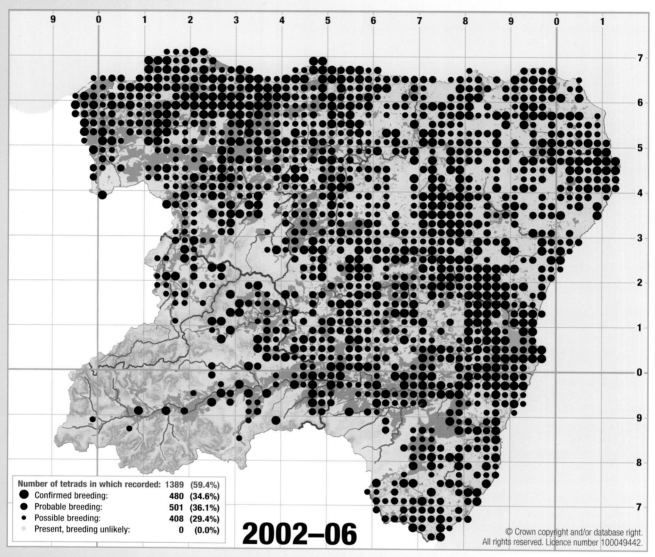

Number of tetrads in which recorded: 1389 (59.4%)

● Confirmed breeding:	480	(34.6%)
● Probable breeding:	501	(36.1%)
● Possible breeding:	408	(29.4%)
Present, breeding unlikely:	0	(0.0%)

2002–06

Dunnock, Alford, June 2008. © Ian Francis

Habitat and breeding biology

The Dunnock is mainly a ground-feeding insectivore found on the edges of a variety of habitats such as open woodland with dense understory. It is mainly a lowland species, common in gardens and farmland where overgrown hedges provide cover. They are absent from open Heather moorland and the high uplands. The Dunnock is unusual among British passerines because both males and females defend territories, and pairs form where these territories overlap. Polyandrous trios (two males and one female) can occur when a female's territory overlaps with those of two males (Davies 1992). Nests are placed 20–100 cm above ground and females typically have 2–3 broods per year.

Scottish distribution and status

Two subspecies of Dunnock breed in Scotland; *hebridium* in the far west of the mainland and in the Inner and Outer Hebrides, and *occidentalis* elsewhere. Dunnocks are widely distributed across the whole of lowland Scotland, with higher numbers in the south and east (Robinson in *BS3*). As Dunnocks do not form traditional territorial breeding pairs it is particularly difficult to assess breeding population size but there are estimated to be 290,000 to

430,000 'pairs' in Scotland, of which nearly three-quarters are *occidentalis* (Robinson in *BS3*).

Distribution and status in North-East Scotland
The highest density of breeding Dunnocks occurs in areas with scrubby cover and overgrown hedgerows which are still common habitats throughout the lowlands of North-East Scotland. However, as birds of habitat margins they are generally absent from dense forests and from coastal sand dunes such as parts of Forvie. Breeding was not confirmed above 450 m, probably due to an absence of appropriate cover on moorland. Densities appear greatest around Aberdeen City, up the Don valley to Inverurie, and beyond to Turriff, as well as in the Moray lowlands. Intensification of farming in the Buchan plain, with consequent removal of suitable breeding and foraging habitat, may help to explain the patchy occupation of this part of Aberdeenshire.

Changes in distribution
The distribution of the Dunnock has remained relatively stable on a 10-km square level since 1968–72 (*BTO 1st Atlas*). There was, however, a small range retraction in 1988–91 (*BTO 2nd Atlas*) which may be attributed to the level of coverage rather than to the absence of birds. There was a 7% increase in occupied recording units in Aberdeenshire/Aberdeen City between 1981–84 and 2002–06; the overall distribution has remained broadly similar, with the increase due to infilling of the existing range, although Dunnocks now appear rather more widespread in the west of the region.

Population and trends
Data from various sources (*NES 1st Atlas*, Jenkins & Watson 1999, Murray *et al*. 1998, *BS3*) suggest that densities of 15–20 territories/km^2 in woodland and up to 60 territories/km^2 in rural and suburban gardens may be applicable to North-East Scotland. Applying these values, and 5–10 territories/km^2 in farmland, to relevant land cover

Dunnock, Airyhall, July 1970. © *John Young*

areas (LC 2000 data) produces a North-East estimate of about 50,000–80,000 occupied territories. Scottish BBS data indicate a 40% increase in the population over the period 1994–2007 (Risely *et al*. 2008). This increase follows a period of apparent decline in the 1970s and 1980s. Factors affecting population size are complex - changes in climate, clutch size and habitat modification may all be implicated (Robinson in *BS3*).

Author: *Jenny Lennon*

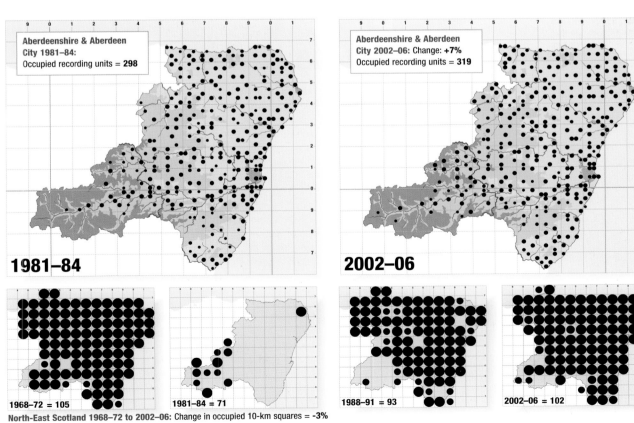

Aberdeenshire & Aberdeen City 1981–84:
Occupied recording units = **298**

1981–84

Aberdeenshire & Aberdeen City 2002–06: Change: +7%
Occupied recording units = **319**

2002–06

1968–72 = 105   1981–84 = 71   1988–91 = 93   2002–06 = 102

North-East Scotland 1968–72 to 2002–06: Change in occupied 10-km squares = -3%

House Sparrow

Passer domesticus

Very common resident. Estimated population in North-East Scotland: *50,000–70,000 pairs* (8% of Scottish population, 2% of UK)

Red list; UK BAP list

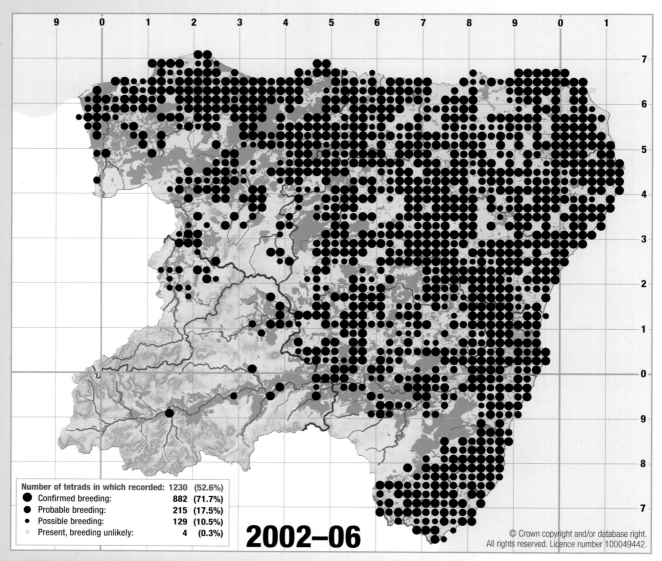

Number of tetrads in which recorded:	1230	(52.6%)
● Confirmed breeding:	882	(71.7%)
● Probable breeding:	215	(17.5%)
● Possible breeding:	129	(10.5%)
● Present, breeding unlikely:	4	(0.3%)

2002–06

House Sparrow, Fife, April 2007. © *John Anderson*

Habitat and breeding biology

Throughout their range in North-East Scotland, House Sparrows live in close association with people in cities, towns and villages as well as in more isolated rural communities, dwellings and hill farms. Studies elsewhere have shown that they breed and survive more successfully in suburban areas where nest sites are plentiful and there are sufficient green areas to provide insect food for the young (Summers-Smith 1988). Nests are usually built in cavities in buildings, typically beneath the eaves, but occasionally the untidy, dome-shaped structures are built in hedges or among similar dense vegetation. Nest boxes are readily used. Egg laying begins in late April or early May with first young on the wing a month later. Two or three broods may be raised in a season.

Scottish distribution and status

Reflecting their close association with human habitation, the highest densities of House Sparrows in Scotland are found in the central lowlands, up the east coast to the south side of the Moray Firth and in Orkney. Following a decline in the 1970s and 1980s, albeit less marked in Scotland than in some other areas of Britain, House Sparrow numbers have increased by 30% over the period 1994–2007 (Risely *et al.* 2008). In 2007 the Scottish population was considered to fall within the broad range of 600,000–900,000 pairs (Dott in *BS3*).

Distribution and status in North-East Scotland

House Sparrows are resident breeders throughout the agricultural lowlands of North-East Scotland and in human settlements of all sizes. Hill farms, up to an altitude of *c*.350 m may also have a colony. They are otherwise absent from the uplands, as they are from extensive tracts of forested ground at all levels. Close examination of the map suggests a patchy distribution in some parts of the lowland range such as the Buchan plain. Here, some tetrads contain only one or two farms and a few birds may easily be missed; or they may be genuinely absent. On some Buchan farms, Tree Sparrows are more numerous than House Sparrows (H. Maggs pers. comm.). Even in apparently more evenly occupied areas, such as the Laich of Moray, a tetrad map can conceal what is in effect a clumped distribution with a colony of House Sparrows around a small human community amid a broad swathe of unoccupied fields and woodland.

Changes in distribution

A comparison of the 1981–84 and 2002–06 maps for Aberdeenshire/Aberdeen City reveals a small, but perhaps significant, difference. From the Ballater area westwards, House Sparrows were found in 18 recording units in 1981–84 but that number had halved to only nine by 2002–06. This may be a genuine reflection of a retraction from marginal habitats such as hill farms, a trend also noted in Lothian, Borders and Ayrshire (Dott in *BS3*). The abandonment of these farms may be linked to changes in agricultural practice, resulting in fewer stubble and weedy 'neep' fields that were once a source of the seeds upon which sparrows relied for winter survival.

Population and trends

No detailed studies have been carried out on the relative numbers of House Sparrows in different habitats in North-

House Sparrow, Newburgh, July 1981. © *John Massie*

East Scotland and this, combined with recent abundance changes, makes a reliable population estimate difficult to calculate. Two recent density estimates from rural areas are of about 50 pairs in 5 km² to the north of Inverurie and about 55 pairs in 4 km² around Clochan (Moray). From this tiny sample a mean density of 48 pairs/tetrad might be derived and if this number is applied to all of the 1,235 tetrads in which House Sparrows were recorded during 2002–06 then a population estimate of 59,280 pairs results. Realistically, all that can be said is that the population is likely to fall within the range of 50,000–70,000 pairs. If suburban densities are considerably higher than the rural density upon which this calculation is based, then the true figure may be closer to the top of this range. Set against a Scottish estimate of 600,000–900,000 pairs this is not unreasonable. If House Sparrow numbers in North-East Scotland have followed the all-Scotland trend then there will have been some decrease during the final quarter of the 20th century. There is, however, no suggestion in the North-East Scotland data from the BBS survey for 1994–2006 of the substantial population increase reported for Scotland as a whole; but the local sample size is too small to draw firm conclusions.

Author: *Martin Cook*

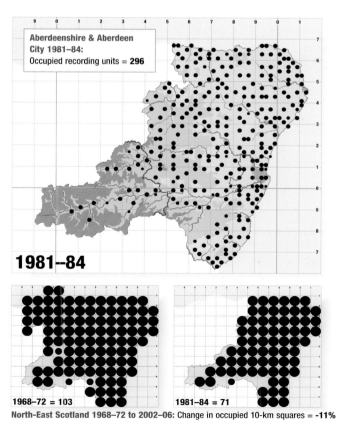

Aberdeenshire & Aberdeen City 1981–84:
Occupied recording units = **296**

1981–84

1968–72 = 103

1981–84 = 71

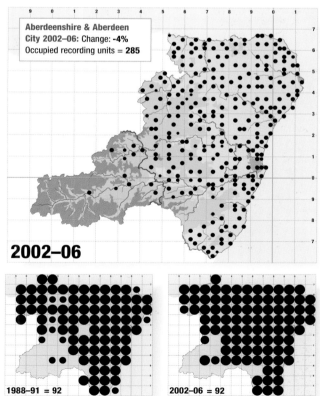

Aberdeenshire & Aberdeen City 2002–06: Change: **-4%**
Occupied recording units = **285**

2002–06

1988–91 = 92

2002–06 = 92

North-East Scotland 1968–72 to 2002–06: Change in occupied 10-km squares = **-11%**

Tree Sparrow

Passer montanus

Common resident. Estimated population in North-East Scotland: **2,500–3,500 pairs** (47% of Scottish population, 4% of UK)

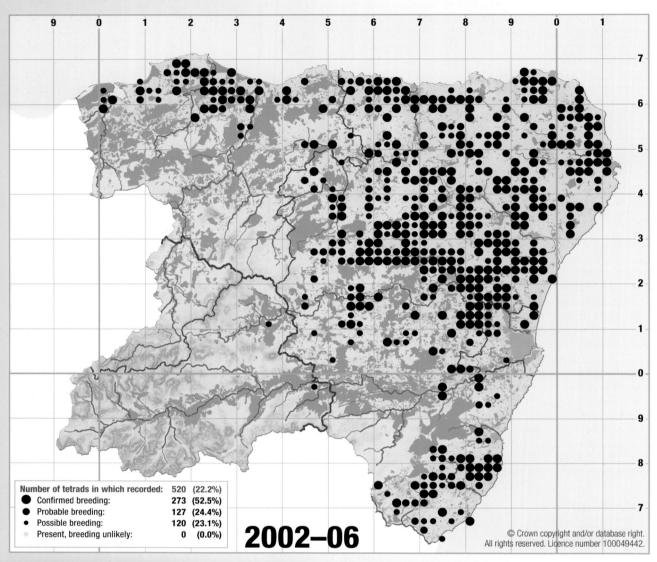

Number of tetrads in which recorded:	520	(22.2%)
● Confirmed breeding:	273	(52.5%)
● Probable breeding:	127	(24.4%)
● Possible breeding:	120	(23.1%)
Present, breeding unlikely:	0	(0.0%)

2002–06

Tree Sparrow, New Deer, January 2011. © *Allan Perkins*

Habitat and breeding biology

Tree Sparrows occupy lowland mixed or arable farming landscapes with scattered copses, open woodland, or hedgerows with large trees. They are semi-colonial, nesting in holes in trees or buildings, nest boxes, and occasionally in dense thorny bushes or even the underside of active Buzzard or Osprey nests. Most pairs rear 2–3 broods, laying clutches of 3–6 eggs from mid April to late July. Incubation lasts for 11–14 days and young fledge at 15–20 days old. The chicks' diet consists mainly of invertebrates, from midges and spiders to larger items such as beetles and caterpillars (Field *et al.* 2008). After fledging, juveniles often flock to feed on weed seeds and ripening cereal grains.

Scottish distribution and status

Tree Sparrows are generally scarce but can be locally common, and are found predominantly in the eastern and central lowlands, around the Moray Firth, and parts of the south-west. In the 1970s, they were much more widespread, with populations as far north and west as Shetland and the Outer Hebrides, including St Kilda. Following severe declines, the Scottish population is now approximately 4,600–8,100 pairs (Coates in *BS3*).

Tree Sparrow, Parkhill, January 2008. © *Ed Duthie*

Distribution and status in North-East Scotland

Locally common in suitable habitat, Tree Sparrows were recorded in 520 tetrads, 22% of those surveyed. They were found on 37 of 39 farms monitored in an RSPB study in Buchan, Moray and Kincardineshire in summers 2003–06. The areas of main distribution lie to the north and east of a line from Aberdeen to Elgin, and in the coastal farmlands south of Stonehaven and west of Elgin. Large gaps in range occur where unsuitable habitat dominates, such as in Aberdeen City, Sands of Forvie and Moss of Cruden, and heavily wooded areas such as those around Keith and Huntly. At the western edge of the range, populations are found in Deeside and Donside around Drumoak, Crathes, Tornaveen, and Alford, with outlying records as far west as Aboyne, Kildrummy and Strathdon. Colonies vary in size from single pairs to loose groups of 10–15 pairs, and they readily take to nestboxes, where densities can be high.

Changes in distribution

One characteristic of the species is that colonies often appear for a few years then disappear, for reasons that are unclear. However, an expansion was reported in range during the 1970s–early 1980s (*NES 1st Atlas*), and this has continued. The number of occupied recording units increased massively by 174% between 1981–84 and 2002–06. North-western Buchan and areas west of Banff are now occupied, and a large gap between St Cyrus and lower Deeside has been bridged. There has also been a westward expansion in Donside, although birds were recorded in some of these areas during winter 1981–84. Many other gaps in Buchan and Moray have also been filled.

Population and trends

There is no BBS trend for Scotland but, in the UK as a whole, the population has at least been stable, with indication of an increase, during 1994–2007 (Risely *et al.* 2008) following severe declines since the 1970s. In Scotland, recent declines in regions such as Borders, Lothian, and Dumfries & Galloway have been in contrast to the North-East, where populations appear to have increased, although BBS data are sparse. Factors which have proved beneficial for Tree Sparrows include mixed farming with predominantly spring-sown cereals and associated over-winter stubbles, plentiful nest sites that now include nest boxes in many places, and the increased provision of seed food in rural and suburban gardens. Milder winters with fewer and shorter periods of snow cover may also have contributed to the local increase. On 37 farms monitored by RSPB where Tree Sparrows were present during 2003–08, the annual mean density varied from 1.2–1.6 pairs/km^2. Multiplied by the 520 tetrads occupied during the Atlas (2,080 1-km squares), this would give a population in the order of 2,500–3,500 pairs for the whole region.

Author: *Allan Perkins*

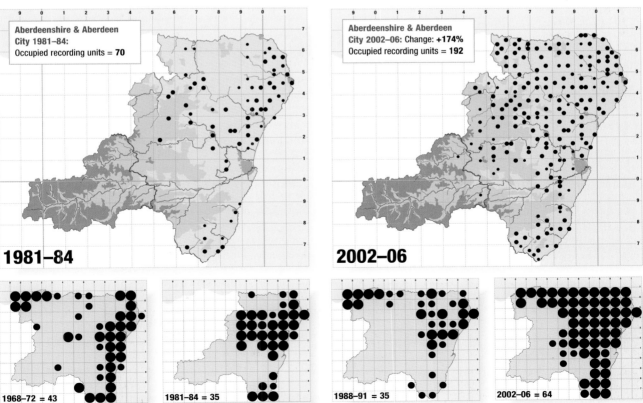

North-East Scotland 1968–72 to 2002–06: Change in occupied 10-km squares = **+49%**

Yellow Wagtail

Motacilla flava

Occasional summer migrant breeder. Passage migrant. Estimated population in North-East Scotland: **0–1 pair** (3% of Scottish population, <1% of UK)

Red list; UK and Scottish BAP lists

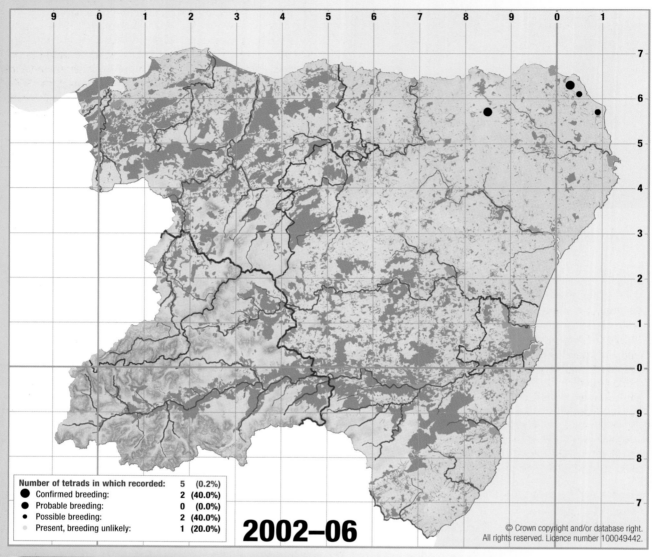

Number of tetrads in which recorded:	5	(0.2%)
● Confirmed breeding:	2	(40.0%)
● Probable breeding:	0	(0.0%)
● Possible breeding:	2	(40.0%)
○ Present, breeding unlikely:	1	(20.0%)

2002–06

Yellow Wagtail, Finnmark, June 2005. © *Harry Scott*

Habitat and breeding biology

In North-East Scotland, Yellow Wagtails occur almost exclusively as migrants near the coast in open, short grass habitats, sometimes associated with water. Dune slacks and links are amongst the favoured places. They nest on the ground in similar open habitats, and breeding is most often established by the presence of adults carrying insect food for the young.

Scottish distribution and status

In the early 20th century, the species bred locally, but widely, in the Clyde area and south-west Scotland, becoming rarer by mid-century. A temporary increase in the west in the 1970s was followed by a decrease and extinction in the early 1990s. This is now a nationally rare breeding species, with about 25–35 pairs in Lothian and the Borders, and scattered pairs elsewhere. The main areas in the south-east are along the haughs of the Rivers Tweed and Teviot, and coastal locations in East Lothian and Berwickshire (Murray in *BS3*). Regularly-occupied territories exist along the river valleys, but most of the coastal sites are less predictable and this echoes the sparse occurrences in North-East Scotland.

Yellow Wagtail, Norfolk, April 2010. © *Chris Upson*

Distribution and status in North-East Scotland

Yellow Wagtails are uncommon but annual migrants on the east coast, and very rare elsewhere; typically, 3–4 birds in spring (mainly in the first two weeks of May, and sometimes singing on apparent territories) and 1–2 in autumn (usually August–September). Most are of the race *flavissima*, but *flava* and *thunbergi* also occur, and birds belonging to all three races have bred, sometimes in mixed pairs. There have been only five breeding records in the last 30 years: 1977 at the Loch of Strathbeg (*flavissima*); 1980 at Meikle Loch (male

thunbergi, female probably *thunbergi*); 1981 at Murcar (male *flavissima*, female *flava*); 2004 at Gowanhill (Cairnbulg) (*flavissima*); 2005 at Hillock o' Leys (New Pitsligo) (race undetermined), where the birds fed in fields grazed by cattle and horses. A published record of breeding at Durris in 1987 referred to Grey Wagtail (A. Duncan pers. comm.).

Changes in distribution

In the late 1800s, Yellow Wagtails nested regularly in the dunes and links along the coast from Aberdeen to the Sands of Forvie, and from Peterhead to Fraserburgh (Sim 1903). Yellow Wagtails also summered for several years in the early 1900s near Boyndie Beach (Banff), leading to a suspicion that they may possibly have bred. Although they were noted as 'abundant' at one east coast locality, the number of breeding birds was probably quite low. Several recent breeding records fall within this historic distribution pattern, though the coastal links have been much changed in the 20th century, through conversion to golf courses, encroaching agriculture and with the drying of many of the dune slacks. One of the recent breeding records was atypically further inland, though still on close-cropped grass. The species has not bred in Moray, where the first record was of a migrant in 1968. In the 16 year period 1968–1983, there were 13 birds in eight years (Cook 1992), then none until a single individual in the autumn of 2003.

Population and trends

The population in North-East Scotland decreased through the early 20th century, with no recorded breeding between the early 1930s and 1977. A 70% decline in the population of *flavissima* in England since 1980 (Baillie *et al.* 2007) has not, apparently, been reflected in the overall pattern of occurrence in the North-East, where this species remains an uncommon migrant and occasional breeder.

Author: *Alan Knox*

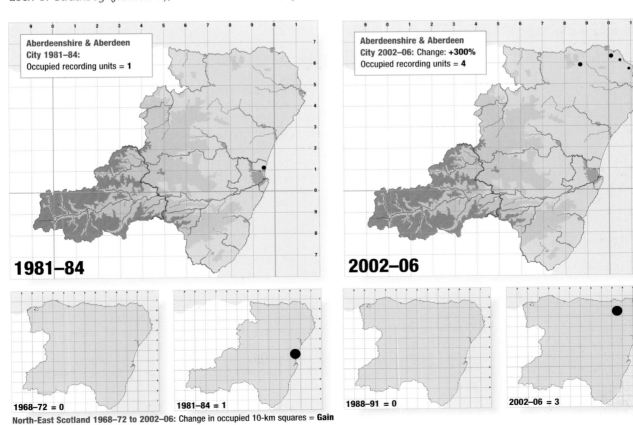

Aberdeenshire & Aberdeen City 1981–84: Occupied recording units = 1

1981–84

Aberdeenshire & Aberdeen City 2002–06: Change: **+300%** Occupied recording units = 4

2002–06

1968–72 = 0   1981–84 = 1

1988–91 = 0   2002–06 = 3

North-East Scotland 1968–72 to 2002–06: Change in occupied 10-km squares = **Gain**

Grey Wagtail

Motacilla cinerea

Common summer migrant breeder. Few in winter. Estimated population in North-East Scotland:
1,000–1,700 pairs (12% of Scottish population, 3% of UK)

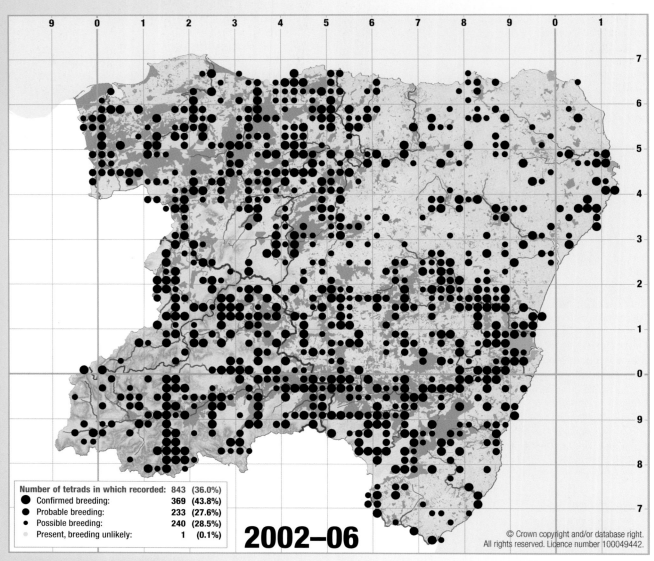

Number of tetrads in which recorded:	843	(36.0%)
● Confirmed breeding:	369	(43.8%)
● Probable breeding:	233	(27.6%)
● Possible breeding:	240	(28.5%)
● Present, breeding unlikely:	1	(0.1%)

2002–06

Habitat and breeding biology

Grey Wagtails are typically found along fast-flowing rivers and streams, with particular preference for river banks lined with broad-leaved trees due to the greater biomass of insects (*BTO 2nd Atlas*). Waterways Bird Survey results for Britain as a whole show that, between 50–300 m, densities increase with altitude and are highest where the gradient is more than 2.5 m/km (Marchant & Hyde 1980). Populations can also be found in lowland areas along slow-moving rivers, mill streams and even Aberdeen city centre. Nests are typically found in rock crevices, between the roots of vegetation and in walls.

Scottish distribution and status

Where suitable habitat is available, Grey Wagtails are common breeders occurring throughout mainland Scotland and the Inner Hebrides. Although still scarce in the north and west, they appear to be increasing and spreading (Young in *BS3*). A lack of data for some habitats creates problems when attempting to derive a Scottish population estimate. In 2007 this was considered to lie within the broad range of 6,000–17,500 pairs (Young in *BS3*).

Distribution and status in North-East Scotland

Grey Wagtails breed extensively along the valleys of the main fast-flowing rivers, such as the Dee, Don, Spey and Avon but they are relatively scarce along the slower rivers in Buchan. The large number of occupied tetrads between the main rivers indicates the ability of the species to occupy very minor streams so long as these present suitable feeding and breeding opportunities. In addition, there are several records of birds breeding very near the coast where the rivers are partly tidal, for example at Peterhead and Stonehaven. Migrant birds typically return to their breeding grounds in March or early April with autumn departures in August or September. A few birds, however, over-winter in the North-East, on or near the coast.

Changes in distribution

In terms of occupied 10-km squares the distribution has changed little over the last 40 years. There has, however, been a substantial increase in occupied recording units in Aberdeenshire/Aberdeen City over the period 1981–84 to 2002–06. This is due to an in-filling within the former range and also to an increase in records in the Buchan area. It is likely that this range expansion is a consequence of population increase and of greater observer effort

Population and trends

Counts along seven sections of fast-flowing river in Moray during 1999–2003, totalling 23 km, found 27 pairs, an average density of 1.2 pairs/km (*MNBRs*). This is similar to densities reported in the south of Scotland (Young in *BS3*). Applying this density to the total river lengths in North-East Scotland will, however, greatly underestimate the population as much smaller streams are frequently occupied. It is therefore necessary to apply an estimate of pairs/tetrad. Such data do not exist for the North-East but, as linear densities are similar, it is probably fair to use tetrad densities from South-east Scotland and Fife. These range from 1.2–2.0 pairs/occupied tetrad (Murray *et al.* 1998, Elkins *et al.* 2003) and when applied to the 842 occupied tetrads in our area suggest a North-East population of 1,000–1,700 pairs. BBS data for the UK as a whole indicate a population increase of 26% over the period 1994–2007 - a trend supported by the sparse local BBS data and the range increase revealed during

Grey Wagtail, Udny, 1980. © *Graham Rebecca*

2002–06. Factors influencing this increase may include improving water quality, with consequent greater invertebrate abundance, and milder winters leading to decreased mortality in wintering areas.

Author: *Ben Macallum*

Grey Wagtail, Glen Muick, June 2009. © *Ed Duthie*

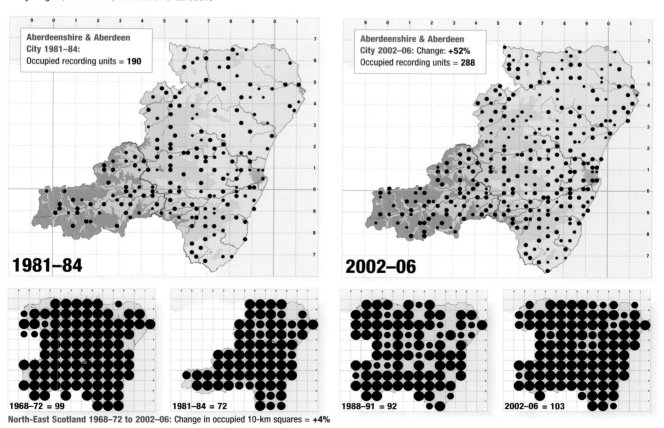

Aberdeenshire & Aberdeen City 1981–84:
Occupied recording units = **190**

1981–84

Aberdeenshire & Aberdeen City 2002–06: Change: **+52%**
Occupied recording units = **288**

2002–06

1968–72 = 99   1981–84 = 72   1988–91 = 92   2002–06 = 103

North-East Scotland 1968–72 to 2002–06: Change in occupied 10-km squares = +4%

Pied Wagtail

Motacilla alba

Common summer migrant breeder and resident. Estimated population in North-East Scotland: **15,000–19,000 pairs** (16% of Scottish population, 6% of UK)

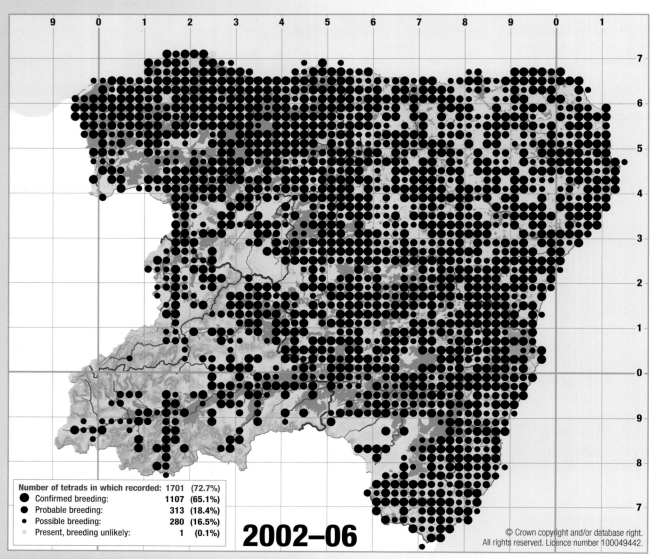

Number of tetrads in which recorded: 1701 (72.7%)		
● Confirmed breeding:	1107	(65.1%)
● Probable breeding:	313	(18.4%)
● Possible breeding:	280	(16.5%)
● Present, breeding unlikely:	1	(0.1%)

2002–06

Pied Wagtail, Drumoak, June 2008. © *Sam Alexander*

Habitat and breeding biology

Pied Wagtails breed in areas where short-cropped pastures, or other short grasslands such as golf courses, provide opportunities for feeding. They can be found from the coast to the uplands, and are most numerous in the vicinity of wetlands, slow-running rivers and upland streams. They build their nests during April in buildings, rock faces, quarries, bridges, steep banks and in dry stone walls. Pairs are often double-brooded, with first clutches laid in early May and second clutches from mid June onwards, although this is less common in northern Scotland where a single brood may be the norm (Dougall in *BS3*).

Scottish status and distribution

The Pied Wagtail (endemic British subspecies *M. a. yarrellii*) is a widespread and abundant species throughout Scotland, although absent from woodland, Heather moorland and bare mountains. The Scottish breeding population was estimated at 90,000–120,000 pairs in 2007 (Dougall in *BS3*). There has been a non-significant 16% increase in Scotland during 1994–2007 in line with a significant 15% increase in the UK as a whole (Risely *et al.* 2008).

Distribution and status in North-East Scotland

Pied Wagtails are very widely distributed in North-East Scotland with 1,701 occupied tetrads. Their range extends from the coast well into the foothills of the uplands. Although scarce above 400 m, birds were recorded up to 500 m in a few localities and even close to 600 m at The Cairnwell and in Glen Avon. They are not found in arable monocultures when feeding habitat and nest sites are lacking, or in large forests. Although generally absent from Heather moorland, a few may inhabit the vicinity of rivers and streams and there is none in the highest uplands. In many rural and upland areas Pied Wagtails are the first summer visitors to return, arriving from early March onwards. Numbers build up rapidly from late March through April, when they may congregate in large

Pied Wagtail, Glen Gairn, May 2004. © Harry Scott

communal roosts, e.g. 500 at Dyce Airport in mid March 1988 (NESBR 1988) and 600 at Loch Spynie in late March 1993 (MNBR 1993). These roosts break up by the end of April as birds disperse to their breeding territories.

White Wagtails M. a. alba are uncommon passage migrants, most often reported in spring but probably overlooked in autumn. There is a single breeding record, at Durris in 1920 (Baxter & Rintoul 1953). During 2002–06, 66 birds were seen in spring; nearly all were close to the coast and there was no suggestion of territorial or breeding activity.

Changes in distribution

There has been no significant change in the distribution of Pied Wagtails over the last 40 years. In 1968–72 they were found in 110 10-km squares in North-East Scotland (BTO 1st Atlas) and this figure is little changed today. At a more detailed scale, the species occupied 340 recording units in Aberdeenshire/Aberdeen City in 1981–84 (NES 1st Atlas) and there was only a 3% increase by 2002–06.

Population and trends

The only density information for the North-East, obtained during 2002–06, was of 16 pairs in 5 km^2 (or 3.2 pairs/km^2) near Inverurie. As a result of local surveys, a similar density of 2.5 pairs/km^2 was used to calculate the population in South-east Scotland (Murray et al. 1998). Relative abundance data presented in BTO 2nd Atlas indicate a similarity between South-east Scotland and our area, and so applying the density of 2.5 pairs/km^2 in the North-East suggests a total population of around 17,000 pairs. A realistically wide estimate would place the likely total between 15,000–19,000 pairs. The BBS in Scotland revealed a 16% increase over the period 1994–2007 (Risely et al. 2008); data for the North-East indicate a stable population but the sample of surveyed plots is small.

Author: Clive McKay

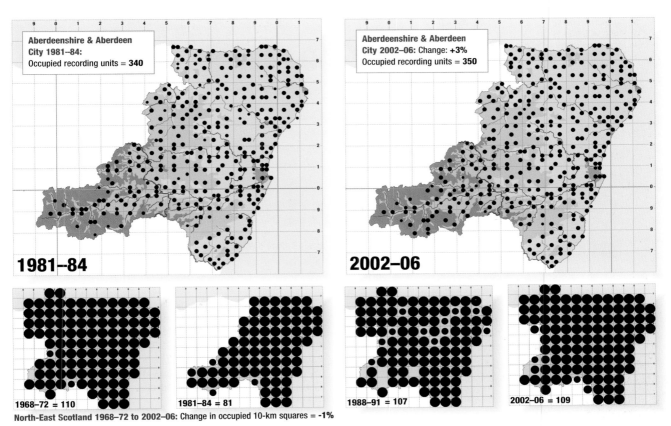

Aberdeenshire & Aberdeen City 1981–84:
Occupied recording units = **340**

1981–84

Aberdeenshire & Aberdeen City 2002–06: Change: +3%
Occupied recording units = **350**

2002–06

1968–72 = 110

1981–84 = 81

1988–91 = 107

2002–06 = 109

North-East Scotland 1968–72 to 2002–06: Change in occupied 10-km squares = **-1%**

Tree Pipit

Anthus trivialis

Common summer migrant breeder. Passage migrant. Estimated population in North-East Scotland:
1,400–2,100 pairs (4% of Scottish population, 2% of UK)

Red list; UK BAP list

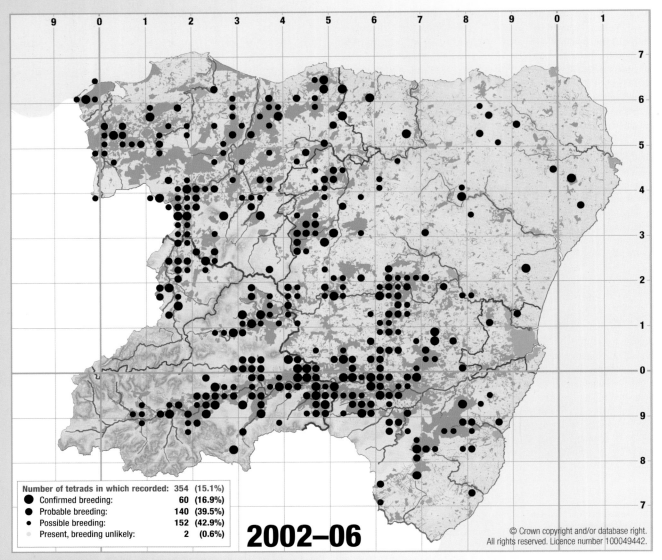

Number of tetrads in which recorded:	354	(15.1%)
● Confirmed breeding:	60	(16.9%)
● Probable breeding:	140	(39.5%)
● Possible breeding:	152	(42.9%)
· Present, breeding unlikely:	2	(0.6%)

2002–06

Tree Pipit, Glen Muick, June 2009. © *Ed Duthie*

Habitat and breeding biology

Tree Pipits are found in a variety of woodland habitats, characterised by a low field layer where they build their nests. They mainly occupy open deciduous woodlands, especially hillside birch woods at altitudes of 100–500 m, but are also found in coniferous woodland. Closed canopy woodland and treeless habitats are avoided, the species favouring areas of scattered trees and shrubs from which it can begin its parachuting song flight. Clear-felled areas in forestry plantations are quickly colonised provided isolated trees are left. Most territories are established in early to mid May and young fledge from early June. Scottish birds appear to be single brooded and breeding areas are deserted by mid July (Shaw in *BS3*).

Scottish distribution and status

Widely distributed across much of Scotland, Tree Pipits breed on most of the mainland and some islands of the Inner Hebrides where suitable habitat exists. Highest densities are found in the open birch woods of the western Highlands and in parts of Dumfries & Galloway. Birds are typically absent from areas of lowland farmland, dense coniferous plantation and treeless uplands. The Scottish population was estimated at 43,000 pairs in 2007 (Shaw in *BS3*). Over the UK as a whole there has been an 11% decline in the population during the period 1994–2007 (Risely *et al.* 2008) but it is uncertain whether this situation is matched in Scotland.

Distribution and status in North-East Scotland

The main breeding areas for Tree Pipits in North-East Scotland are mid and upper Deeside and Donside, together with the River Spey and Avon valleys upstream from Craigellachie. There are also smaller concentrations in the forests south of Forres and south of Huntly. Elsewhere the species is widely but thinly distributed through wooded parts of Moray and Aberdeenshire but there are few in lowland arable areas such as the Laich of Moray, Buchan and the Mearns. Within forested areas, occupancy is uneven, reflecting the changing attractiveness to Tree Pipits of different stages in forestry rotation. The earliest returning birds are usually singing in the woods by around 20th April.

Changes in distribution

There appears to have been a substantial expansion of the range of Tree Pipits in North-East Scotland since the 1980s. In 1968–72 (*BTO 1st Atlas*) and in 1988–91 (*BTO 2nd Atlas*) the species was found in 45–46 10-km squares but by 2002–06 this had risen to 74 squares. Similarly, at the finer scale of the recording units used in the 1981–84 Atlas (*NES 1st Atlas*), there has been a doubling in the number of occupied units. This increase is due both to consolidation within core areas and to an extension of the range northwards and eastwards. These findings are surprising in view of the UK decline in numbers revealed by BTO surveys. Despite the fact that maturing and felled plantations may have created some additional habitat, there must be a suspicion that some at least of the apparent spread is due to more intensive fieldwork during 2002–06.

Tree Pipit, Glen Muick, May 2009. © *Rab Rae*

Population and trends

Tree Pipits were recorded in breeding habitat in 354 tetrads, with probable or confirmed breeding in 200 of these. There is little local information on which to base a population estimate; 0–4 territories/km^2 were recorded in various woodland types in a small area of Deeside (Jenkins & Watson 1999). However, abundance in the North-East may be comparable to that in South-East Scotland (*BTO 2nd Atlas*) and here a range from 1–10 pairs/tetrad has been found (Murray *et al.* 1998). Applying the middle of this range (4–6 pairs/tetrad) to 354 tetrads in North-East Scotland suggests a population in the range of 1,400–2,100 pairs. It is likely that Tree Pipits are under recorded in North-East Scotland, with many upland birch woods visited infrequently by birders, and it is possible that the species is more numerous than this estimate suggests.

Author: *Andy Jensen*

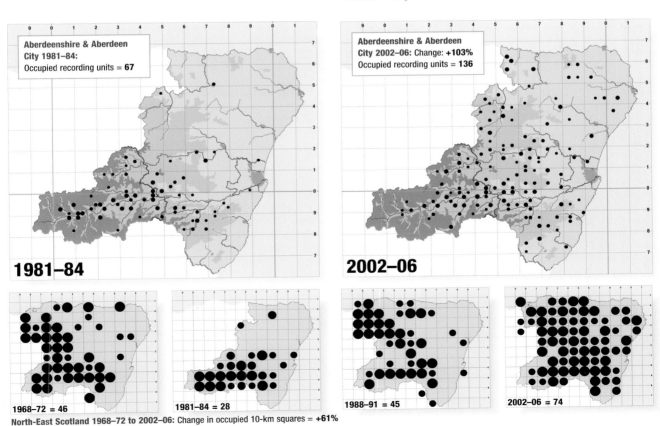

Aberdeenshire & Aberdeen City 1981–84:
Occupied recording units = **67**

1981–84

Aberdeenshire & Aberdeen City 2002–06: Change: **+103%**
Occupied recording units = **136**

2002–06

1968–72 = 46   1981–84 = 28   1988–91 = 45   2002–06 = 74

North-East Scotland 1968–72 to 2002–06: Change in occupied 10-km squares = **+61%**

Meadow Pipit

Anthus pratensis

Very common summer migrant breeder and resident. Passage migrant. Estimated population in North-East Scotland: ***120,000–140,000 pairs*** (9% of Scottish population, 8% of UK)

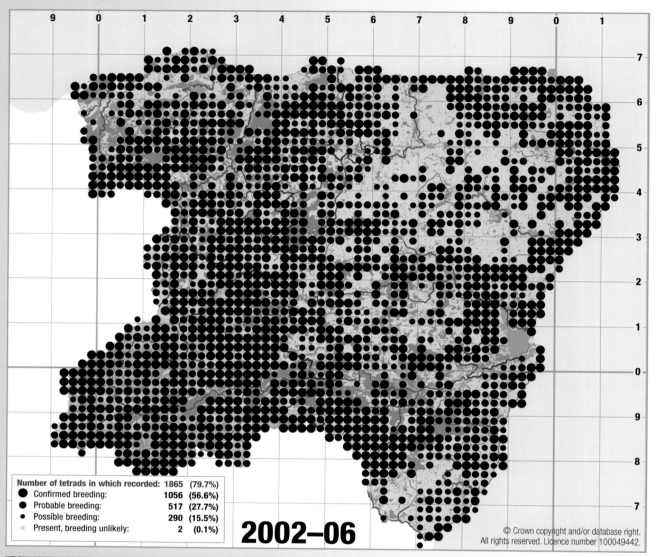

Number of tetrads in which recorded:	1865	(79.7%)
● Confirmed breeding:	1056	(56.6%)
● Probable breeding:	517	(27.7%)
● Possible breeding:	290	(15.5%)
· Present, breeding unlikely:	2	(0.1%)

2002–06

Meadow Pipit, Glen Finglas, June 2008. © *Gina Prior*

Habitat and breeding biology

Meadow Pipits breed in a wide range of rough grassland and moorland habitats including dunes on the coast, uncultivated ground in agricultural areas, lowland mosses and on hill ground up to the mountain summits. Virtually all upland habitats are utilised; Heather and grass moorland, blanket bog, flushes and montane areas. They require a mixture of tall or tussocky vegetation for nesting, adjacent to short-cropped, open areas for feeding (Douglas *et al.* 2008). The nest is placed on the ground, usually hidden under a grass tussock or other tall vegetation, often on steep slopes. The breeding season extends from late April to late July but can be earlier on the coast. Here they are double-brooded, whereas birds in the uplands may be limited to single broods, and may not breed at all in years with late snowfall (*NES 1st Atlas*). Meadow Pipits are a key prey item of Hen Harriers and Merlins and a primary host species for the Cuckoo in Scotland.

Scottish distribution and status

The Meadow Pipit is a widespread and abundant species throughout Scotland, although perhaps less so in the lowlands of the south and east. They are absent only from

Meadow Pipit, Glen Girnock, June 2010. © Ian Francis

woodland, intensive arable farmland and built up areas. The Scottish breeding population was estimated at 1.3–1.6 million breeding pairs in 2007 (Dougall in *BS3*).

Distribution and status in North-East Scotland

The Meadow Pipit is the most widely distributed bird in the uplands of North-East Scotland; it was found in virtually all moorland and mountain tetrads, extending up to the highest altitudes. It is also common in coastal areas. However, it is absent from the most intensively cultivated arable areas around Turriff, Huntly, Ellon and Laurencekirk; Buckland *et al.* (1990) found a negative correlation between

Meadow Pipit distribution and Wheat growing areas. Many tetrads in these areas are strongly influenced by modern arable monocultures and do not support enough rough grassland or marsh for this small bird to breed, reflecting the influence of modern arable monocultures. They are also scarce in heavily forested areas such as parts of Deeside, Speyside and south of Forres. Birds start to return to upland breeding areas during March, and leave their territories for lower ground in August and September (Dougall in *BS3*). Most leave North-East Scotland in September, for wintering grounds in England, France and Portugal (Dougall in Wernham *et al.* 2002).

Changes in distribution

There has been no major change in distribution since 1981–84, although the number of occupied recording units in Aberdeenshire/Aberdeen City rose by 5.2% from 347 in 1981–84 to 365 in 2002–06, perhaps as a consequence of greater observer effort.

Population and trends

There are very few local data on which to base a population estimate. Abundance measures in 1988–91 (*BTO 2nd Atlas*) suggest that the North-East is comparable to South-East Scotland, where an overall density of 24 pairs/km^2 in occupied tetrads was calculated from local surveys (Murray *et al.* 1998). Applying this to the 1,865 tetrads in North-East Scotland which contained Meadow Pipits during 2002–06, and taking into account the significant 23% decline indicated by Scottish BBS data during 1994–2007 (Risely et al. 2008), suggests a population of around 140,000 pairs. There is, however, much uncertainty because the balance of habitats in the North-East may not precisely match that in South-East Scotland. It is safer, therefore, to propose a population in the range of 120,000–140,000 pairs, which represents about 10% of the Scottish total.

Author: *Clive McKay*

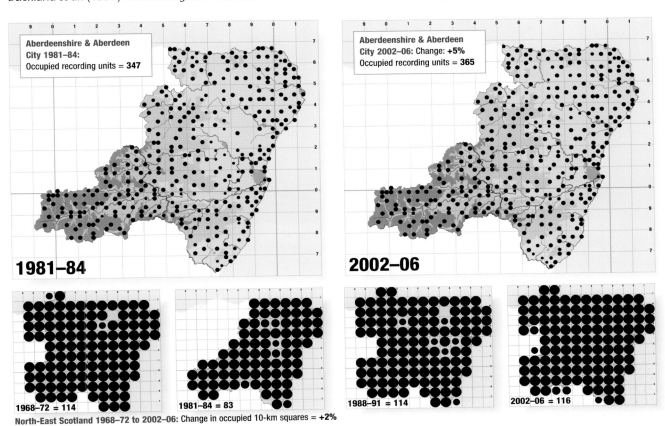

Aberdeenshire & Aberdeen City 1981–84:
Occupied recording units = **347**

1981–84

Aberdeenshire & Aberdeen City 2002–06: Change: +5%
Occupied recording units = **365**

2002–06

1968–72 = 114

1981–84 = 83

1988–91 = 114

2002–06 = 116

North-East Scotland 1968–72 to 2002–06: Change in occupied 10-km squares = +2%

Loch of Strathbeg

One of the UK's premier wetland sites, and a renowned winter goose roost, the RSPB Loch of Strathbeg reserve and surrounding area is also by far one of the most important locations for breeding birds in North-East Scotland. The Special Protection Area citation includes terns, though the Sandwich Tern colony has not been present here for 10 years, having shifted to the Sands of Forvie. Nevertheless, the breeding bird community here is very rich and diverse, and includes many species for which this is the only site in the region. Birds which nest regularly or have done so include Shelduck, Gadwall, Garganey, Shoveler, Great Crested Grebe, Marsh Harrier, Water Rail, Black-headed Gull and Common Tern. Pectoral Sandpipers displayed here in 2004. Potential future breeding wetland colonists could include Spoonbill, Little Egret, Avocet, Crane and Bearded Tit, all of which have been present in the breeding season. The surrounding farmland also holds Grey Partridge, Quail, Barn Owl and Corn Bunting. September 2009 © *Duncan Goulder*

Fowlsheugh

One of the largest seabird colonies in mainland Britain, Fowlsheugh is a classic 'seabird city' and is an RSPB reserve. Tens of thousands of Kittiwakes and Guillemots breed here, with good numbers of other species such as Razorbill, Puffin (mainly at the northern end), Fulmar, Shag, Great Black-backed and Herring Gulls. Feral Pigeons, Rock Pipits, Starlings and Jackdaws also nest on the cliffs. Small numbers of Eiders nest along the coast here, Peregrines breed close by, and Raven has recently bred. Cliff top scrub holds Linnets and Yellowhammers. June 2009 © *Ian Francis*

Rock Pipit

Anthus petrosus

Scarce resident. Estimated population in North-East Scotland: ***525 pairs*** (2% of Scottish population, <2% of UK)

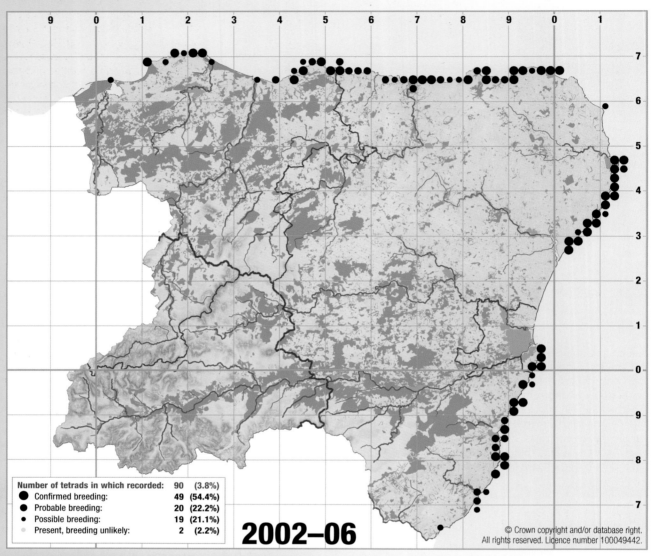

Number of tetrads in which recorded:	90	(3.8%)
● Confirmed breeding:	49	(54.4%)
● Probable breeding:	20	(22.2%)
• Possible breeding:	19	(21.1%)
Present, breeding unlikely:	2	(2.2%)

2002–06

Rock Pipit, Buchanhaven, December 2008. © *Ed Duthie*

Habitat and breeding biology

During the breeding season, Rock Pipits are never found far from rocky coastlines, foraging along the tideline or in short vegetation behind the beach. They occupy undeveloped coasts and also areas of suitable habitat in built-up areas such as Banff and Peterhead. They build their nests close to the shore in cliff crevices and hollows among rocks, under vegetation and sometimes in man-made structures such as derelict buildings and boats. The conspicuous song flights begin in March and a clutch of 4–5 eggs is laid during April or early May.

Scottish distribution and status

Rock Pipits are restricted to rocky and cliff-bound sections of the coastline, occurring continuously along the north and west coasts of mainland Scotland and around all the major islands (Woodbridge in *BS3*). They are far more local along the east coast due, in part at least, to the reduced availability of suitable habitat. The most recent population estimate, in 2007, suggests 20,000–23,000 pairs in Scotland (Woodbridge in *BS3*).

Rock Pipit, Girdle Ness, May 2011. © *Amanda Biggins*

Distribution and status in North-East Scotland

Rock Pipits are closely associated with all stretches of the North-East Scotland coastline where cliffs or rocks prevail. The main concentrations are to be found between Burghead and Lossiemouth, from Buckie eastwards along the Moray Firth coast to Fraserburgh, between Peterhead and Collieston, and south from Aberdeen to Inverbervie. In other areas the coastline is dominated by sand or shingle - although Rock Pipits shun such areas for breeding they may be found foraging there in winter.

Changes in distribution

At the 10-km square level there has been little change in range from the 22 occupied squares in 1968–72 (*BTO 1st Atlas*) to 24 in 2002–06. The apparent reduction to 13 squares in 1988–91 (*BTO 2nd Atlas*) is likely to be attributable to reduced observer effort. Closer examination at the scale of the recording units used in Aberdeenshire/Aberdeen City in 1981–84 reveals a substantial 44% increase over the 20 year period between the two local atlases. Such an increase is due to infilling within the stretches of suitable habitat and this appears most marked along the Aberdeen to Inverbervie section of coast where an increase of 71% in occupied recording units is apparent. However, observer effort could have influenced this apparent increase.

Population and trends

The population is hard to assess. Rock Pipits were recorded in 90 tetrads in 2002–06, but the length of coastline included within a tetrad may range from over 2 km down to a few metres depending on the incidence of map gridlines and the shore. For this reason it is inappropriate to apply a density measured in pairs/tetrad. Measures of pairs/linear km of occupied coast are required. The only recent local counts are of six pairs in 2 km between Tronach Head and the Bow Fiddle Rock (Moray) in 2000 (*MNBR* 2000) and four singing males in 1.5 km at Lossiemouth in 2004 (*MNBR* 2004). This is not dissimilar from densities reported elsewhere in Scotland such as Fife (1–3 pairs/km) (Elkins *et al.* 2003) and Shetland (1.3–2.7 pairs/km in 2002) (Harvey 2003) although rather lower than recorded in Lothian & Borders (5–10 pairs/km in 1988–94) (Murray *et al.* 1998). If we accept a North-East Scotland density of 3 pairs/km and apply this figure to approximately 175 km of occupied coastline then an estimated population of 525 pairs results.

Author: *Dominic Funnell*

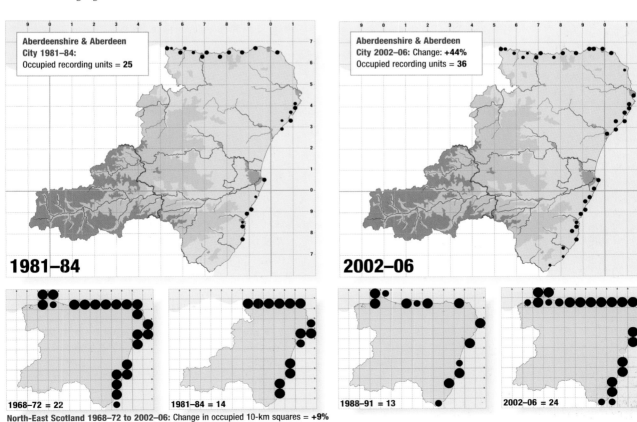

Aberdeenshire & Aberdeen City 1981–84:
Occupied recording units = **25**

1981–84

Aberdeenshire & Aberdeen City 2002–06: Change: +44%
Occupied recording units = **36**

2002–06

1968–72 = 22   1981–84 = 14

1988–91 = 13   2002–06 = 24

North-East Scotland 1968–72 to 2002–06: Change in occupied 10-km squares = **+9%**

Chaffinch

Fringilla coelebs

Very common resident. Winter visitor and passage migrant. Estimated population in North-East Scotland: **140,000–150,000 pairs** (12% of Scottish population, 2% of UK)

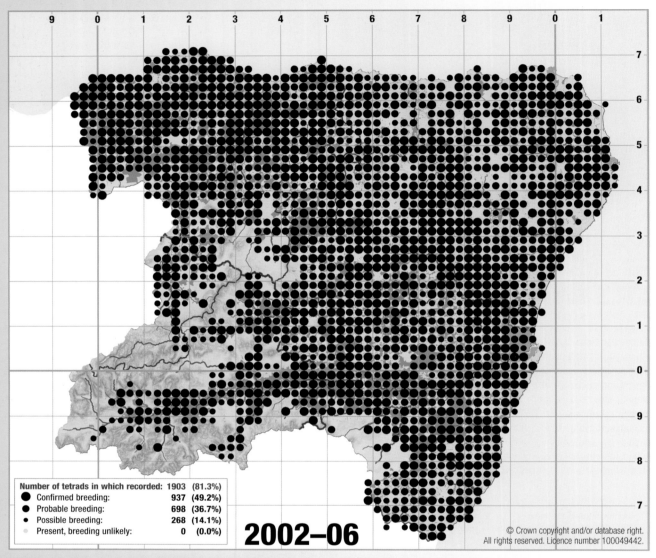

Number of tetrads in which recorded: 1903	(81.3%)
● Confirmed breeding: 937	(49.2%)
● Probable breeding: 698	(36.7%)
● Possible breeding: 268	(14.1%)
● Present, breeding unlikely: 0	(0.0%)

2002–06

Chaffinch, Dinnet, May 2009. © Harry Scott

Habitat and breeding biology

Chaffinches breed wherever there are trees or shrubs, preferably with some above 3 m in height. They are common in gardens, copses, woodland, including coniferous plantations, and also in upland areas in small patches of birch and Juniper scrub. Their nests are well camouflaged with moss and lichen and are usually built in a shrub or small tree 1–3 m above ground. The clutch of 3–6 eggs is usually laid in May, with the young fledging about four weeks after the clutch is completed. Most pairs are single brooded.

Scottish distribution and status

Chaffinches breed widely in Scotland and are absent on the mainland only from the highest treeless uplands. Greatest densities are found in the lowlands of eastern, central and southern Scotland. They are uncommon in the Outer Hebrides and Orkney, and only rarely breed in Shetland. In 2007, the Scottish population was estimated to lie within the range of 1,000,000–1,500,000 pairs (Newton in *BS3*).

Distribution and status in North-East Scotland

The Chaffinch is the most widely distributed breeding species in North-East Scotland, having been found in 81% of tetrads. The range extends far up glens into the uplands,

Chaffinch, Drum, 1975. © *Graham Rebecca*

achieving altitudes exceeding 500 m in Glens Derry, Ey and Quoich. They are therefore absent only from the highest uplands which lack suitable breeding vegetation. They are also apparently missing from a small number of lowland tetrads but it is likely that they have been overlooked except, possibly, in the most arable areas of Buchan.

Changes in distribution

Over the past 40 years there is no evidence of any major change in the breeding distribution of Chaffinches. At the 10-km square level, the number of occupied squares has remained virtually unchanged between 1968–72 (*BTO 1st Atlas*), 1988–91 (*BTO 2nd Atlas*) and 2002–06. Similarly, the small increase in occupied recording units in Aberdeenshire/Aberdeen City between 1981–84 and 2002–06 is unlikely to be meaningful. This may be a little surprising in view of the increase in upland afforestation but it may be that these areas already contained enough patches

of breeding habitat to enable the species to be registered as present - although in smaller numbers than now.

Population and trends

Evidence from various sources (*BS3, 1st NES Atlas,* Jenkins & Watson 1999) suggests that average densities in different habitats in North-East Scotland might be about 70 pairs/km^2 in broad-leaf woodland, 50 pairs/km^2 in coniferous woodland, 15 pairs/km^2 in farmland and 20 pairs/km^2 in suburban and rural gardens. By applying these densities to the area of relevant land cover types (LC 2000 data) a total population of around 146,000 pairs can be calculated. Realistically, the range might be widened to 140,000–150,000 pairs - 12% of the Scottish population. The BBS in Scotland reveals a 10% population increase during 1994–2007 (Risely *et al.* 2008).

Author: *Melvin Morrison*

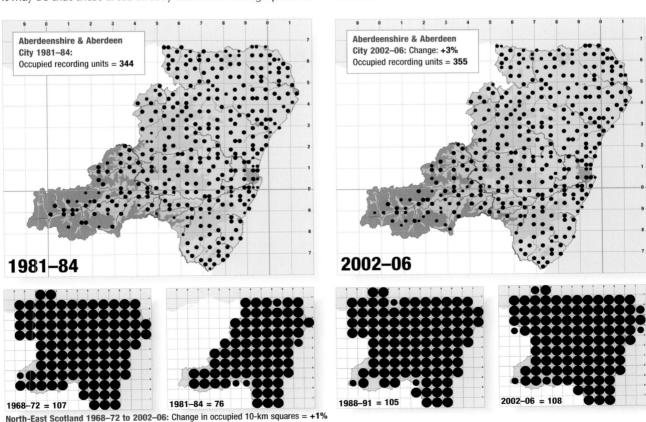

Aberdeenshire & Aberdeen City 1981–84: Occupied recording units = 344

Aberdeenshire & Aberdeen City 2002–06: Change: +3% Occupied recording units = 355

1981–84

2002–06

1968–72 = 107   1981–84 = 76   1988–91 = 105   2002–06 = 108

North-East Scotland 1968–72 to 2002–06: Change in occupied 10-km squares = +1%

Brambling

Fringilla montifringilla

Occasional possible, and former, breeder. Winter visitor and passage migrant. Estimated population in North-East Scotland: usually **0 pairs**

Schedule 1; Scottish BAP list

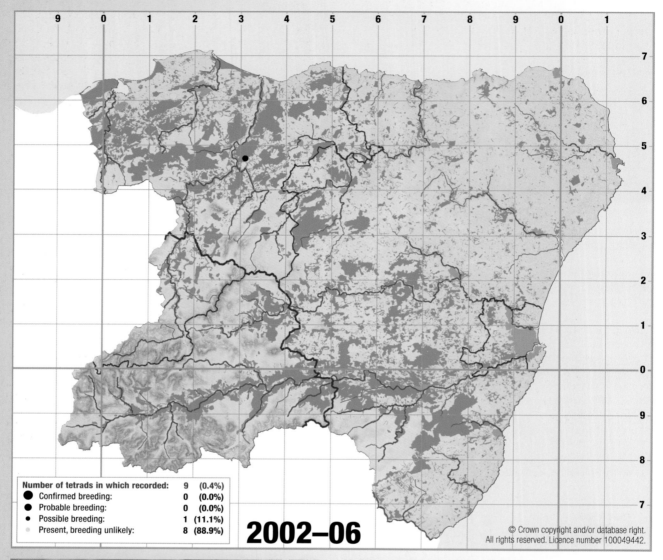

Number of tetrads in which recorded:	9	(0.4%)
● Confirmed breeding:	0	(0.0%)
● Probable breeding:	0	(0.0%)
● Possible breeding:	1	(11.1%)
Present, breeding unlikely:	8	(88.9%)

2002–06

Brambling, Finland, May 1990. © *Ed Duthie*

Habitat and breeding biology

Over their northern Eurasian range, Bramblings breed chiefly in open upland birchwoods and in mixed forests of birch and conifers. Similarly, the few instances of breeding in Scotland have mostly been in birch woodland but also occasionally in conifers (*BWP, BTO 2nd Atlas*). Nests are sited in trees, usually between 2–10 m above the ground. Egg laying takes place between mid May–early July, depending at least partly on latitude. In Scotland, nests have contained eggs in late May and early July (*BWP*).

Scottish distribution and status

Bramblings are primarily winter visitors to Scotland and are most numerous in agricultural eastern Scotland and the central lowlands. Numbers vary greatly from year to year, depending on the extent of immigration and the availability of food supplies. In a good winter up to 100,000 may be present (Newton in *BS3*). They are also passage migrants, most commonly in autumn. The first record of confirmed breeding in Scotland was in Easter Ross in 1899, and they nested again in Sutherland in 1920. The next proved breeding took place in 1979, and between then and 2004 there were nine further attempts (Newton in *BS3*).

The Breeding Birds of North-East Scotland

Distribution and status in North-East Scotland

Winter numbers of Bramblings are variable but they can be numerous and flocks of several hundred are not unusual. The last migrants may not depart until late April or early May and singing passage males may briefly appear to be territorial. A very late bird was still at Inchmarlo (Banchory) on 10th June 2008 (*NESBR* 2008). There were no records during 1968–72 (*BTO 1st Atlas*). The first confirmed breeding in North-East Scotland was in 1979 at Inverey in a mature birchwood of about 2 ha. The female appeared to be incubating on 2nd July and the deserted nest contained at least three eggs six days later (Buckland & Knox 1980). During 1981–84, possible breeding was noted at two sites in the Aboyne area and a female was seen building a nest at Old Deer in May 1983 (*NES 1st Atlas*). There was no further indication of breeding until 2006 when a pair was seen on the lower slopes of Ben Aigan on 30th July (*MNBR* 2006). In view of the date, however, it is by no means certain that they bred in that immediate locality if, indeed, they did so at all.

Although it is not unusual for late-staying and migrant males to sing for several days, there is little evidence that these birds often attract females or attempt to breed. However, large areas of apparently suitable habitat are infrequently visited by birders and it is possible that breeding attempts may pass un-noticed. Nonetheless, there is nothing to indicate that North-East Scotland is likely to be colonised by a significant breeding population of Bramblings.

Author: *Martin Cook*

Brambling, Finnmark, June 2003. © *Rab Rae*

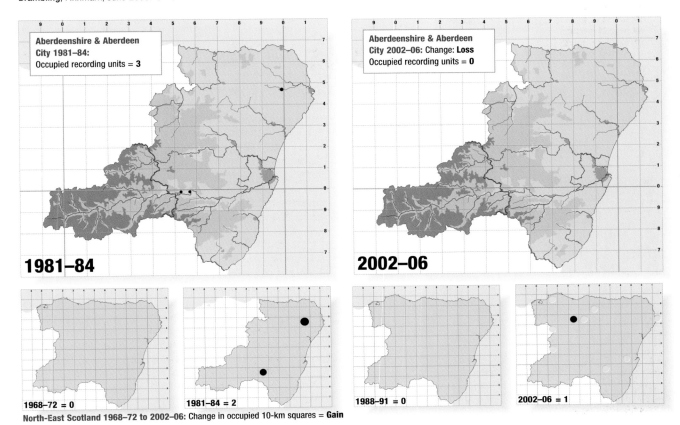

Aberdeenshire & Aberdeen City 1981–84:
Occupied recording units = **3**

Aberdeenshire & Aberdeen City 2002–06: Change: **Loss**
Occupied recording units = **0**

1981–84

2002–06

1968–72 = 0

1981–84 = 2

1988–91 = 0

2002–06 = 1

North-East Scotland 1968–72 to 2002–06: Change in occupied 10-km squares = Gain

Greenfinch

Carduelis chloris

Very common resident. Winter visitor. Estimated population in North-East Scotland: *25,000–30,000 pairs* (15% of Scottish population, 4% of UK)

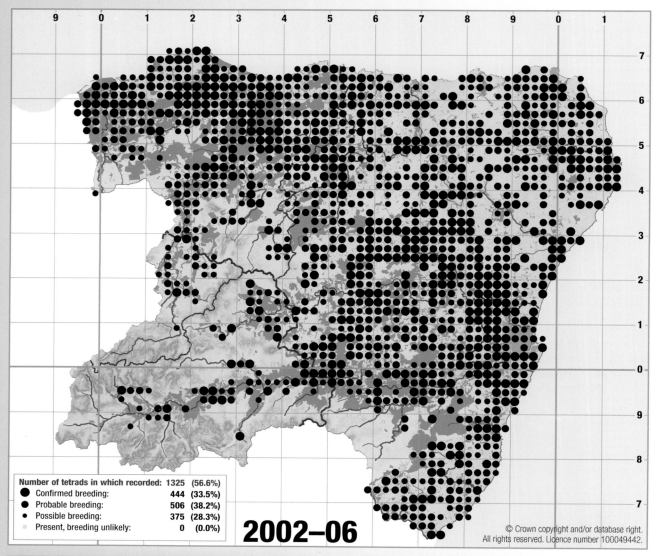

Number of tetrads in which recorded:	1325	(56.6%)
● Confirmed breeding:	444	(33.5%)
● Probable breeding:	506	(38.2%)
● Possible breeding:	375	(28.3%)
● Present, breeding unlikely:	0	(0.0%)

2002–06

Greenfinch, Montrose, July 2010. © *John Anderson*

Habitat and breeding biology

Greenfinches are birds of large gardens and parks in towns and villages but they also occupy arable farmland and conifer plantations. They often breed in small loose colonies of 4–6 pairs, preferring to build their nests in tall thick hedges and evergreens between 1.5–5 m above ground. Display flights, and the distinctive wheezy song, begin in March and the first eggs are laid in late April or May. The clutch, usually consisting of 3–6 eggs, hatches after two weeks and the young fledge around 16 days later. The breeding season is long, with the last young fledging in September, enabling pairs to raise two or three broods in a year.

Scottish distribution and status

Greenfinches are widespread over much of lowland Scotland but are absent from the treeless uplands, especially most of the north-west highlands, and from Shetland. They achieve their highest densities on the low ground of eastern Scotland from the Moray Firth south to the Borders. In much of western Scotland and the Outer Hebrides they occupy only the coastal fringe. The population is thought to lie within the range of 120,000–250,000 pairs (Newton in *BS3*).

Distribution and status in North-East Scotland

Greenfinches have an extensive range in lowland North-East Scotland with central and southern Aberdeenshire, along with Moray, being especially well populated. The distribution is patchy in Buchan where suitable breeding habitat may be unavailable. Extensive mature forestry blocks often lack Greenfinches unless they are interspersed with plantations of younger trees. They are largely absent from the uplands, failing to utilise the birch woods which allow Chaffinches to penetrate far up the glens. Few are found above 300–350 m although they exceed this altitude at Inchrory and in Glen Muick, and even ascend to around 500 m in Glen Derry and Glen Quoich where there are relatively young plantations.

Changes in distribution

Between 1968–72 and 1988–91 there was an apparent range reduction of ten 10-km squares, almost entirely in the upland areas of south-west Aberdeenshire (*BTO 2nd Atlas*). Assuming effective observer coverage was achieved, this reduction may have been attributable to upland farms in these areas switching away from mixed farming with the consequent loss of small arable fields and the foraging opportunities they provide (Newton in *BS3*). By 2002–06, many of these unoccupied upland squares have been re-populated with Greenfinches. This is well illustrated by comparison of the more detailed recording units used in 1981–84 (*NES 1st Atlas*) with the same units in 2002–06. This reveals that, despite only a 7% increase overall in the North-East, there has been a 58% increase in occupied recording units in upper Donside and in Deeside above Ballater. This range extension may be due to colonisation of recently established conifer plantations in these areas though the influence of observer effort in these changes cannot be discounted.

Population and trends

Evidence from *BS3* and Jenkins & Watson (1999) suggests that average densities in different habitats in North-East Scotland might be about 11 pairs/km^2 in broad-leaved woodland, 3 pairs/km^2 in coniferous woodland, 5 pairs/km^2 in farmland and 8 pairs/km^2 in suburban and rural gardens. By applying these densities to the area of relevant land cover types (LC 2000 data) a total population of around 28,000 pairs can be calculated. Clearly there can be no claim of great precision attached to this estimate but the total is likely to fall within the range of 25,000–30,000 pairs - 10% of the Scottish population. The BBS in Scotland reveals a 10% population increase during 1994–2007 (Risely *et al.* 2008).

Author: *Melvin Morrison*

Greenfinch, Alford, May 2009. © *Ian Francis*

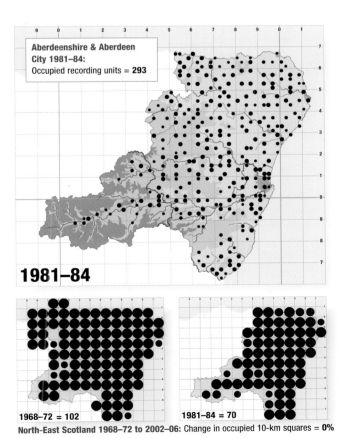

Aberdeenshire & Aberdeen City 1981–84:
Occupied recording units = 293

1981–84

1968–72 = 102   1981–84 = 70

North-East Scotland 1968–72 to 2002–06: Change in occupied 10-km squares = 0%

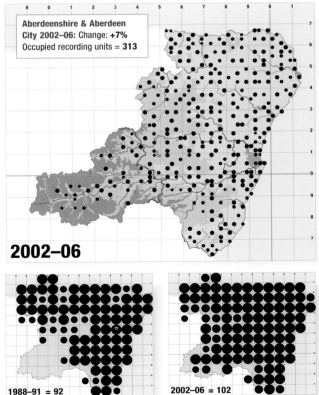

Aberdeenshire & Aberdeen City 2002–06: Change: +7%
Occupied recording units = 313

2002–06

1988–91 = 92   2002–06 = 102

Goldfinch

Carduelis carduelis

Common resident and migrant breeder. Estimated population in North-East Scotland: *6,000–9,000 pairs* (15% of Scottish population, 2% of UK)

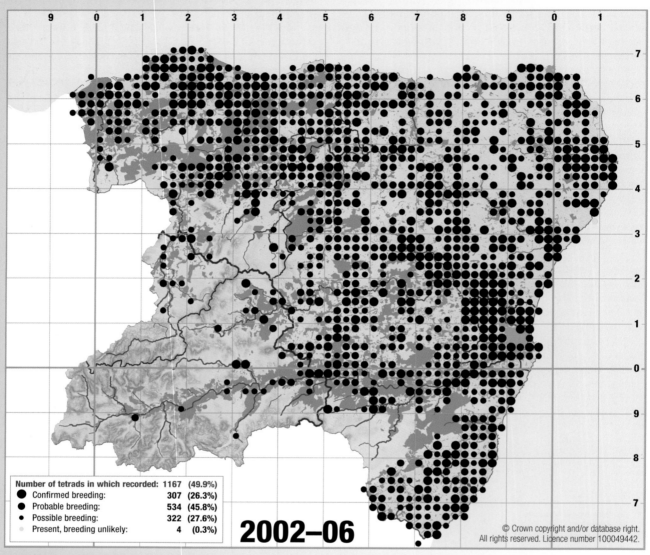

Number of tetrads in which recorded: 1167	(49.9%)
● Confirmed breeding:	307 (26.3%)
● Probable breeding:	534 (45.8%)
• Possible breeding:	322 (27.6%)
Present, breeding unlikely:	4 (0.3%)

2002–06

Habitat and breeding biology
Goldfinches breed in open country such as farmland with scattered trees, tall hedges and scrub but can also make use of parks and gardens. At other times of year they can be found feeding in birch and Alder woodland and in conifer plantations (Newton in *BS3*). They breed singly or in small groups. Nests are usually built in the outermost branches of trees at heights up to 10 m, but may be much lower in shrubs and hedges. The first clutch, of 4–6 eggs, is usually laid in mid May and up to three broods may be raised. Many early nests are lost due to adverse weather and predation so more young are produced in the latter half of the season (Newton in *BS3*).

Scottish distribution and status
Goldfinches are widely distributed throughout the lowlands of Scotland, mostly below 300 m. They are absent from the north-west of the mainland, the Northern Isles and most of the Outer Hebrides. They were said to be common in the 18th and 19th centuries but declined markedly during the latter part of the 19th century, possibly due to their popularity as cage birds and due to changes in agricultural practice (Baxter & Rintoul 1953). There was a general increase and northward

spread in the Scottish population during the 20th century and the population is now estimated at 40,000–60,000 pairs (Newton in *BS3*).

Distribution and status in North-East Scotland
Goldfinches are widespread throughout agricultural areas of North-East Scotland but are absent from most of the uplands. A few pairs inhabit moorland glens around Tomintoul but they are virtually absent to the west of Ballater; the few exceptions include isolated records at Spittal of Glenmuick and at Inverey, above Braemar. Very few breed above 300 m although breeding was proved as high as 400 m in Glen Buchat. Also evident is the species' aversion to breeding in extensive coniferous plantations, and the distribution is patchy in central Buchan where the lack of suitable habitat may be limiting. The low proportion (26%) of tetrads where breeding was confirmed may be due to the relative scarcity of successfully fledged broods in the early part of the season when most fieldwork was carried out.

Changes in distribution
Comparison of the 10-km square maps reveals a steady spread of Goldfinches over North-East Scotland since 1968–72. At that time the Goldfinch distribution in the North-East was

The Breeding Birds of North-East Scotland

focussed to the south of Aberdeen and they were virtually absent from land bordering the Moray Firth (*BTO 1st Atlas*). Breeding was confirmed in Moray in 1977 (Cook 1992) and by 1988–91 Goldfinches were widely but thinly spread through Moray and, indeed, all around the Moray Firth (*BTO 2nd Atlas*). Evidence of consolidation within the range is provided by comparison of the Aberdeenshire/Aberdeen City maps which reveal an almost three-fold increase in occupied recording units since the early 1980s.

Population and trends

Production of a meaningful estimate of the Goldfinch breeding population is fraught with difficulty for a number of reasons - no local studies have been carried out, the range and population have expanded substantially over the last 20 years, and even density estimates from elsewhere in Scotland are based on small data sets up to 20 years old. Reference to the mapped distribution in *BS3* indicates that North-East Scotland contains about 15% of the Scottish range; 15% of the Scottish population estimate would suggest 6,000–9,000 pairs in the North-East. Scottish BBS figures indicate a 91% increase over 1994–2007 (Risely *et al.* 2008) so our population may well approach or even exceed the upper limit of this range. It is likely that increased planting of rape and wild bird cover crops, as well as provision of Niger seed in many gardens, is providing some protection from winter food shortage and therefore contributing to the survival of birds which remain in the North-East in winter. Our breeding population may therefore continue to increase.

Author: *Melvin Morrison*

Goldfinch, Newburgh, 1980. © *Graham Rebecca*

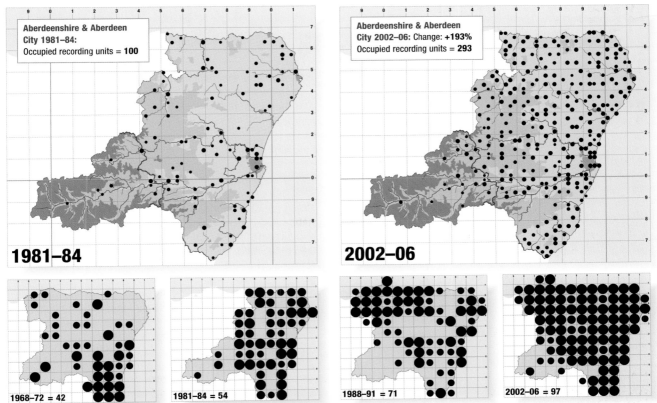

Aberdeenshire & Aberdeen City 1981–84:
Occupied recording units = **100**

1981–84

Aberdeenshire & Aberdeen City 2002–06: Change: **+193%**
Occupied recording units = **293**

2002–06

1968–72 = 42

1981–84 = 54

1988–91 = 71

2002–06 = 97

North-East Scotland 1968–72 to 2002–06: Change in occupied 10-km squares = **+131%**

Siskin
Carduelis spinus

Very common resident and migrant breeder. Winter visitor. Estimated population in North-East Scotland: **60,000–400,000 pairs** (12% of Scottish population, <12% of UK)

Scottish BAP list

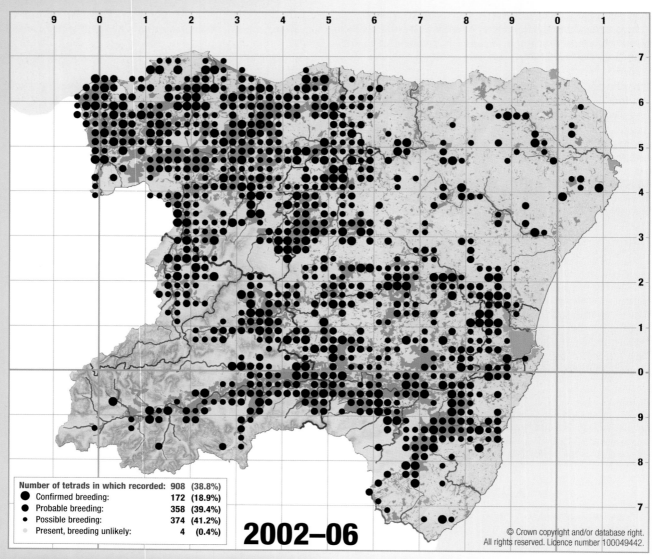

Number of tetrads in which recorded: 908 (38.8%)
- ● Confirmed breeding: 172 (18.9%)
- ● Probable breeding: 358 (39.4%)
- · Possible breeding: 374 (41.2%)
- ○ Present, breeding unlikely: 4 (0.4%)

2002–06

Siskin, Dunecht, May 1982. © *John Massie*

Habitat and breeding biology

Siskins are specialist feeders on conifer seed, using larch and spruce in winter and Scots Pine in spring, as cones open (Newton 1972). In summer, they shift to seeds of herbs such as Dandelions, docks and thistles. Birch seed is first used in late summer, but from autumn through to midwinter it can be a staple food along with Alder, larch and Sitka Spruce. Siskins often use garden feeders, taking peanuts when foods elsewhere are at a seasonal low, or in years of low spruce seed production (McKenzie *et al.* 2007). The main habitats used are therefore plantation forests, woodlands and gardens. In spruce 'mast' years, most return to their breeding areas during winter and breed from March onwards, with most young fledged by May (Shaw 1990). In Scots Pine forest they breed a month later (Newton 1972).

Scottish distribution and status

Formerly, the Siskin was a Scottish pinewood specialist species (Nethersole-Thompson & Watson 1974) but with the widespread planting of exotic trees, the species has spread to occupy coniferous woodland wherever it occurs (Jardine in *BS3*). Particularly large breeding populations are found during conifer seed 'mast' years in the spruce forests of the Borders, Dumfries & Galloway, Argyll, the Great Glen,

The Breeding Birds of North-East Scotland

Easter Ross and the North-East. Although formerly restricted in both range and abundance, Siskins are now ubiquitous with a population estimated as varying between 500,000–3,500,000 pairs (Jardine in *BS3*).

Distribution and status in North-East Scotland

The distribution and status of Siskins in the North-East is primarily influenced by the amount of coniferous woodland and how much of it is producing seed. During 2002–06, Siskins occupied most tetrads with coniferous woodland, breeding in Scots Pine virtually every year and spruces during 'mast' years. They were also found in some tetrads with little woodland because they use garden feeders in spring. Nevertheless there were far fewer occupied tetrads in the intensive farmlands of the Buchan plain and the Mearns, and virtually none in the mountain and moorland of the Cairngorms. The variation in annual abundance shown by the local BBS (despite the limited data sample) reflects the variation in production of spruce seed, which was high in 1998–99 and 2005–06 (M. Marquiss unpubl.).

Changes in distribution

In the 19th century, breeding Siskins were largely restricted to semi-natural Scots Pine forest, and some mature Scots Pine plantations (Holloway 1996). The huge expansion into the new forests of exotic conifers took place in the 1970s as those trees started to produce seed at about 20 years of age. By comparison, the recent change in distribution shown between 1981–84 (*NES 1st Atlas*) and 2002–06 was less dramatic but nevertheless substantial, with an 81% increase in occupied recording units. Much of this increase has taken place in Buchan where far more 10-km squares were occupied in 2002–06 than formerly; this is associated with more plantation woodland there, now established under the Grampian Challenge Scheme during the late 1990s and early 2000s.

Siskin, Daviot, Inverness-shire, June 2008. © *Allan Perkins*

Population and trends

Over the last century, the Siskin breeding population has increased dramatically with the increase in planted coniferous woodland. In the short term the population is volatile, fluctuating approximately seven-fold between years with copious spruce seed and years without (Jardine in *BS3*). In the North-East, there are roughly 1,230 km² of coniferous woodland - about 15% of the total for Scotland (Mackey *et al.* 1998, Forestry Commission 2001). If we assume that the Siskin breeding population exists in direct proportion, the population here might be calculated as between 60,000–400,000 pairs, depending on the abundance of the spruce seed crop. However, the population could be far less because conifer forest in the North-East has substantially more pine where Siskin breeding density is much lower.

Author: *Mick Marquiss*

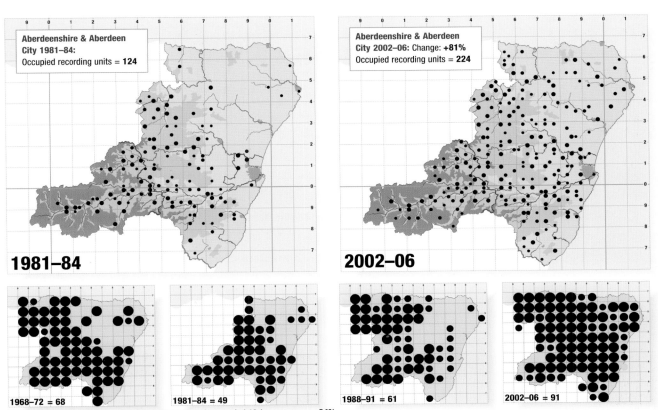

Aberdeenshire & Aberdeen City 1981–84: Occupied recording units = **124**

1981–84

Aberdeenshire & Aberdeen City 2002–06: Change: +81% Occupied recording units = **224**

2002–06

1968–72 = 68

1981–84 = 49

1988–91 = 61

2002–06 = 91

North-East Scotland 1968–72 to 2002–06: Change in occupied 10-km squares = +34%

Linnet

Carduelis cannabina

Very common resident. Estimated population in North-East Scotland: *18,000–22,000 pairs* (25% of Scottish population, 4% of UK)

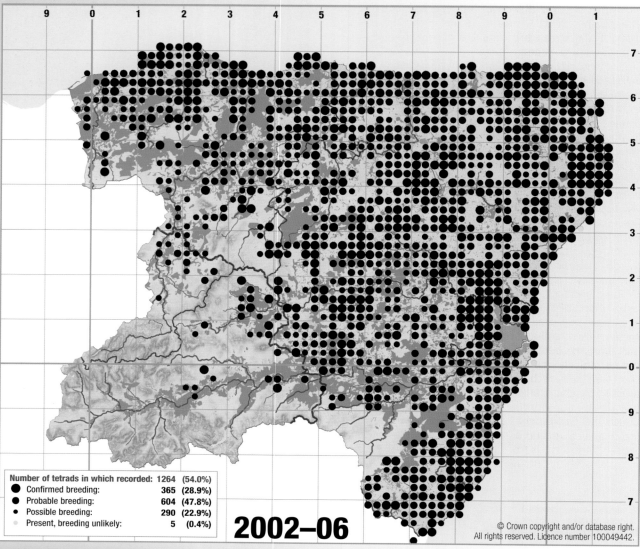

Number of tetrads in which recorded: 1264 (54.0%)
- ● Confirmed breeding: 365 (28.9%)
- ● Probable breeding: 604 (47.8%)
- ● Possible breeding: 290 (22.9%)
- ∙ Present, breeding unlikely: 5 (0.4%)

2002–06

Linnet, Whinnyfold, June 1998. © *Ed Duthie*

Habitat and breeding biology

Linnets breed throughout lowland North-East Scotland wherever scrub provides suitable nest sites and food plants provide a source of seeds. Gorse scrub is the favourite nesting habitat and is particularly used early in the nesting season before other species are in leaf; other scrub, bushes and hedges are also used. Linnets feed their young largely on seeds, with Dandelion and Oil-seed Rape appearing particularly important (Moorcroft *et al.* 2006). During the nesting season, rape fields, grazed pasture, weedy patches in arable fields and areas of set-aside provide foraging habitat. Wintering flocks have mostly broken up by April when nesting territories start to be occupied. Reports of small groups of birds through the summer may relate to loose nesting colonies. Flocks, probably of adults and juveniles, usually start to form in August but are recorded during July in some years. Laying can continue into August giving time for three broods, but two are probably normal.

Scottish distribution and status

The endemic Scottish subspecies, *C. c. autochthona,* occurs widely across most of lowland Scotland, being most abundant in eastern, arable areas. Linnets are scarce and localised above 300 m. The Scottish population is estimated as 70,000 to 90,000 pairs (Newton in *BS3*) and is thought to have declined in line with the rest of the British breeding population which fell by more than 50% between the 1970s and 2000 (BTO). More recently, the Scottish population may be increasing with the BBS recording a 26% increase between 1994–2007 (Risely *et al.* 2008).

Distribution and status in North-East Scotland

The Linnet is a widespread and common species across lowland areas of North-East Scotland. It is frequent in areas of arable and mixed farmland and coastal areas, particularly in the Howe of the Mearns, lower Donside, the Howe of Alford, Buchan, north-west Aberdeenshire and the Laich of Moray. It is much less numerous on ground above 300 m although, during 2002–06, breeding was confirmed near Balmoral at an altitude of more than 400 m and a single bird was recorded at around 600 m at Carn an Tuirc. Large areas of forestry, even on low ground, are generally avoided, with the possible exception of recently restocked areas where young trees can provide suitable nest sites for a few years. The species also appears to be absent from urban areas of Aberdeen City.

Changes in distribution

The Linnet's distribution in lowland areas of North-East Scotland appears similar to the distribution in 1968–1972 (*BTO 1st Atlas*). The main change in distribution between 1968–72 and 1981–84 (*NES 1st Atlas*) was a contraction in hill areas - for example it was not recorded in upper Deeside west of Ballater during 1981–84. In 1988–91 (*BTO 2nd Atlas*) this contraction in distribution was confirmed. The current distribution shows some expansion in range since 1981–84 with 293 occupied recording units in 2002–06 in Aberdeenshire/Aberdeen City compared with 209 occupied recording units in 1981–84. The most marked recent change in distribution has been a re-occupation of upland areas in upper Donside and upper Deeside with records from six tetrads west of Ballater. The reason for this recent change is unclear.

Linnet, Aberdeen, June 2006. © *John Chapman*

Population and trends

North-East Scotland probably supports a substantial proportion of Scotland's breeding population of Linnets. Assuming that the North-East contains around 25% of the area of suitable habitat in Scotland, then a North-East Scotland population of 18,000–22,000 can be estimated. BBS data for 1994–2006 indicates a slight decline in abundance in the North-East which may be linked to changes in agricultural land use. The withdrawal of compulsory set-aside in 2008 is likely to result in a decrease in availability of weed seeds which may have an effect on Linnet abundance.

Author: *David Law*

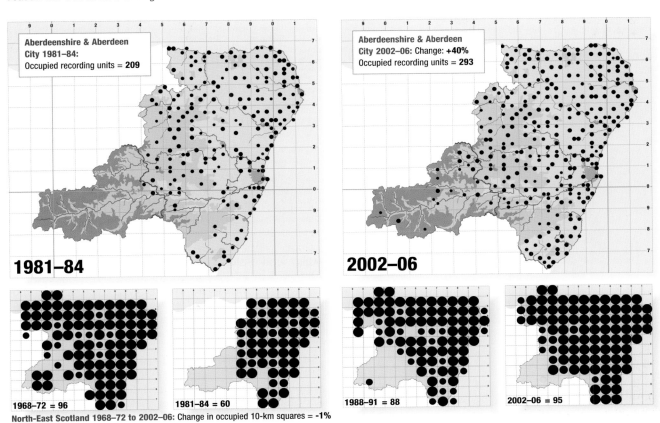

Aberdeenshire & Aberdeen City 1981–84:
Occupied recording units = **209**

1981–84

Aberdeenshire & Aberdeen City 2002–06: Change: +40%
Occupied recording units = **293**

2002–06

1968–72 = 96

1981–84 = 60

1988–91 = 88

2002–06 = 95

North-East Scotland 1968–72 to 2002–06: Change in occupied 10-km squares = -1%

Scarce resident and migrant breeder. Winter visitor. Estimated population in North-East Scotland: **110–330 pairs** (2% of Scottish and UK populations)

Red list; UK BAP list

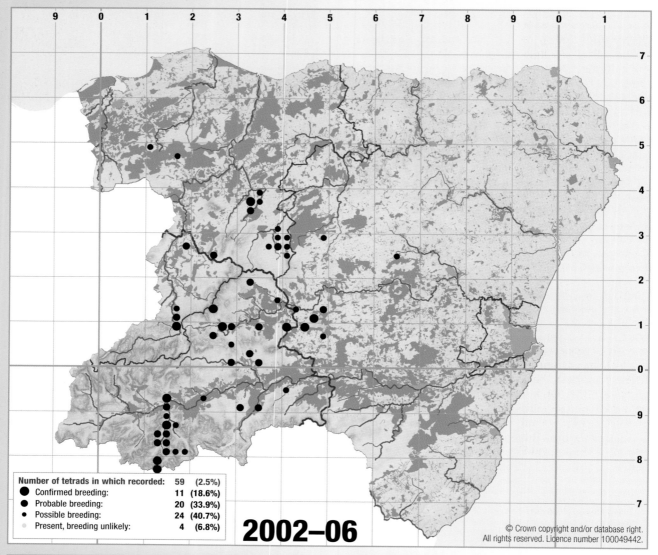

Number of tetrads in which recorded:	59	(2.5%)
● Confirmed breeding:	11	(18.6%)
● Probable breeding:	20	(33.9%)
● Possible breeding:	24	(40.7%)
· Present, breeding unlikely:	4	(6.8%)

2002–06

Twite, North Uist, May 2008. © *Derek McGinn*

Habitat and breeding biology

Twite breed on open Heather moorland, in upland areas, but also in coastal areas in the north and on Scottish islands. They are known to visit nearby pasture to feed (Orford 1973). Most birds return to their breeding grounds in April with eggs laid from the end of April to mid July, and the young fledging from June to August. In Glen Clunie, pairs are double brooded (Wilkinson in *BS3*). Twite are colonial, often nesting in small groups with nests on rocky outcrops or near the ground amongst tall Heather, Bracken and grass tussocks. They have an extended breeding season and remain for a relatively long period in their breeding areas. Factors that have a negative effect on breeding success are the loss of hay meadows and the increase in silage production, the loss of tall Heather through overgrazing, poor muir-burn practice and the loss of Bracken beds (Langston *et al.* 2006). The conservation of these habitats is crucial to the survival of Twite populations (Wernham *et al.* 2002).

Scottish distribution and status

The core breeding areas are Orkney, the north coasts of Caithness and Sutherland, the Outer Hebrides (especially the Uists), Coll, Tiree and Colonsay. The estimated breeding population is between 5,600 and 13,800 pairs (Wilkinson in

BS3). Twite have undergone a severe long-term decline over the last two hundred years (*BTO 2nd Atlas*, Gregory *et al.* 2002). The Scottish population comprises about 94% of the world population of the subspecies *C. f. pipilans*, and is thus of international importance (Davis 1988, Batten *et al.* 1990).

Distribution and status in North-East Scotland

The Twite's breeding range is concentrated in moorland areas in Moray and in upper Deeside and Donside. Here, it avoids the very high ground and is found mainly among lower hills often bordering farmland and rough pasture with the altitudinal breeding range extending from around 200–650 m. During 2002–06, favoured areas for breeding Twite included country to the south of Braemar (up Glen Clunie to Cairnwell), the Cabrach, up Glen Avon (to the south of Tomintoul) and near Dufftown. They were also widely but thinly spread around Strathdon. The wintering population is variable, and far exceeds the breeding population in most years (*NES 1st Atlas*). Winter ringing has shown breeding birds from Glen Clunie wintering on the coastal plain south of Stonehaven while birds from Donside have been found wintering in the Newburgh area. It also revealed the presence of birds from the west coast of Scotland within these flocks. (R. Duncan, R. Rae pers. comm.).

Changes in distribution

There is conflicting evidence relating to range changes. At the 10-km square level, the range has steadily decreased over the last 40 years from 32 squares in 1968–72 (*BTO 1st Atlas*) to 21 squares in 2002–06. This supports the evidence of a national decline (Wilkinson in *BS3*, Langston *et al.* 2006). By contrast, the number of occupied recording units in Aberdeenshire has increased from 20 in 1981–84 to 26 in 2002–06. This does, however, reflect an infilling of the 1981–84 distribution rather than an extension of the range to new areas. Indeed, there was a loss of two recording units between Banchory and Stonehaven.

Twite, Scotland 1980s. © *John Edelsten*

Population and trends

The estimates of breeding density given by Gibbons *et al.* (1993) vary widely between a mean of 2 pairs/100 ha (Davies 1988) and 9 pairs/100 ha (B. Campbell from nest record cards). These population estimates equate to between 8–36 pairs/tetrad but are considered too high by Langston *et al.* (2006) for the Scottish population. Their study found that densities were generally higher along coastal fringes of the north and west but lower across inland Scotland. Average densities ranged from 0.51 pairs/km^2 in eastern Scotland to 1.47 pairs/km^2 in south-west Scotland. Applying these densities to the 55 tetrads with confirmed, probable or possible breeding records in North-East Scotland in 2002–06, gives a population estimate within the range of 110–330 pairs. These figures should be regarded only as very approximate as Twite are difficult to census and there are few published quantitative data on the status of Scottish breeding Twite. In particular, applying average densities of pairs per tetrad to a colonial species must be treated with caution.

Author: *Alister Clunas*

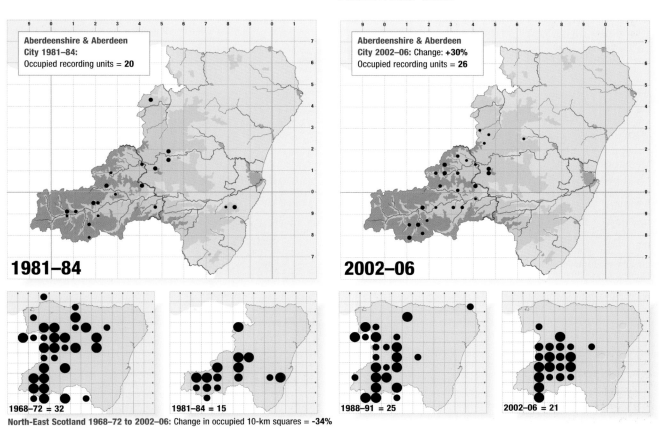

Aberdeenshire & Aberdeen City 1981–84:
Occupied recording units = **20**

1981–84

Aberdeenshire & Aberdeen City 2002–06: Change: **+30%**
Occupied recording units = **26**

2002–06

1968–72 = 32   1981–84 = 15   1988–91 = 25   2002–06 = 21

North-East Scotland 1968–72 to 2002–06: Change in occupied 10-km squares = **-34%**

Lesser Redpoll

Carduelis cabaret

Common resident and migrant breeder. Estimated population in North-East Scotland: *1,000–2,000 pairs* (13% of Scottish population, 6% of UK)

Red list; UK BAP list

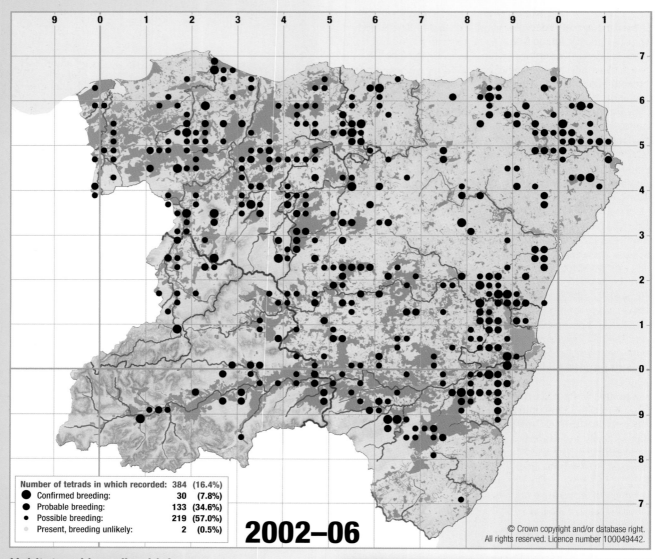

Number of tetrads in which recorded:	384	(16.4%)
● Confirmed breeding:	30	(7.8%)
● Probable breeding:	133	(34.6%)
● Possible breeding:	219	(57.0%)
Present, breeding unlikely:	2	(0.5%)

2002–06

Habitat and breeding biology

Lesser Redpolls breed in small, loose groups in birch woods and young conifer plantations, as well as scrub and sometimes large gardens. In plantations, as the canopy closes over, the redpolls leave as the habitat becomes unsuitable. The nests are built in trees and bushes. There is little local information on the breeding cycle but elsewhere in Scotland active nests are found mostly from late May until July. Clutches usually contain 4–6 eggs with fledglings appearing from late June. Lesser Redpolls are commonly double brooded (Petty & Pennington in *BS3*). After the breeding season the birds form flocks, often with other species, from August through to the following spring. At these times they can be found feeding on birches and Alders and in more open habitats, including weedy fields.

Scottish distribution and status

In the breeding season, they are distributed widely on the Scottish mainland where suitable habitat occurs at mid-altitudes and are therefore absent from the higher hills and most of the agricultural lowlands. They breed thinly in the Western Isles but are largely absent from Orkney and Shetland (Petty & Pennington in *BS3*). They are more widespread in winter, when birds are generally found at lower

Lesser Redpoll, Park, 1979. © *John Massie*

altitudes. The Lesser Redpoll is a partial migrant with a variable number leaving the area after breeding and moulting. In 2007, the Scottish breeding population was estimated at 7,500–15,000 pairs (Petty & Pennington in *BS3*).

Distribution and status in North-East Scotland
Lesser Redpolls breed widely through the wooded and scrubby areas of inland Moray, Buchan, Donside and Deeside, though they are absent from mature forestry plantations and more elevated regions above about 350 m. There are few breeding records from coastal Moray, the lower Deveron, the Ythan basin and the Mearns. Whilst it is likely that the species is indeed less common in the more intensively agricultural areas, the issue is confounded by less thorough tetrad coverage in the lower Deveron and Ythan basin in particular, where the species may occur more frequently.

Changes in distribution
There is no evidence to suggest any major change in distribution in North-East Scotland over the last 100 years, though local populations will have come and gone with habitat succession and scrub and woodland clearances. In 1968–72, breeding Lesser Redpolls were found in 97 10-km squares across the whole of the North-East except on the very highest hills (*BTO 1st Atlas*). The second national atlas showed major losses and drew attention to reductions in the lowlands of eastern Aberdeenshire (*BTO 2nd Atlas*). There must be a suspicion that these 'losses' were attributable to problems with coverage since there is little substantial difference at the 10-km square level between the distributions reported in the first local atlas and the current one.

Population and trends
The Lesser Redpoll population varies locally with changes in the availability of habitat (mainly through woodland succession), and quite substantially from year to year with fluctuations in the seed crops. UK national surveys indicate dramatic reductions in redpoll numbers following a rapid

Lesser Redpoll, Clyde, April 2006. © *John Anderson*

build-up in the 1970s, apparently due to changes in habitat availability in forestry plantations. In Scotland, the population showed little change between 1994 and 2007 (Risely *et al.* 2008), but this masks evidence of a decline of 23% (confidence limits -34% to +3%) in the BBS over the period 2000–05 (Baillie *et al.* 2007). Atlas fieldwork in 2002–06 revealed 383 occupied tetrads so an assumption of 3–5 pairs per tetrad would indicate a population in the range of 1,000–2,000 pairs.

Author: *Alan Knox*

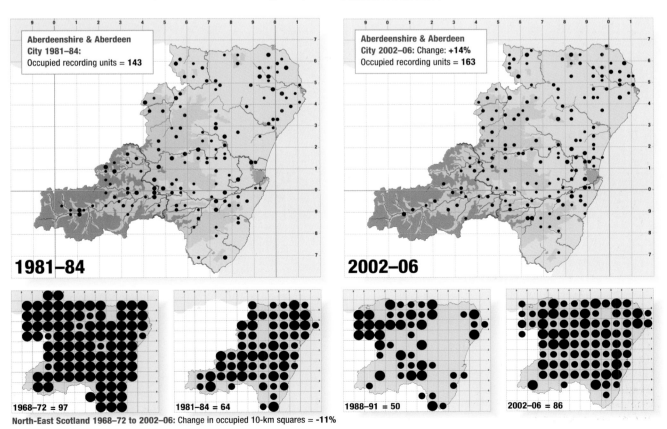

Aberdeenshire & Aberdeen City 1981–84: Occupied recording units = **143**

1981–84

Aberdeenshire & Aberdeen City 2002–06: Change: +14% Occupied recording units = **163**

2002–06

1968–72 = 97   1981–84 = 64   1988–91 = 50   2002–06 = 86

North-East Scotland 1968–72 to 2002–06: Change in occupied 10-km squares = **-11%**

Cairn Lochan to Ben Macdui

This alpine plateau in the Cairngorm Mountains holds a specialised community of birds which breed only in such high montane areas of Scotland. Ptarmigan are widespread and there are smaller numbers of Dotterel and Snow Bunting. Wheatears and Meadow Pipits are here in summer although greater numbers breed at slightly lower altitudes. Snowy Owls were present in spring or summer in several years between 1979 and 1998, but breeding never took place. August 2005 © *Martin Cook*

Muir of Dinnet

Few sites in North-East Scotland contain such a wide range of habitats as the Muir of Dinnet National Nature Reserve. Two important lochs are surrounded by regenerating broad-leaved and coniferous woodland extending out onto high level moorland, and scattered within this lie numerous marshes and wetlands, with patches of grazed and cultivated farmland. The land was almost completely open 60 years ago, but now there is extensive woodland cover. Breeding birds in this area include Mute Swan, Greylag Goose, Wigeon, Tufted Duck, Goosander, Goldeneye (an important national concentration), Black Grouse, Great Crested Grebe, Water Rail, seven species of wader, Black-headed and Common Gulls, Cuckoo, Barn Owl, Long-eared Owl, Green Woodpecker, Tree Pipit, Redstart, Grasshopper and Sedge Warblers. February 1999 © *Harry Scott*

Common Crossbill   *Loxia curvirostra*

Common resident and irruptive migrant breeder. Estimated population in North-East Scotland: *variable - hundreds to many thousands* (>10% of Scottish population; unknown % of UK)   Schedule 1

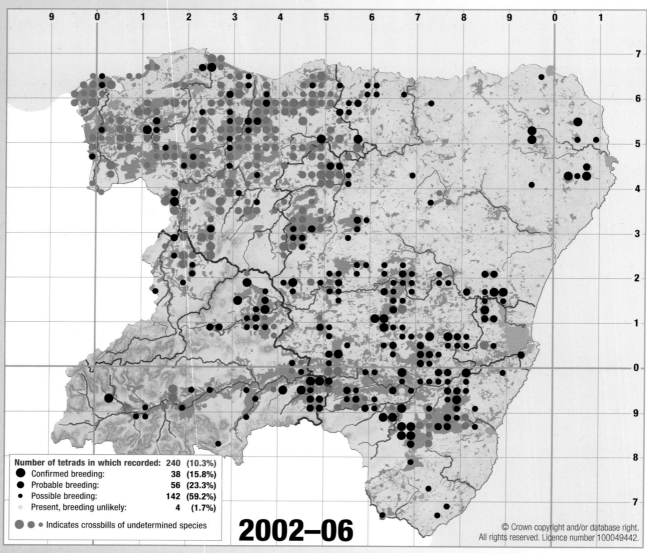

Number of tetrads in which recorded: 240 (10.3%)
● Confirmed breeding: 38 (15.8%)
● Probable breeding: 56 (23.3%)
● Possible breeding: 142 (59.2%)
· Present, breeding unlikely: 4 (1.7%)

● ● ● Indicates crossbills of undetermined species

2002–06

Habitat and breeding biology

Crossbills are specialist finches that feed on conifers year round, using their crossed mandibles to extract seeds from closed cones. Common Crossbills have relatively narrow bills best suited for prising the scales of Norway Spruce cones. In any single region, Norway Spruce seed is produced in quantity only sporadically. From late summer, crossbills aggregate in areas of seed abundance. They breed as cones start to open in late winter, and then switch in spring to breed and then fatten on Scots Pine seed prior to mass movement (irruption) in search of new areas of spruce seed abundance (Newton 1972). In North-East Scotland there is a variety of planted conifers, and Common Crossbills switch between species as each seed type becomes seasonally available (Marquiss & Rae 1994) enabling them to breed in autumn and winter (on larch and Sitka Spruce), late winter (on Norway Spruce) and spring (on Scots Pine), before moving on in June.

Scottish distribution and status

Formerly, the only coniferous habitat in Scotland was Scots Pine and mass arrivals of Common Crossbills led to only temporary abundance as their breeding in Scots Pine is short-lived. From the 19th century, the substantial plantations of exotic conifers have enabled immigrants to establish progressively larger breeding populations, at least in the year following an irruption. Such populations are occasionally sustained for several years thereafter as Sitka Spruce crops can be asynchronous on a Scotland-wide scale, and larch retains seed for several years. The Scottish breeding population varies enormously - perhaps between 10,000 and 50,000 pairs with 250,000 pairs or more following exceptional immigration (Summers in *BS3*).

Common Crossbills, Glen Gairn, April 2001. © *Ed Duthie*

Distribution and status in North-East Scotland

Common Crossbills are similar to Scottish Crossbills and, without the advantage of familiarity with head shape or calls, many observers were reluctant to allocate species to the crossbills they observed. This was particularly the case in areas north and west of Huntly. Despite this bias the distribution of tetrads occupied by Common Crossbill showed good correspondence with plantations of conifers. This is as expected considering there were major immigrations in 2001 and 2002 (Summers in *BS3*). It is well established that following large irruptions, Common Crossbills can occupy even the most isolated blocks of coniferous woodland and will settle wherever there is seed production. During 2002–06, crossbills were recorded in most areas of conifer woodland sufficiently mature to produce seed.

Common Crossbill, Glen Gairn, April 2002. © *Ed Duthie*

In many cases, observers were unable to confirm with certainty which species of crossbill was involved. Tetrads which contain such records are indicated on the main map with grey dots.

Common Crossbills vary in their morphology and calls in a discontinuous way suggesting several types, possibly adapted to a particular region or food type, and each irruption is characterised by a particular type (see review in Summers in *BS3*, Marquiss & Newton 2008). The distribution of at least three call types has been mapped (Summers *et al.* 2002) with little obvious assortment according to habitat, and all three occurred in the North-East.

Changes in distribution

The comparison between the two atlases was compromised again by the uncertainty of the species concerned in many records. Nevertheless, the distributions of those identified as Common Crossbills were similar in Aberdeenshire/Aberdeen City in the two atlas periods. There were fewer records in 1981–84, probably because the main irruption during this period (in 1982) was substantially smaller than that in 2002. There was a notable lack of records from the earlier atlas in upper Deeside (*NES 1st Atlas*) but this was probably biased as observers were more wary of identifying birds as Common Crossbills if they were observed within this area renowned for Scottish Crossbills. It is now well known that Common Crossbills use semi-natural Scots Pine forests in spring once cones start to open.

Population and trends

Over the long term, the substantial increase in planted exotic conifers, particularly Sitka Spruce, has led to progressively larger populations of immigrant Common Crossbills settling. Moreover, the presence of larch has enabled the birds to persist in years between irruptions. The fluctuations in population size are nevertheless high, perhaps with only hundreds in low years but rising to many thousands as immigrants settle in Sitka Spruce seed production years.

Authors: *Mick Marquiss & Robert Rae*

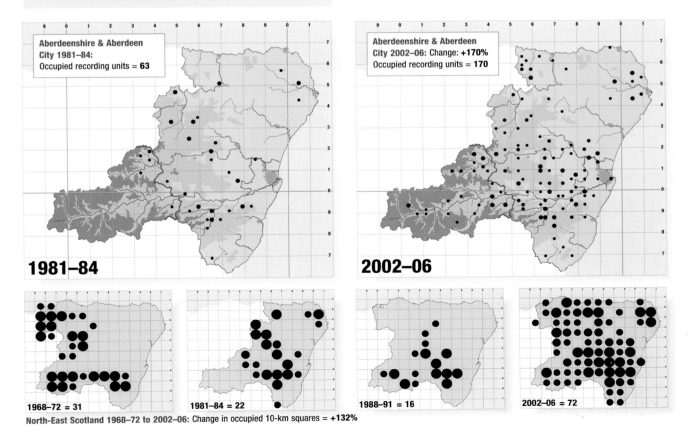

Aberdeenshire & Aberdeen City 1981–84:
Occupied recording units = **63**

1981–84

Aberdeenshire & Aberdeen City 2002–06: Change: **+170%**
Occupied recording units = **170**

2002–06

1968–72 = 31

1981–84 = 22

1988–91 = 16

2002–06 = 72

North-East Scotland 1968–72 to 2002–06: Change in occupied 10-km squares = +132%

Scottish Crossbill

Loxia scotica

Common resident. Estimated population in North-East Scotland: up to *1,000–2,000 pairs* (in peak years about 30% of Scottish and UK populations)

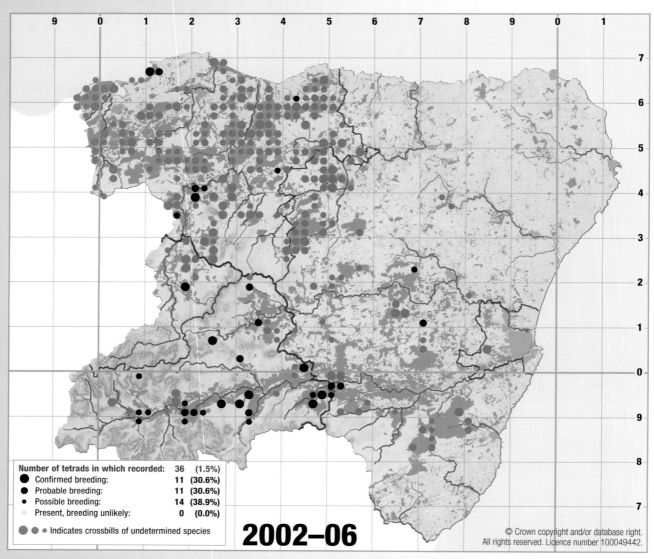

Number of tetrads in which recorded: 36 (1.5%)

● Confirmed breeding: 11 (30.6%)

● Probable breeding: 11 (30.6%)

● Possible breeding: 14 (38.9%)

○ Present, breeding unlikely: 0 (0.0%)

● ● ● Indicates crossbills of undetermined species

2002–06

Habitat and breeding biology

Scottish Crossbills are slightly larger than Common Crossbills and have a deeper, more curved bill adapted to prise the tough woody scales of Scots Pine cones (Newton 1972, Knox 1975). They are relatively sedentary, moving short distances to track conifer seed production (Marquiss *et al.* 1995). They can feed on Scots Pine seed year round but only do so in the absence of other conifer seed. In most years they switch between species using Scots Pine from early spring to summer, then exotics (larch, Sitka Spruce, Lodgepole Pine and Norway Spruce) in autumn and winter (Marquiss & Rae 2002). Spruce seed is only available in 'mast' years, larch more so because it retains seed in upright cones, and pine seed is produced in all years. The habitats used by Scottish Crossbills are therefore primarily centred on pine woodland, but include plantations of other species (Summers *et al.* 2002). Optimal habitat is probably an intimate mosaic of Scots Pine and larch. They can breed in mid winter in spruce mast years but most start nesting in March, and produce most fledged young in May and June.

Scottish distribution and status

The Scottish Crossbill is a Scottish endemic crossbill. Scottish Crossbills can be difficult to distinguish from other crossbills in the field and the best assessments of distribution have therefore come from widespread surveys to record calls (Summers *et al.* 2002). Most Scottish Crossbills are found in the forested parts of the east coast river systems from Deeside north to Caithness. There are a few scattered records south to the central belt (Summers *et al.* 2004). A survey in 2008 estimated the (world) population

Scottish Crossbill, Glen Tanar, April 2009. © *Rab Rae*

size at 6,800 pairs (95% CI 4,050–11,350 pairs; Summers & Buckland 2010). Population fluctuation remains obscure; it is known that numbers vary much from year to year within some woods, but there is insufficient broad scale survey to determine how much this is due to movement and how much to flux in the total population.

Distribution and status in North-East Scotland
Following the decision not to accept non-specialist records which separated Scottish from Common Crossbills in Moray (*MNBR* 2000) and recommendations that records of Scottish Crossbill in North-east Scotland should be substantiated with acoustic or biometric evidence (*NESBR* 2002), the number of claimed records for the present atlas was small and there was bias; Scottish Crossbills were particularly under recorded away from the historically well known stronghold in upper Deeside. Nevertheless, there were records in all the most wooded parts of the North-East, and (unlike Common Crossbills) they were not recorded in the small woods of the arable lowlands, or along the east coast. The pattern of occupied tetrads was thus consistent with the distribution of Scottish Crossbill mapped from acoustic surveying for diagnostic calls in 1995–2003 (Summers *et al.* 2004) but differed significantly from that in 2008 (Summers & Buckland 2010) when Scottish Crossbills were recorded further east in spruce forests where seed production peaked.

Changes in distribution
The comparison between published atlases was compromised by the uncertainty of the crossbill species concerned amongst earlier records; the 1981–84 Aberdeenshire distribution, confined to middle and upper Deeside (*NES 1st Atlas*), was influenced by the known historical records, as was the next atlas distribution map from 1988–91 (*BTO 2nd Atlas*). By then it was thought that Scottish Crossbills were living outside the previously known strongholds, but to an unknown degree. With little spatial information any changes in distribution remain obscure.

Scottish Crossbill, Ballater, March 2006. © *Jenny Lennon*

Population and trends
It is difficult to estimate the Scottish Crossbill population in the North-East, other than as a proportion of the national estimate. This is unsatisfactory because it is known that they can concentrate in areas of seed abundance, and in theory the bulk of the population might in some years be located within the North-East. Certainly, the converse occurs for, in 2000, Scottish Crossbills were so scarce in the forests of Deeside and Strathdon that no nesting pairs were found. With no quantitative estimate of population movement, we can only guess at peak numbers here involving 1,000–2,000 pairs. For lack of long-term survey information, we are ignorant of trends. We can speculate that as conifer woodland has increased, so must have numbers of Scottish Crossbills. Their future population could well increase alongside increases in Scots Pine forest, but not necessarily if there is concomitant decrease in other conifers, particularly larch.

Authors: *Mick Marquiss & Robert Rae*

In many cases, observers were unable to confirm with certainty which species of crossbill was involved. Tetrads which contain such records are indicated on the main map with grey dots.

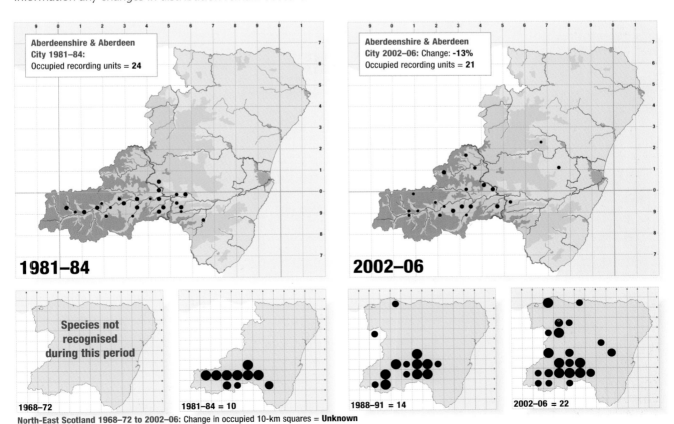

Aberdeenshire & Aberdeen City 1981–84:
Occupied recording units = **24**

1981–84

Aberdeenshire & Aberdeen City 2002–06: Change: **-13%**
Occupied recording units = **21**

2002–06

Species not recognised during this period

1968–72

1981–84 = 10

1988–91 = 14

2002–06 = 22

North-East Scotland 1968–72 to 2002–06: Change in occupied 10-km squares = **Unknown**

Parrot Crossbill

Loxia pytyopsittacus

Rare resident. Estimated population in North-East Scotland: **50–100 pairs** (about 50% of Scottish and UK populations)

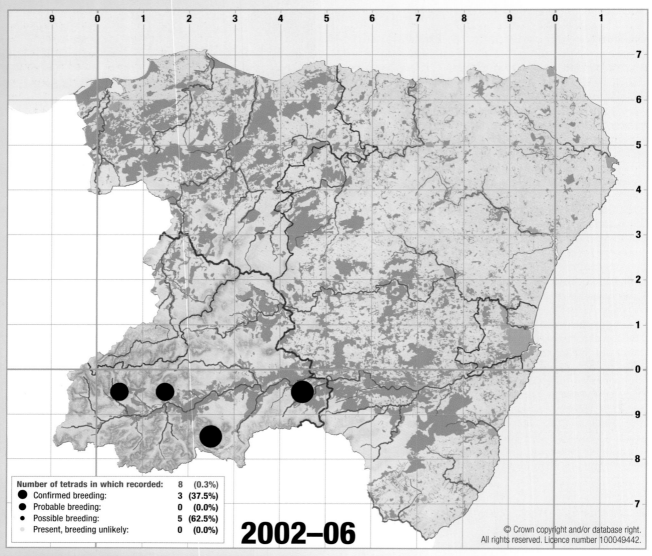

Number of tetrads in which recorded:	8	(0.3%)
● Confirmed breeding:	3	(37.5%)
● Probable breeding:	0	(0.0%)
● Possible breeding:	5	(62.5%)
● Present, breeding unlikely:	0	(0.0%)

2002–06

Parrot Crossbill, Dinnet, May 2003. © *Harry Scott*

Habitat and breeding biology

Parrot Crossbill is the largest of the crossbill species; it is larger than Scottish Crossbill and has an even deeper and more curved bill, especially suited to prise apart the tough woody scales of Scots Pine cones (Newton 1972, Knox 1975) to extract seeds. They forage on Scots Pine year round (Marquiss & Rae 2002) but in winter prefer the relatively small cones found on the broad canopy of the most mature trees (Summers in *BS3*) so their main habitat is semi-natural native pine forest. They also use plantations where old pines have been left *e.g.* to provide seed for 'natural' regeneration in continuous cover forestry. Breeding is closely timed to exploit food abundance as cones open in spring and crossbills can then extract seeds more efficiently. In some years, breeding attempts start in February but most first nests are in March. Many early nests fail due to snow and rain but repeat attempts continue through to June. Early successful pairs can produce a second brood. Scots Pines' seed production can vary ten-fold over a three to five year cycle, but even in poor years there is always some seed available so, as the last of the ripe seed is shed from open cones in summer, Parrot Crossbills switch to the next generation of maturing seed. Compared with Common Crossbills, Parrot Crossbills are relatively sedentary, often remaining within the same forest although some birds move short distances, including late breeding adults still with dependant young. Nevertheless, mass movement does occur in search of a better cone crop, with exodus from places where seed production is low and crossbill numbers high. Such longer distance movements take place in autumn and, by November, Parrot Crossbills have settled in the area where they will subsequently winter and breed (Marquiss 2002).

Scottish distribution and status
From the 1990s to date, Parrot Crossbills have been recorded in all of the larger native pinewoods of Scotland, and in plantations with mature trees in mid Deeside, lower Speyside, and on the Black Isle (Summers in *BS3*). These records are derived from birds identified using measurements of wing and bill (live caught birds and a few dead specimens) and by the sonograms of their calls. There were probably birds breeding in the past following previous irruptions (*e.g.* Millais 1884) but the lack of definitive criteria for identification at that time obscured numbers and trends. Summers (in *BS3*) suggested a Scottish population of about 100 pairs during the period 1997 to 2002 and there is no evidence of marked population change since then.

Distribution and status in North-East Scotland
Throughout the Atlas period, Parrot Crossbills were observed in the semi-natural pine forests of the North-East, with pairs and small groups of birds during the breeding season, larger groups of up to 30 in autumn, and between 6 and 20 in mid winter. To judge from newly fledged juveniles seen, breeding occurred in 2004 (Glen Tanar), 2005 (Ballochbuie) and 2006 (Mar Forest).

Changes in distribution
There were no records of Parrot Crossbills in previous atlases and as far as is known, a nest found by the authors in the Quoich woodlands on 6th June 1993 was the first proof of breeding in the North-East. The nest contained four young about 10 days old and all subsequently fledged. Over the next three years Parrot Crossbills were found in all the semi-natural Scots pine forests in Deeside, and in mature pine plantations at Invercauld, Dinnet and by Strachan.

Population and trends
In 1993 we guessed the population was over 50 breeding pairs, and probably close to 100 pairs in 1995, a year of good pine seed production. Re-sightings of colour ringed birds showed that individuals moved between years, from the upper Quoich woodlands to Ballochbuie Forest, and from the Derry woodlands to Invercauld, and to Glen Tanar. To judge from the present atlas records, there has been little change in breeding distribution or numbers but in the absence of systematic counts during the breeding season, trends in numbers are unknown.

Authors: *Mick Marquiss & Robert Rae*

Parrot Crossbill nest (lower left), Deeside, April 2005. © *Ed Duthie*

Common Rosefinch *Carpodacus erythrinus*

Occasionally present in summer. Passage migrant. Estimated population in North-East Scotland: **0 pairs**

Schedule 1; Scottish BAP list

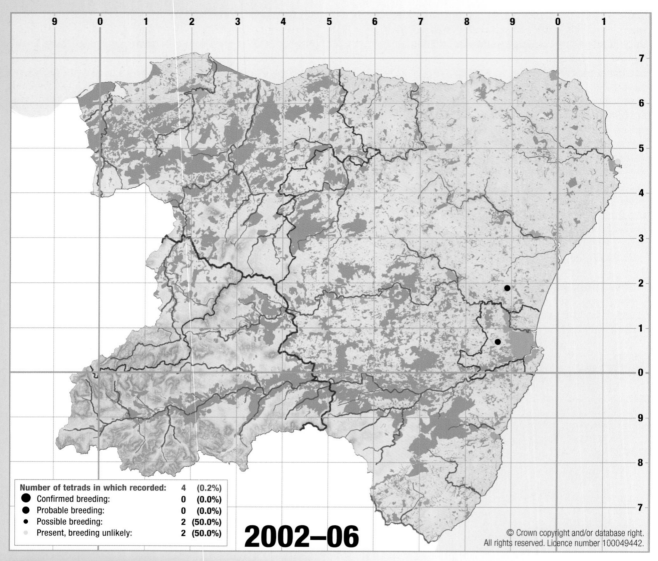

Number of tetrads in which recorded:	4	(0.2%)
● Confirmed breeding:	0	(0.0%)
● Probable breeding:	0	(0.0%)
• Possible breeding:	2	(50.0%)
· Present, breeding unlikely:	2	(50.0%)

2002–06

Common Rosefinch, Oulanka NP, Finland, June 2007. © *Allan Perkins*

Habitat and breeding biology

Across their northern Eurasian range, Common Rosefinches breed in woodlands, scrub, marshy areas and mature suburban gardens. On the few occasions when the species has nested in Scotland, this has taken place in open birch scrub and other rough vegetation. Throughout their range they typically breed late in the season, laying their clutch of 4–6 eggs during late May–mid June, with young fledging 21–25 days later.

Scottish distribution and status

In Scotland, spring migrants mostly arrive between mid May–late June. Autumn migrants appear from mid August with peak numbers in late August and early September. The great majority of records at both seasons are from the Northern Isles but a few appear throughout Scotland, especially in spring when there is a north-westerly bias to mainland records (Proctor in *BS3*). Common Rosefinches occasionally linger to breed; on five occasions, all between 1982–1997. Localities have included Ross & Cromarty, Sutherland, Argyll and Skye & Lochalsh.

Distribution and status in North-East Scotland

There have been 25 records in North-East Scotland since the first in 1979; eight in spring and 15 in autumn. The great majority have been at, or very close to, the coast (Phillips 1997). There have also been two summer records of lingering birds; a singing adult male in gardens at Kingswells near Aberdeen for 3–4 weeks from 26th May 2003, and another singing adult male at Newmachar between 22nd June–16th July 2006. There has been a substantial increase in Scottish passage migrants since the 1970s, reflecting the recent range expansion in western Europe (Proctor in *BS3*). If this continues then there is clearly the possibility that a lingering adult male will attract a mate and a breeding attempt in North-East Scotland will follow.

Author: *Martin Cook*

Common Rosefinch, Newmachar, July 2006. © *Harry Scott*

Common Rosefinch habitat, Newmachar, November 2010. © *Ian Francis*

Common Rosefinch habitat, Newmachar, November 2010. © *Ian Francis*

Bullfinch
Pyrrhula pyrrhula

Common resident. Estimated population in North-East Scotland: *3,000–5,000 pairs* (6% of Scottish population, 2% of UK)

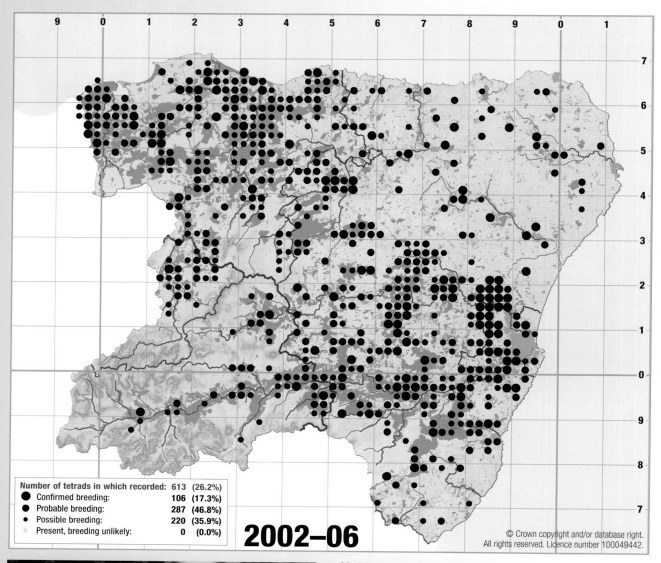

	Number of tetrads in which recorded:	613	(26.2%)
●	Confirmed breeding:	106	(17.3%)
●	Probable breeding:	287	(46.8%)
●	Possible breeding:	220	(35.9%)
·	Present, breeding unlikely:	0	(0.0%)

2002–06

Bullfinch, Bieldside, May 2004. © *Harry Scott*

Habitat and breeding biology

Bullfinches seldom stray far from cover and are typically found in deciduous and coniferous woodlands, scrub, large hedgerows, and shrubby gardens in suburban areas. Males are not strongly territorial, so pairs often nest close to one another. They nest in thick shrubs 1–3 m above the ground, laying clutches of 3–6 eggs from May to August, and can rear 2–3 broods (Proffitt *et al.* 2004, Newton in *BS3*). The female incubates for 12–14 days, when the male feeds her at the nest. Chicks are similarly fed by regurgitation on seeds such as Chickweed, dock and Wood Sorrel, supplemented by caterpillars and spiders (Marquiss 2007). They fledge at 15–17 days old, becoming independent after a further 2–3 weeks.

Scottish distribution and status

The species is widespread and relatively common throughout Scotland, absent only from unforested upland areas, and the virtually treeless Outer Hebrides and Northern Isles. The Scottish population is estimated at 50,000–90,000 pairs, and it may be more numerous now than at any time during the last 200 years, due partly to the increase in area of forestry (Newton in *BS3*).

Distribution and status in North-East Scotland

Bullfinches were recorded in a quarter of the tetrads surveyed, and the distribution largely mirrors that of woodland throughout the region. The core of the range lies in a broad band from Stonehaven and Aberdeen north-westwards to Cullen and Forres. The Buchan plain, where woodland, hedgerows and scrub are relatively scarce, is sparsely populated, as is the open agricultural landscape south of Stonehaven. To the west, birds are found along Deeside and Donside as far as Linn of Dee and Corgarff, with glens such as Muick and Gairn also occupied. Populations in Strathdon and Glenlivet are separated by the Ladder Hills, and other gaps occur south of Huntly, north of Keith, and east of Findhorn. Birds are also absent from much of Aberdeen City, and there are also apparent gaps in some wooded areas such as Clashindarroch, and Drumtochty Forest in the south.

Bullfinch, Cults, May 1989. © *Ed Duthie*

Changes in distribution

The number of occupied recording units increased by 50% between 1981–84 and 2002–06. Most of this increase has been infilling of gaps within the core of the range, although new areas appear to have become occupied in parts of the Buchan plain and in upper Deeside, perhaps associated with woodland plantings and maturation of existing plantations. Losses between the two Atlas periods are few, and even these may not be real, given the secretive nature of a species that is easily overlooked. Of course, a similar caveat must also be applied to the apparent gains in some areas since the previous Atlas fieldwork in 1981–84.

Population and trends

Bullfinches occur in too few BBS squares in North-East Scotland to assess their local trend, but in Scotland as a whole the population was at least stable, and probably increased during the period 1994–2007 (Risely *et al.* 2008). This contrasts with severe declines in most of southern Britain. Multiplying habitat-specific densities (Newton in *BS3*) by the area of woodland in Grampian (Alexander *et al.* 1998), a crude population estimate can be made. With a density of 1 pair/km^2 in conifer plantations (multiplied by 1,200 km^2), 8.4 pairs/km^2 in native pinewood (37 km^2) and broad-leaved woodland (240 km^2), the woodland population would be approximately 3,000–3,500 pairs, allowing for gaps in distribution. Another 500–1,000 pairs in farmland and suburban areas would seem reasonable, based on the distribution of occupied tetrads, and a density of 2.1 pairs/km^2 in these habitats. This would give a population for the whole region in the order of 3,000–5,000 pairs.

Author: *Allan Perkins*

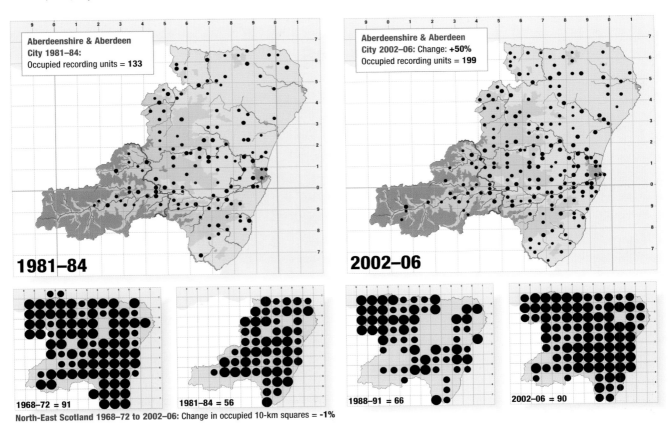

Aberdeenshire & Aberdeen City 1981–84: Occupied recording units = **133**

1981–84

Aberdeenshire & Aberdeen City 2002–06: Change: **+50%** Occupied recording units = **199**

2002–06

1968–72 = **91**   1981–84 = **56**   1988–91 = **66**   2002–06 = **90**

North-East Scotland 1968–72 to 2002–06: Change in occupied 10-km squares = -1%

Hawfinch

Coccothraustes coccothraustes

Very rare resident. Passage migrant. Estimated population in North-East Scotland: **1–5 pairs** (5% of Scottish population, <1% of UK)

Red list; UK and Scottish BAP lists

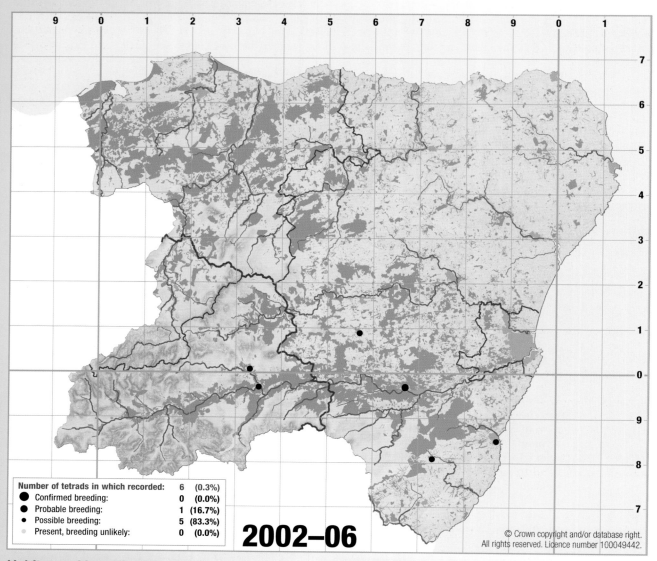

Number of tetrads in which recorded:	6	(0.3%)
● Confirmed breeding:	0	(0.0%)
● Probable breeding:	1	(16.7%)
• Possible breeding:	5	(83.3%)
Present, breeding unlikely:	0	(0.0%)

2002–06

Habitat and breeding biology

Hawfinches are found mainly in deciduous and mixed woodland. In Scotland, they particularly favour mature ornamental woodlands containing a range of tree species, often including Yew and oak (Zonfrillo in *BS3*). They are able to crack open cherry seeds with their powerful beaks and they will also eat hips, haws, buds, shoots, and, mainly during the breeding season, caterpillars and other invertebrates. They are rather elusive, flying rapidly between trees, high in the canopy. Pairs form in February and March with nest building from late March. Nests consist of cups of small twigs lined with fine grasses and are placed in trees on level branches or in forks at heights of 2–40 m. The clutch consists of 3–5 eggs and incubation takes 9–14 days with young fledging after 10–14 days. Sometimes a few pairs may nest in close proximity, forming a loose colony.

Scottish distribution and status

During the first half of the 20th century there was a big increase in the Scottish population due possibly to the maturing woodlands planted in the 18th and 19th centuries. Breeding was recorded in East Lothian, Borders and Dumfries & Galloway between 1900 and the 1920s. Between the 1940s and 1980s breeding was confirmed in

Hawfinch, Aberlour, April 2009. © *Robert Tribe*

The Breeding Birds of North-East Scotland

Hawfinch, Kinneff, October 2010. © *Maria Perera*

the Borders, Dumfries & Galloway, Upper Forth, Perth & Kinross and Angus & Dundee. By the 1990s the only regular records came from the Borders, Perth & Kinross and lower Deeside, with only occasional records from elsewhere (Zonfrillo in *BS3*). In 2007, the Scottish population was thought to number 40–75 pairs (Zonfrillo in *BS3*) but since that time there have been few or no records from former regular sites away from Perth & Kinross which probably leaves that population as the only regular Scottish site (J. Calladine pers. comm.). In Britain as a whole, the breeding population is believed to have declined markedly towards the end of the 20th century (Langston *et al.* 2002).

Distribution and status in North-East Scotland

Most records during 2002–06 came from lower Deeside but they are very scattered. The only probable breeding site was at Inchmarlo (Banchory) where two males and two females were seen in March 2005, with other records during March–November, and there were two pairs in late March 2006. More recently there have been only two sightings, of a female in 2007 and one in 2008. In addition, single birds were seen in possible breeding habitat at Stonehaven and Craigievar Castle in 2003, Lary (Glen Gairn) in 2004, and near Ballater and near Auchenblae in 2005. Other recent records, almost certainly relating to migrants have come from Strichen in April 1999, Newmachar, Collieston and near Lossiemouth in April 2000, Newburgh in December 2001, Bennachie in September 2004, near Johnshaven in October 2004, Rattray Head in April 2005, Aberdeen in October 2005 and Boddam in January 2006.

Changes in distribution

In North-East Scotland, breeding probably took place in the Aberdeen area during 1968–72 (*BTO 1st Atlas*) and there were further records of single birds on Deeside near Ballater in June 1980, Bieldside in July 1985 and Aboyne in May–June 1986 (*NES 1st Atlas*). During the 1990s a few birds were seen at Banchory in several years and breeding was proved in 1993 when adults were watched feeding a juvenile in July (*NESBR* 1993). In 1996, breeding again took place, this time in west Aberdeen where a pair fed a juvenile in a garden in late summer (*NESBR* 1996).

Population and trends

In view of the ongoing series of records of this secretive species from lower Deeside it seems possible that a small population of up to five pairs may survive there. However sightings have declined around the Inchmarlo area in recent years and the future of Hawfinches as breeding birds in North-East Scotland is far from assured.

Author: *Richard Cinderey*

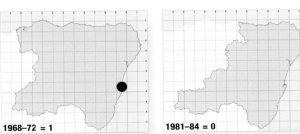

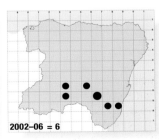

1968–72 = 1   1981–84 = 0   1988–91 = 0   2002–06 = 6

North-East Scotland 1968–72 to 2002–06: Change in occupied 10-km squares = **+500%**

Snow Bunting

Plectrophenax nivalis

Rare resident. Winter visitor and passage migrant. Estimated population in North-East Scotland: *15–20 pairs* (33% of Scottish and UK populations)

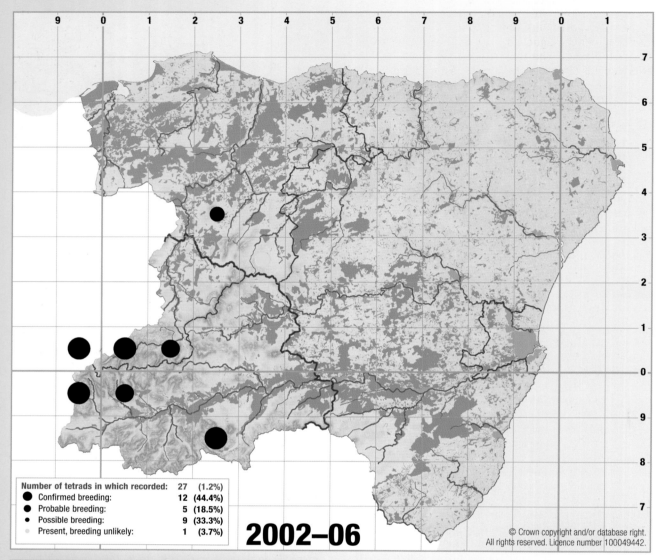

Number of tetrads in which recorded:	27	(1.2%)
● Confirmed breeding:	12	(44.4%)
● Probable breeding:	5	(18.5%)
● Possible breeding:	9	(33.3%)
Present, breeding unlikely:	1	(3.7%)

2002–06

Snow Bunting, Cairn Lochan, June 2006. © *Derek McGinn*

Habitat and breeding biology

Snow Buntings are small passerines of arctic habitats, from sea-level to the mountains. In the main part of the breeding range, they are birds of rocky, barren tracts of land with eroded soils, gravels and wet flushes. In Scotland they use areas with sparse vegetation, boulder fields and late-lying snowfields, gleaning seeds and invertebrates from wind-swept ridges, grasslands, shrinking snowfields and moss-dominated wet flushes. Scottish breeders winter close by, return to their territories early and often produce two broods. They build nests from mid May in cavities among boulders; eggs are laid and young fledged from June onwards. Second nests are less productive and few of the late fledged young subsequently recruit to the breeding population (Smith & Marquiss 1994, 1995).

Scottish distribution and status

Scottish breeding Snow Buntings are mainly dark *P. n. insulae* but include pale nominate *nivalis* (Smith 1996). There is occasional breeding on the coast and on isolated northern hilltops but the only sustained populations have been on the high tops of the Central Highlands, the Nevis Range and the Cairngorms. It was formerly thought that breeding numbers were so small that they must have been supplemented periodically by recruitment from winter visitors that settled here, but a population study in 1987–93 showed that breeding production was more than sufficient to sustain numbers (Smith 1991). Despite a long history of breeding records, there was no estimate of total numbers until 1991 when Watson & Smith (1991) tallied breeding records from a series of years, suggesting a maximum population of about 100 pairs. The numbers recorded reflect search effort, so it is difficult to be sure of past trends other than that the population was probably low in the mid 20th century, peaked in 1991 and has declined since.

Distribution and status in North-East Scotland
North-East Scotland includes much of the Scottish breeding range. During 2002–06 there were records in 27 tetrads, at least one of which involved no breeding. Of the remaining 26, there was confirmed breeding in only 12 tetrads and no more than six in any single year (2006). The records are clustered on the highest, snowiest parts of the Cairngorms range within well-documented breeding areas (Marquiss 2007).

Changes in distribution
It was said that Snow Buntings bred at Invercauld in 1769 (Pennant 1771) and MacGillivray (1837, 1855) describes adults with juveniles on Lochnagar in August 1830, and on Braeriach and Cairn Toul in 1850. Breeding habitat is so restricted that there is little scope for change, and the present distribution encompasses historical records and is similar to that described for 1968–72 (*BTO 1st Atlas*) and 1981–84 (*NES 1st Atlas*).

Snow Bunting, Beinn a' Bhuird, August 2010. © *Hugh Addlesee*

Snow Bunting, Cairn Toul, June 1988. © *Rab Rae*

Population and trends
During 1999–2006, the North-East Scotland breeding population was probably between 15 and 20 pairs. Although no more than six 'confirmed breeding' records arose in any particular year, there were many other records of birds 'probably breeding', mostly singing males as females can be elusive. Some records from adjacent squares might have involved the same individuals ranging across mountain summits. In particular, unmated males wander later in the breeding season to sing beside breeding pairs in attempts to lure females (Smith *et al.* 2009). Nevertheless, duplicate records were probably few, and in one year (2005) visits to the known breeding areas located 19 singing males (M. Marquiss unpubl.).

Trends are difficult to prove because observations of breeding are heavily influenced by search effort and weather. However, documented changes within North-East Scotland included decline from the 1920s to the 1960s (Nethersole-Thompson 1966, 1976) and increase through the 1970s and 1980s (Milsom & Watson 1984, Watson & Smith 1991) to a peak in 1991. Subsequent decline was associated with a series of markedly mild winters.

Author: *Mick Marquiss*

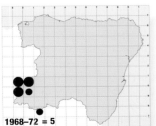

1968–72 = 5

Species not mapped at this resolution during this period

1981–84

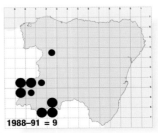

1988–91 = 9

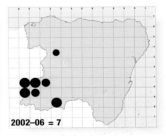

2002–06 = 7

North-East Scotland 1968–72 to 2002–06: Change in occupied 10-km squares = +40%

Yellowhammer

Emberiza citrinella

Very common resident. Estimated population in North-East Scotland: ***40,000–45,000 pairs*** (24% of Scottish population, 5% of UK)

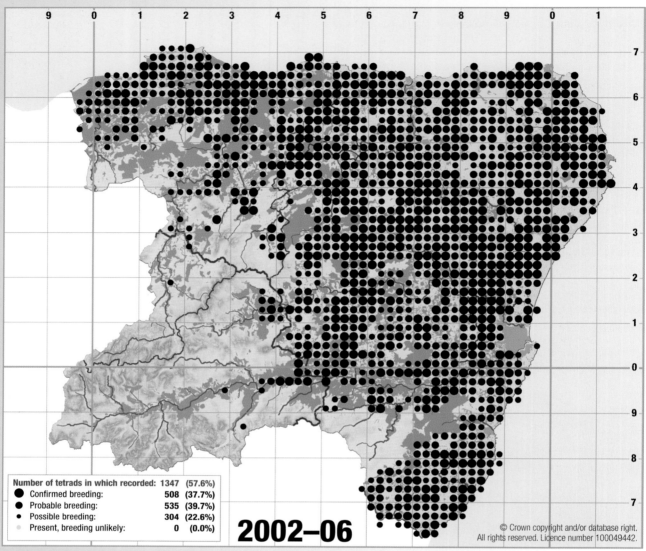

Number of tetrads in which recorded: 1347 (57.6%)
- ● Confirmed breeding: 508 (37.7%)
- ● Probable breeding: 535 (39.7%)
- • Possible breeding: 304 (22.6%)
- ⸰ Present, breeding unlikely: 0 (0.0%)

2002–06

Yellowhammer, St Cyrus, June 2008. © *Harry Scott*

Habitat and breeding biology

Yellowhammers favour open habitats, especially low-altitude mixed farmland where there are hedgerows, scrub or shelter belts. They can also be found in coastal Gorse scrub and young plantations. Nests are open and typically on or near the ground in rough vegetation or in scrub such as at the base of hedges or Gorse bushes. Clutches of 3–6 eggs are laid from April onwards and there is a protracted breeding season during which three broods can possibly be raised, although it is uncertain whether this often happens in North-East Scotland. They feed their young on invertebrates, and the supply of these is key to their breeding success (Bradbury *et al.* 2003).

Scottish distribution and status

The range formerly covered much of lower-altitude Scotland but since the 1970s many western breeding populations have been lost due, probably, to a reduction in arable farming in these areas. Yellowhammers are now found predominantly in southern and eastern Scotland with the highest densities in the eastern lowlands between Fife and Moray, and along the Solway coast. The most recent population estimate is in the range 140,000–220,000 pairs (Calladine in *BS3*). In the UK as a whole, Yellowhammers have declined as a consequence of

The Breeding Birds of North-East Scotland

changes in farming practices but in Scotland, possibly due to a larger proportion of fields being spring-sown and left as stubble over the winter (SEERAD 2000), the decline has been less severe and in recent years an increase in population has taken place (Risely *et al.* 2008).

Distribution and status in North-East Scotland
The distribution of Yellowhammers in North-East Scotland closely matches the extent of lowland arable countryside. Within these lowlands they avoid dense forests, notably in Moray and Deeside, but they can be found in clear-felled areas where scrub has developed, especially close to the forest edge which gives access to fields for feeding. They are also absent from the centres of urban areas such as Aberdeen but may occur in suburban fringes. Their altitudinal range is closely governed by the existence of arable farming and for this reason the species is absent from most of the uplands. The highest breeding populations are likely to be at around 320 m at Tomintoul and the Cabrach, although breeding was not confirmed here.

Yellowhammer, Newburgh, July 2008. © *Rab Rae*

Changes in distribution
While the lowland breeding distribution of Yellowhammers has remained virtually unchanged over recent decades, there has been a marked retraction from marginal upland breeding habitats in upper Deeside and Donside, and across to Strath Avon. Of 11 10-km squares in this area, ten were occupied in 1968–72 (*BTO 1st Atlas*) and the seven falling within Aberdeenshire were still occupied in 1981–84 (*NES 1st Atlas*). By 1988–91, however, only five of the 11 squares held Yellowhammers (*BTO 2nd Atlas*) and this had dropped to three by 2002–06. The decline in these areas since the early 1980s is also clearly demonstrated at the level of occupied recording units where the number west of Ballater has reduced from 15 in 1981–84 to only one in 2002–06. It is likely that the reasons behind this withdrawal from the uplands lie with agricultural change, notably a move away from mixed farming to an emphasis on livestock rearing.

Population and trends
Little recent information has been gathered in the North-East on which to base a reliable population estimate; three density measurements in individual tetrads during 2002–06 were 5.5, 7.5 and 10.8 territories/km^2, although other tetrads held much lower densities. Surveys in Lothian farmland recorded an average density of 10 pairs/km^2 in farmland, with much higher densities of up to 115 pairs/km^2 in scrub (da Prato 1985). If we assume a North-East density of 10 pairs/km^2 over the land cover area which is likely to support Yellowhammers (LC 2000 data) then the population may fall between 40,000–45,000 pairs. Local BBS data indicate a decline in numbers from 1994–2001 and a recovery since then - but the sample size is small.

Author: *Paul Doyle*

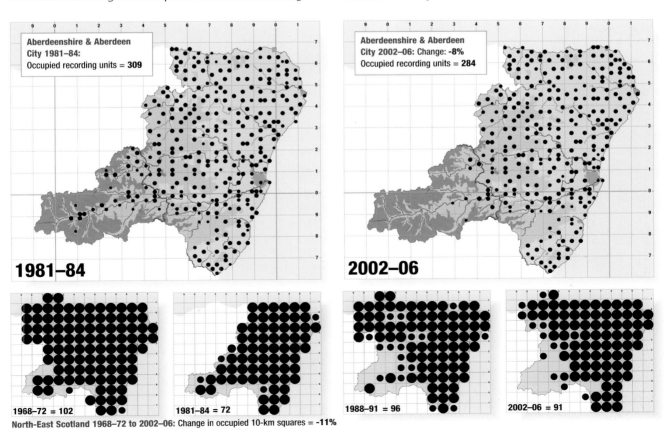

Aberdeenshire & Aberdeen City 1981–84:
Occupied recording units = 309

1981–84

Aberdeenshire & Aberdeen City 2002–06: Change: -8%
Occupied recording units = 284

2002–06

1968–72 = 102   1981–84 = 72   1988–91 = 96   2002–06 = 91

North-East Scotland 1968–72 to 2002–06: Change in occupied 10-km squares = **-11%**

Reed Bunting

Emberiza schoeniclus

Common resident. Passage migrant. Estimated population in North-East Scotland: **3,000–4,000 pairs** (16% of Scottish population, 2% of UK)

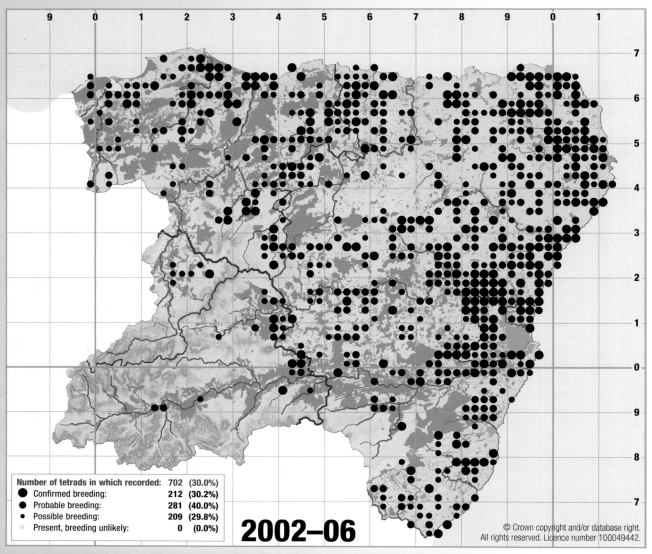

Number of tetrads in which recorded:	702	(30.0%)
● Confirmed breeding:	212	(30.2%)
● Probable breeding:	281	(40.0%)
● Possible breeding:	209	(29.8%)
Present, breeding unlikely:	0	(0.0%)

2002–06

Reed Bunting, Meikle Loch, May 2009. © Ian Francis

Habitat and breeding biology

Reed Buntings breed in a variety of habitats and not exclusively reedbeds. Although many habitats do include water fringes, such as river margins, bogs and carr areas, Reed Buntings can also be found breeding in coastal salt marshes, semi-natural grasslands, field fringes, arable farmland and young plantations prior to canopy closure. In good habitats the number of breeding pairs can be high; for example, 13 territories in around 0.4 km² of marsh at Loch Spynie in 1999 (*MNBR* 1999), but usually territories are larger than this. Males occupy breeding territories in March, and clutches, usually of 4–5 eggs, are laid in May. Hatching takes place after 12–15 days and the subsequent fledging period is short with young sometimes leaving the nest, unable to fly, after 9–12 days (*BWP*). Some pairs are double-brooded and birds can still be breeding in August.

Scottish distribution and status

Breeding occurs mainly in lowland areas, particularly in southern Scotland, the Central Lowlands, up the east coast to the Moray Firth, Caithness and north Sutherland. They can be found in parts of the Outer Hebrides and throughout Orkney, but ceased to breed in Shetland in the late 1990s (Pennington *et al.* 2004). A reasonable estimate of the breeding population in Scotland falls between 15,000–30,000 pairs (Walton in *BS3*).

Distribution and status in North-East Scotland

Reed Buntings occupy an extensive range through North-East Scotland but are particularly concentrated in the lowlands of eastern Aberdeenshire and along the north coastal lowlands to the west of Banff. Within this range their absence from apparently suitable landscapes may be due to the fact that they are easily overlooked if relevant habitat is scarce and fieldwork is limited. Although the distribution becomes more patchy, Reed Buntings are found over much of the interior. Very few pairs breed above 300 m although birds were found in a few marshes up to 350 m in Glenlivet and the Cabrach. Extensive blocks of mature forestry plantation are avoided although young plantations on damp ground may be utilised.

Changes in distribution

In terms of occupied 10-km squares there has been little change in overall numbers since 1968–72 (*BTO 1st Atlas*), assuming that the apparent decline in 1988–91 (*BTO 2nd Atlas*) was a consequence of reduced recording effort. There has, however, been a reduction in the upland range in south-west Aberdeenshire; this appears to have taken place prior to 1981–84 (*NES 1st Atlas*). An encouraging trend is revealed by comparison of the Aberdeenshire/Aberdeen City maps where an 80% increase in occupied recording units is revealed. This is largely the result of infilling among previously occupied sites; perhaps this is a consequence of the population increase recorded in Scotland during 1994–2007 (Risely *et al.* 2008), although land use changes during the years of the set-aside and agri-environment schemes may have helped.

Population and trends

The population size was estimated in 23 tetrads during 2002–06, ranging from 1–10 pairs/tetrad at an average of 3 pairs/tetrad, or 0.75 pairs/km^2. In the most favourable habitats, however, such as the marshes and reedbeds around Loch Spynie, densities up to 30 pairs/km^2 have been recorded (*MNBR* 1999). This, however, is exceptional and if we apply an average density of 1 pair/km^2 to the 712 tetrads where Reed Buntings were recorded during 2002–06 then a population estimate of 2,848 pairs results. Reed Buntings can, however, be elusive at low densities and so a population within the range 3,000–4,000 pairs seems likely.

Author: *Bob Proctor*

Reed Bunting, Bridge of Don, May 2005. © *Chris Jones*

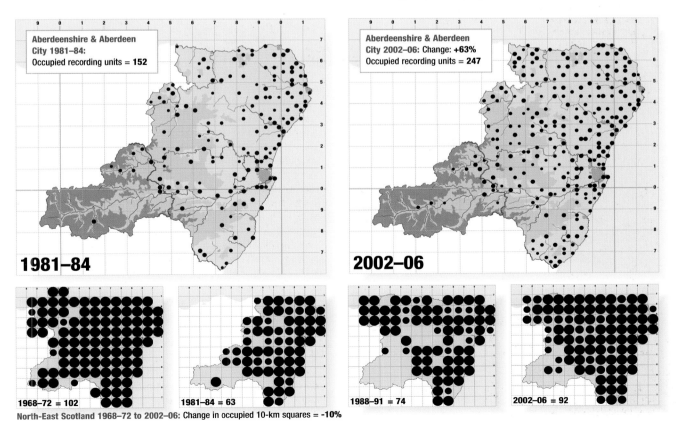

Aberdeenshire & Aberdeen City 1981–84: Occupied recording units = **152**

1981–84

Aberdeenshire & Aberdeen City 2002–06: Change: **+63%** Occupied recording units = **247**

2002–06

1968–72 = 102

1981–84 = 63

1988–91 = 74

2002–06 = 92

North-East Scotland 1968–72 to 2002–06: Change in occupied 10-km squares = **-10%**

Corn Bunting

Emberiza calandra

Scarce resident. Estimated population in North-East Scotland: **550–600 territories** (64% of Scottish population, 6% of UK)

Red list; UK and Scottish BAP lists

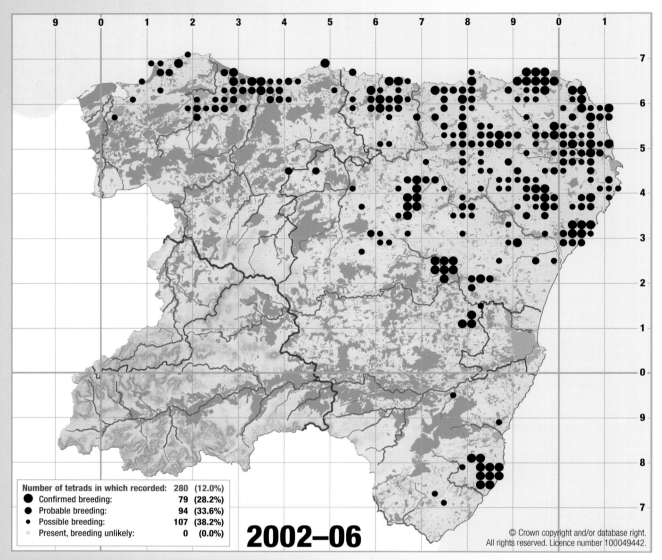

Number of tetrads in which recorded:	280	(12.0%)
● Confirmed breeding:	79	(28.2%)
● Probable breeding:	94	(33.6%)
● Possible breeding:	107	(38.2%)
· Present, breeding unlikely:	0	(0.0%)

2002–06

Corn Bunting, Fife, May 2007. © *John Anderson*

Habitat and breeding biology

Corn Buntings in the UK occur on lowland arable and mixed farms. Adults feed largely on grain and large weed-seeds, but take insects to feed chicks. They nest on the ground within crops or dense grass. In North-East Scotland, nesting usually commences from late May, but some males sing at favoured song posts from early in the year. Early nests are often in autumn-sown cereals or grass managed for silage, later nests usually in spring-sown cereals. Corn Buntings often rear two broods per summer and some males attract more than one female. The duration between laying of the first egg and fledging is about a month, although chicks may leave the nest before being able to fly.

Scottish distribution and status

In 1993, a sample survey estimated 1,977 territories in east Scotland, and 231 in the west (Donald & Evans 1995). BTO data suggest an estimated Scottish breeding population of 966–1,387 males (calculated as a percentage of UK figures for *Birds in Europe*) in 2000. However, recent local surveys suggest that the number of singing males across Scotland could now be as low as 800–1,000 (Maggs in *BS3*).

Distribution and status in North East Scotland

Most birds occur on the Buchan plain of Aberdeenshire. In several 'hotspots' between Rattray and Rosehearty, densities can reach 21 males/km^2, which are probably amongst the most densely populated areas in the UK. Inland they are less numerous and more widely spread, and have disappeared from several areas since the 1990s. For example, numbers at Inverurie and Blackburn fell from 30 and 18 in the early 1990s to none in 2006, associated with nest destruction by grass mowing for silage. In southern Aberdeenshire, an isolated population persists at Barras, declining from 134 singing males in 1990 to ten in 2006. There is a continuous spread of birds along the northern coastal strip into north-west Aberdeenshire, where the distribution becomes more widespread. The Moray population lies almost entirely between Elgin and Spey Bay and eastwards to Buckie. The number of singing males has remained stable at Spey Bay, with approximately 12 each year since 2003. Small numbers are more widely spaced along the coast from Forres north-east towards Lossiemouth.

Changes in distribution

Corn Buntings were widespread in Deeside west of Ballater during the mid 1940s (Watson 1992) but were sparse in Deeside by the 1950s (Goodbody 1955). Between 1968–72 and 1988–91, there was retraction to a more coastal distribution. Many inland populations have been lost and recent fragmentation has isolated others. Since 1981–84 there has been a range reduction of 26% in Aberdeenshire/Aberdeen City and birds have become extinct in ten 10-km squares, where agricultural intensification and urban development have been recorded. Big losses have also occurred on the outskirts of Aberdeen, *e.g.* around Westhill and Dyce. In southern Aberdeenshire, populations have been lost from near Portlethen, Fettercairn and St Cyrus. However, some populations in extensively managed, mixed farming systems have remained apparently unchanged during this period, with range stability in 17 10-km squares.

Corn Bunting, Fisherbriggs Farm, 2004. © *Hywel Maggs*

Populations and trends

In a Grampian SOC survey during 1998–99, 221 singing males were recorded in 27 10-km squares in Aberdeenshire (Rae 1999), although underestimation was highly likely in some areas. Occupied sites west of Fraserburgh and south of Stonehaven were omitted by the SOC survey. With their addition, an estimate of 500 singing males was suggested. The Moray population was surveyed during 1997 and estimated at 40–50 singing males (Shewan 1997). A survey between Elgin and Forres in 1987 revealed 21 singing males (Mackie 1987), but only eight during the 1997 survey. Across 30 Aberdeenshire study areas, including Barras, numbers declined by 83% between 1989 and 2007, to extinction at all but two (Watson *et al.* 2009). During the 2002–06 Atlas period, surveys by RSPB and Adam Watson across 214 km^2 yielded a yearly average of 260 territories. These study areas overlapped with 127 (45%) of the 280 tetrads in which Corn Buntings were recorded. If one assumes similar numbers in the remaining 55% of tetrads, this would give a population estimate of 550–600 territories across the region.

Authors: *Hywel Maggs, Adam Watson & Allan Perkins*

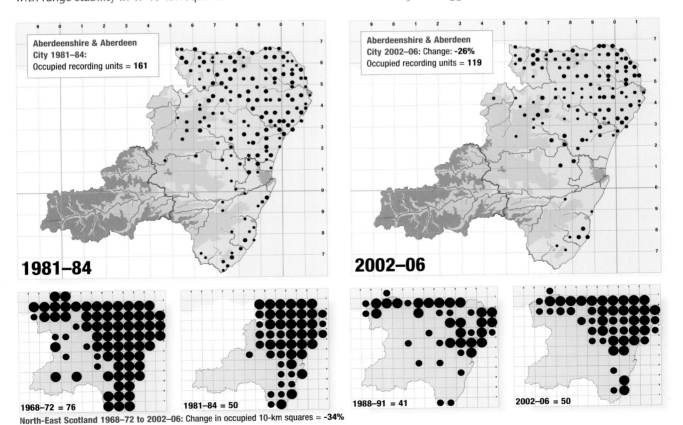

Aberdeenshire & Aberdeen City 1981–84: Occupied recording units = **161**

1981–84

Aberdeenshire & Aberdeen City 2002–06: Change: **-26%** Occupied recording units = **119**

2002–06

1968–72 = 76

1981–84 = 50

1988–91 = 41

2002–06 = 50

North-East Scotland 1968–72 to 2002–06: Change in occupied 10-km squares = **-34%**

Additional species

All species for which breeding evidence of any sort was obtained during 2002–06 are covered earlier in this chapter. There are, in addition, a number of other species which have occurred in North-East Scotland during the breeding season in recent years. These fall within the following categories:

a) Species for which there is breeding evidence in North-East Scotland since the start of the *BTO 1st Atlas*, in 1968, but not during 2002–06.

b) Species which were recorded in North-East Scotland in the breeding season (April–July) during 2002–06, but with no suggestion of breeding.

c) Escaped or released species recorded in North-East Scotland during 2002–06 which have failed to establish a sustained feral breeding population.

a) Species with breeding evidence in North-East Scotland since 1968, but not in 2002–06

Green Sandpiper *Tringa ochropus*
On 9th July 1999, an adult giving alarm calls was found in suitable breeding habitat in Deeside, but no young were seen (*NESBR 1999*, Ogilvie *et al.* 2001).

Wood Sandpiper *Tringa glareola*
Birds have been present in suitable breeding habitat in the North-East in six years between 1973 and 2000. In the Kincardine & Deeside District of the former Grampian Region, possible breeding was recorded at four sites; one site held birds in two years (1978 and 1980), while the other three sites were occupied in just one year (1973, 1978 and 2000). Elsewhere, possible breeding was reported at one site in Gordon District in 1977 and at one site in Moray in 1981 (Chisholm 2007).

Eagle Owl *Bubo bubo*
In 1984, a pair bred near Fogwatt (Moray) but the nest failed. In 1985, they moved a short distance to a disused quarry where they bred again and reared one chick. Unfortunately, the adult male was killed on a nearby road in September of that year. The female remained at the site, laying clutches of infertile eggs, until at least 1994 (Dennis & Cook 1996). The origin of this pair is unknown but they probably had escaped, or been released, from captivity (*see photographs page 430*).

Snowy Owl *Bubo scandiacus*
Males were present in spring or summer in suitable breeding habitat in the Cairngorms in 1979–81 and 1984, and females were there in 1987 and 1990–91 (Cook 1992). More recently, a male was seen in 1996 and 1998 (and nearby in Highland in 1997) (Ogilvie *et al.* 1999, Rogers *et al.* 1997, 1999).

Little Owl *Athene noctua*
A record of probable breeding in 10-km square NO67 (the Mearns area) was obtained in 1968–72 (*BTO 1st Atlas*); recent enquiries have failed to trace further detail. In 1986, one was found at Rothienorman on 2nd April. It died the following day and a post-mortem revealed it to be a female with active ovaries. The bird was received from a farmer who reported that two had been in the area in 1985 (*NESBR 1986*). The only other record of this species was a single bird at Loch of Strathbeg on 4th–5th May 1991 (*NESBR 1991*).

Golden Oriole *Oriolus oriolus*
A pair was present in suitable breeding habitat in Deeside for about two weeks in mid-late June 1985. The male was heard singing on several days and a female was seen on two occasions (*NES 1st Atlas*).

Reed Warbler *Acrocephalus scirpaceus*
One sang at Loch of Strathbeg during 11th–25th June 1987 (*NESBR 1987*) and another was singing there in July 1989 (*NESBR 1989*). In 2008, juveniles were trapped and ringed at Loch Spynie on 3rd and 22nd August but it is not certain that they were reared there (*MNBR 2008 in prep.*). Also in 2008, a singing bird was present in suitable habitat at Old Rattray farm in July, and a pair may have bred at Loch of Strathbeg, with late juveniles seen (*NESBR 2008*). In 2009, one also sang at Loch of Strathbeg (*NESBR 2009*).

Black Redstart *Phoenicurus ochruros*
A male was present, often singing, in Aberdeen between April and mid July 1976. A female was also present (*NESBR 1976*) and breeding was confirmed (R. Rae pers. comm.).

Lapland Bunting *Calcarius lapponicus*
Breeding was first proved in 1977, on Ben Macdui, when four young were seen on 6th August after two adults had been watched for over a week. In that year, other adults were seen in the Ben Macdui and Cairn Gorm area, on Cairn of Claise and on Beinn a' Bhuird. In 1978, there were three pairs, of which at least two pairs nested, between Cairn of Claise and Carn an Tuirc, and further single nests were found on Ben Macdui and Ben Avon. In 1979, there were 9–12 territories on the plateau between Cairn of Claise and Carn an Tuirc with birds present at a few other of the 1977–78 sites and on Lochnagar. In 1980, only one pair bred on Cairn of Claise and there has been no confirmed breeding since then (McNee in BS3). There have been a few subsequent records in suitable habitat in the North-East, but without proof of breeding. In 1988, a male was seen on Cairn Lochan on 10th May and a juvenile was in the same area on 11th August (*MNBR 1992*). In 1992, a singing male was on the Cairn Gorm–Ben Macdui plateau on 20th June and a female was at the same site on 26th; neither bird was seen subsequently (*MNBR 1992*). In 1995, a male was in breeding habitat in June and one was singing on Sron nan Gabhar on 17th July (McNee in BS3).

b) Species recorded in 2002–06 for which no breeding evidence was obtained
Table 3.2 lists late-staying winter visitors, migrants, vagrants, seabirds on passage, and wildfowl and waders which are predominantly winter visitors with a non-breeding summer population which remains in the North-East. Most of these species are considered to be unlikely potential breeders.

c) Escaped or released species recorded during the breeding seasons of 2002–06

Black Swan *Cygnus atratus*
A single bird was seen on several occasions at St. Fergus gas terminal in March and April 2002 (a pair had nested on a fire pond here in 2001, hatching two young of which one fledged - *NESBR 2001*). What was presumably the same bird spent the summer at Loch of Strathbeg, where it remained until at least the end of August. A different individual was on the Ythan estuary on 22nd July and 4th August 2002 (*NESBR 2002*).

Domestic goose *Anser anser* (varieties)
Recently fledged young were seen at Whitestones (near Kemnay) in 2005.

Lesser White-fronted Goose *Anser erythropus*
One visited Loch of Strathbeg from 4th–6th June 2005 (*NESBR 2005*).

Bar-headed Goose *Anser indicus*

Up to three at Rattray Head on 22nd June 2005 were subsequently seen on the Ythan estuary on nine dates between 30th June and 7th September. One was a hybrid, perhaps with an Emperor Goose *Chen canagica* (*NESBR* 2005).

Ruddy Shelduck *Tadorna ferruginea*

A pair was on the Ythan estuary on 6th July 2004 and at Loch of Strathbeg the following day. A female remained at Loch of Skene from 9th–22nd August 2004 (*NESBR* 2004). Two were also at Kingston (Speymouth) on 6th July 2004 - but would appear to have been different birds to those in Aberdeenshire (*MNBR* 2004). In 2005, one was at Cotehill Loch from 16th–31st July (*NESBR* 2005) and the same bird (presumably) was reported at Meikle Loch.

Chiloe Wigeon *Anas sibilatrix*

Adult males frequented several waters in Moray during 2004–06. In 2004, one was at Loch Spynie, briefly, in early July before moving to Kingston until the end of the year, while another was at Cloddach quarry between May and September (*MNBR* 2004). In 2005, the Kingston bird remained there throughout the year (*MNBR* 2005). In 2006, one (probably the same bird) was seen at Kingston, Loch Spynie and the Lossie estuary between April and August (*MNBR* 2006).

Wood Duck *Aix sponsa*

Two males were at Girdleness on 20th April 2002 (*NESBR* 2002) and one male was on Loch Avon on 6th and 11th June 2006 (*MNBR* 2006).

Muscovy Duck *Cairina moschata*

A pair reared young to fledging at the Cooper Park pond in Elgin in 2006.

Northern Bobwhite Quail *Colinus virginianus*

A male sang regularly in various gardens near Alford from 14th July to 11th August 2006 (*NESBR* 2006).

Reeves's Pheasant *Syrmaticus reevesii*

A male was at Mains of Balmaud, north of Turriff, on 12th June 2005 (*NESBR* 2005).

Indian Peafowl *Pavo cristatus*

Feral breeding was recorded in four tetrads during 2002–06; in the Mearns near Kincardine Castle (NO67S) in 2006 and near Alpity (north of Arbuthnott) (NO77Y) in 2005, near Lochside (St. Cyrus) (NO76H) in 2005 and near Aberdour House (south of Rosehearty) (NJ96C) in 2006. Breeding possibly took place in one tetrad near Fordoun (also in the Mearns) (NO77N) in 2006 and a bird was seen at Tynet, near Fochabers in 2004.

Rose-ringed Parakeet *Psittacula krameri*

One was in Elgin on 21st June 2002 (*MNBR* 2002).

Budgerigar *Melopsittacus undulatus*

One was flying around buildings at Foresterhill Hospital, Aberdeen on 6th June 2005 (*NESBR* 2005).

Zebra Finch *Taeniopygia guttata*

A female was in a Clochan garden on 16th April 2006 (*MNBR* 2006).

Table 3.2. Species without breeding evidence during 2002–06 and the years in which they were recorded in the breeding season. Details of these records can be found in North-east Scotland Bird Reports and Moray & Nairn Bird Reports for relevant years.

	2002	2003	2004	2005	2006
Bean Goose *Anser fabalis*	■				
Pink-footed Goose *Anser brachyrhynchus*	■	■	■	■	■
White-fronted Goose *Anser albifrons*	■	■	■	■	■
Snow Goose *Anser caerulescens*					■
Brent Goose *Branta bernicla*	■				■
American Wigeon *Anas americana*	■				■
Ring-necked Duck *Aythya collaris*			■	■	
King Eider *Somateria spectabilis*				■	
Long-tailed Duck *Clangula hyemalis*	■	■	■	■	
Common Scoter *Melanitta nigra*	■	■	■	■	
Surf Scoter *Melanitta perspicillata*	■	■	■		
Velvet Scoter *Melanitta fusca*	■	■		■	
Barrow's Goldeneye *Bucephala islandica*				■	
Smew *Mergellus albellus*	■	■			■
Great Northern Diver *Gavia immer*	■	■	■	■	
White-billed Diver *Gavia adamsii*			■	■	
Sooty Shearwater *Puffinus griseus*	■		■	■	
Manx Shearwater *Puffinus puffinus*	■	■	■	■	
Balearic Shearwater *Puffinus mauretanicus*				■	
Storm Petrel *Hydrobates pelagicus*	■		■		
Leach's Petrel *Oceanodroma leucorhoa*			■	■	
Great White Egret *Ardea alba*			■		■
Black Stork *Ciconia nigra*					■
White Stork *Ciconia ciconia*	■		■		
Red-necked Grebe *Podiceps grisegena*	■				
Montagu's Harrier *Circus pygargus*		■	■		
Rough-legged Buzzard *Buteo lagopus*			■	■	
Stone-curlew *Burhinus oedicnemus*	■				
Grey Plover *Pluvialis squatarola*	■	■	■	■	
Knot *Calidris canutus*	■	■	■	■	
Sanderling *Calidris alba*	■	■	■	■	
Little Stint *Calidris minuta*	■	■	■	■	
Curlew Sandpiper *Calidris ferruginea*	■	■	■	■	■
Broad-billed Sandpiper *Limicola falcinellus*			■		
Buff-breasted Sandpiper *Tryngites subruficollis*				■	
Jack Snipe *Lymnocryptes minimus*	■	■	■	■	
Bar-tailed Godwit *Limosa lapponica*	■	■	■	■	■
Green Sandpiper *Tringa ochropus*	■	■	■	■	■
Spotted Redshank *Tringa erythropus*	■	■	■	■	■
Wood Sandpiper *Tringa glareola*	■	■	■	■	■
Turnstone *Arenaria interpres*	■	■	■	■	■
Pomarine Skua *Stercorarius pomarinus*	■	■	■	■	■
Arctic Skua *Stercorarius parasiticus*	■	■	■	■	■
Long-tailed Skua *Stercorarius longicaudus*				■	
Great Skua *Stercorarius skua*	■	■	■	■	■
Little Gull *Hydrocoloeus minutus*	■	■	■	■	■
Ring-billed Gull *Larus delawarensis*	■	■			
Yellow-legged Gull *Larus michahellis*			■		
Iceland Gull *Larus glaucoides*	■	■	■	■	■
Glaucous Gull *Larus hyperboreus*	■	■	■	■	■
Whiskered Tern *Chlidonias hybrida*					■
Black Tern *Chlidonias niger*				■	■
Little Auk *Alle alle*		■	■		■
Turtle Dove *Streptopelia turtur*	■	■	■	■	■
Snowy Owl *Bubo scandiacus*			■		
Belted Kingfisher *Megaceryle alcyon*				■	
Golden Oriole *Oriolus oriolus*				■	
Great Grey Shrike *Lanius excubitor*	■	■	■		■
Firecrest *Regulus ignicapilla*	■	■	■		■
Red-rumped Swallow *Cecropis daurica*				■	■
Subalpine Warbler *Sylvia cantillans*				■	
Waxwing *Bombycilla garrulus*	■	■		■	■
Rose-coloured Starling *Pastor roseus*	■				
Black Redstart *Phoenicurus ochruros*	■	■	■	■	■
Tawny Pipit *Anthus campestris*	■				■
Common Redpoll *Carduelis flammea*					■

Eagle Owl nest site, Netherglen Quarry, April 2011. © *Martin Cook*

Eagle Owl, Netherglen Quarry, April 1994.
© *Martin Cook*

Eagle Owl, Netherglen Quarry, May 1985.
© *Martin Cook*

Chapter 4. *Distribution patterns and species richness*

The breeding distributions of different groups of birds can tell us much about environmental conditions, help target conservation work or assist in the development of land use plans. In this chapter we consider some of these group distribution patterns and present information about the relative abundance of birds in North-East Scotland, focusing mainly on the extent to which they are widespread or otherwise within the 2,340 tetrads covered in the project. No detailed statistical analyses of the atlas data have been undertaken, in contrast to the first local atlas (Buckland *et al.* 1990). There is, though, an enormous amount of information contained within our atlas dataset and we invite researchers to use it. Most data can be viewed using the National Biodiversity Network (see Chapter 1) and obtained by contacting the editors.

How many breeding species per tetrad?

Figure 4.1 shows the number of species recorded as either possibly, probably or definitely breeding in each tetrad - a map of species richness across North-East Scotland. It excludes escaped species and also the records of birds observed but not thought to be breeding (the yellow dots on the species maps in Chapter 3).

The low number of species breeding in the western and south-western uplands is clear, and not surprising - this is a landscape of moorland, bogs and mountain tops with little woodland. The other area with apparently generally low breeding bird richness lies in the north-east - from north Formartine up to Banff and then southwards towards Huntly. This is perhaps less expected. In part it is likely to reflect less thorough survey coverage, but it also reflects the fact that this area is intensively farmed and generally has low woodland cover, so consequently lacks some woodland birds that add diversity elsewhere. Further north-east in Buchan, the range of breeding species increases with greater habitat diversity, including rough grassland and peat mosses.

Within the zones of greater species richness (yellows and reds) several apparent 'hotspots' stand out; parts of north

No of spp
- 1–9
- 10–18
- 19–27
- 28–36
- 37–45
- 46–54
- 55–63
- 64–72
- 73–91

Figure 4.1. Species richness - all species present (excluding escaped species and records of 'observed only').

Moray, the lower Don around Kintore, and, at a smaller scale, the Dinnet area in Deeside plus coastal sites around Loch of Strathbeg, the Ythan, Donmouth and St. Cyrus in the south. These areas held *c.* 70–90 species that at least 'possibly' bred during 2002–06. The 'top ten' tetrads in these terms are listed in Table 4.1. Some are at, or close to, the coast, while others include lochs and rivers with a wide range of other habitats within the tetrads. The high scoring of some individual tetrads may relate to chance combinations of varied habitat and high observer effort, so the exact totals per tetrad should only be considered a guide to their richness in terms of breeding birds; the number of confirmed breeding species is also shown in Table 4.1 and these totals are considerably lower, though NJ25E and NJ26I were also the highest ranking tetrads in the area from this perspective. However, the overall patterns across the area can be seen clearly and further detailed investigation would make the relationship between species totals and habitat clearer. Over all the 2,340 tetrads, the mean (and median) number of possible, probable and confirmed breeding species per tetrad was 34.

Table 4.1. The 'top ten' tetrads with the highest number of 'breeding' species during the 2002–06 atlas.

Tetrad	Location	No. possible	No. probable	No. confirmed	Total
NJ26I	Loch Spynie	15	13	63	91
NK05P	Loch of Strathbeg	24	17	49	90
NJ36M	Speymouth	36	14	37	87
NK05U	Loch of Strathbeg	34	16	35	85
NJ40K	Loch Davan, Muir of Dinnet	25	16	39	80
NJ25E	Cloddach, Elgin	6	10	63	79
NO49P	Loch Davan, Muir of Dinnet	24	17	38	79
NJ36H	Kingston, Speymouth	26	7	44	77
NO19K	Braemar	9	14	53	76
NJ26V	Loch Oire/Loch na Bo	17	15	43	75

How do these totals compare with other tetrad-based breeding bird atlases? Many local atlases do not provide detailed information of this kind. In terms of the mean number of species per tetrad, this figure was 40 in South-east Scotland (Murray *et al.* 1998). That atlas also tabulated totals per tetrad for 12 other atlases from England; all had higher mean values than North-East Scotland, except for Northumberland with 29 breeding species per tetrad (other atlases recorded 40–58 species per tetrad, with a trend for higher species richness further south in England). North-East Scotland contains a high proportion of upland tetrads with few breeding species, so the lower figure for our area is not surprising. For the highest number of breeding species per tetrad, in South-east Scotland, four tetrads held 90 species or over (Murray *et al.* 1998), but this information is not given for Fife (Elkins *et al.* 2003) and no other local atlases have been published in Scotland. It is not possible to compare such figures with the first North-East atlas (Buckland *et al.* 1990) due to the different recording units used.

Which are the most widespread breeding species?
There is usually a positive relationship between the extent of the breeding range of a species in any area and how numerous it is (Donald & Fuller 1998, Sara 2008 and see below). This may seem obvious, in that the most widespread species tend to be more common, but there are exceptions to this, especially in the case of colonially-nesting species such as seabirds, which are highly localised but abundant. We did not attempt to count numbers of breeding birds in

this atlas, so the extent of the breeding range (the number of occupied tetrads) is the best method we have of deriving some form of relative abundance from the atlas data. Table 4.2 shows the 20 most widespread breeding species during the atlas period, together with the number of tetrads in which each species was recorded. The rank order of each species in terms of occurrence in local BTO Breeding Bird Survey (BBS) squares in 2006 is also shown. This correlates significantly with the atlas rank order, showing that the species most frequently encountered in the 34 randomly selected BBS squares in 2006 were also those with the widest breeding distributions in the atlas. However, these figures relate only to how widespread species are - they do not measure their real breeding populations. BBS data can only do this if the sample size is large, and the number of squares covered in our area is not sufficient to allow this.

Table 4.2. The 20 most widespread breeding species during the atlas period.

Rank	Species	Number of tetrads occupied (possible, probable or confirmed breeding) out of 2,340	Rank according to number of BBS squares occupied in N-E Scotland in 2006
1	Chaffinch	1,904	1
2	Wren	1,883	5
3	Meadow Pipit	1,869	11
4	Woodpigeon	1,813	2
5	Willow Warbler	1,740	4
6	Blackbird	1,722	6
7	Pied Wagtail	1,704	16
8	Carrion Crow	1,701	3
9	Buzzard	1,690	10
10	Robin	1,667	8
11	Swallow	1,665	9
12	Skylark	1,651	13
13	Pheasant	1,560	7
14	Oystercatcher	1,530	18
15	Song Thrush	1,528	17
16	Blue Tit	1,480	14
17	Starling	1,446	25
18	Jackdaw	1,415	21
19	Dunnock	1,393	12
20	Great Tit	1,358	15

In the 1981–84 Aberdeenshire/Aberdeen City atlas (Buckland *et al.* 1990), the eight most widely distributed breeding birds were Meadow Pipit, Oystercatcher, Carrion Crow, Chaffinch, Skylark, Pied Wagtail, Blackbird and Willow Warbler. The fall in rank position of Oystercatcher may reflect the decline in this species recently, and the elevation of Willow Warbler could also be related to increased woodland cover. However, the 1981–84 atlas recording units were larger, which may distort direct comparison.

Of the 20 species listed above, 17 were also amongst the 20 most widespread birds in the South-east Scotland atlas during 1988–94 (Murray *et al.* 1998), the omissions in the list from that area being Buzzard, Oystercatcher and Great Tit. Only 15 of the top 20 species are shared with Fife (Elkins *et al.* 2003), where Meadow Pipit does not feature, but the presence there of Linnet and Greenfinch reflects the higher proportion of farmland in Fife. Sixteen of the species listed above were also the most frequently counted in tetrads as part of the UK and Ireland atlas 1988–91 (Gibbons *et al.* 1993), the exceptions being Pied Wagtail, Buzzard, Pheasant and Oystercatcher. Clearly, the most widespread birds in North-East Scotland reflect those of most of Scotland and the UK, but there are a few common species such as Oystercatcher that are more characteristic of our area.

Estimates of breeding populations

Despite the absence of quantitative species counts in our atlas, we have made efforts to estimate breeding populations in North-East Scotland. The author of each species account attempted to estimate breeding numbers, using some standard information sources and methods (see Chapters 1 and 3). The complete list of population estimates is given in Annex 4, but Table 4.3 below gives the twenty most abundant species according to these methods.

Twelve of these most abundant species are also amongst the 20 most widespread in North-East Scotland (see above), and there is a significant positive correlation between the estimated size of breeding populations in the area and the number of occupied tetrads. Guillemot and Kittiwake stand out in the table - their large populations at coastal seabird colonies make them amongst our most abundant birds, yet their breeding range is highly localised. Siskin is also slightly anomalous. This can be our second most abundant species, especially in peak years, but it is less widespread, largely restricted to conifer plantations, where densities clearly can become very high.

In a wider context, 16 of the species listed are also amongst the 20 most abundant breeding birds in the UK (Baker *et al.* 2006) and 18 are amongst the 20 most abundant in Scotland - for the country as a whole, Puffin and Fulmar are very abundant, but less so in North-East Scotland, where they are replaced by Siskin and Kittiwake. Elsewhere in Scotland, the 20 most abundant species in South-east Scotland are very similar - 18 are shared, with Great Tit and Yellowhammer in our area replacing Starling and Gannet there.

Table 4.3. The 20 most abundant breeding species in North-East Scotland.

Rank	Species	Estimated breeding population in N-E Scotland (pairs/AOS*)	Rank according to number of occupied tetrads
1	Wren	250,000	2
2	Siskin	230,000	38
3	Chaffinch	145,000	1
4	Meadow Pipit	130,000	3
5	Robin	115,000	11
6	Blackbird	105,000	9
7	**Guillemot**	**100,425***	122
8	Woodpigeon	100,000	4
9	Rook	86,000	24
10	Willow Warbler	85,000	5
11	Blue Tit	80,000	16
12	**Kittiwake**	**70,000***	116
13	Dunnock	65,000	19
14	Goldcrest	65,000	27
15	Coal Tit	60,000	21
16	House Sparrow	60,000	26
17	Skylark	50,000	12
18	Starling	45,000	25
19	Yellowhammer	42,500	22
20	Great Tit	40,000	20

Note: all population figures given are estimates; those in bold are Apparently Occupied Sites (AOS) based on better information and are more accurate. See Chapter 1 (methods), introduction to Chapter 3 and Annex 4 for full list.

Plate 4.1. Wren, Berneray, July 2009. © *Derek McGinn* The most abundant breeding species in North-East Scotland during the 2002–06 atlas period.

Distribution patterns - species groups

Species with similar ecology, or those that are closely related, can be grouped together and mapped to show the best areas to see members of any group, or to suggest parts of the region where habitat quality for them may be particularly good. Some groupings produce results that are obvious, but others are more revealing. The following maps show some of the main bird 'taxonomic' and 'ecological' groupings. Groups of species according to legislation or conservation status are shown later in this chapter. In all maps, the coincidence of all possible, probable and confirmed breeding records for the group of birds selected is plotted - effectively the 'breeding presence' for all relevant species combined.

All wildfowl plus Coot and Moorhen

Seven major concentrations of breeding wildfowl stand out: the Loch Spynie and Speymouth areas, the Loch of Strathbeg, the Ythan estuary, Loch of Skene, the Dinnet lochs and St. Cyrus. Surprisingly, Findhorn Bay itself does not appear to hold a wide range of breeding wildfowl. The poorest areas for this group are the high tops, coniferous plantations and the most intensively farmed lowlands.

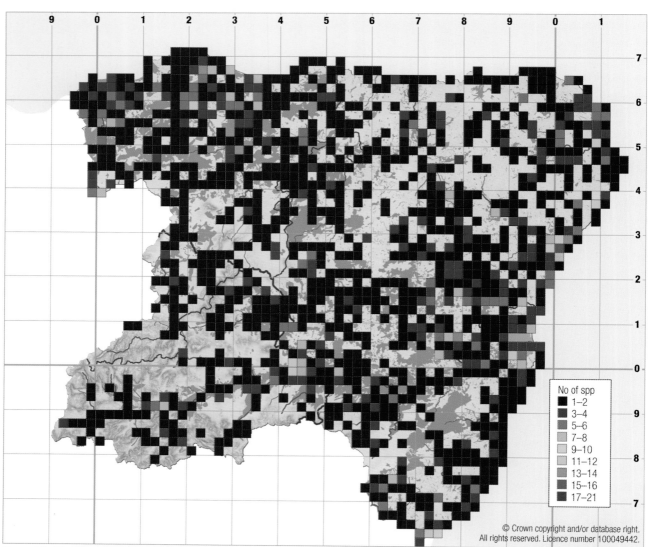

No of spp
- ■ 1–2
- ■ 3–4
- ■ 5–6
- ☐ 7–8
- ☐ 9–10
- ■ 11–12
- ■ 13–14
- ■ 15–16
- ■ 17–21

Figure 4.2. All wildfowl, Moorhen and Coot. [Species combination mapped: Mute Swan, Whooper Swan, Greylag Goose, Canada Goose, Barnacle Goose, Shelduck, Mandarin, Wigeon, Gadwall, Teal, Mallard, Pintail, Garganey, Shoveler, Pochard, Tufted Duck, Scaup, Eider, Red-breasted Merganser, Goosander, Goldeneye, Ruddy Duck, Moorhen, Coot]

The Breeding Birds of North-East Scotland

All birds of prey

This map has been plotted at coarser resolution and shows the coincidence of possible, probable and confirmed breeding for birds of prey in each 10-km square (excluding owls). Since so many raptors are rare, threatened or specially protected, we felt that a detailed tetrad resolution map would be inappropriate, drawing attention to small groups of tetrads (especially in the uplands) that might be prone to disturbance. The richest areas for breeding birds of prey are in the west and south, where both upland moorland and woodland habitats are found within a 10-km square. Very high altitude ground is less suitable.

Plate 4.3. Buzzard, Balvack, May 2011. © Ian Francis

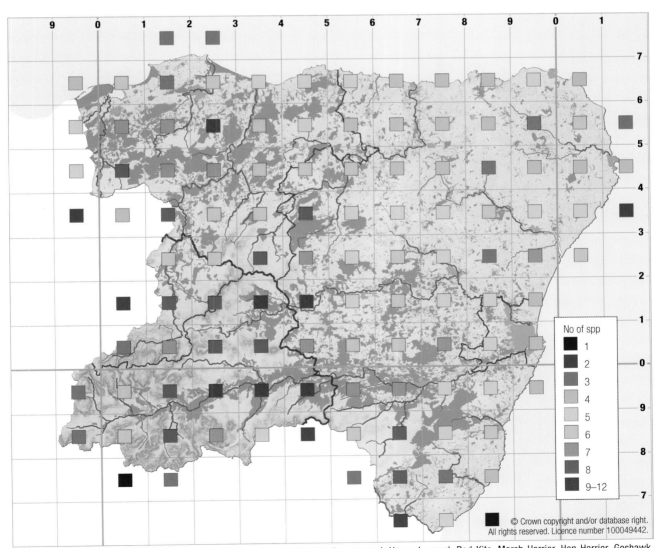

Figure 4.3. All birds of prey, at 10-km square resolution. [Species combination mapped: Honey-buzzard, Red Kite, Marsh Harrier, Hen Harrier, Goshawk, Sparrowhawk, Buzzard, Golden Eagle, Osprey, Kestrel, Merlin, Hobby, Peregrine]

Plate 4.4. **Golden Plover**, Norway, 1997. © *John Young*

All waders

The species grouped here vary widely in their habitat preferences, but most share a requirement for access to moist ground for feeding. This can be found on upland peat bogs, on farmland and near the coast, so there are few patterns here. The importance of key coastal and lowland sites such as the Loch Spynie and lower Spey areas, the Loch of Strathbeg and the Ythan estuary can be seen, but some low-lying mixed farmland in the lower River Don is clearly important, as is a large swathe of marginal uplands holding mixed farmland and moorland fringe. Concentrations of waders on upland moorland and peatland areas in the south-west can also be seen. The waders mapped include some rare species, at least some of which are highly localised and which have not been confirmed to breed in North-East Scotland.

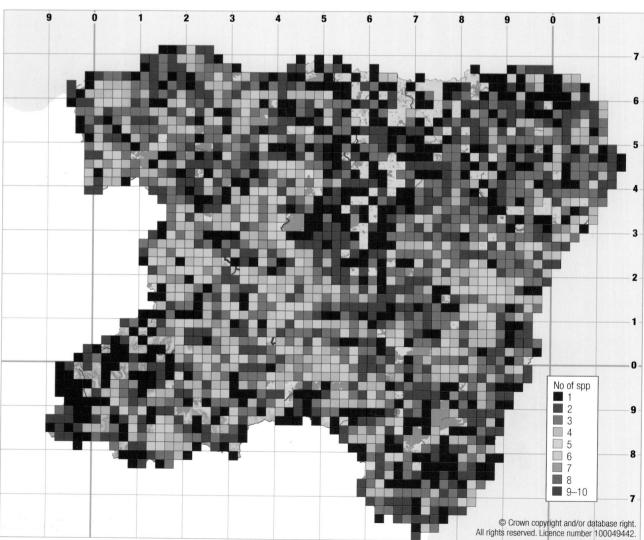

Figure 4.4. All waders. [Species combination mapped: Oystercatcher, Avocet, Little Ringed Plover, Ringed Plover, Dotterel, Golden Plover, Lapwing, Pectoral Sandpiper, Purple Sandpiper, Dunlin, Ruff, Snipe, Woodcock, Black-tailed Godwit, Whimbrel, Curlew, Common Sandpiper, Greenshank, Redshank]

The Breeding Birds of North-East Scotland

Farmland waders

North-East Scotland still holds many breeding waders, though the numbers and range of most have declined (Chapter 5). Five species are typical of the mixed farmland present in the North-East, and the bright yellows in the map show where all five occur together. Such areas are scattered over the north of Moray and are more concentrated in south-west Moray near Dava and around Tomintoul. Much of upper Donside and Deeside is also important for these birds. Further east, Buchan holds numerous farmland wader concentrations but the most obvious block with all five species is around the lower Don, between Inverurie and Aberdeen. This may in part be influenced by particularly intensive observer coverage, and some of the low density areas and gaps, especially in the north of Aberdeenshire towards Banff, may conversely be affected by less thorough observer coverage. However, at least three of these waders are very conspicuous and should not be missed easily, suggesting that their apparent absence from these tetrads is real. The other main gaps in the range are the high tops and tetrads with the most extensive coniferous woodlands.

Plate 4.5. Snipe, Midtown, Kerloch Moor, May 1970. © *Nick Picozzi*

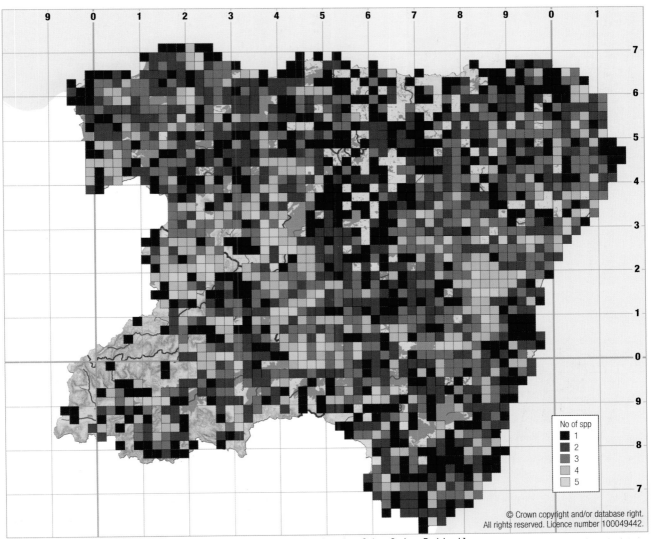

Figure 4.5. Farmland waders. [Species combination mapped: Oystercatcher, Lapwing, Snipe, Curlew, Redshank]

Chapter 4. Distribution patterns and species richness

Seabirds

The presence of many nesting gulls (of four species) leads to a 'seabird' map with extensive breeding evidence across inland parts of the North-East, concentrated towards the upland fringes. In addition, Common Terns can also be widely scattered, especially along the main rivers and in some industrial estates. Some of the prominent yellow dots inland relate to our large upland gull colonies. The main concentrations of all seabirds are of course along the coast, and the main breeding colonies stand out, especially in the east (Fowlsheugh, Sands of Forvie and Collieston to Buchan Ness) and at Troup Head, which has mainland Scotland's only Gannet colony. Most seabird colonies hold many of the species present in the area, at least as possible breeders. The Moray coast is lower-lying and has fewer suitable nesting cliffs, but some areas still hold the possibility of breeding for several species and stand out on this map.

Plate 4.6. Common Gull, Baads Moss, 1978. © *Graham Rebecca*

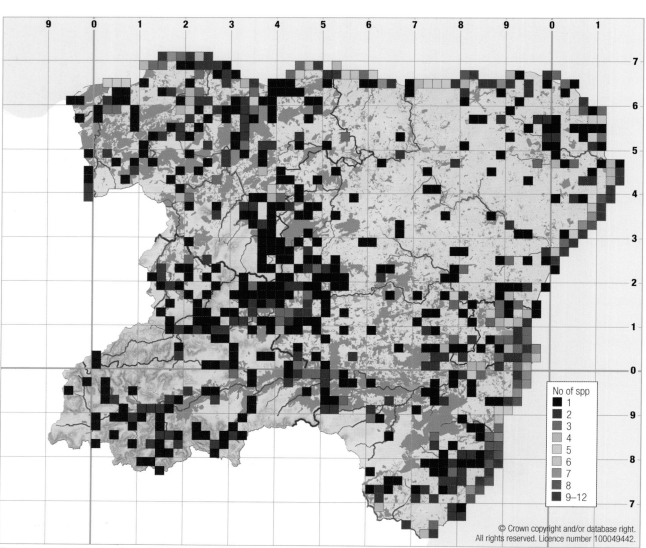

No of spp
1
2
3
4
5
6
7
8
9–12

Figure 4.6. All seabirds. [Species combination mapped: Fulmar, Gannet, Cormorant, Shag, Kittiwake, Black-headed Gull, Mediterranean Gull, Common Gull, Lesser Black-backed Gull, Herring Gull, Great Black-backed Gull, Little Tern, Sandwich Tern, Common Tern, Roseate Tern, Arctic Tern, Guillemot, Razorbill, Black Guillemot, Puffin]

The Breeding Birds of North-East Scotland

All woodland birds

The 'all woodland birds' map is dominated strongly by the inhabitants of coniferous woodland and effectively mirrors the main extents of coniferous plantations and native pine woodland. The main upland areas have no trees at all, though some Juniper scrub communities can hold breeding 'woodland' birds. The heavily wooded part of the area, running south-east from Moray down to lower Deeside contrasts clearly with the Buchan area, which has low woodland cover and often low diversity of woodland species. The species chosen for mapping here are those judged to be most closely linked to woodland, rather than habitat generalists that also use woodland.

Plate 4.7. **Siskin**, Parkhill, April 2010. © *Ed Duthie*

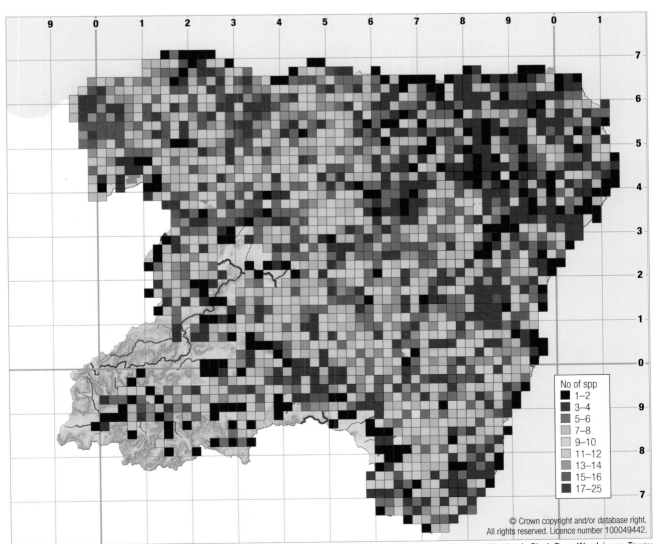

No of spp
- 1–2
- 3–4
- 5–6
- 7–8
- 9–10
- 11–12
- 13–14
- 15–16
- 17–25

Figure 4.7. All woodland birds. [Species combination mapped: Capercaillie, Honey-buzzard, Goshawk, Sparrowhawk, Buzzard, Woodcock, Stock Dove, Woodpigeon, Tawny Owl, Long-eared Owl, Green Woodpecker, Great Spotted Woodpecker, Jay, Rook, Goldcrest, Crested Tit, Coal Tit, Wood Warbler, Chiffchaff, Blackcap, Garden Warbler, Treecreeper, Spotted Flycatcher, Redstart, Pied Flycatcher, Tree Pipit, Siskin, Lesser Redpoll, Common Crossbill, Scottish Crossbill, Parrot Crossbill, Bullfinch, Hawfinch]

Birds of deciduous woodland

The distribution of species strongly associated only with deciduous woodland is shown below, and indicates the influence of habitats in north Moray, lower Donside and mid Deeside.

Plate 4.8. Blackcap, Norwood, May 1983. © *John Young*

Plate 4.9. Craigendarroch Oakwood, May 2010. © *Harry Scott*

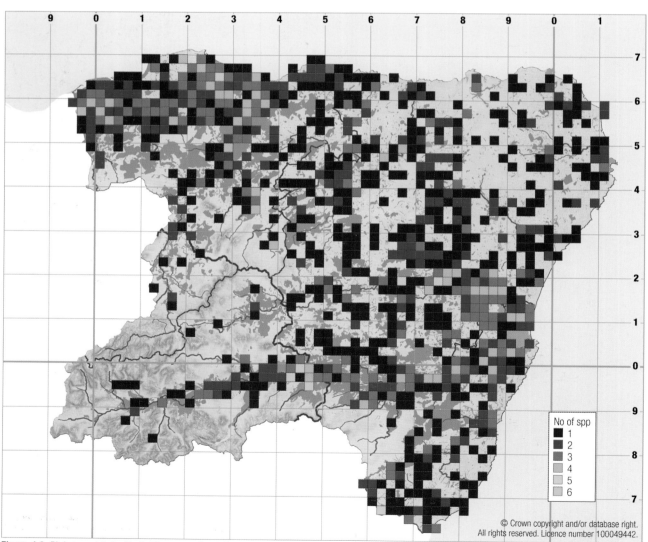

Figure 4.8. Birds associated with deciduous woodland. [Species combination mapped: Stock Dove, Green Woodpecker, Wood Warbler, Chiffchaff, Blackcap, Garden Warbler, Pied Flycatcher, Hawfinch]

Groups of species according to legislation or conservation status

Of the birds breeding in North-East Scotland, some are rare, threatened or have experienced serious declines in numbers in recent decades. This section illustrates the coincidence of groups of species specially protected under EU or UK legislation, as well as those considered to be priorities for conservation because of their status. Areas holding concentrations of these species should be considered as potentially sensitive in connection with land use change or development projects, as well as potential targets for bird conservation projects and environmental funding.

Birds of Conservation Concern - Red List species

Birds of the highest conservation concern are classed as 'Red-listed' (Eaton *et al.* 2009). These are species that are classed as globally rare, those whose numbers have declined severely in historic times or whose breeding population or range have declined in the UK by more than 50% over 25 years. The application of these criteria produces a set of species with little in common, and their distribution is shown below. The high number of birds associated with farmland and woodland gives a strong lowland element to the distribution pattern.

Plate 4.10. Cuckoo, Rhynie, May 2008. © *Ed Duthie*

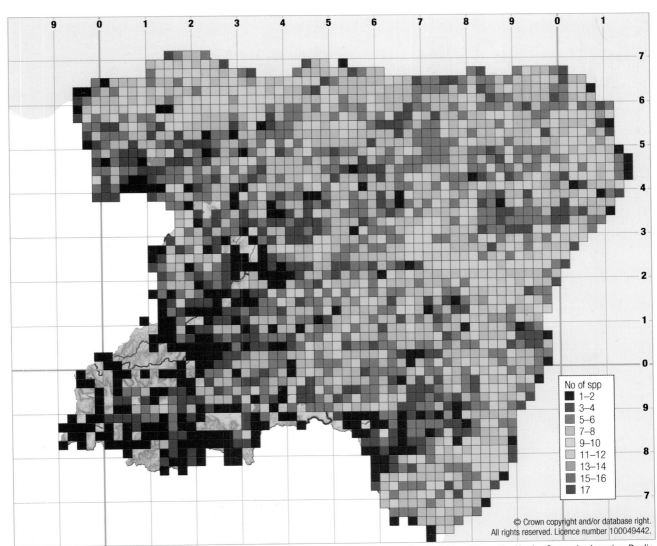

Figure 4.9. All Red-listed species. [Species combination mapped: Scaup, Black Grouse, Capercaillie, Grey Partridge, Bittern, Hen Harrier, Corncrake, Lapwing, Dunlin, Ruff, Black-tailed Godwit, Whimbrel, Herring Gull, Roseate Tern, Cuckoo, Nightjar, Wryneck, Red-backed Shrike, Skylark, Wood Warbler, Grasshopper Warbler, Starling, Ring Ouzel, Fieldfare, Song Thrush, Redwing, Spotted Flycatcher, House Sparrow, Tree Sparrow, Yellow Wagtail, Tree Pipit, Linnet, Twite, Lesser Redpoll, Hawfinch, Yellowhammer, Corn Bunting]

Chapter 4. Distribution patterns and species richness

EU 'Birds' Directive - Annex 1 species

The 1979 EU Directive on the Conservation of Wild Birds led to the UK Wildlife and Countryside Act and subsequently to the designation of Special Protection Areas (SPAs - see Chapter 6) for the protection of species listed on Annex 1 of the directive. These designations were applied following a national review of 'suitable areas', and usually SPAs cover areas holding more than 1% of the UK breeding numbers of each relevant species. However, Annex 1 species are much more widely distributed than just within SPAs, and the map below illustrates their occurrence. The species listed in Annex 1 have an upland and coastal bias, and their distribution in many ways is the opposite of the 'Red-list' species shown above, due to the application of different criteria. It should be stressed that the map shows all possible, probable and confirmed breeding records, so their distribution is much more extensive than would appear on a map that showed only confirmed breeding sites.

Plate 4.11. Hen Harrier, Deeside, May 2009. © *Ed Duthie*

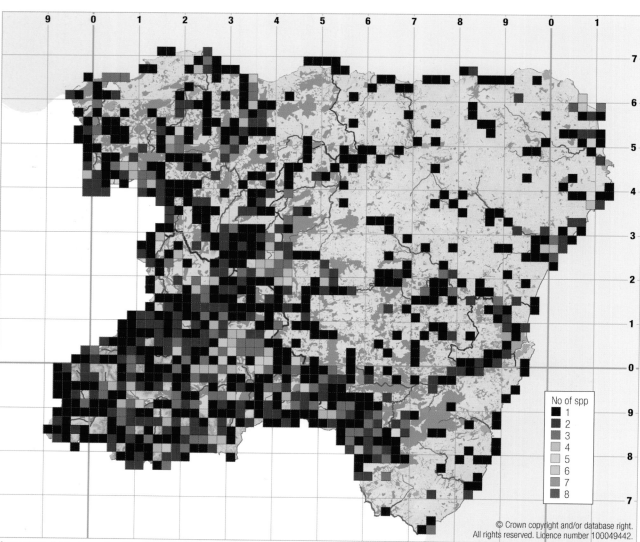

Figure 4.10. Annex 1 species. [Species combination mapped: Whooper Swan, Capercaillie, Red-throated Diver, Black-throated Diver, Bittern, Slavonian Grebe, Honey-buzzard, Red Kite, Marsh Harrier, Hen Harrier, Golden Eagle, Osprey, Merlin, Peregrine, Spotted Crake, Corncrake, Avocet, Dotterel, Golden Plover, Ruff, Mediterranean Gull, Little Tern, Sandwich Tern, Common Tern, Roseate Tern, Arctic Tern, Short-eared Owl, Nightjar, Kingfisher, Red-backed Shrike, Scottish Crossbill]

The Breeding Birds of North-East Scotland

Wildlife and Countryside Act - Schedule 1 species

UK legislation protects certain birds while they are nesting, with special penalties under Schedule 1 of the Wildlife and Countryside Act 1981, as amended in Scotland by the Nature Conservation (Scotland) Act 2004. These are, in general, rare breeding species and include most raptors. As with the Annex 1 birds above, it should be stressed that the map shows all possible, probable and confirmed breeding records, so their distribution is much more extensive than would appear on a map that showed only confirmed breeding sites. There is a much more even spread of locations for Schedule 1 birds compared to Annex 1 species, due to the greater number of species included and their more diverse habitat preferences.

Plate 4.12. Little Ringed Plover, near Aberdeen, June 2008. © *Chris Jones*

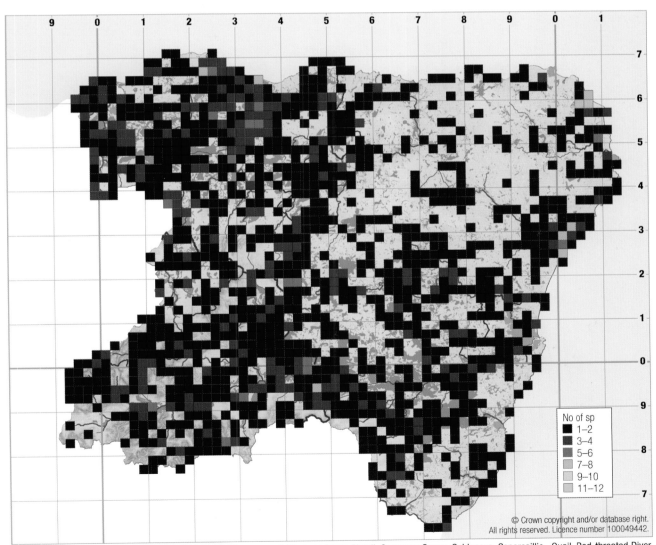

Figure 4.11. All Schedule 1 species. [Species combination mapped: Whooper Swan, Pintail, Garganey, Scaup, Goldeneye, Capercaillie , Quail, Red-throated Diver, Black-throated Diver, Bittern, Spoonbill, Slavonian Grebe, Black-necked Grebe, Honey-buzzard, Red Kite, Marsh Harrier, Hen Harrier, Goshawk, Golden Eagle, Osprey, Merlin, Hobby, Peregrine, Spotted Crake, Corncrake, Avocet, Little Ringed Plover, Dotterel, Purple Sandpiper, Ruff, Black-tailed Godwit, Whimbrel, Greenshank, Mediterranean Gull, Little Tern, Roseate Tern, Barn Owl, Kingfisher, Wryneck, Red-backed Shrike, Crested Tit, Fieldfare, Redwing, Bluethroat, Brambling, Common Crossbill/crossbill sp., Scottish Crossbill, Parrot Crossbill, Common Rosefinch, Snow Bunting]

Plate 4.13. Spotted Flycatcher, Drums, September 2002. © *Sam Alexander*

UK Biodiversity Action Plan 'Priority' species

Chapter 6 explains the background to the development of Biodiversity Action Plans (BAPs) for a wide range of species. The criteria used for species to be included differ from those above, but there is considerable overlap and the UK BAP priority species mapped below include birds listed on Annex 1 and Schedule 1 as well as Red-list species. As with the Red-list map above, the species included are strongly influenced by lowland farmland and woodland habitats.

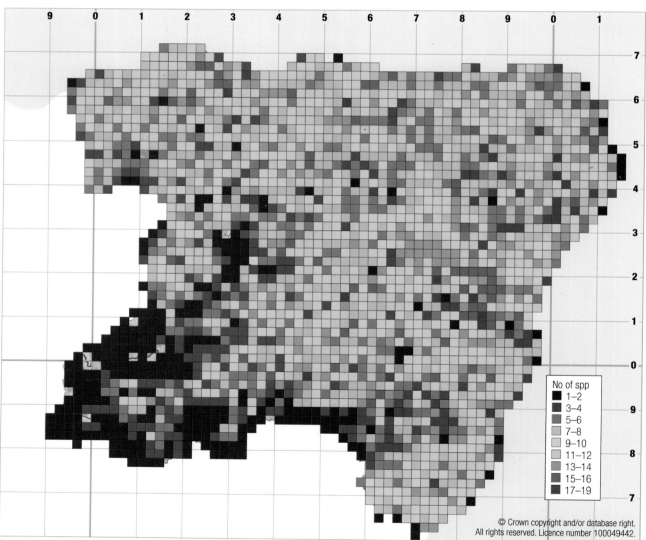

Figure 4.12. All UK BAP priority species. [Species combination mapped: Scaup, Red Grouse, Black Grouse, Capercaillie, Grey Partridge, Black-throated Diver, Bittern, Corncrake, Lapwing, Black-tailed Godwit, Curlew, Herring Gull, Roseate Tern, Cuckoo, Nightjar, Wryneck, Red-backed Shrike, Skylark, Wood Warbler, Grasshopper Warbler, Starling, Ring Ouzel, Song Thrush, Spotted Flycatcher, Dunnock, House Sparrow, Tree Sparrow, Yellow Wagtail, Tree Pipit, Linnet, Twite, Lesser Redpoll, Scottish Crossbill, Bullfinch, Hawfinch, Yellowhammer, Reed Bunting, Corn Bunting]

The Breeding Birds of North-East Scotland

Scottish Biodiversity List species

The Nature Conservation (Scotland) Act 2004 incorporated reference to species covered by the Scottish Biodiversity Strategy, which was developed as Scotland's response to the UK BAP. The strategy included the 'Scottish Biodiversity List' of priority species for nature conservation in Scotland. The list is very wide-ranging and includes many of the birds mapped in the categories above. The general distribution pattern resembles the overall species richness map for the atlas, and combines species from both lowland and upland areas. The range of species included also implies that the map could be subject more to the influence of observer effort than the other conservation priority maps above, which tend to include species with more systematic recording effort.

Plate 4.14. Sandwich Tern, Sands of Forvie, June 2009. © *Chris Jones*

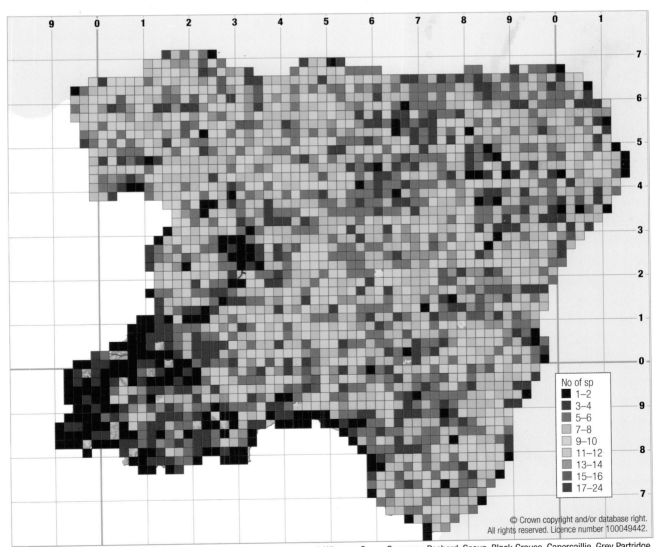

No of sp
- 1–2
- 3–4
- 5–6
- 7–8
- 9–10
- 11–12
- 13–14
- 15–16
- 17–24

Figure 4.13. All Scottish Biodiversity List species. [Species combination mapped: Whooper Swan, Garganey, Pochard, Scaup, Black Grouse, Capercaillie, Grey Partridge, Red-throated Diver, Black-throated Diver, Bittern, Slavonian Grebe, Black-necked Grebe, Honey-buzzard, Red Kite, Marsh Harrier, Hen Harrier, Golden Eagle, Osprey, Kestrel, Merlin, Hobby, Peregrine, Spotted Crake, Corncrake, Dotterel, Golden Plover, Lapwing, Purple Sandpiper, Dunlin, Ruff, Woodcock, Black-tailed Godwit, Curlew, Black-headed Gull, Herring Gull, Little Tern, Sandwich Tern, Common Tern, Roseate Tern, Arctic Tern, Barn Owl, Short-eared Owl, Nightjar, Swift, Kingfisher, Wryneck, Red-backed Shrike, Hooded Crow, Bearded Tit, Skylark, Wood Warbler, Ring Ouzel, Song Thrush, Spotted Flycatcher, Robin, Tree Sparrow, Yellow Wagtail, Brambling, Siskin, Linnet, Scottish Crossbill, Parrot Crossbill, Common Rosefinch, Bullfinch, Hawfinch, Snow Bunting, Reed Bunting, Corn Bunting]

Chapter 5. *Changes in bird distributions and numbers*

Summary of changes

During 2002–06, 189 species showed some evidence of at least possibly breeding, and 153 species were confirmed to have done so. The number of 'new' breeding species outnumbered those lost since previous atlases, more species showed evidence of an increase in their breeding range than showed a decrease, and more species appeared to have increased in numbers than decreased. However, these conclusions were certainly influenced by varying levels of observer effort and coverage, which it was not possible to fully quantify. Despite this, circumstantial evidence reinforces the conclusion that the breeding ranges (and populations) of many species have increased over the past four decades, and probably more species now breed in North-East Scotland than ever before. It is clear, though, that some species are declining, with much reduced ranges, and these tend to be birds that are 'red-listed' at a national level.

Changes in number of recorded breeding species between atlases

Over the 42 years from the start of the first UK atlas in 1968 until 2009, 173 species have definitely bred in North-East Scotland, excluding recently escaped or feral species (see Chapter 3). In the 1968–72 atlas period, 150 species were confirmed to breed, and during 2002–06, this figure was 153 species (Table 5.1). For the whole area (updated to 2009) we have gained 14 species and lost six since 1968. From 1981–84 to 2002–06, in Aberdeenshire/Aberdeen City we gained 13 and lost four confirmed breeding species (Table 5.2).

Details of breeding *distribution* changes (numbers of occupied recording units) are discussed below, but in summary, using the raw data, since 1981–84, 146 species have apparently increased or shown indications of becoming a new breeder, 16 have decreased or have probably become extinct and 23 stayed roughly the same. These figures were probably influenced by observer effort, as considered below. In terms of occupied 10-km squares across the whole of North-East Scotland from 1968–72 to 2002–06, 72 species became more widespread, 36 became less so and 49 stayed roughly stable; 32 other species were also recorded as potential breeding species in the area during 2002–06 that were not found in 1968–72 (see Table 5.3). Figure 5.1 shows the years of first recorded breeding and last known confirmed breeding for species that have been 'gained' or 'lost' since 1968.

In comparison, 219 species have been confirmed as ever having bred in Scotland, with an increase from 155 known species during 1800–1850 to 214 for the 1951–2004 period (Murray in *BS3*).

Table 5.1. Summary of changes in breeding species and distributions 1968–1972 to 2002–2006.

No. of species confirmed breeding:	
North-East Scotland, 2002–2006	153
North-East Scotland, 1988–1991	150
'North-east' Scotland (Aberdeen/shire), 1981–1984	140
North-East Scotland, 1968–1972	150
North-East Scotland, whole 1968–2009 period	173

No. of species possibly, probably or confirmed breeding (any potentially or definite breeding presence) in North-East Scotland 2002–2006: 189

Table 5.2. 'Losses' and 'gains' of confirmed breeding species.

Species confirmed breeding in 2002–2006 but not 1968–1972	12
Species confirmed breeding in 1968–1972 but not 2002–2006	9
Species confirmed breeding since 2006 (not in atlas period)	2
Species confirmed only breeding between atlas periods since 1968, but not now still breeding (not classed as 'gain')	6
Species 'gained' in 2002–2006 compared with 1981–1984	13
Species 'lost' in 2002–2006 compared with 1981–1984	4

Table 5.3. Breeding distribution changes (No. of occupied 10-km squares or recording units - confirmed, probable and possible).

	New presence	Range increase	Range decrease	Range similar (+/-5%)
10-km square changes 1968–72 to 2002–06:	32	72	36	49
Recording Unit changes 1981–84 to 2002–06:	31	115	16	23

n.b. All comparisons between 1981–84 and 2002–06 in the tables above relate to the 'Aberdeenshire/Aberdeen City' area covered by Buckland *et al.* 1990 and exclude Moray. Recording Unit changes use the original 'raw' data. 1968–72 and 1988–91 comparisons with 2002–06, plus the whole 1968–2009 period relate to the entire area covered by our atlas and include Moray.

Plate 5.1. **Goldfinch**, Aberdeen, January 2009. © *Ed Duthie* The breeding range of Goldfinch has increased almost threefold since 1981–84.

Species first known to have bred ('gained')	Year (known breeding years for occasional breeders)	Species last known to have bred ('lost')
	2009	
Red Kite	2008	
Black-throated Diver	2007	
	2006	
	2005	
	2004	
Bearded Tit, Barnacle Goose	2003	
	2002	
Gadwall	2001	
Marsh Harrier	2000	
	1999	
	1998	
	Pied Flycatcher	
	1997	
	Pied Flycatcher	
	1996	Greenshank
	Pied Flycatcher	
Little Ringed Plover	1995	
	1994	
Parrot Crossbill	1993	
	1992	
	1991	Wryneck
	1990	
Mandarin	1989	
	1988	
	Pied Flycatcher	
	1987	
Gannet	1986	
	Pied Flycatcher	
	1985	Corncrake
	Pied Flycatcher	
Kingfisher[1]	1984	
	1983	
Goldeneye	1982	
	1981	
	Red-backed Shrike, Pied Flycatcher	
	1980	
	Lapland Bunting	
Red-throated Diver	1979	
	Red-backed Shrike, Brambling, Lapland Bunting	
Purple Sandpiper	1978	
	Lapland Bunting	
Yellow Wagtail[2], Honey-buzzard	1977	
	Red-backed Shrike, Shore Lark, Lapland Bunting	
	1976	
	Black Redstart	
	1975	
	1974	
	1973	
	1968–72	Pintail, Nightjar, Hawfinch[3]
	Pied Flycatcher	

Notes: **1.** Known to have bred in 1910. **2.** Known to have bred prior to the 1930s. **3.** No exact date available.

Figure 5.1. Years of first recorded breeding and of last known confirmed breeding for species that have been 'gained', 'regained' or 'lost' since 1968, or which have bred occasionally.

Records relate to the whole of North-East Scotland using all sources. Any historical breeding (if relevant) in past centuries or the first half of the 20th century has not been included here. It is important to stress that apparent gains or losses relate purely to known records - it is possible that some species have bred undetected. In 'occasional breeders' column, species are placed below relevant years. Diagram concept after Norman (2008).

Changes in breeding distributions and evidence for population changes

In the following sections we examine in more detail the changes in breeding *distributions* that have apparently taken place, and also consider some likely changes in breeding bird *numbers*. We deal firstly with changes between our two local atlases, then longer-term changes using the two UK atlases combined with our results, then finally look at other information sources including the BTO Breeding Bird Survey.

1. Breeding distribution changes in Aberdeenshire and Aberdeen City between the two atlases 1981–84 and 2002–06

In the South-east Scotland atlas, Murray *et al.* (1998) suggested (using intensive fieldwork) that even common species which were easy to detect, such as Chaffinch, were under-recorded by 5–10% compared to their likely true occurrence. This implies that even in well-visited tetrads with many species, there could be further species present, and that there will be a degree of under-recording that is likely to be related to varying effort. This problem is almost impossible to resolve definitively. In the North-East, we have had two atlases, each of which produced distribution maps that can be compared for every species (when tetrad data are converted to the 1981–84 atlas units). The raw figures for the changes in numbers of occupied recording units are shown on the 'change' maps in each species account in Chapter 3. However, the possible degree of under- or over-recording in each atlas needs to be considered, since this will have influenced the apparent changes for many species.

Summary of raw atlas distribution changes in species selected for analysis

We looked at 154 species that were confirmed to breed in either or both of the two atlas periods. Of these, 115 (75%) showed an increase of >5% in the number of occupied recording units, compared with 23 (15%) indicating no clear change and just 16 (10%) showing a decrease of >5% (including species not now breeding) (see Figure 5.2). On the face of it, then, this suggests that the breeding ranges of the vast majority of species have undergone substantial expansion and very few have contracted.

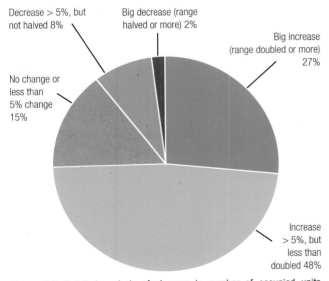

Figure 5.2. Detailed analysis of changes in number of occupied units between 1981–84 and 2002–06, based on a simple count of the number of occupied units per species in each atlas. 'Occupied recording units' includes confirmed, probable or possible breeding, and changes take account of losses and gains between the two atlases. 5% change was adopted arbitrarily to exclude very small variations in distribution.

Effects of observer coverage levels

However, before concluding that these apparent changes in distributions between the two local atlases are real, we must take into account the potential effects of differing levels of observer coverage in each. We have considered this in more depth in Annex 3, where several lines of evidence suggest that the major trend towards widespread range increases is probably true, but almost certainly it was exaggerated by observer effort. We conclude that the issue cannot be resolved definitively, and it is important to bear in mind this probable underlying influence when interpreting the changes below.

Species showing the greatest changes in occupied units

Increases: Using both raw and adjusted figures (see Annex 3), the 20 species showing the greatest increases in range are listed in Table 5.4. When considering these changes, bear in mind that some species have very low populations so changes can seem very large even though only small numbers of breeding units are involved. Species marked in bold are in the top 20 assessed in two different ways, which between them probably include most species showing the greatest real increases. Full details of recorded changes for all species are listed in Annex 4. Some are analysed further later in this chapter, but many of the species listed come as no surprise considering what is known about long-term population changes in Scotland (see Murray in *BS3*). However, some may still be subject, to an unknown degree, to differing recording effort levels, and in Section 7 below we have highlighted those where species authors have considered this to be potentially more serious.

Table 5.4. Species showing the greatest increases in breeding distribution in Aberdeenshire/Aberdeen City from 1981–84 to 2002–06. Percentage change figures are given in species accounts. Those marked * are thought to be more influenced by observer effort levels (see Table 5.10).

Greatest relative increase (see Annex 3)	Rank	Greatest % increase in raw data	Increase (raw data)
Buzzard	1	Kingfisher	10x increase or greater
Goldfinch	2	Barn Owl*	
Stonechat	3	Canada Goose	
Great Sp. Woodpecker	4	Greylag Goose	
Barn Owl*	5	Quail*	
Stock Dove*	6	Stonechat	More than doubled but less than 10x increase
Tawny Owl*	7	Goldeneye	
Blackcap	8	Red-legged Partridge	
Red-legged Partridge	9	Pochard	
Tree Sparrow	10	Raven	
Com. Crossbill/crossbill sp.	11	Cormorant	
Jay	12	Yellow Wagtail	
Sparrowhawk*	13	Blackcap	
Chiffchaff	14	Little Grebe	
Sand Martin	15	Buzzard	
Siskin	16	Ruddy Duck	
Quail*	17	Water Rail*	
Long-tailed Tit*	18	Long-eared Owl*	
Reed Bunting*	19	Great Sp. Woodpecker	
Long-eared Owl*	20	Jay	

Decreases: The species showing the greatest relative decreases in range are listed in the first column below in descending order. Nine of them (in bold) also fall in the 'bottom 20' using the raw, unadjusted data (second column). Again, some species have low populations so changes can seem very large even though only small numbers of breeding units are involved. As above, the two methods between them probably include most species showing the greatest real

Plate 5.2. Greenshank, Sutherland, May 1982. © *Ed Duthie* The Greenshank has declined to extinction in North-East Scotland.

decreases, but some may still be subject to the impact of differing recording levels. Details of distribution changes for all species are listed in Annex 4. As with the birds showing an increase in number of units, there are many expected species in the list in Table 5.5.

Table 5.5. Species showing the greatest decreases in breeding distribution in Aberdeenshire/Aberdeen City from 1981–84 to 2002–06. Percentage change figures are given in species accounts.

Relative decrease (biggest decrease at bottom of list)	Rank	% decrease in raw data (biggest decrease at bottom)	Decrease (raw data)
Woodpigeon	20	Fulmar	
Swallow	19	Curlew	
Grey Partridge	18	House Sparrow	
Willow Warbler	17	Rook	
Starling	16	Spotted Flycatcher	
Pied Wagtail	15	Lapwing	
Chaffinch	14	Yellowhammer	
Jackdaw	13	Grey Partridge	Decrease
Corn Bunting	12	Golden Plover	in range,
Redshank	11	Scottish Crossbill	but not
Skylark	10	Ring Ouzel	halved
House Sparrow	9	Arctic Tern	
Curlew	8	Lesser Whitethroat	
Blackbird	7	Corn Bunting	
Rook	6	Red-breasted Merganser	
Oystercatcher	5	Redshank	
Hooded Crow	4	Capercaillie	
Carrion Crow	3	Greenshank	Range
Yellowhammer	2	Hooded Crow	more than
Lapwing	1	Little Tern	halved

2. Breeding distribution changes over the whole of North-East Scotland using atlas sources from 1968–72 to 2002–06

Prior to the first national atlas (1968–72) there is little detailed information about breeding distributions for most species. This section highlights changes that may have occurred over the roughly 40 years since that time, using previous UK national atlases in combination with our 2002–06 survey, after tetrad data have been converted to 10-km square resolution (see Chapter 1). This involves the direct comparison of the numbers of occupied 10-km squares (confirmed, probable and possible breeding), and excludes data from the 1981–84 atlas (since this atlas period did not cover the whole area, with Moray excluded). However, once again, the issue of coverage levels needs to be considered (see

Annex 3). The evidence presented there suggests that there was a substantial reduction in recorder effort during the second national atlas (1988–91) in North-East Scotland compared with the first national atlas (1968–72) and our 2002–06 atlas. This can affect the interpretation of apparent changes in range over the last four decades.

Distribution changes at the 10-km level from 1968–72 to 2002–06

Figure 5.3 shows that from 1968–72 to 2002–06, of 157 species that were present in both atlas periods, 72 (46%) showed an increase in the number of occupied 10-km squares by 2002–06 of more than 5% (an arbitrary figure adopted to exclude small fluctuations). In addition, 32 species not recorded in 1968–72 were present in 2002–06. Forty-nine species (31%) showed little change (within +/- 5%) and 36 (23%) showed a decrease of more than 5% in number of occupied squares. No species totally disappeared in terms of *presence* in 10-km squares, though a few were lost as confirmed breeders - see Table 5.2 above. In making these assessments, we used records from all 10-km squares overlapping with our recording area. This may have led to the inclusion of some extra-limital records, but in assembling the data, we removed any species in marginal squares that clearly could not have occurred in the habitats present on our side of local authority boundaries. We did not adjust records from marginal squares in a systematic way similar to Buckland *et al.* (1990).

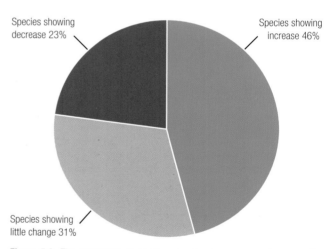

Figure 5.3. The proportion of species showing increases or decreases in number of occupied 10-km squares between the first UK atlas (1968–72) and the North-East Scotland atlas (2002–06).

Table 5.6 summarises the species which have shown the greatest gains and losses between 1968–72 and 2002–06 in terms of occupied 10-km squares (possible, probable and confirmed breeding). Again, some species have low populations so changes can seem very large even though only small numbers of 10-km squares are involved. The percentage change figures are shown in context in the species accounts.

Of the 20 species with the greatest gains, 11 are also those within the top 20 gains when comparing the 1981–84 and 2002–06 atlases for Aberdeenshire/Aberdeen City (Table 5.4). Ten of the species showing the greatest 10-km level decreases are also included in the 20 species showing the greatest decrease in our local atlases (Table 5.5). Both comparative atlas measures, then, show considerable similarity in the assessment of distribution change, and are significantly positively correlated.

The Breeding Birds of North-East Scotland

Table 5.6. The 20 greatest increases and decreases in occupied 10-km squares between the 1968–72 and 2002–06 UK atlases. Species in bold are also included in the 20 greatest increases or decreases between 1981–84 and 2002–06 local atlases (see Tables 5.4 and 5.5 above). Those marked * are thought to be more influenced by observer effort levels.

Top 20 increases 68/72–02/06	% increase	20 greatest decreases 68/72–02/06	% decrease
Goshawk		**Golden Plover**	
Goldeneye		**Ring Ouzel**	
Red-legged Partridge	10x increase	Short-eared Owl	
Canada Goose	or greater	**Red-breasted Merganser**	
Marsh Harrier		Shoveler	
Gadwall		Common Tern	Decreasing in range,
Kingfisher		Pied Flycatcher	but not halved
Quail*		**Corn Bunting**	
Osprey		Twite	
Greylag Goose		Dunlin*	
Jay		**Hooded Crow**	
Hobby	More than doubled	**Redshank**	
Hawfinch	but less than	**Little Tern**	
Scaup	10x increase	Redwing	
Green Woodpecker		Pochard	
Chiffchaff		Arctic Tern	
Blackcap		Roseate Tern	
Black Guillemot		**Capercaillie**	Range more
Barn Owl*		Corncrake	than halved
Stonechat		**Greenshank**	

3. Relationship between apparent change in atlas distributions and population change

Above, we consider only changes in *distribution* - not in population levels. Although there is a relationship between them, it is not straightforward. There could be large fluctuation in numbers of common species without this showing on a map of presence or absence within recording units. However, for scarcer species, Smith *et al.* (1993) showed a significant correlation between atlas changes and national population changes measured by the Common Birds Census, though the magnitude of change in the number of occupied tetrads was not necessarily the same as the change in population. In North-East Scotland, we have too few national Breeding Bird Survey squares in our area to draw reliable conclusions about population changes locally. However, BBS data for the whole of Scotland (Risely *et al.* 2008) allow comparison between the period from 1994 to 2007 with the longer period between our atlases from 1981–84 to 2002–06. The percentage changes in numbers of species measured by the BBS are significantly positively correlated with changes in number and in proportions of occupied units between our two atlases, suggesting that the two measures reflect genuine changes.

4. Changes in numbers of some common species recorded in the Breeding Bird Survey

Breeding Bird Survey transect counts have been available for our area and for Scotland since 1994. Francis (2007) analysed data from North-East Scotland for 1994–2006 and Risely *et al.* (2008) gave summary figures for Scotland from 1994–2007. BBS transects count all species in a sample of 1-km squares across Scotland. The Scottish sample size allows statistical significance to be assessed; in our area, the number of squares surveyed is too small for this, but an indication of possible trends over time can be obtained. Not all species are detected effectively by the technique, and the results are more reliable for the commoner and more widespread species.

In North-East Scotland, 21 BBS squares were surveyed ten times or more in the 13 years analysed, and using trends in numbers of the 75 most often recorded species, most (42%)

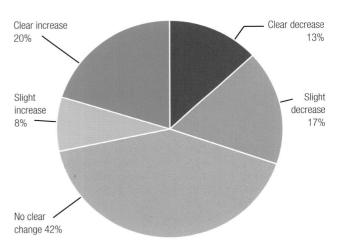

Figure 5.4. Trends in 75 species monitored by BBS in North-East Scotland 1994–2006.

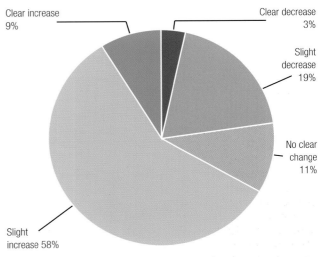

Figure 5.5. Trends in 57 species monitored by BBS in Scotland 1994–2007.

showed no clear change over time. Of the remainder, slightly more species (30%) showed evidence of decrease than increase (28%). This result (Figure 5.4) differs from that nationally (see below), and from the atlas distribution changes described above. However, the sample is small, and these local trends are less reliable than the other data sources.

For all Scottish BBS samples (Risely *et al.* 2008), 57 species were recorded in more than 30 squares and were used for analysis. Of the 57, 13 (22%) showed evidence of a decrease, six (11%) showed little trend (less than 5% either way), and 38 (67%) showed evidence of increase. More species (20) showed a *statistically significant* increase than showed a decrease (7).

This proportion was similar for the UK as a whole (Risely *et al.* 2008), with 26% of 104 species assessed at that level showing a significant decline during 1994–2007 and 44% showing a significant increase (the rest showed no significant change).

In conclusion, then, BBS data for Scotland suggest more species increasing than decreasing, though a more limited local sample suggests, marginally, the opposite picture. Full details of changes in numbers as assessed by BBS are given for each species in Annex 4.

5. Change in numbers of seabirds and birds of prey

For these two groups of birds, dedicated survey and monitoring schemes exist for most or some species and more detailed, long-running information is available. Neither group is well-monitored using other methods such as the Breeding Bird Survey.

Seabirds

The three main surveys, *Operation Seafarer* 1969–71, *Seabird Colony Register* 1985–87 and *Seabird 2000* (1998–2002), together with regular seabird colony monitoring, allow some long term trends to be identified. These are summarised in Mitchell *et al.* (2004), with updated information in annual seabird monitoring reports (*e.g.* Mavor *et al.* 2008) and on the JNCC website www.jncc.gov.uk/seabirds.

Although there are exceptions, such as Gannet, which has shown continued increase, and most terns, which have shown variable numbers, most seabirds increased strongly from 1969–71 to 1985–87 and continued to increase until 2000, though some gulls, especially Kittiwake and Herring Gull, had began to decline by then. Since 2000, there has been no further complete census, but several species are showing evidence of a decline (Table 5.7). These trends reflect those that have been found for the UK as a whole.

Table 5.7. Long-term trends in numbers of some breeding seabirds in North-East Scotland. The central date in the surveys listed above is given for each period. For each species, numbers from the constituent survey areas listed in Mitchell *et al.* (2004) have been used to calculate the trends for the whole of N-E Scotland.

Species	Breeding population 1970	Breeding population 1986	Breeding population 2000	Population trend from 1970 to 2000 (% change)	More recent trend from 1986 to 2000 (% change)	Probable local trend since 2000
Fulmar 1	4487	8891	10092	125%	14%	Decrease
Gannet * 1/2	0	2	530		26400%	Increase (1810 AOS, 2007)
Cormorant 2	1	13	145	14400%	1015%	Increase
Shag 2	293	634	730	149%	15%	Unknown
Black-headed Gull + 2	2253	1999	692	-69%	-65%	Unknown
Common Gull + 2	126	83	302	140%	264%	Decrease
Lesser B. B. Gull + 2	61	105	178	192%	70%	Unknown
Herring Gull + 2	43640	19034	15853	-64%	-17%	Decrease
Great B.B. Gull 2	45	43	82	82%	91%	Unknown
Kittiwake 2	66910	80525	70843	6%	-12%	Decrease
Sandwich Tern 2	740	1212	524	-29%	-57%	Increase/Variable
Common Tern 2	551	447	338	-39%	-24%	Unknown
Arctic Tern 2	261	165	504	93%	205%	Variable
Little Tern 2	67	49	60	-10%	22%	Variable
Guillemot 3	69092	85556	149889	117%	75%	Decrease
Razorbill 3	10044	8681	18070	80%	108%	Decrease
Black Guillemot 3 £		19	26		37%	Increase
Puffin 4	775	883	2488	221%	182%	Decrease

1 = Apparently Occupied Site; 2 = Apparently Occupied Nest; * = Survey dates for Gannet were 1994–95 and 2004, not 2000; + = not complete survey (inland sites not covered); 3 = individuals at colony; £ = not counted fully in 1969–1971; 4 = Apparently Occupied Burrows.

Table 5.8. Numbers of known breeding pairs of six bird of prey species in Aberdeenshire/Aberdeen City

Species	Earlier		1987	1992	1997	2002	2007	Trend
Hen Harrier	15 (min.)	1971–74	10	15	8	11	4	Decrease
Goshawk	1	1972	3	6	18	21	28	Increase
Golden Eagle	18	1945	17	16	18	19	17	Roughly stable
Osprey	1	1977	4	5	7	16	19	Increase
Merlin	41	1983	42	32	32	33	37	Roughly stable
Peregrine	22	1981	34	61	52	54	38	Increase then decrease

Birds of prey

For some birds of prey, there are also long-running datasets, maintained by Raptor Study Groups and latterly the Scottish Raptor Monitoring Scheme. These relate to a small selection of breeding raptors - mostly the rarer species, where full population monitoring has taken place on an annual basis in North-East Scotland for many years. However, there are differences in boundaries between Raptor Study Group monitoring areas and our boundary, so the details in Table 5.8 refer only to the North-east Scotland recording area (Aberdeenshire and Aberdeen City). The data are taken from species accounts in this atlas and North-east Scotland Bird Reports, but Scottish Raptor Monitoring Scheme reports (*e.g.* Etheridge *et al.* 2008) and their predecessors, annual 'Raptor Round Up' reports published annually as a supplement to *Scottish Birds,* have also been used where necessary.

Of the six species, two have shown a steady increase over time following re-colonisation of the area after elimination in the past, and one, the Peregrine, increased following recovery from pesticide impacts and persecution but is now declining again. Two species have been roughly stable over the past few decades, though Golden Eagles do not occupy all the sites that have been used previously. The Hen Harrier, after having recolonised the area by the mid 20th century, peaked in the 1970s and 1980s and is now declining again.

6. Conclusions about changing bird distributions and numbers in North-East Scotland

For Scotland, Murray (in *BS3*) suggested that, overall, there had been an increase in the number of species breeding in the country and that an increase was also shown in terms of the total number of species that could be classed as 'common' or 'abundant'. By 2004, some 92 species were considered to be 'abundant' (over 10,000 breeding pairs in Scotland), an increase from 85 in the period 1851–1950. Some species have undergone a considerable range expansion in Scotland; many of these are woodland birds. Since 1951, eight species have moved into the abundant category in Scotland; Greylag Goose, Pheasant, Oystercatcher, Woodcock, Stock Dove, Collared Dove, Chiffchaff and Siskin. Murray also documents many instances of first breeding, colonisation and spread, as well as some clear declines - species such as Capercaillie, Corncrake, Roseate Tern, Nightjar and Corn Bunting. The pattern of more increases than decreases was also reported for Britain and Ireland (Robinson 2010), for Scotland (amongst 62 species monitored since 1994) by Mackey & Mudge (2010) and by Jenkins & Watson (2005) amongst 23 species within our area in upper Feughside, Deeside; 15 of these showed significant increases and five showed significant decreases between 1987 and 2004.

Most of these overall patterns also apply to our North-East Scotland atlas data, with many species sharing national trends. In Annex 4, we have presented a full list of likely changes in distribution and populations, based on the evidence above, together with Scottish and local BBS data, seabird colony counts, raptor monitoring and other available sources. It appears, from all available measures, that, as in Scotland as a whole, more species have shown increases than decreases in our area, and there have been many more 'colonisations' than losses as breeding birds, whether expressed as confirmed breeding or simply 'breeding presence', or at a 10-km square or tetrad scale. In addition, evidence from BBS and other sources suggests that, at least for those species covered effectively by available techniques, more species have increased in numbers since 1994 than

have decreased. Some possible reasons for such changes are considered further in Chapter 6.

When comparing our local atlas results (for Aberdeenshire/ Aberdeen City, 1981–84 to 2002–06), some interesting general patterns of distribution change emerge.

Relationship between distribution change and abundance

1. More widespread species are significantly less likely to show a substantial percentage change in the number of occupied units between the two atlases. This may largely be a statistical artefact in that it is harder for a species that is already widespread to show a big proportional change in number of units.

2. The most numerous species (by estimated population size) are also less likely to show a large percentage change in the number of occupied recording units between the two atlases. This is not surprising since the estimated population sizes and the number of occupied units per species are significantly positively correlated.

Relationship between distribution change and species groupings

Where suitable comparative data were available, we examined three main types of species groups (Table 5.9). The birds included in each are indicated in Annex 4. The apparent increases and decreases in distribution should be viewed against the general 27% increase in the number of records across the 395 recording units.

1. **Comparison between Red, Amber and Green list species (see Eaton *et al.* 2009).** The average change for Red list species was well below the overall 27% increase and seven of the 25 species showed a decline in the number of occupied units (such as Capercaillie, Corn Bunting and Ring Ouzel). The proportion of records accounted for by Red list species also fell, with 15 species showing a decline. Red list species are clearly still generally in unfavourable condition. The 57 Amber list species showed an average change close to the overall figure and the 53 Green list species considered were higher than this.

Table 5.9. Average values of distribution changes for certain groupings of species.

Grouping (see text for explanation)	Average % change in distribution (raw data)	Change in proportion of total records accounted for by group (see Annex 3)	Number of species included
Birds of Conservation Concern			
Red list species	9	-3.02	25
Amber list species	29.4	0.48	57
Green list species	35.5	2.75	53
'African migrants'	34.7	0.84	28
Non-'African migrants'	26.5	-0.63	106
Habitat groups			
Birds of prey	98	1.72	5
Woodland birds	51	2.93	25
Seabirds	46	0.21	14
Upland birds	26	-0.03	7
Wetland birds	21	-0.89	36
Farmland birds	18	-0.60	8
Overall % change in total no. of occupied unit records, 1981-84 to 2002-06	27	n/a	142

2. Comparison between long-distance African migrants and all other species. Surprisingly, both the comparative increase in distribution and the change in proportion of records were higher for the 28 African migrant summer visitors than for the remaining birds analysed. This suggests that overall these birds are doing better than other species which are resident or move locally within the UK or Europe. Although this seems contrary to the general picture relating to long-distance migrants, some species such as Garden Warbler or Chiffchaff may be shifting their distribution northwards such that their status in Scotland is more favourable than further south. The trends here may reflect that.

3. Comparison between species characteristic of different habitats. We assigned (subjectively) most species to a habitat type or grouping that best represents them in our area. The categories are shown for each species in Annex 4, but 10 species did not fit easily into any of the categories used (such as Swift or Stonechat) and were not included. In Table 5.9, they are listed in descending order of change in distribution. When interpreting this, the relationship between change and abundance described above should be borne in mind, in that some of the groups showing lower levels of increase also include most of the common, widespread species with less capacity to show large increases. Only five **birds of prey** were considered, being the only species with accurate comparative change maps, and their strong average increase is influenced mainly by Buzzard and Merlin, which have shown large percentage increases. The 25 **woodland bird** species also showed a strong average increase in occupied units and a higher proportion of the records. Amongst these, a few such as Capercaillie and Spotted Flycatcher showed a decrease, but there were also some very strong increases to compensate. In part, this reflects the considerable growth in woodland area, but in some cases, trends are contrary to those recorded nationally. Fourteen **seabird** species were included in the analysis and these too showed a general increase, with decreases mainly in terns. The general increase in seabird numbers over recent decades is well documented, and the recent downturn in numbers is not sufficient to cancel out the longer term increases.

The remaining four groups considered showed increases in distribution below the overall average and also showed a negative change in the proportion of records they accounted for by the time of the 2002–06 atlas. A small group of seven **upland** birds showed low levels of positive change, with a large increase in Ravens counterbalancing a decline in Ring Ouzels. **Wetland** bird species showed a below-average increase, with a declining proportion of the records and this was also true of eight **farmland** species. Here, the decline of Corn Bunting, Grey Partridge and Yellowhammer was more than balanced by increases in Tree Sparrow and Quail. The remaining **generalist** species group includes only four species with a reduced distribution; most birds showed below average apparent increases, and overall a decreased proportion of the total records.

7. Conclusions about the potential impact of differing levels of recording effort

All of the changes assessed above depend on the assumption that they are not the result of distortion due to differing levels of fieldwork intensity. The shared trends in all the lines of evidence discussed suggest that this factor does not undermine the general analysis, but it is likely to have been influential. The analyses in Annex 3 and above include several possible measures of the level of impact of recording effort. Most imply that greater recording intensity in 2002–06 in the local atlas led to an increase in records - perhaps as much as 27% overall, but varying greatly between species (from relatively low, around 4%, for common widespread species, to much higher for some scarcer birds). We believe though that many of the general trends described above and in the species accounts do reflect real changes in the breeding distributions of many species. It is impossible to be sure which species have been most influenced by effort levels, rather than real change - it seems likely that most if not all species have been influenced to some degree. However, for a few species, there may be more grounds to suspect a strong distorting influence (Table 5.10). These are largely anecdotal, based upon knowledge of specialist recording, and upon the conclusions of species authors in this atlas. More than other species, this possibility should be borne in mind when interpreting the results of all of the breeding bird atlases considered in this book.

Table 5.10. Species for which recording effort probably had the greatest distorting effect on apparent distribution changes between atlases.

Local breeding bird atlases, North-east Scotland, 1981–84 and 2002–06.

For these species, it is likely that the apparent increases were exaggerated, as birds were probably overlooked in 1981–84. The list includes a few species (marked *) whose distribution maps are probably even more influenced by observer effort.

Tufted Duck	Long-eared Owl*
Sparrowhawk	Tree Pipit
Quail	Grey Wagtail
Water Rail*	Redstart
Dunlin*	Wheatear
Snipe	Grasshopper Warbler*
Woodcock	Long-tailed Tit
Feral Pigeon	Linnet
Stock Dove	Bullfinch
Barn Owl*	Reed Bunting
Tawny Owl	

National BTO breeding atlases, 1968–72, 1988–91 and comparison with 2002–06.

The strongly reduced distributions in 1988–91 are likely to be spurious. This list shows only those species whose breeding distributions in 10-km squares dropped from an index value of 100 in 1968–72 to below 80 in 1988–91 then back up to 100 or more in 2002–06 (see Annex 3).

Tufted Duck	Barn Owl
Black Grouse	Long-eared Owl
Sparrowhawk	Great Spotted Woodpecker
Water Rail	Rock Pipit
Snipe	Long-tailed Tit
Stock Dove	

Chapter 6. *Conservation of the breeding birds of North-East Scotland*

Bird populations and distributions are rarely static. They are subject to a wide range of influences, some of which are clear and well understood, whilst others are subtle, complex or novel. In this chapter we examine the wider context of the breeding birds of North-East Scotland and consider the main influences on their conservation status, both negative and positive. Our aims are both to examine the current situation and to speculate about possible changes over the next few decades.

North-East Scotland's birds in a wider context

North-East Scotland holds disproportionately high numbers of many breeding species when viewed in a Scottish, UK or even European context. Table 6.1 lists the top ten species for these geographic areas whose local populations are thought to be particularly important at these levels. In terms of proportional land area, North-East Scotland occupies around 11% of Scotland, 4% of the UK and well under 1% of Western Europe.

Plate 6.2. Crested Tit, Aviemore, May 2010. © *Kev Jones* North-East Scotland holds 25% of Scotland's breeding Crested Tits.

Although some of the estimates are very approximate, the list in Annex 4 shows that North-East Scotland holds around 14 species which have 1% or more of their European breeding population in our area, 22 species with 10% or more of the UK population and 31 species with 20% or more of the Scottish population. The Scottish Crossbill is currently accepted as Scotland's (and the UK's) only endemic bird species and North-East Scotland forms one of the main parts of its world range. We also hold significant populations of three subspecies endemic to Scotland (see *BS3*) - Ptarmigan, Crested Tit and Linnet (25% of Scottish population). The concentration in North-East Scotland of these breeding populations imposes a responsibility on us to ensure their conservation, and the main issues which influence the population levels and breeding success of all birds nesting in North-East Scotland are considered below.

Plate 6.1. Scottish Crossbill, Deeside, June 2003. © *Harry Scott* A high proportion of Europe's Scottish Crossbills breed in North-East Scotland.

Table 6.1. Some important breeding bird populations of North-East Scotland; the ten most important species at each geographic level in terms of the approximate percentage of breeding populations nesting within North-East Scotland. The European geographic area is as used in the EBCC Atlas of European Breeding Birds (Hagemeijer & Blair 1997) and excludes Russia and Turkey. UK populations are taken largely from Baker *et al.* 2006, and Scottish figures from *BS3*. These percentages vary in their accuracy according to level of knowledge of local and wider populations. A more extended list is given in Annex 4, Table B.

European population	% in North-East Scotland	UK population	% in North-East Scotland	Scottish population	% in North-East Scotland
Scottish Crossbill	29	Purple Sandpiper	50	Sandwich Tern	74
Siskin	8	Parrot Crossbill	50	Corn Bunting	64
Guillemot	5	Dotterel	35	Purple Sandpiper	50
Oystercatcher	3	Fieldfare	33	Parrot Crossbill	50
Curlew	3	Snow Bunting	33	Tree Sparrow	47
Kittiwake	3	Ptarmigan	30	Quail	46
Razorbill	2	Scottish Crossbill	30	Goshawk	42
Rook	2	Crested Tit	25	Dotterel	35
Herring Gull	2	Common Gull	<22	Fieldfare	33
Meadow Pipit	2	Goldeneye	20	Snow Bunting	33

General picture - the 'state of North-East Scotland's birds'

We have enough information now to assess the status of most of our local breeding birds within a wider context and to describe change in recent decades. It is much more difficult to take a longer-term view on this, say further back than 40 years, due to the lack of information from that time, especially about populations. Meaningful statements become possible for most species from around 1968, the start of the first national breeding atlas.

Chapter 5 outlines the changes in the numbers of birds confirmed to breed in the area between the 1968–72 atlas (150 species) and 2002–06 (153 species), with 173 species over the whole 42 year period since 1968. The evidence also suggests that more species increased their breeding distribution than showed a decline. However, despite these indications of range changes, we know little about changes in breeding bird *numbers* since 1968–72. For some raptors and seabirds we have numerical information but for most we can only guess. It is likely that some general UK countryside trends, such as those for farmland birds revealed by the Common Bird Census, were representative to some extent of North-East Scotland over that period, though there were very few such census plots in our area. For Scotland as a whole, Murray (*BS3*) has analysed how the levels of abundance of breeding birds may have changed since 1800, and much of that analysis is relevant to North-East Scotland. We can also use knowledge of habitat changes to speculate how bird numbers might have changed; Fuller & Ausden (2008, 2009) present a detailed analysis of this issue and review bird conservation measures, much of which is relevant to North-East Scotland. They suggest that most species that have increased in Britain during the last century are those associated with lowland water bodies (for example, gravel pits) and conifer plantations. In contrast, many formerly common birds of farmed land are faring less well now, mainly due to agricultural intensification.

North-East Scotland now almost certainly holds fewer seed-eating farmland birds and fewer breeding waders than would have been the case in the late 1960s. However, there are more breeding geese and seabirds than there were 40 years ago. Some birds of prey are more numerous now, such as Buzzard, but others, such as Hen Harrier, are less so. Most native grouse and partridge species have declined, but we now have many more introduced Pheasants and Red-legged Partridges. A wide range of birds associated with large conifer plantations, such as Goldcrest, Siskin and Coal Tit are without doubt much commoner than decades ago. There are other such examples of change, but for some species, long-term numerical trends are obscure. In general, the evidence suggests we have gained more breeding species than we have lost; in fact, there are probably more species breeding in North-East Scotland now than for many decades, and the total may even be the highest it has ever been. Similar conclusions were also reached by Murray (*BS3*) for Scotland, Fuller & Ausden (2009) for Britain, and Yalden & Albarella (2009) for the British Isles. In part, this reflects much more observation and recording (see Chapter 5 for discussion of this), but there have been many genuine additions to the breeding species of North-East Scotland. The status of our local breeding birds is therefore complex and constantly changing. There are some general influences on population changes though, and we consider these below - for each, some adverse and beneficial trends and then some likely developments that might enhance bird conservation or present future threats. This assessment uses information presented in this atlas but also draws on Fuller & Ausden (2008, 2009), Walton & Housden (in *BS3*), Parkin & Knox (2010) and Robinson (2010); speculation about the future is our responsibility.

Conservation issues for birds in North-East Scotland

Agricultural change

The agriculture of North-East Scotland has changed greatly in recent decades (Chapter 2). Large-scale influences such as the Common Agricultural Policy have shaped the crops grown, the kinds of habitat features on farms, and the timing and nature of farm operations. In turn, these have affected the numbers of birds nesting on farms and some of these effects are shown in Table 6.2. North-East Scotland remains a classic area of mixed agriculture, with large areas of cereals grown for feeding livestock and for malting, forming a

Table 6.2. Some examples of change on farmland in North-East Scotland between 1981–84 and 2002–06.

Change	Negative effects on birds	Positive effects on birds
Winter/spring cereals balance; increase in winter cereals; loss of cereals in upland areas.	Winter cereals provide less overwinter stubble for seed eaters.	Spring-sown crops still comprise two-thirds cover of cereals, so N-E Scotland relatively favourable.
Increased fertiliser use, more frequent & intensive grass cutting.	Less suitable for Curlew, Corn Bunting, Corncrake, Skylark.	Some crow species have increased with better feeding on farmland, (but predation by crows on other birds may be an issue).
Greater extent of Oil-seed Rape.	Associated reduction of cereals reduces food for some species.	Rape used by Woodpigeon, Linnet, Sedge Warbler, Reed Bunting, so benefits for some species.
More farm woodland and hedges, mainly 1990s onwards.	Loss of field habitat for some open ground farmland birds	Increase in nesting and feeding for common farmland birds and some rarer species.
Loss of small pockets of rough, wet or semi-improved ground through farmland intensification; narrower field margins.	Reduced habitat for waders, warblers and buntings.	Probably none - negative effects offset any occasional benefit such as removal of predator cover.
Creation of new habitat features such as hedges and field margins and management methods through agri-environment schemes.	Some conflict between value of new and existing habitats, such as ponds in marshy areas or fenced and planted open river banks.	Demonstrated benefits for Corn Buntings and some other seed-eaters (Perkins *et al.* 2008); likely benefits for generalist bird species. Hedges likely to be important.

mosaic with grass fields grazed by livestock or cut for winter feed, mainly as silage. This mixed farmland landscape, which provides a greater variety of food and nesting habitat, has probably helped to slow the declines of some breeding bird species compared with some other parts of the country, where agriculture has become more specialised.

Future change for farmland birds in North-East Scotland

Increasing pressure on farmland seems inevitable. Although this trend seemed to recede in the 1990s and the early part of this century, demand for food and for energy crops appears likely to grow again. Autumn sown cereals may possibly increase at the expense of spring barley as malting premiums decline and bigger feed Barley yields are sought. The big losses suffered in malting Barley enterprises could also lead to a switch to intensive grassland. These changes will lead to increased intensification and loss of areas of semi-improved or rough farmland habitat. Numbers of waders and seed-eating birds are unlikely to recover greatly and the former may become increasingly confined to scattered, suitable areas. At the same time, demand for what are termed 'environmental services' (such as flood storage, water quality and carbon sequestration) is likely to

increase. This may bring funding sources that can offset commercial pressures and lead to some beneficial habitat management on farms, along with continued funding for agri-environment schemes - though these will always be small in extent. Grazing levels may diverge to become intensive on some land and low or non-existent on other areas (mostly moorland fringes). Both effects would have negative impacts on birds unless scrub and woodland communities developed on the ungrazed areas (which itself would depend on the numbers of wild deer).

For bird conservation over the coming years, it will be crucial to ensure that measures to manage birds and their habitat are promoted in all government funding sources and regulations; there is clear evidence that these, when applied in the right areas, can reduce the rate of farmland bird declines and even increase numbers. An example of this is the RSPB's scheme for Corn Buntings in East Scotland, which benefited this species when combined with government agri-environment measures (Perkins *et al.* 2008). If such measures are absent, it will be increasingly hard to maintain the numbers of birds nesting on farmland.

Plate 6.3. Drainage of wet areas on farmland, Dallas, June 2009. Intensification of farming is likely to continue. © *I. Francis*

Plate 6.4. Short rotation willow coppice grown as a biomass crop on a farm near Banchory, September 2009. Such crops are becoming more frequent on farmland but birds using them have not been studied in Scotland. © *I. Francis*

Wetlands, water and environmental quality

North-East Scotland is generally a dry part of the country. It experiences low precipitation in the east and most major wetlands were drained long ago. Remaining wetlands are few, small and scattered, but even these are vulnerable, with many losses during the past 20 years. Although some wetlands have been created as part of agri-environment schemes, their nature has changed; for example, moist, soft-edged corners or flood areas, favoured by Lapwing and Snipe have become scarcer and new wetlands often now tend to be steep, hard-edged ponds. The suitability of some wet fields for breeding waders has also declined in places due to inappropriate grazing practices - at times, ironically, stemming from the rules of environmental schemes. This has led to insufficient grazing and rush encroachment in numerous areas.

Natural lowland wetlands such as raised bogs are now rarely grazed, burned or cut and fens have tended to become unmanaged, leading to vegetation succession, rank herb growth and, on some, colonisation by scrub and trees. The important network of raised bog remnants is still present in Buchan, but elsewhere most have been lost to conifer planting or woodland succession. There are many scattered fens but little is known about their current condition or bird life, though vegetation growth and drying of sites may have led to a decline in the occurrence of Spotted Crake in North-East Scotland. Nevertheless, all these wetlands still act as valuable refuges for some birds; if they were not present, species such as Curlew, Grasshopper Warbler, Reed Bunting, Mallard and even Meadow Pipit would be much less widespread. Many areas of low-lying land still flood, in some places greatly, particularly recently in north Moray, prompting the creation of several flood relief schemes such as at Lhanbryde, Forres, and Rothes. These rarely incorporate significant wetland habitat creation and the large scheme proposed for Elgin is also likely to lack such features. Where land does flood, water usually drains away quickly through well-developed ditch networks. Long-lasting inundation of grassland is rare, with the result that some large tracts of farmland are largely dry and hold few waders. Some floodplains have also been lost to development, with examples of this on the edge of Aberdeen and at Inverurie.

Precipitation and runoff in watercourses are both subject to the influence of various pollutants, though impacts on birds are either indirect or unclear. The acidity of rainfall appears to be declining (e.g. see Environmental Change Network 2009) but deposited nitrous oxides are still causing the nutrient enrichment of some habitats, including grasslands which themselves are subject to fertiliser application. Much of the eastern and northern parts of North-East Scotland are designated as a 'Nitrate Vulnerable Zone' with restrictions on farming practice designed to reduce nutrient inputs and nitrate and phosphate runoff. The water quality of some watercourses in intensively farmed areas is poor (for example, several wetland birds such as Common Sandpiper are scarce on the Ythan, one of the most enriched of our rivers) and measures are being developed to deal with such issues. Some stem from the EU Water Framework Directive, though other initiatives are also underway such as the Dee catchment management plan (see http://www.theriverdee.org). These will take time to have an impact, especially on lowland lochs, most of which are eutrophic and have suffered declines in plant communities and changes in the birds using them (e.g. Loch of Strathbeg - Francis 1996 and Loch of Skene - Wills 2009).

Plate 6.5. Wetlands continue to be lost. The top photograph of a long-established pond and wetland in Deeside, that held breeding Redshanks and numerous Lapwings, was taken in 1999. The bottom one shows the site in June 2006 after drainage in April that year. Although the site has re-wetted again slightly since then, it no longer holds the numbers of waders it once did. © I. Francis

Plate 6.6. Wetland at Tarland Waste Water Treatment Works, April 2006. This wetland was created by Scottish Water as part of the '3Dee Vision' partnership to take treated effluent water from the sewage works and so continue to act as a valuable habitat for waders, ducks, gulls and geese. Five pairs of Redshanks bred here in 2008 and 2009. © N. Penford

Other pollutants are not considered further here, but it is worth noting that some previously-used pesticides (now banned) such as DDT and Dieldrin still occur in the food chain and may affect, for example, coastal Feral Pigeons, and potentially Peregrines (Hardey 2002). Methods of disposing of sewage have changed greatly, with effluent that used to provide food sources for birds at many short coastal outfalls now being pumped far out to sea, and many inland sewage discharges have been cleaned up, with potential improvements in water quality. Rarely, such as at Tarland and Ballater, wetland features have been built into modern sewage treatment works, with considerable benefits for birds (see Plate 6.6).

Future changes in wetland habitats and their birds

There is unlikely to be any *large-scale* drainage of wetlands in the coming years due to stricter regulation stemming from the Water Framework Directive, but the attrition of small-scale wetlands is likely to continue, linked to the intensification of agricultural land. Wading birds will continue to be found largely in small, scattered, wetland patches and most drainage schemes that currently exist will remain intact with no significant re-wetting; indeed, a climatic trend for drier summers in future (Chapter 2) may exacerbate summer dryness and reduce the extent of wet soils. Set against this, some creation of wetlands will continue. These may, as now, be linked to agri-environment schemes or for shooting wildfowl, and the trend for the excavation of small ponds seems likely to be maintained. Some provision for small-scale wildlife habitats may be built into future flood alleviation schemes, and wetlands created to store water, regulate summer flows, deposit organic sediment to store carbon, or other forms of 'environmental service', may become more prevalent, with some potential beneficial impacts on birds. Some larger-scale schemes to restore wetland habitat will probably occur but these will be few. Overall, then, it seems unlikely that there will be any wide-scale resurgence in the numbers of wetland breeding birds in North-East Scotland during the coming decades.

Plate 6.7. New pond at Asloun, Alford, April 2006. The resurgence of pond creation is likely to continue in the coming years, though perhaps at a lower rate; there are probably now thousands in North-East Scotland, though not all are optimally designed for wildlife. © I. Francis

Plate 6.8. The Dee floodplain between Braemar and Mar Lodge, May 2008. This 220 ha area benefited from wetland restoration following ditch blocking in 1996 in a joint project between NTS Mar Lodge and Invercauld Estates, SNH and RSPB Scotland, and led to increases in the breeding populations of six species of wading birds since that time. © *I. Francis*

Woodland management and new planting

Around 18% of North-East Scotland is covered by woodland (Chapter 2), mostly coniferous plantations, though there are some large areas of Caledonian pinewood and birch woodland. The threefold increase in area of conifer plantation between the 1940s and the 1980s continued into the 1990s but planting rates have declined to very low figures now. This increase has benefited numerous passerines such as Goldcrest, Coal Tit, Siskin and Common Crossbill, but there has been a large loss of open ground habitat, especially moorland, and this has contributed to declines of some species such as Red Grouse and Golden Plover. Some afforestation schemes in the 1990s were of 'New Native Pinewoods' and these are now gradually becoming established as young open woodland. The majority of recent planting has been of broad-leaved trees, often in small blocks or strips and sometimes rather artificial in structure and composition. Coniferous and broad-leaved planting was concentrated during the 1990s and early 2000s in the north-east of the area, under the Grampian Challenge Fund and successor schemes. Species that may have benefited include warblers such as Whitethroat, Blackcap, Garden Warbler and Sedge Warbler

in young plantations. Further information on changes in woodland bird populations nationally, and possible reasons for these can be found in Amar *et al.* 2006 and Smart *et al.* 2007. Although none of their detailed study sites lay in our area, some of the trends identified are likely to be relevant to North-East Scotland.

Many conifer plantations have been restructured in the last 25 years as they have matured, and all have become more diverse, with greater planting of broad-leaves within them, and generally smaller areas of felling and restocking. This can provide structural diversity, variation in tree age, increased open space and edge habitat, variety in tree species and woodland type and lead to improvement of water quality in watercourses within plantations. There has almost certainly been a diversification of the breeding bird community, though there is little information from North-East Scotland. Restocking with a range of conifer species including larch has probably offered diverse food sources to crossbills, and conditions available to the three local species are probably as favourable as they have ever been. Black Grouse have probably also benefited from the opening up and replanting of previously mature plantations.

Plate 6.9. New Scots Pine and broad-leaved woodland on Mar Lodge Estate, 2008. Such areas benefit Black Grouse and a range of song birds. Large-scale establishment of 'New Native Pinewoods' largely ceased in the late 1990s due to changes in grant support, but new grants are likely to encourage native woodland once more, especially along watercourses. © I. Francis

Plate 6.10. New broad-leaved woodland planted on rough acid grassland on a farm at Breda, Alford, 2008. Tree planting on farms may become increasingly confined to small areas on marginal ground, threatening less-intensive grassland bird habitat. © I. Francis

Caledonian pinewoods have gained a high profile since the 1990s, but their management (or lack of it) has not always been beneficial to birds. In particular, the continued use of deer fences creates strong differences in vegetation structure, as shown in Plate 6.11. Upland broad-leaved woodlands are also often in a similar condition - either open to grazing animals and heavily grazed with few ground nest sites and lack of woodland regeneration, or fenced to exclude stock and deer, leading to rank vegetation, domination by a few plant species and less varied feeding for birds.

Nevertheless, the general picture for most woodland birds in North-East Scotland is probably favourable, and by 2009 many species were at their highest population levels for a very long time - aided by relatively mild winters (though the hard winter of 2009–10 will probably have had an impact on some species). Even the long-distance migrants nesting in woodlands, such as Tree Pipit, Redstart and Wood Warbler appear to be stable in distribution and Willow Warblers, which are seriously declining in southern Britain, are very abundant here. Spotted Flycatchers though, appear to be declining in range. The woodland species at greatest risk of extinction remains Capercaillie, and much effort has been directed towards its conservation; it is not yet clear though whether this will succeed in maintaining and increasing the currently very low population in North-East Scotland.

Plate 6.11. Caledonian pine woodland, Ballochbuie, Deeside, 2006. Grazing and browsing pressure from Red Deer remains a serious management issue in Deeside, Donside and parts of Moray. Deer fences separate heavily grazed areas from areas receiving little grazing. Neither extreme is ideal for many pinewood species and even marked fences like this still provide a collision risk for Capercaillie. The problem of landscape-scale sustainable deer numbers shows little sign of being resolved. © I. Francis

Future change for woodland birds in North-East Scotland

There is likely to be a resurgence of commercial woodland planting and management, especially linked to growing trees for biomass incinerators and for storing or sequestering carbon. This may lead to intensive management of some plantations and renewed commercial planting of spruce in places. Otherwise, the trend towards more diverse forests managed for a range of purposes is likely to continue, with wider mixes of species and age structures leading to more bird species using most plantations. Increased management through 'selection' systems of harvesting and regeneration rather than clear-felling is likely to occur, and a focus on native woodlands, biodiversity and water quality management will continue in planting and forest operations, including on some of the larger private estates which have already developed long-term forest plans with these objectives. All evidence suggests that bird conservation will be paid more attention, though management methods for some of the nationally-declining woodland birds have not yet been developed. It is also likely that there will be more public recreation in woodlands, together with associated trails, signs and facilities, which could increasingly disturb some species, including Capercaillie.

Woodland expansion will probably continue at a slow rate. Recent tree planting has been offset by some deforestation related to wind farm projects sited in plantations, and this may continue, but the woodland area will probably continue to expand gradually; the majority almost certainly will still be of broad-leaved species. There will be little land available for woodland expansion, especially on farmland and there is likely to be more afforestation on marginal moorland. Some of this will be encouraged to form part of 'forest habitat networks' to provide linkages between woodlands, and there will also be emphasis on woodland along watercourses. If climate changes in ways that have been predicted, this may affect the choice of tree species in future planting, and have impacts on existing forests. However, overall, habitat conditions for most woodland birds seem likely to become more favourable in the coming decades.

Plate 6.12. Woodland near Ballater, from Coilacriech, May 2007. The creation of 'forest habitat networks' linking existing woodlands is being widely promoted, especially in the Cairngorms National Park. © I. Francis

Plate 6.13. Broad-leaved trees planted on Heather moorland at Hill of Foudland, Gartly, June 2006. Marginal, unmanaged Heather moorland is likely to see more woodland establishment schemes in future as less land becomes available elsewhere. This will see the loss of habitat for some open-ground birds but also habitat creation for some woodland species. © I. Francis

The Breeding Birds of North-East Scotland

Plate 6.14. Although the North-East Scotland coast is generally undeveloped, habitat losses can occur, most notably here at Menie Estate, Balmedie, where the sand dunes and dune heath are being developed as a golf resort, despite their protected status as a SSSI. © I. Francis (2008)

Semi-natural habitat change and protected sites

Chapter 2 summarises the considerable changes in land cover and bird habitats between the 1940s and the 1980s, some of which have continued to the present day. For 'semi-natural' habitats of higher nature conservation value, there have been large losses of Heather moorland, peatlands, scrub, hedgerows and broad-leaved woodland. Not all types of land cover have been measured consistently over time, but it appears that few semi-natural habitats have *increased* to any large degree, though there have been some shifts in their nature. For example, birch woodland and scrub have invaded numerous wetlands or unmanaged moorland; this can be seen well at the Muir of Dinnet, where a formerly open moorland landscape has become naturally established native woodland. The planting of New Native Pinewoods or broad-leaved woodland on moorland can also perhaps be seen as an artificially-induced change from one 'semi-natural' type to another in the long term.

Change over time through vegetation succession, grazing or nutrient enrichment has affected many semi-natural habitats and these problems remain. In the last ten years or so though, intentional damage to, or destruction of, semi-natural habitats has slowed. Most local development plan policies and agricultural or forestry regulations are now designed to prevent such actions, requiring, for example, Environmental Impact Assessments (including for the ploughing or conversion of rough grazing and permanent pasture). Still, there have been exceptions, and one important area of coastal habitat at Menie Estate north of Aberdeen will be lost to the 'Trump International Golf Links' leisure development. Such events are now rarer than they were, but add incrementally to earlier habitat losses and adverse ecological changes taking place on 'intact' sites.

The future for semi-natural habitats in North-East Scotland

Compared to the period from the 1960s to the mid 1990s, direct loss of semi-natural habitats in recent years has slowed, though gradual change induced by land management practices (or their absence) is still taking place. In the coming decades, the legislative framework will probably be sufficient to prevent most serious direct losses, with some exceptions, such as at Menie Estate. As noted above, wetlands and small remnant patches of semi-natural habitat on farms are likely to remain threatened and a range of factors may lead to some SSSIs not being managed appropriately, despite government targets. In the uplands, there may be some tree and scrub regeneration and planting on moorland as single-purpose shooting management is reassessed in some places and land management becomes influenced by requirements to produce broader benefits to the ecosystem. However, moorland on many shooting estates will remain intensively managed with regular and widespread burning. In addition to this, deer browsing and grazing almost certainly will remain locally high, leading to damage to some designated areas, suppressed natural tree regeneration and continuing imbalance in the levels of grazing in woodlands. With intensification on more productive land it seems likely that renewable energy projects, such as wind farms and possibly biomass planting, will be concentrated on semi-natural land of perceived lower value. The main expansion in semi-natural habitats will be in regenerated and planted woodland, especially along watercourses and within the Cairngorms National Park, particularly in upper Deeside.

These changes suggest that we may expect some species to become scarcer across the area, including Red Grouse, Grey Partridge, most wading birds and some passerine inhabitants of marginal land such as Wheatear, Whinchat, Twite and Yellowhammer. Most woodland birds will continue to increase, though. There may also be impacts from climate change, which are considered further below.

Site protection, conservation action and nature reserve management

One key aspect of the conservation of semi-natural bird habitats in North-East Scotland is the network of protected sites, and how they are managed. The situation in 2009 is shown in Table 6.3. Many SSSIs are not designated directly for birds, but the habitat contained in them is likely in many cases to benefit them. It seems unlikely that there will be additions of large size Special Protection Areas beyond the designation in 2010 of Golden Eagles. Designation is only one step towards bird conservation, and ensuring that appropriate management occurs is also critical. The extent to which this is happening is still unclear because monitoring is a slow process with insufficient detail for many species. It is clear though that some birds experience wide-ranging problems that site designations alone cannot easily tackle - perhaps the best examples are Capercaillie and Hen Harrier, whose numbers are perilously low despite sites being designated to protect them. Designations though can bring extra funding for management, so at least there may be options on these sites that are not found elsewhere.

Table 6.3 shows that almost 7% of North-East Scotland is protected by SSSI designation (with the exception of two sites on the Royal estate at Balmoral, all SPAs, SACs and Ramsar sites are also designated as SSSIs so are contained within this figure). Just under 5% is protected by SPA designation specifically aimed at bird conservation (Figure 6.1). Within the Cairngorms National Park, 39% is designated for nature conservation, with 25% of the Park area designated as SPAs and SACs and therefore of European importance (Cairngorms National Park Authority 2007).

In both North-East Scotland and the overlapping Cairngorms National Park, all statutory bodies have responsibilities to ensure that designated sites achieve 'favourable status' for the important habitats and species within them. Scottish Natural Heritage monitors this using a 'Site Condition Monitoring' (SCM) system, with

Table 6.3. Sites protected under nature conservation designations in North-East Scotland (Source: Scottish Natural Heritage www.snh.org.uk/snhi/default.asp - accessed 31 August 2009).

Local Authority	No. of SSSI	Area of SSSI (ha)	% of land SSSI	No. of SAC	Area of SAC (ha)	% of land SAC	No. of SPA	Area of SPA (ha)	% of land SPA	No. of Ramsar sites	Area of Ramsar (ha)	% of land Ramsar site
Aberdeen City	3	47	0.23	1	142	0.76	0	0	0	0	0	0
Aberdeenshire	82	39,778	6.28	19	35,196	5.55	10	29,926	4.72	4	1,239	0.20
Moray	35	19,466	8.63	5	15,412	6.83	4	11,617	5.15	2	1,953	0.87
TOTAL N-E Scotland (total land area = 868,699 ha)	120	59,291	6.82	25	50,748	5.82	14	41,543	4.78	6	3,192	0.36

n.b. - Site nos. may span Local Authorities including cross-border outside area: area figures in hectares are accurate to each LA though. **SSSI:** Site of Special Scientific Interest (under Wildlife & Countryside Act 1981 as modified); **SAC:** Special Area of Conservation (for other wildlife and habitats - under EU 'Habitats' Directive 1992); **SPA:** Special Protection Area (for birds - under EU 'Birds' Directive 1979; **Ramsar Site:** wetlands designated under the international Ramsar Convention 1971.

Figure 6.1. Special Protection Areas (designated under the EU 'Birds' Directive) in North-East Scotland (SNH/RSPB data).

Table 6.4. The condition of designated protected sites in North-East Scotland 2009.

North-East Scotland SCM Bird Feature condition (2009) (source: SNHi)	No.(%) of SSSI bird features in each condition state	No.(%) of SPA bird features in each condition state	No.(%) of Ramsar site bird features in each condition state	Total (%)
Favourable maintained	35 (52%)	39 (62%)	12 (86%)	86 (59%)
Favourable declining	3 (4%)	1 (2%)		4 (3%)
Unfavourable recovering		1 (2%)	1 (7%)	2 (1%)
Unfavourable no change	10 (14%)	6 (10%)		16 (11%)
Unfavourable declining	18 (26%)	13 (21%)	1 (7%)	32 (23%)
Not assessed	3 (4%)	2 (3%)		5 (3%)
Total	69	62	14	145

standard methods common to other UK countries. The condition of designated sites in North-East Scotland as assessed in 2009 is shown in Table 6.4. There is a government target to reach a level of 95% of features on designated sites in favourable condition, or the necessary management in place to achieve this, by 2010. Clearly there has been some progress but with around one-third of all features assessed as 'unfavourable' it seems that favourable conditions for birds on protected sites even beyond the planned timescale will not be achieved.

Species and habitat action plans
Originating from the 1992 United Nations Biodiversity Convention in Rio de Janeiro, a set of species and habitat action plans has developed as part of the UK Biodiversity Action Plan and Scottish Biodiversity Strategy. This process began in North-East Scotland in 1996 and in the precursor of the Cairngorms National Park in 1999. Local Biodiversity Action Plan (LBAP) partnerships formed in each area, lists of qualifying species and habitats were developed, biodiversity 'audits' were undertaken (Alexander *et al*. 1998, Leaper 1999) and local action plans produced (North-East Scotland LBAP Partnership 2000, Cosgrove 2002). These audits and plans cover many bird species in a general sense, but there are no action plans dealing specifically with birds in our area; instead, where relevant, management of habitats is intended to meet the requirements of birds. The plans depend heavily on other mechanisms for delivery of this management (such as agri-environment programmes) but their existence has led to the insertion of protection policies in Local Authority plans and other strategies, covering 'LBAP' species. The partnerships involved in this process have also led to a wider public awareness of the idea of the conservation of biodiversity. In theory, through this, a wider range of species (including birds) in addition to those statutorily protected should be taken account of during decisions about economic development. Practically, those species formally protected under national or European nature conservation legislation (see below) still carry the greatest weight.

Although there are now many conservation plans, strategies and designations, financial resources are strongly limiting. With sufficient funding and scientific underpinning, benefits can be delivered for many species and their status improved. In comparison, though, with the resources available to development and other economic activities, the level of funding available for bird and biodiversity conservation is insufficient to achieve most government targets, and this needs to be addressed.

Nature reserves
Management directed at bird conservation is most likely to take place on nature reserves and similar properties. Within North-East Scotland, the National Trust for Scotland owns by far the greatest proportion of such land,

followed by RSPB Scotland, then SNH (Table 6.5). The NTS has a variety of objectives for its land and not all areas are managed primarily for nature. Although the National Nature Reserve area is large, the degree to which positive management is possible varies between sites, as some are privately owned. The Local Nature Reserve network is dominated in area by Findhorn Bay, but here there has been little active nature conservation work; all other LNRs are small and, except for the Waters of Philorth near Fraserburgh, are in or near Aberdeen.

Table 6.5. Nature reserves and land managed for nature conservation in North-East Scotland.

Nature reserve type or owner/manager	No. of sites	Area covered (ha)
National Nature Reserve (SNH)	6	17,770
Local Nature Reserve (Local Authorities)	7	1,354
RSPB Scotland	6	3,822
National Trust for Scotland	10	30,295
Scottish Wildlife Trust	5	232
Woodland Trust	1	19
TOTAL (area adjusted - see text)	35	44,259 (5.1% of land area)

Note 1: NNR total excludes Dinnet Oakwood and Morrone Birkwood (both to be de-declared); **Note 2:** Most of the NNR area is not actually owned by SNH and is private land.

The NTS Mar Lodge estate at 29,380 ha is by far the largest individual site in North-East Scotland that has conservation management as a major objective (by itself it accounts for 3.4% of North-East Scotland), and the background to management here is described by Rao (2004). It overlaps with the Cairngorms NNR, and part of RSPB's property in Upper Glen Avon also lies within an NNR. All other sites are mutually exclusive, giving a total 'nature reserve' area (including all NTS properties) of 44,259 ha, or 5.1% of the North-East Scotland land area. RSPB Scotland's land holding includes the Loch of Strathbeg and part of the high tops of the Cairngorms, both prime areas for breeding birds. In fact, most of the highest mountains in North-East Scotland are owned at least in part by these two conservation organisations. SNH owns the important sand dune and heath complex at Sands of Forvie. The most important bird sites managed by SWT are Spey Bay and Longhaven Cliffs.

Habitat restoration and creation work now and in the future
Most large-scale habitat management projects have taken place on land owned by nature conservation bodies, though there are a few exceptions - principally New Native Pinewood Schemes or native pinewood management on

Plate 6.15. RSPB Loch of Strathbeg, 2007. The restoration of open wetlands with more 'natural' watercourses and free of scrub involved considerable planning and machine time, but the result is likely to be of great long-term benefit to breeding and wintering birds. The re-creation of the meandering Savoch Burn can be seen clearly, as can the previously canalised embankments. © *Caledonian Air Surveys Ltd, Inverness/RSPB*

some private estates such as Glen Tanar, Altyre or Moray Estates. Mar Lodge is undertaking some large-scale Caledonian pinewood expansion (see above) and the Dee Floodplain example of a wetland restoration project (Plate 6.8) lies on Mar Lodge and Invercauld Estates. As noted above, the concept of habitat networks is well developed in the Cairngorms National Park and this is most advanced for woodlands. It is likely that woodland expansion will continue in future, enabling coalescence and linkages across open ground. Achieving this faces major challenges due to deer pressure, but in the next few decades it seems likely that almost continuous woodland will be developed through some of the straths between Deeside/Donside and Strathspey, which may help the colonisation of Aberdeenshire by Crested Tits.

Woodland reconnection like this can be viewed as lying at the 'naturalistic' end of the spectrum of habitat restoration. Floodplain and river channel restoration can also be seen as such but, often, active intervention is needed to restore canalised or embanked rivers and burns to their more meandering former natural courses. At RSPB's Loch of Strathbeg nature reserve a major project was undertaken between 2006 and 2009 to do this, as well as create large buffering wetland areas designed to reduce the influx of nutrient-rich sediment to the loch. This work, together with the clearance of much scrub that had colonised, has restored a much more open wetland

landscape on a large scale. This should prove attractive to more breeding waders and waterfowl.

Work such as this is expensive and involves a great deal of organisation; necessarily it is likely to take place in very few areas, and these will principally be nature reserves. In future, there may be a few similar projects, but most habitat restoration and creation is likely to be small-scale and funded by government agri-environment schemes. Habitats so created may not last for long periods since their dependence on grant funding can lead to conversion to other management once schemes end. Other relatively small-scale habitat creation or management may come as so-called 'offset mitigation' for schemes such as the proposed Aberdeen Western Peripheral route bypass - in such cases habitats over a few tens of hectares may be created or managed, but the bypass project itself will directly destroy over six square kilometres of farmland. Management of land as mitigation or compensation for potentially damaging impacts may also be included within some wind farm projects (see below). In the coming decades, therefore, habitat restoration and creation is likely to be limited in extent with few large sites, and probably involving mainly woodland and wetlands. There will be some benefits for breeding birds, but these will need to be set against the other continuing adverse semi-natural habitat changes considered above, as well as increasing urbanisation and other development.

Increased development pressure

Chapter 2 showed that the urban area in North-East Scotland increased by 43% between the 1940s to the 1980s. This has continued, but differences in definitions in the main land cover recording systems mean that quantifying it is difficult. Depending on source, up to 4% of the land surface is covered by urban and related developments.

Away from urban areas, development can be extended even into remote rural parts because of the widespread and continuing development of wind farms. At the end of 2009, around 70 wind farm projects were being pursued across North-East Scotland (RSPB data) with more proposed since then, though as yet relatively few have been built. Most projects are small-scale (1–3 turbines) though some large developments (up to 57 turbines) have also been proposed. There are also proposals for offshore projects, such as in Aberdeen Bay. Evidence about the impacts of wind farms on birds is mixed and the issue is beyond the scope of this chapter. It is clear though that in most cases the effects are unlikely to be *beneficial*, due to the necessary habitat losses and the fact that collisions and disturbance do occur, even if only at low levels for the majority of species. The evidence is still growing on this issue - for example, see Pearce-Higgins *et al.* (2009), whose study included one local site.

Future trends in urban and rural development

The development plan for Aberdeen City and Shire (2009 Structure Plan) will encourage up to 56,000 new houses and a growth in population of 9% by 2030. Across the North-East, urban expansion, new industrial estates, golf courses, garden centres and associated road developments and improvements will bring increased pressure on the countryside, its habitats and birds, adding to general land use intensification. There are very few examples of land abandonment or change to a less intensive use, so overall, because of increased development and intensification, the extent and diversity of available habitat will diminish for most birds, except for some garden and urban species which are already numerous.

Plate 6.16. New industrial estate, Westhill, Aberdeen, 2009. Construction of such areas on the edges of settlements displaces farmland and woodland birds, though a few species do adapt to the new environment. At Westhill and elsewhere, Oystercatchers and Ringed Plovers have nested between units, and gulls and Common Terns can nest on roof tops. Aberdeen has the largest population of roof-nesting gulls in Britain, with over 3,861 pairs of five species counted in 2002 (NESBR/JNCC) and almost 270 pairs of Oystercatchers have nested within the city. © *I. Francis*

It is possible that where large scale and meaningful land management occurs alongside a wind farm development there could be some benefits for birds. This has happened at two sites in Moray, and has been proposed for others, but it is necessary for it to be sustained and at a big enough scale, and this is unlikely to be forthcoming for most wind farms. Thus, the net effect of wide-scale wind farm development is to add, even if incrementally, to the other development pressures on birds and their habitats, and this is unlikely to diminish in future.

Plate 6.17. Paul's Hill wind farm, Ballindalloch, Moray, February 2006. A habitat management plan for birds was developed at this site as a condition of planning permission. Despite annual monitoring for more than five years, the impacts of this wind farm on birds are not yet clear, but Hen Harriers have continued to nest in the nearby management area. © *J. Matthews*

Increased recreational pressure

Levels of recreational pressure in North-East Scotland are probably lower than in many other parts of the country, due to the relatively low population. Nevertheless, they are increasing and in some places there are potential conflicts in terms of possible disturbance to nesting birds. These are likely to occur in a small number of localities rather than generally across the countryside, and key areas are the high mountains, woodlands holding Capercaillie and on water bodies, particularly lochs. Statutory rights introduced by the Land Reform Acts 2003 gave everyone the legal right of access to most land, but so far there is little evidence of this having had adverse effects on birds generally, since recreation and access levels remain low in most places. Few studies have been undertaken in North-East Scotland, but in general, based on most reviews of access, the increased presence of people rarely if ever has *beneficial* effects on birds, even if adverse impacts may not be apparent. The legislation also required the creation of 'core paths' in all parts of Scotland, and some of these may have the effect of encouraging people to go to places that previously were less accessible. This may be a problem in some of the most scenic woodlands which also hold Capercaillie. Another area where public recreational pressure remains a potential issue is in the mountains. More people ascend summits than previously, but the overall impacts are not clear. The construction of the funicular railway up Cairn Gorm had the effect of reducing the number of walkers on the plateau (compared to the previous chair lift) due to the closed system in operation. If this is ever relaxed, and access through the railway allowed, there could be a serious issue for nesting Dotterel, and possibly Ptarmigan. In this same area, Ptarmigan numbers have already declined due to increased nest and chick losses to predators attracted by food scraps left by tourists (Watson & Moss 2004), indicating another localised adverse impact of recreational activity.

The Land Reform Acts also allowed access to any water body to recreational users with boats, as long as they are not powered. North-East Scotland has very few water bodies of any size (fewer than 150 over 2–3 ha, mostly in the lowlands, with only around 30 in total over *c.*10 ha) and there is inevitably an attraction for water-based access to the same lochs used by breeding and roosting birds. Discussions to reconcile potential problems have been underway at Loch of Skene and Dinnet lochs, but it seems likely that this issue will occur at other lochs in future. Water-based recreation disturbs birds at Findhorn Bay at times, but information about impacts from other coastal areas is lacking. Some boat-based tourism to view birds in cliff colonies takes place near Fowlsheugh, at Troup Head and along the Moray coast, apparently without serious impacts on breeding species, but there has been no scientific monitoring of this.

Plate 6.18. Walkers on the Cairn Gorm plateau, May 2006. Most walkers tend to remain on standard routes, but general levels of recreation in the mountains have increased in recent decades. The effects of this on birds are unlikely to be beneficial, but hard evidence is lacking. © *I. Francis*

Plate 6.19. Kayaks on the lower River Dee, 2009. The Dee and the Spey are the main canoeing rivers, and Loch of Skene the main freshwater sailing site, though recreation is increasing on other lochs. Coasts near Stonehaven and in north Buchan are popular with sea kayakers, and Findhorn Bay is busy with many types of craft including windsurfers. The effects on birds in most areas are largely unknown. © *A. Young*

Plate 6.20. Prawn fishing off Macduff, September 2006. Fishing practices are directly influential on some nesting seabirds (those that may feed on discarded fish and waste from trawlers), though for others it is the whole marine ecosystem that influences food resources. © *I. Francis*

Changes in the marine and coastal environment

North-East Scotland holds some very important colonies of seabirds which rely on the sea completely (such as auks and terns) as well as some species that use both sea and land for foraging (such as gulls). In general terms, most seabirds increased in number in our colonies from the 1960s to the 1990s, after which declines set in for most species (Mitchell *et al*. 2004, Grandgeorge *et al*. 2008), though the patterns have been very variable. Breeding success has fluctuated, but the effects of this take a long time to be seen in the population levels of such long-lived species. The evidence suggests that changes in the marine environment have been occurring, such as a slow warming of sea surface temperatures with effects on plankton (Edwards & Richardson 2004, Dybas 2006), and that food resources such as sand eels have become unreliable. The impacts of this on colonies in North-East Scotland do not yet appear to have been as severe as in Orkney and Shetland, but nonetheless population levels of several seabirds have declined in some colonies in our area in recent years. Kittiwake numbers at Fowlsheugh, for example, have almost halved since 1992 and most other seabirds at this site have declined over that time period (RSPB data). The major seabird colonies are protected by designation as Special Protection Areas and in 2009 these were extended to include offshore areas next to the colonies. However, nesting seabirds forage many kilometres from colonies and management that takes account of the entire marine ecosystem is needed.

The future for seabirds and the marine environment

It is conceivable that if long-term declines in numbers and breeding productivity continue then perhaps in 30 years time our renowned seabird cliff colonies could be greatly depleted or even extinct. This would be a catastrophic outcome of environmental change, and preventing it will be extremely difficult. The establishment of effective offshore management systems through new legislation may take place and marine protected areas in places other than adjacent to colonies may help. The development of coastal and marine conservation partnerships on the East Grampian Coast (www.egcp.org.uk) and in the Moray Firth (www.morayfirth-partnership.org) has led to increased awareness of issues and the initiation of some projects. But if the main influences on adverse trends in the marine environment are changing climate and sea temperatures, then possibilities to address them at local or national levels will be very limited.

Legislation and species protection

The numbers of some of our breeding birds are very directly influenced by people - they are controlled or persecuted because of perceived or actual impacts on other animals (usually game birds). In turn, the numbers of some game birds are also strongly influenced by releases on sporting estates. The principal legislation covering wild birds is the Wildlife and Countryside Act 1981 (WCA) (as amended in Scotland by the Nature Conservation (Scotland) Act 2004 amongst other legislation). This sets out protection for all birds but then establishes circumstances where there is less protection (*e.g.* for legitimate hunting) or, in the case of birds on Schedule 1, greater protection. Game birds are covered by much older legislation, currently under review by government.

The species most affected by direct killing are birds of prey and also several species of crow (see, for example, Jenkins & Chapman 2008), though gulls and pigeons are controlled in places too. Some killing is legally permitted through general licences issued under the WCA (see 'Predation' below), and this covers most instances of control of crows and gulls during the breeding season, though the extent to which licences are properly complied with is not monitored. In Aberdeen, for several years now there has been a control programme under the general licence for roof nesting Herring Gulls, involving nest destruction and egg oiling. The results of this have been monitored, though not as part of a scientific experiment, so the outcome is not clear; there appears though to be little overall population impact on the nesting gulls in the city.

The illegal killing of some birds of prey is still widespread and directly influences the overall breeding population levels in North-East Scotland of Hen Harrier, Golden Eagle and Goshawk, and locally has impacts on Peregrines (on upland estates). Other raptors such as Buzzards and Sparrowhawks are also killed intentionally, as are Ravens. Killing can involve many methods from shooting and nest disturbance or destruction to the placing of poisons - many of which are prohibited substances and highly toxic to other animals including humans. This problem is well publicised and analysed (see RSPB Scotland 2009; Taylor *et al.* 2009) and is condemned strongly by politicians and landowning bodies. Unfortunately the killing of raptors still occurs widely on shooting estates, especially in the uplands (Scottish Raptor Study Groups 1997; Whitfield *et al.* 2003, 2007; RSPB Scotland 2009) and some see the issue as a wider political conflict. It is beyond the scope of this chapter to explore this further, but it is important to stress that it is still a major controlling influence on the numbers and distribution of some of our predatory birds (see Whitfield *et al.* 2008). This is because killing birds of prey in any individual place not only reduces numbers locally, but also affects the overall abundance of these species across the wider countryside due to a 'sump' effect. Areas with suitable habitat but no breeding adults continually attract new birds so the numbers killed can be substantial. This directly affects their potential spread across the wider countryside.

There are also other forms of killing and disturbance, some now relatively minor in incidence. Licences are still issued annually by the Scottish Government to permit the killing of certain fish-eating birds "for the purpose of preventing serious damage to fisheries". Licence returns show that on rivers in North-East Scotland (the Dee, Deveron, Esk, Findhorn, Spey and Ythan) during the 2002–2006 atlas period, 335 Goosanders, 119 Red-breasted Mergansers and 131 Cormorants were reported as being killed under licence, though these figures cannot be confirmed, nor can the identity of all the birds shot. Neither the purported benefits for river fisheries nor the impacts on the populations of birds killed are clear. All these licences did not extend beyond the end of April. The hunting of most birds during the breeding season is prohibited, so the only bird-killing at this time of year should be for the control of various crow species and some gulls as outlined above, though Woodpigeons are also shot during their nesting period to prevent crop damage.

Egg collecting has declined generally, and there have been few known instances in recent years. It remains a serious threat only for a small number of very rare breeders. For

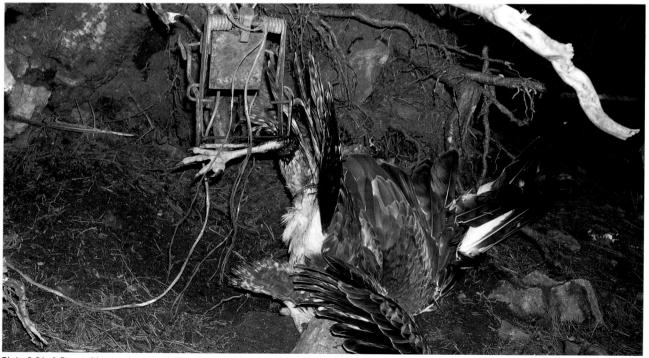

Plate 6.21. A Buzzard in a spring trap set in an open woodland glade in Donside, March 2005. Despite police investigations, no-one was prosecuted for this offence. © *I. Francis*

Plate 6.22. A poisoned adult male Golden Eagle found on Morven, Deeside in May 2006. This death led to a nest failure and there has been no successful nesting in this home range since. No-one was caught or prosecuted for the offence. There was also another confirmed Golden Eagle poisoning in 2009 only a few hundred metres outside North-East Scotland in Angus. Golden Eagles are still largely absent from lower altitude grouse moors. © *D. MacKinnon, Grampian Police*

example, egg theft for two consecutive years (2006 and 2007) helped to push Slavonian Grebes to the verge of extinction in North-East Scotland. There have also been very few suspected incidences recently of raptor chicks being taken for falconry, although recent relaxations in the regulation of the keeping of birds of prey may reverse this trend. Finally, there have been no known recent occurrences of intentional bird disturbance sufficient to cause nest desertion, but 'reckless' disturbance is possible and there was one offence in 2008 where the construction of a track near a Golden Eagle nest was thought to have caused desertion of a site; a formal warning was issued in this instance.

Reintroduction projects

One way of reversing the impacts of past persecution is to reintroduce species made extinct long ago to their former haunts. This has been done from 2007 onwards in North-East Scotland by RSPB Scotland and partners for Red Kites and in Fife for Sea Eagles. The Red Kites are now beginning to establish a breeding population (see species account) and young White-tailed Eagles from the reintroduction scheme are spending time in our area, with the possibility that one day they may colonise. The two projects are based on the assumption that factors which brought about their extinction over a century ago are not now operating. This appears to be generally the case in lowland areas, but poisoning on some upland estates still brings annual casualties to both species in some areas, mostly away from North-East Scotland (RSPB Scotland 2009; Taylor *et al.* 2009).

Future issues in species protection

In urban areas, some control of nesting gulls seems likely to continue, but this may be revised as Herring Gull populations continue to decline nationally. The problem of bird of prey killing has been so long-lasting that it seems certain to continue in the coming years. It is possible that Hen Harriers will remain extremely scarce for years to come, and that Golden Eagles and Peregrines will not reoccupy many former home ranges on managed grouse moors. One factor that might help is that there will be further tightening of restrictions on the use of banned pesticides that potentially could poison birds, making such substances harder to obtain (although only very small quantities are needed to carry out widespread and damaging illegal poisoning). Some other changes such as tighter regulation of crow cage trap design (see below) so as to make it more difficult to catch raptors such as eagles, may also be forthcoming. There has been much legislative reform in the past six years, and penalties are available to allow, for example, jail sentences for those convicted. It remains difficult to catch the perpetrators though and the chances of the penalties being imposed are low. This needs to be addressed, as well as constant reinforcement of the message that such activities are highly antisocial and contrary to the will of most people in Scotland. Other deterrents, such as licensing of grouse shooting, with the capacity to lose such a licence following incidents of killing, would be effective but are unlikely to be introduced yet by government.

Predation of breeding birds

Predation has always been a factor in the breeding success and population levels of birds. Recently, the issue has become more hotly debated as numbers of generalist predators such as crows and Foxes, as well as rarer species such as Goshawks and Pine Martens, have risen. This has followed the gradual relaxation in levels of killing and control of such species and a recovery following their virtually complete disappearance in Victorian times and up until the post-war period, when pesticide impacts were also prevalent. We now live in a landscape with higher predation levels, though during the heyday of the sporting estate, numbers of all predators were, conversely, artificially very low (see Lovegrove 2007). This is a complex issue and beyond the scope of this chapter, but the question remains - what evidence is there that predation is a major influence on breeding bird numbers in North-East Scotland? There is little specific information from our area, but based on generalised results from studies elsewhere (summarised in Gibbons *et al.* 2007; see also Ausden *et al.* 2009), it is likely that crows and especially Foxes do have an impact on numbers of some ground nesters such as game birds, breeding waders, and perhaps some other species. Crow control is permitted under Open General Licences within the Wildlife and Countryside Act, and Foxes do not require any licence for control. Such control is still carried out widely in North-East Scotland on many landholdings, not just sporting estates. To what extent it improves breeding success of other birds is unknown, since there is a complex interaction with habitat and other factors. The consensus though is that it can help some species to breed and survive better than in its absence; this may be one reason, for example, why Black Grouse appear to thrive on open moorland edge habitats in Deeside.

Despite claims by some land managers, the extent to which protected predators such as Buzzards, Ravens, Goshawks or Pine Martens affect populations of other wild breeding birds is not known. The general issue is perennially debated but evidence from our area is almost totally absent. It is certain though that Hen Harriers, Golden Eagles and Peregrines can have little impact on Red Grouse numbers because they are so uncommon on most upland moorlands in North-East Scotland.

Predation as an issue in the future

It is highly likely that there will be no return to the levels of predator control seen in the early 20th century, and that many potential predators of wild birds will continue to be widespread and abundant. Sustained control of crows and Foxes will reduce numbers on extensive tracts of upland sporting estates, but in the lowlands the equivalent effect over large areas will continue to be absent. Habitat management and other techniques aimed at reducing the impact of predation on wild birds will continue to be investigated and this may produce useful results. Predation by several protected birds and mammals will continue as their numbers are maintained (Pine Marten numbers may even increase as they continue to recover from a very restricted range in the past), but the interactions *between* predators are hard to predict and as some become more abundant these interactions will change. For example, Goshawks, Buzzards and Red Kites all kill substantial numbers of young crows; Goshawk diet locally can be made up of 15% crow species and as much as one quarter of items brought to nests in summer (M. Marquiss pers. comm.). Golden Eagles may have negative impacts on other predatory birds such as Hen Harriers, and Goshawks similarly on Kestrels and Long-eared Owls, though the degree to which this has a significant effect remains unclear. It is conceivable that, in the future, the government may issue some licences to permit the killing of otherwise fully protected predators (possibly to address claimed predation of 'livestock'), but there are some complex legal and scientific questions to be addressed before this happens, and they are unlikely to be issued explicitly for the conservation of other wild birds.

Plate 6.23. 'Ladder' style crow trap, Donside, May 2006. This trap had caught a number of Rooks and Jackdaws. There are many hundreds of such devices across North-East Scotland, which collectively catch probably tens of thousands of Rooks, Jackdaws, Carrion and Hooded Crows per year (see Jenkins & Chapman 2008). They are legally permitted if checked every 24 hours, have food, water and shelter, are tagged with reference code, disabled when not in use and if non-target species are released rather than killed. Buzzards and other raptors (even Golden Eagles) regularly enter crow traps. © *I. Francis*

Climate change

Climate change is predicted to have a strong influence on bird communities within the British Isles during the coming decades. Huntley *et al.* (2007) used an analysis of relationships between current bird distributions and various measures of climate to predict how the occurrence of the 'climate space' (the climatic characteristics required) for each species might change geographically, given expected scenarios under global warming. For our area, there are numerous predicted changes by the end of the 21st century, as summarised in Table 6.6. The species listed are those for which the predicted climate space maps show clear changes affecting our area; slightly more ambiguous or marginal range changes are indicated with a question mark.

Table 6.6. Possible losses and gains for North-East Scotland's birds under predicted climate space scenarios for the end of the 21st century (Huntley *et al.* 2007).

Climate space becomes unsuitable for species currently present: predicted loss from our area or significant decline	Climate space becomes suitable for species not currently present (or very scarce): predicted movement into our area
Red-throated Diver	Gadwall
Black-throated Diver	Turtle Dove
Slavonian Grebe	Little Owl
Eider?	Nightjar?
Golden Eagle	Lesser Sp. Woodpecker
Osprey	Yellow Wagtail
Ptarmigan	Nightingale?
Capercaillie	Reed Warbler
Dotterel	Lesser Whitethroat
Arctic Tern	Pied Flycatcher
Crested Tit	Marsh Tit
Scottish Crossbill	Willow Tit
Snow Bunting	Nuthatch

n.b. - for explanations of the predicted changes see Huntley *et al.* 2007.

There is little direct evidence to date of breeding bird numbers or distribution in North-East Scotland having responded clearly to trends in climate. It is possible that some of the range expansion between the two atlases of birds susceptible to cold weather, such as Grey Heron, Kingfisher or Barn Owl may be due to longer-term climate change; weather on an annual basis is certainly an influence (the hard winter of 2009–2010 is likely to have affected some birds locally). The Capercaillie's decline is also in part linked to weather and perhaps even longer-term climate change (Watson & Moss 2008). Of the other species in Table 6.6 above, Slavonian Grebes appear to be declining rapidly in Scotland, possibly also linked to climate, as numbers rise further north, in Iceland (Thórarinsson *et al.* in press; S. Benn, RSPB, pers. comm.). Many seabirds (for example, Kittiwakes and Arctic Terns) have recently experienced very poor breeding success, also thought to be due in part to warming sea temperatures with consequent effects on food resources, particularly sand eels (Dybas 2006, Wanless *et al.* 2007, JNCC 2009). Few of the species listed in Table 6.6 that may colonise or increase have done so yet, though recently-fledged Reed Warblers were seen in late summer at Loch of Strathbeg in 2008 and a bird sang there in 2009 (*NESBR* 2008, 2009) and Nuthatch was recorded for the first time in Moray in 2003 (*MNBR* 2003) and in Aberdeenshire in 2010 (North-east Scotland Bird Records), within a wider expansion of range in Scotland (*BS3*). There may also be some range shifts underway, with declines in some warbler species such as Willow and

Garden Warblers in southern Britain but increases further north, including our area (Amar *et al.* 2006, K. Mustin pers. comm.). This may be reflected in the finding that African migrants in our area are performing relatively well compared with other birds (Chapter 5). There are also indications that, in line with wider UK findings (Sparks *et al.* 2007), some of our summer migrants are arriving earlier, with weaker evidence for later departure in a few cases (Tables 6.7, 6.8).

The possible changes in Table 6.6 are projections based on currently available knowledge. Other species not listed may colonise, or some birds may adapt and prove far more resilient to change in climate space than predicted here, since habitat, land use and climate interact in complex ways (Watson 2007, Scott 2009). When a future breeding bird atlas for North-East Scotland is produced, the possible changes outlined above should by then be far more obvious.

Changes in arrival and departure dates for summer migrants in North-East Scotland

A preliminary analysis of arrival and departure dates (Dixon *et al.* in prep), suggests that there have been some changes in our area. Using simply the dates for first and last sightings in the North-east Scotland Bird Reports since 1974, the following trends are apparent.

Table 6.7. Arrival dates of summer migrants: species showing significant or near-significant trends. All other species showed non-significant first date trends since 1974.

Significant (p<0.05)	Arrival now:
Chiffchaff	Earlier
Garden Warbler	Earlier
Osprey	Earlier
Swallow	Earlier
Sand Martin	Earlier
Sedge Warbler	Earlier
Sandwich Tern	Earlier
Wood Warbler	Earlier
Yellow Wagtail	Later
Near-significant (0.05<p<0.1)	
Garganey	Earlier
Little Tern	Earlier
Swift	Earlier
Whinchat	Later
Whitethroat	Earlier

Table 6.8. Departure dates of summer migrants: species showing significant or near-significant trends. All other species showed non-significant last date trends since 1974.

Significant (p<0.05)	Departure now:
Cuckoo	Earlier
Common Sandpiper	Earlier
Garganey	Later
Grasshopper Warbler	Later
Marsh Harrier	Later
Osprey	Later
Whimbrel	Earlier
Wood Warbler	Later
Near-significant (0.05<p<0.1)	
Sand Martin	Later
Wheatear	Earlier

Eight out of the 31 summer migrants analysed showed a statistically significant trend for earlier arrival, with one (Yellow Wagtail) suggesting later arrival, though this was strongly influenced by a couple of outlying dates. A further four species showed almost-significantly earlier arrival dates, with one species, Whinchat, suggesting later arrival. The remaining 17 species show no clear trend.

For departure dates, trends are weaker since the last sightings of birds are often not as well-recorded or meaningful. Trends are more variable, with five species showing significantly later departure dates and three earlier, with two further species showing almost significant trends. The remaining 24 species show no apparent trends since 1974.

The details of the analysis and various possibly complicating factors are beyond the scope of this chapter and are considered further by Dixon *et al.* (in prep.). Jenkins & Watson (2000) and Jenkins & Sparks (2010) have also analysed migrant arrival dates in part of our area (mid Deeside) since 1974, and Cook (2003) examined some changes in migrant dates in Moray.

Bird knowledge and information management

The quantity of information about birds in North-East Scotland has never been greater; indeed, we hope this atlas has added substantially to it! The number of birdwatchers is higher than ever, and techniques for collating and analysing the records generated are improving constantly. Chapter 1 has described the methods used in this atlas, and their links to the SOC's bird recording project and the National Biodiversity Network. As our atlas goes to press, we are nearing the end of the third major UK-wide breeding bird atlas organised by the BTO and SOC, and the online methods for capturing the vast number of bird records generated are very efficient and impressive. In our atlas, we benefited from the expertise of many local nest finders, bird ringers and raptor study group members, and we hope that we have been able to include most major sources of information so that the picture we have given of our local breeding birds is substantially correct.

The future for gathering breeding bird information

The key to ensuring we can continue to monitor our local breeding birds effectively is to have a large number of knowledgeable and motivated local birdwatchers of all levels of skill. While the current BTO/SOC UK atlas is experiencing record levels of contribution, will this still be the case in any

Plate 6.24. Lochan Buidhe, Cairngorms, 17th May 2008. Late spring snow-lie is important for several high altitude breeding birds. © *I. Francis*

The Breeding Birds of North-East Scotland

repeat atlas in 20 years time? It will depend on a new generation of recorders, and they will need to gain their experience against a background of many indoor techno-logical distractions - though technological competence will become increasingly important too. 'Citizen Science' projects will no doubt continue to be promoted and receive substantial participation (including through large data handling networks such as the National Biodiversity Network - see Chapter 1), but ensuring the necessary expertise to prove breeding for the more difficult birds is important. Such experience comes from more detailed ornithological work such as bird ringing, studying raptors or other specialist projects; though there has been a recent increase in interest in ringing, the prospects for a new generation of experienced raptor monitors looks less certain. It is also important to ensure that information on rarer breeding birds is handled sensitively and securely; but equally there has to be a way of ensuring that all necessary breeding information is available so that conservation bodies can use it to help defend nesting areas and valuable habitats against the growing pressures on land. The Rare Breeding Birds Panel has recently issued guidance on this (www.rbbp.org.uk/downloads/rbbp-recording-standards.pdf) and the recording standards described there would greatly help the gathering and use of breeding bird information in future.

Conclusions

North-East Scotland is a very important part of the country for many birds, with some species, such as Scottish Crossbill, Guillemot, Razorbill, Kittiwake and Oystercatcher present in disproportionately high numbers at a European scale and numerous others such as Parrot Crossbill, Crested Tit, Ptarmigan, Goldeneye and Common Gull important within the UK. This places a major responsibility on us to ensure that their populations thrive. We know that overall the number of breeding species has increased over the last century, and is now probably higher than it has ever been. Some species are also more abundant than historically, but others have suffered declines too. These have been more frequent amongst farmland birds, including some seed-eaters such as Corn Buntings, but also waders. Over the next two to three decades, we see no real chance of the numbers of these birds increasing to a large extent across the farmed landscape, as intensification of management is most likely and wetland losses will not be reversed. Localised habitat creation and management though will at least help retain most of these declining species, but at lower population levels. Farmland occupies over half of the land surface, and here, in addition to likely intensification of agricultural management, there will be continued incursion of development of urban areas, roads and associated infrastructure, with increased recreational pressure linked to this. There will be relatively little habitat creation to compensate, apart from some small ponds, wetlands and small-scale tree planting. Overall, conditions on farmland will lead to a bird community that looks similar to today, but with a different balance of numbers and certainly with fewer waders.

The woodland extent will probably increase slightly, especially broad-leaved trees, and most plantations will be better managed, probably favouring the majority of woodland birds. Caledonian pinewoods and other native woodlands will be protected but ideal management is likely still to be compromised by excessive grazing from high numbers of deer. Their condition may improve, but some threatened woodland species such as Capercaillie will continue to face problems, especially as disturbance from recreation increases. Deliberate killing of some birds, especially raptors, is still a problem and it is difficult to predict how this issue, and arguments about predation and its impact, will change in the coming years. It seems likely that similar debates and some illegal acts will still be influencing bird conservation in 2030. It would be reassuring though to think that Golden Eagles might have increased in numbers and range by then, and that the Hen Harrier will not be the extremely rare breeding bird it is now.

The extent of other semi-natural habitats (including protected sites) will probably remain similar, with few large-scale losses. However, gradual and sometimes adverse habitat changes will continue, with divergence of management so that some sites, such as raised bogs and fens, may become ranker, whereas other areas such as grasslands may become more intensively managed, or perhaps used for developments such as wind farms. In a few places, for example nature reserves, some effective large-scale habitat management projects will take place, but otherwise, habitat creation will be scattered, small in extent and subject to the existence of government funding schemes. The condition of protected areas such as Special Protection Areas will probably improve as further measures to manage them come forward, but some of the larger scale trends affecting them will remain intractable. This will be especially true of the marine environment, where climate change already appears to be having impacts on offshore conditions and the numbers of a range of seabirds. Climate change may also begin to have some more obvious impacts on terrestrial habitats and their birds, affecting breeding numbers and the range of species nesting. It is possible though that we may see new breeding birds arriving before we lose any, so the number of breeding species may increase still further over the next 20 years or so.

We have made some suggestions about how our breeding bird community might change in the coming decades, but such things are in reality highly unpredictable. We have increasingly sophisticated information about breeding birds in North-East Scotland, and as long as we can maintain the interest in bird recording then we will be well-placed to monitor the forthcoming changes in great detail. During the next two decades, we are still likely to have most of the species we have now, and North-East Scotland will still be an immensely rich part of the country for breeding birds. But there will be some clear changes in the breeding numbers of a range of species, as well as some gains and perhaps a few losses. By 2030, it seems likely we will have nesting Little Egrets and Avocets, White-tailed Eagles breeding on the coast, and Red Kites and Little Ringed Plovers will be widespread. Corncrakes will have recolonised, Reed Warblers will be nesting and Tree Sparrows and Corn Buntings will have rebounded from population low points. Conversely, we may have lost at least one species, the Slavonian Grebe, which is perhaps the most vulnerable of our breeding birds. Some of the other northern rare breeders will probably still be present, in small numbers, and with good management, the sound of lekking Capercaillie should still be heard in our woodlands in early spring. Breeding bird populations will always change. The best conservation strategy is to maintain the conditions necessary to allow our current breeders to continue to survive, and create habitats for new breeding species to use as they move into North-East Scotland. Monitoring this needs sound information, and we hope that this atlas has fulfilled a vital role in setting out the status of our breeding birds at the beginning of the 21st century.

References

Frequently used and shorthand references
(see below for full details)

BS3	- Forrester *et al.* 2007 - *Birds of Scotland*
BTO 1st Atlas	- Sharrock 1976
BTO 2nd Atlas	- Gibbons *et al.* 1993
BWP	- Cramp *et al.* (eds) 1977–93. *Birds of the Western Palearctic*
Cook (1992)	- *Birds of Moray and Nairn*
MNBR	- Cook 1985–2007 - *Birds in Moray & Nairn* (Moray & Nairn Bird Reports)
NES 1st Atlas	- Buckland *et al.* 1990 - *Birds of North-East Scotland*
NESBR	- *North-east Scotland Bird Reports*
Phillips (1997)	- *Rare and Scarce Birds in North East Scotland*
Risely *et al.* (2008)	- *The Breeding Bird Survey 2007*

Alexander, G., Leaper, G., Francis, I. & Tulloch, M. 1998. *Biodiversity in North-east Scotland: an audit of priority species and habitats*. NE Scotland Local Biodiversity Action Plan Steering Group, Aberdeen. Available at: http://www.nesbiodiversity.org.uk/publications/audit.htm

Amar, A., Hewson, C.M., Thewlis, R.M., Smith, K.W., Fuller, R.J., Lindsell, J., Conway, G., Butler, S. & MacDonald, M.A. 2006. *What's happening to our woodland birds? Long-term changes in the populations of woodland birds*. RSPB research report number 19, BTO research report number 169. RSPB/BTO.

Anderson, A. 1961. The breeding of the Starling in Aberdeenshire. *Scottish Naturalist* 1961: 60–74.

Anderson, D.I.K. & Petty, S.J. 1996. Population growth and breeding of Mandarin *Aix galericulata* in Cowal, Argyll. *Argyll Bird Report* 12: 82–84.

Ausden, M., Bolton, M., Butcher, N., Hoccom, D.G., Smart, J. & Williams, G. 2009. Predation of breeding waders on lowland wet grassland - is it a problem? *British Wildlife* 21: 29–39.

Baillie, S.R., Marchant, J.H. *et al.* 2007. Breeding Birds in the Wider Countryside: their conservation status 2007. *BTO Research Report No. 487*. BTO, Thetford. (www.bto.org/birdtrends, updated 7 November 2008).

Baker, H., Stroud, D.A., Aebischer, N.J., Cranswick, P.A., Gregory, R.D., McSorley, C.A., Noble, D.G. & Rehfisch, M.M. 2006. Population estimates of birds in Great Britain and the United Kingdom. *British Birds* 99: 25–44.

Banks, A.N., Coombs, R.H. & Crick, H.P.Q. 2003. *The Peregrine Falcon breeding population of the UK and Isle of Man in 2002*. BTO Research Report, BTO, Thetford.

Barne, J.H., Robson, C.F., Kasnowska, S.S., Doody, J.P. & Davidson, N.C. 1996. Coasts and seas of the United Kingdom. Region 3, North-east Scotland: Cape Wrath to St Cyrus. JNCC, Peterborough. Available at: http://www.jncc.gov.uk/page-2477

Barnett, C., Hossell, J., Perry. M., Procter, C. & Hughes, G. 2006. *A Handbook of Climate Trends across Scotland*. SNIFFER project CC03. Scotland and Northern Ireland Forum for Environmental Research. Available from: http://www.sniffer.org.uk/Webcontrol/Secure/ClientSpecific/ResourceManagement/UploadedFiles/CC03_1_Handbook.pdf

Batten, L.A., Bibby, C.J., Clement, P., Elliott, G.D. & Porter, R.F. 1990. *Red Data Birds in Britain*. T. & A.D. Poyser, London.

Baxter, E.V. & Rintoul, L.J. 1909. Nesting of the Gadwall in Scotland. *Annals of Scottish Natural History* 1909: 184.

Baxter, E.V. & Rintoul, L.J. 1922. Some *Scottish Breeding Duck: their arrival and dispersal*. Oliver & Boyd, Edinburgh, UK.

Baxter, E. V. & Rintoul, L. J. 1953. *The Birds of Scotland*. Oliver and Boyd, Edinburgh.

Baxter, P.A.A. & Broadbent, I.D. 2005. The Central Asian Lesser Whitethroat in Aberdeen. *Birding Scotland* 8: 87–92.

Beale, C. M., Burfield, I. J., Sim, I. M. W., Rebecca, G. W., Pearce-Higgins, J. W. & Grant, M. C. 2006. Climate change may account for the decline in British Ring Ouzels *Turdus torquatus*. *Journal of Animal Ecology* 75: 826–835.

Berry, J. 1939. The Status and Distribution of Wild Geese and Wild Duck in Scotland. International Wildfowl Enquiry: Vol. 2. Cambridge University Press, Cambridge, UK.

Berthold, P. & Terrill, S.B. 1988. Migratory behaviour and population growth of Blackcaps wintering in Britain and Ireland: some hypotheses. *Ringing and Migration* 9: 153–159.

Bibby, C.J., Bain, C.G. & Burges, D.J. 1989. Bird Communities of Highland Birch Woods. *Bird Study* 36: 123–133.

Biggins, A. & Francis, I. 2007. *North East Scotland Wetlands Inventory*. North East Scotland Biodiversity Action Plan Partnership, Aberdeen. Available at: www.nesbiodiversity.org.uk/publications

BirdLife International 2004. *Birds in Europe: Population estimates, trends and conservation status*. BirdLife Conservation Series No. 12. BirdLife International, Cambridge.

Bourne, W.R.P. 1979. Prolonged parental care in Herring Gulls nesting in towns in eastern Scotland. *Bird Study* 26: 196–197.

Bourne, W.R.P. 1982. Greylag Geese breeding at the Loch of Skene. *North-East Scotland Bird Report* 1981: 42.

Bourne, W. R. P. 1992. Alarm calls used by a presumed Spotted Crake in the Grampian Region. *Scottish Birds* 16: 220–221.

Bourne, W.R.P. 2004. Gulls nesting inland in Moray and North-east Scotland. *Birds in Moray & Nairn* 2003: 91–101.

Bourne, W.R.P. 2008. Problems with North-east Scottish Common Gulls. *Birds in Moray & Nairn* 2007: 98–100.

Bourne, W.R.P. & Dixon, T.J. 1974. Gulls breeding inland in Aberdeenshire. *Scottish Birds* 8: 73–75.

Bourne, W.R.P. & Smith, A.J.M. 1974. Threats to Scottish Sandwich Terns. *Conservation Biology.* 6: 222–224.

Bourne W.R.P. & Smith A.J.M. 1978. Seabirds in North-East Scotland. *North-East Scotland Bird Report* 1977: 55–62.

Bradbury, R.B., Wilson, J.D., Moorcroft, D., Morris, A.J. & Perkins, A.J. 2003. Habitat and weather are weak correlates of nestling condition and growth rates of four UK farmland passerines. *Ibis* 145: 295–306.

Braithwaite, M.E., Ellis, R.W. & Preston, C.D. 2006. *Change in the British Flora 1987–2004*. Botanical Society of the British Isles, London.

British Association 1963. *The North-East of Scotland*. British Association for the Advancement of Science. The Central Press, Aberdeen.

Brown, A. & Grice, P. 2005. *Birds in England*. T. & A.D. Poyser, London.

Brown, A.W. & Brown, L.M. 1985. The Scottish Mute Swan Census in 1983. *Scottish Birds* 13: 140–148.

Brown, A.W. & Brown, L.M. 2005. The 2002 census of the Mute Swan in Scotland. *Scottish Birds* 25: 1–16.

Buchanan, G. M., Pearce-Higgins, J. W., Wotton, S. R., Grant, M. C. & Whitfield, D. P. 2003. Correlates of the change in Ring Ouzel *Turdus torquatus* abundance in Scotland from 1988–91 to 1999. *Bird Study* 50: 97–105.

Buckland, S.T. & Knox, A.G. 1980. Brambling breeding in Scotland. *British Birds* 73: 360–361.

Buckland, S.T., Bell, M.V. & Picozzi, N. (eds.) 1990. *The Birds of North-East Scotland*. North-East Scotland Bird Club, Aberdeen.

Burfield, I.J. 2002. The breeding ecology and conservation of the ring ouzel *Turdus torquatus* in Britain. Ph.D. thesis, Queen's College, Cambridge.

Burton, H., Evans, T.L. & Weir, D.N. 1970. Wrynecks breeding in Scotland. *Scottish Birds* 6: 154–156.

Byars, T., Curtis, D.J. & McDonald, I. 1991. The breeding distribution and habitat requirements of the Lesser Whitethroat in Strathclyde. *Scottish Birds* 16: 66–76.

Cadbury, C.J. 1980. The status and habits of the Corncrake in Britain. *Bird Study* 27: 203–18.

Cadman, M.D., Sutherland, D.A., Beck, G.G., Lepage, D. & Couturier, A.R. (eds.) 2007. *Atlas of the Breeding Birds of Ontario, 2001–2005*. Bird Studies Canada, Environment Canada, Ontario Field Ornithologists, Ontario Ministry of Natural Resources and Ontario Nature. Toronto.

Cairngorms National Park Authority 2007. *Cairngorms National Park Plan 2007*. CNPA, Grantown.

Campbell, J. 1955. *The Rarer Birds of Prey*. RSPB.

Carey, P.D., Wallis, S.M., Emmett, B.E., Maskell, L.C., Murphy, J., Norton, L.R., Simpson, I.C. & Smart, S.S. 2008. *Countryside Survey: UK headline messages from 2007*. Centre for Ecology and Hydrology. Available from www.countrysidesurvey.org.uk

Carter, I. 2001. *The Red Kite*. Arlequin Press, Chelmsford.

Castle, M.E. 1977. Rookeries in Scotland - 1975. *Scottish Birds* 9: 327–334.

Chisholm, K. 2007. History of the Wood Sandpiper as a breeding bird in Britain. *British Birds* 100: 112–121.

Christer, G. 1991. Garganey breeding attempt at Loch of Strathbeg RSPB reserve *North-East Scotland Bird Report* 1990: 71–72.

Clark, H. & Sellers, R.M. 1998a. Winter habitats of Twites in Scotland. *Scottish Birds* 19: 262–269.

Clark, H. & Sellers, R.M. 1998b. Movements of Twites in Scotland. *Scottish Birds* 19: 270–279.

Clements, R. 2001. The Hobby in Britain: a new population estimate. *British Birds* 94: 402–408.

Colquhoun, M.K. 1951. *The Wood Pigeon in Britain*. Abridged report. H.M.S.O., London.

Conway, G.J., Burton, N.H.K., Handschuh, M. & Austin, G.E. 2008. *UK population estimates from the 2007 Breeding Little Ringed Plover and Ringed Plover surveys*, BTO Research Report No. 510, BTO, Thetford.

Cook, M.J.H. 1982. Breeding status of the Crested Tit. *Scottish Birds* 12: 97–106.

Cook, M. (ed.) 1985–2007. Birds in Moray & Nairn. (*Moray & Nairn Bird Report*) Privately published.

Cook, M. 1992. *The Birds of Moray and Nairn*. Mercat Press, Edinburgh.

Cook, M. 1997. Herring and Lesser Black-backed Gulls breeding on Elgin rooftops in 1996. *Moray & Nairn Bird Report* 1996: 85–86.

Cook, M. 1999. Bearded Tits at Loch Spynie - new to Moray & Nairn. *Moray & Nairn Bird Report* 1998: 80–81.

Cook, M. 2003. Changes in summer migrant arrival dates. *Birds in Moray & Nairn* 2002: 93–94.

Cook, M. 2005. The Status of Birds at Loch Spynie (Part 1). *Birds in Moray & Nairn* 2004: 85–98.

Cook, P. & L. and Partners 2008. *Agriculture in Aberdeenshire: looking to the future*. A study for NESAAG, Aberdeenshire Council and Scottish Enterprise, November 2008. Aberdeenshire Council.

Cosgrove, P. 2002. *The Cairngorms Local Biodiversity Action Plan*. Cairngorms Partnership Board, Grantown.

Cosnette, B. L. & Rebecca, G. W. 1997. Breeding Merlins in Aberdeenshire during 1993–1996. *North-East Scotland Bird Report* 1996: 71–80.

Cramp, S., Bourne, W.R.P. & Saunders, D. 1974. *The Seabirds of Britain and Ireland*. Collins. London.

Cramp, S. *et al.* (eds.) 1977–93. *The Birds of the Western Palearctic*. 9 volumes. Oxford University Press, Oxford.

Crick, H.Q.P. & Ratcliffe, D.A. 1995. The Peregrine *Falco peregrinus* breeding population of the United Kingdom in 1991. *Bird Study* 42: 1–19.

Crick, H.Q.P., Robinson, R.A., Appleton, G.F., Clark, N.A. & Rickard, A.D. 2002. *Investigation into the Causes of the Decline of Starlings and House Sparrows in Great Britain*. British Trust for Ornithology, Thetford.

da Prato, S.R.D. 1985. The Breeding Birds of Agricultural Land in South-East Scotland. *Scottish Birds* 13: 203–216.

da Prato, S.R.D. & da Prato, E.S. 1986. Appearance and song of possible Chiffchaff x Willow Warbler hybrid. *British Birds* 79: 341–342.

Davies, M. 1988. *The importance of Britain's twite*. RSPB Conservation Review No 2 (1988): 91–94.

Davies, N. B. 1992. *Dunnock Behaviour and Social Evolution*. Oxford University Press, Oxford.

Dazley, R.A. & Trodd, P. 1994. *An Atlas of the Breeding Birds of Bedfordshire 1988–92*. Bedfordshire Natural History Society.

Dennis, R.H. 1983. Purple Sandpipers breeding in Scotland. *British Birds* 76: 563–566.

Dennis, R. 1995. *The Birds of Badenoch & Strathspey*. Colin Baxter Photography, Grantown-on-Spey.

Dennis, R. 2002. Birds and Mammals. Chapter 4 in Gimingham, C. (ed.): *The Ecology, Land use and Conservation of the Cairngorms*. Packard Publishing Ltd. Chichester.

Dennis, R. 2008. *A Life of Ospreys*. Whittles Publishing, Dunbeath.

Dennis, R. & Cook, M. 1996. Eagle Owl breeding in Moray. *Moray & Nairn Bird Report* 1995: 79–80.

Dickson, R.C. 1997. Red-backed Shrike breeding records in Scotland. *Scottish Birds* 19: 114.

Dixon, N., Francis, I. & Perkins, A. (in prep., 2011). Arrival and departure dates of summer and winter migrants in North-East Scotland. *North-east Scotland Bird Report 2009*.

Donald, P.F. & Evans, A.D., 1995. Habitat selection and population size of Corn Buntings *Miliaria calandra* breeding in Britain in 1993. *Bird Study* 42: 190–204.

Donald, P. F. & Fuller, R.J. 1998. Ornithological atlas data: a review of uses and limitations. *Bird Study* 45: 129–145.

Doody, J. P., Johnston, C. & Smith, B. (eds.) 1993. *Directory of the North Sea Coastal Margin*. Joint Nature Conservation Committee, Peterborough.

Dougall, T., Craig, S., Thorne, D. & Thorne, M. 1989. Oystercatcher nesting in a tree. *Scottish Bird News* 15: 9.

Dougall, T.W., Holland, P.K. & Yalden, D.W. 2004. A revised estimate of the breeding population of Common Sandpiper in Great Britain and Ireland. *Wader Study Group Bulletin* 105: 42–49.

Douglas, D.J.T., Evans, D.M. & Redpath, S.M. 2008. Selection of foraging habitat and nestling diet by Meadow Pipits *Anthus pratensis* breeding on intensively grazed moorland. *Bird Study* 55: 290–296.

Dudley, S. P., Gee, M., Kehoe, C., Melling, T. M. and the BOURC Records Committee. 2006. The British List: A Checklist of Birds of Britain (7th Edition). *Ibis* 148: 526–563.

Duncan, A., Duncan, R., Rae, R., Rebecca, G. & Stewart, B. 2001. Roof and ground nesting Eurasian Oystercatchers in Aberdeen. *Scottish Birds* 22: 1–8.

Dybas, C.L. 2006. On a collision course: ocean plankton and climate change. *BioScience* 56: 642–646.

Eaton, M.A., Dillon, I.A., Stirling-Aird, P.K. & Whitfield, D.P. 2007. The status of Golden Eagle *Aquila chrysaetos* in Britain in 2003. *Bird Study* 54: 212–220.

Eaton, M., Marshall, K.B. & Gregory, R.D. 2007. The status of Capercaillie *Tetrao urogallus* in Scotland during winter 2003/04. *Bird Study* 54: 145–153.

Eaton, M.A., Brown, A.F., Noble, D.G., Musgrove, A.J., Hearn, R., Aebischer, N.J., Gibbons, D.W., Evans, A. & Gregory, R.D. 2009. Birds of Conservation Concern 3: the population status of birds in the United Kingdom, Channel Isles and the Isle of Man. *British Birds* 102: 296–341.

Edlin, H. L. (ed.) 1963. *Forests of North-East Scotland.* Forestry Commission Guide. HMSO.

Edward, T. 1854. The birds of Strathbeg and its neighbourhood, with a few remarks upon their habits etc. *Naturalist* 4: 239–247, 263–271.

Edward, T. 1856–1860. A list of the birds of Banffshire, accompanied with anecdotes. *Zoologist* 14: 5117–5122, 5199–5202, 5258–5268; 17: 6595–6601, 6631–6637, 6665–6672; 18: 6841–6849, 6964–6975.

Edwards, M. & Richardson, A.J. 2004. Impact of climate change on marine pelagic phenology and trophic mismatch. *Nature* 430: 881–884.

Elkins, N., Reid, J.B., Brown, A.W., Robertson, D.G. & Smout, A.M. 2003. *The Fife Bird Atlas.* Fife Ornithological Atlas Group. Woodlands Studios, Dunfermline.

Ellis, P. M. 1990. Shore Larks nesting in Scotland in 1977. *Scottish Birds* 16: 43–44.

Environmental Change Network (ECN) 2009. see http://www.ecn.ac.uk/Database/index.html

Etheridge, B., Holling, M., Riley, H., Wernham, C. & Thompson, D. 2008. *Scottish Raptor Monitoring Report 2006.* SOC/Scottish Raptor Monitoring Scheme/SNH.

Ewins, P.J., Dymond, J.N. & Marquiss, M. 1986. The distribution, breeding and diet of Ravens *Corvus corax* in Shetland. *Bird Study* 33: 110–116.

Ferguson-Lees, I. J. & the Rare Breeding Birds Panel. 1977. Rare breeding birds in the United Kingdom in 1975. *British Birds* 70: 2–23.

Field R.H., Anderson G.Q.A. & Gruar D. 2008. Land-use correlates of breeding performance and diet in Tree Sparrows *Passer montanus*. *Bird Study* 55: 280–289.

Forestry Commission 1997. National *Inventory of Woodland and Trees. Scotland: Grampian Region.* Forestry Commission http://www.forestry.gov.uk/forestry/HCOU-54PG9T

Forestry Commission 2001. *National Inventory of Woodland and Trees. Scotland.* Forestry Commission http://www.forestry.gov.uk/forestry/HCOU-54PG9T

Forestry Commission 2003. *National Inventory of Woodland and Trees. Great Britain.* Forestry Commission http://www.forestry.gov.uk/forestry/HCOU-54PG9T

Forestry Commission 2008. Forestry Statistics 2008. Forestry Commission. http://www.forestry.gov.uk/forestry/infd-7j5evb

Forrester, R.W., Andrews, I.J., McInerny, C.J., Murray, R.D., McGowan, R.Y., Zonfrillo, B., Betts, M.W., Jardine, D.C. & Grundy, D.S. (eds.) 2007. *The Birds of Scotland.* The Scottish Ornithologists' Club, Aberlady. 2 volumes.

Francis, I. 1996. Reserve Focus: Loch of Strathbeg, Aberdeenshire. *British Wildlife* 8: 109–111.

Francis, I. 1997. A survey of Lapwings in North-East Scotland 1996. *North-east Scotland Bird Report* 1996: 81–85.

Francis, I.S. 1998. Observations at a winter Rook and Jackdaw roost in Aberdeenshire. *Scottish Birds* 19: 129–133.

Francis, I. 2008a. Recent trends in numbers of some breeding birds in North East Scotland: a summary of Breeding Bird Survey data 1994–2006. *North East Scotland Bird Report 2006:* 125–128. North East Scotland Bird Club, Aberdeen.

Francis, I. 2008b. Birds of the Moray Moors: a resurvey of the Ladder Hills area 2007. *Birds in Moray & Nairn* 2007: 89–97.

Francis, I. 2009. *Black Grouse in North-East Scotland 2009: a lek survey and collation of records in Moray and Aberdeenshire.* Unpublished report, RSPB Scotland, Aberdeen.

Francis, I. & Pout, A. 2006. Black Grouse in North East Scotland in 2005. North East Scotland Bird Report 2005: *116–119.* North East Scotland Bird Club, Aberdeen.

Francis, I. & Thorpe, A. 1999. The breeding status of the Spotted Crake in north east Scotland. *Scottish Birds* 20: 14–17.

French, D.D., Jenkins, D. & Conroy, J.W.H. 1986. Guidelines for managing woods in Aberdeenshire for song birds. Pp.129–143 in: *Trees and Wildlife in the Scottish Uplands.* Institute of Terrestrial Ecology/NERC. ITE Symposium 17. ITE, Banchory.

Fuller, R.J. & Ausden, M. 2008. Birds and habitat change in Britain. Part 1: a review of losses and gains in the twentieth century. *British Birds* 101: 644–675.

Fuller, R.J. & Ausden, M. 2009. Birds and habitat change in Britain. Part 2: past and future conservation responses. *British Birds* 102: 52–71.

Garcia, E.F.J. 1983. An experimental test of competition for space between Blackcaps *Sylvia atricapilla* and Garden Warblers *Sylvia borin* in the breeding season. *Journal of Animal Ecology* 52: 795–805.

Garden, E.A. 1958. The national census of heronries in Scotland 1954, with a summary of the 1928/29 census. *Bird Study* 5: 90–109.

Garson, P.J. 1980. Male Behaviour and female choice: Mate Selection in the Wren? *Animal Behaviour* 28: 491–502.

Gibbons, D. W., Reid, J. B. & Chapman, R. A. 1993. *The New Atlas of Breeding Birds in Britain and Ireland: 1988–1991.* T. & A.D. Poyser, London.

Gibbons, D.W., Donald, P.F., Bauer, H-G., Fornasari, L. & Dawson, I.K. 2007. Mapping avian distributions: the evolution of bird atlases. *Bird Study* 54: 324–334.

Gibbons, D.W., Amar, A., Anderson, G.Q.A., Bolton, M., Bradbury, R.B., Eaton, M.A., Evans, A.D., Grant, M.C., Gregory, R.D., Hilton, G.M., Hirons, G.J.M., Hughes, J., Johnstone, I., Newbery, P., Peach, W.J., Ratcliffe, N., Smith, K.W., Summers, R.W., Walton, P. & Wilson, J.D. 2007. *The predation of wild birds in the UK: a review of conservation impact and management.* RSPB Research Report no. 23. RSPB, Sandy.

Gill, D. 1992. Quail activity at Gowanwell, *North-east Scotland Bird Report* 1992: 14–15.

Gillings, S. & Fuller, R.J. 1998. The breeding bird community of upland Juniper scrub in eastern Scotland. *Scottish Birds* 19: 231–238.

Gillings, S., Fuller, R.J. & Henderson, A.C.B. 1998. Avian community composition and patterns of bird distribution within birch-heath mosaics in north-east Scotland. *Ornis Fennica* 75: 27–37.

Gimingham, C. (ed.) 2002. *The Ecology, Land use and Conservation of the Cairngorms*. Packard Publishing Ltd. Chichester.

Goodbody, I.M. 1955. Field notes on the Corn Bunting (*Emberiza calandra*): habitat and distribution in Aberdeenshire. *Scottish Naturalist* 67: 90–97.

Gordon, G. 1844. A Fauna of Moray. II: Birds. *Zoologist* 2: 502–15.

Gordon, S. 1912. *The Charm of the Hills*. Cassell.

Gorman, M. (ed.) 1997. *The Ythan: a festschrift for George Dunnet*. University of Aberdeen, Department of Zoology.

Grampian FWAG (2006). Farming and Biodiversity in Strathdon, A study into the future of farming in Strathdon and implications for biodiversity. Unpublished report available from Grampian FWAG (Grampian@ fwagscotland.org.uk)

Grampian Regional Council 1988. *Grampian Natural Habitats Survey*. Planning Department, GRC. Data available at www.nesbrec.org.uk

Grampian Regional Council 1991. Minerals Policy Review 1990. Department of Economic Development and Planning, Grampian Regional Council.

Grandgeorge, M., Wanless, S., Dunn, T.E., Maumy, M., Beaugrand, G. & Gremillet, D. 2008. Resilience of the British and Irish seabird community in the 20th century. *Aquatic Biology* 4: 187–199.

Graham, I. M., Redpath, S. M. & Thirgood, S.J. 1995. The diet and breeding density of Common Buzzards *Buteo buteo* in relation to indices of prey abundance. *Bird Study* 42: 165–173.

Gray, D.B. 1974. Breeding behaviour of Whinchats. *Bird Study* 21: 280–282.

Gray, R. 1871. *Birds of the West of Scotland including the Outer Hebrides*. T. Murray & Son, Glasgow.

Green, R. 1983. Spring dispersal and agonistic behaviour of the Red-legged Partridge *Alectoris rufa. Journal of Zoology* 201: 541–555.

Green, R. E. 1984. Double nesting of the Red-legged Partridge *Alectoris rufa. Ibis* 126: 332–346.

Gregory, R.D., Wilkinson, N.I., Noble, D.G., Robinson, J.A., Brown, A.F., Hughes, J., Procter, D.A., Gibbons, D.W. & Galbraith, C.A. 2002. The population status of birds in the United Kingdom, Channel Islands and Isle of Man: an analysis of conservation concern 2002–2007. *British Birds* 95: 410–450.

Hagermeijer, E.J.M. & Blair, M.J. (eds.) 1997. *The EBCC Atlas of European Breeding Birds: their Distribution and Abundance*. T. & A.D. Poyser, London.

Halley, D. J. 1993. Population changes and territorial distribution of Common Buzzards *Buteo buteo* in the Central Highlands, Scotland. *Bird Study* 40: 24–30.

Hancock, M.H., Gibbons, D.W & Thompson, P.S. 1997. The status of breeding Greenshank *Tringa nebularia* in the United Kingdom in 1995. *Bird Study* 44: 290–302.

Hardey, J. 2002. *Analysis of pesticide levels in feral pigeons in north-east Scotland*. Scottish Natural Heritage Commission Research Report F01AC327.

Hardey, J.J.C., Rae, R. & Rae, S. 1978. Breeding success of Dippers in the Grampian Region. *Grampian Ringing Group Report* 1: 23–25.

Hardey, J. & Craib, J. 2001. Survey of breeding Hen Harriers, Ladder Hills, 2001. Unpublished report to Scottish Natural Heritage.

Hardey, J., Craib, J. & Cosnette, B. 2002. Survey of breeding Hen Harriers in selected areas in Moray and Aberdeenshire, 2002. Unpublished report to Scottish Natural Heritage.

Hardey, J., Craib, J. & Cosnette, B. 2003. Survey of breeding Hen Harriers in selected areas in Moray and Aberdeenshire, 2003. Unpublished report to Scottish Natural Heritage.

Harvey, P. V. 2003. The Shetland Breeding Bird Survey 2002 and an estimate of the population size of some of Shetland's commoner breeding birds. *Shetland Bird Report* 2002: 108–110.

Harvie-Brown, J.A. 1906. A fauna of the Tay Basin and Strathmore. David Douglas, Edinburgh.

Harvie-Brown, J.A. & Buckley, T.E. 1895. *A vertebrate fauna of the Moray Basin*. 2 vols. David Douglas, Edinburgh.

Harris, M.P. & Birkhead, T.R. 1985. Breeding ecology of the British Alcidae. In: Nettleship, D.N. & Birkhead, T.R. (eds) *The Atlantic Alcidae*. Academic Press, London.

Harrison, J., Winterbottom, S. & Johnson, R. 2001. *Climate Change and Changing Patterns of Snowfall in Scotland*. Scottish Executive Central Research Unit. Edinburgh.

Hatton, P.L. & Marquiss, M. 2004. The origins of moulting Goosanders on the Eden Estuary. *Ringing & Migration* 22: 70–74.

Hawthorn, I. & Mead C.J. 1975. Wren movements and survival. *British Birds* 68: 349–358.

Haynes, P.J., Inglis, I.R., Isaacson, T.J. & Fryday, S.L. 2003. Woodpigeon *Columba palumbus* movements in eastern England. *Bird Study* 50: 33–38.

Hilden, O. 1982. Winter Ecology and the Partial Migration of the Goldcrest (*Regulus regulus*) in Finland. *Ornis Fennica* 59: 99–122.

Holling, M. & the Rare Breeding Birds Panel. 2007a. Rare breeding birds in the United Kingdom in 2003 and 2004. *British Birds* 100: 321–367.

Holling, M. & the Rare Breeding Birds Panel. 2007b. Non-native breeding birds in the United Kingdom in 2003, 2004 and 2005. *British Birds* 100: 638–649.

Holling, M. & the Rare Breeding Birds Panel. 2008. Rare breeding birds in the United Kingdom in 2005. *British Birds* 101: 276–316.

Holling, M. & the Rare Breeding Birds Panel. 2009. Rare breeding birds in the United Kingdom in 2006. *British Birds* 102: 158–202.

Holling, M. & the Rare Breeding Birds Panel. 2010. Rare breeding birds in the United Kingdom in 2007. *British Birds* 103: 2–52.

Holloway, S. 1996. *The Historical Atlas of Breeding Birds in Britain and Ireland: 1875–1900*. T. &. A.D. Poyser, London.

Hoodless, A. 2005. How Many Woodcock Breed in Britain? *Game Conservancy Trust Review* 2004: 34–35.

Horn, W. 1881. Collected notes on the birds of Buchan. *Proceedings of Natural History Society of Glasgow* 4: 231–256.

Huntley, B., Green, R.E., Collingham, Y.C. & Willis, S.G. 2007. *A climatic atlas of European breeding birds*. Durham University, RSPB and Lynx Edicions, Barcelona.

Jenkins, D. 1957. The breeding of the Red-legged Partridge. *Bird Study* 4: 97–100.

Jenkins, D. (ed.) 1985. The *Biology and Management of the River Dee*. Institute of Terrestrial Ecology/NERC. ITE Banchory.

Jenkins, D. (ed.) 1987. *Land use in the River Spey catchment*. Aberdeen Centre for Land Use Symposium No. 1. ACLU, Department of Zoology, University of Aberdeen.

Jenkins, D. & Chapman, P. 2008. Birds in mid Deeside, 1970–2008. *North East Scotland Bird Report* 2007: 124–144. North East Scotland Bird Club, Aberdeen.

Jenkins, D. & Sparks, T. 2010. The changing bird phenology of Mid Deeside, Scotland 1974–2010. *Bird Study* 57: 407–414.

Jenkins, D. & Watson, A. 1999. Bird numbers in an Aberdeenshire glen in March–June 1987–99. *Scottish Birds* 20: 81–93.

Jenkins, D. & Watson, A. 2000. Dates of arrival and song of birds during 1974–99 in mid-Deeside, Scotland. *Bird Study* 47: 249–251.

Jenkins, D. & Watson, A. 2005. Bird numbers in an Aberdeenshire glen (1987–2004). *Scottish Birds* 25: 50–53.

Johnston, R.F., Siegel-Causey, D. & Johnson, S.G. 1988. European Populations of the Rock Dove *Columba livia* and Genotypic Extinction. *The American Midland Naturalist* 120: 1–10.

JNCC 2009. *UK Seabirds in 2008.* Joint Nature Conservation Committee. www.jncc.gov.uk/seabirds

Knox, A.G. 1975. Appendix I. *Crossbill taxonomy*. In: Nethersole-Thompson, D. *Pine Crossbills*. T. & A.D. Poyser, Berkhamsted.

Lack, D. & Venables, L.S.V. 1939. The habitat distribution of British woodland birds. *Journal of Animal Ecology* 8: 39–71.

Lack, P. 1986. *The Atlas of Wintering Birds in Britain and Ireland.* T. &. A.D. Poyser, Calton.

Langslow, D.R. 1979. Movements of Blackcaps ringed in Britain and Ireland. *Bird Study* 26: 239–252.

Langston, R., Gregory, R. & Adams, R. 2002. The status of the Hawfinch in the UK, 1975–1999. *British Birds* 95: 166–173.

Langston, R.H.W., Smith, T., Brown, A.F. & Gregory, R.D. 2006. The Status of Breeding Twite *Carduelis flavostris* in the UK. *Bird Study* 53: 55–63.

Leaper, G. 1999. *Biodiversity of the Cairngorms: assessment of priority habitats and species.* Cairngorms Partnership, Grantown (now Cairngorms National Park Authority).

Lees, A.C. & Gilroy, J.J. 2004. Pectoral Sandpipers in Europe: vagrancy patterns and the influx of 2003. *British Birds* 97: 638–646.

Leverton, R. 2002. Grasshopper Warblers at a regular breeding site in Banffshire, 1990–2002. *North-East Scotland Bird Report* 2001: 94–97. North East Scotland Bird Club, Aberdeen.

Lewis, S., Sherratt, T.N., Hamer, K.C. & Wanless, S. 2001. Evidence of intra-specific competition for food in a pelagic seabird. *Nature* 412: 816–818.

Lloyd, C., Tasker, M.L. & Partridge K. 1991. *The status of seabirds in Britain and Ireland.* Poyser Ltd. London.

Love, J. & Stevenson, A. 2006. The birds of North Rona, 13th–18th June 1998. *Hebridean Naturalist* 15: 47–53.

Love, J.A. & Summers, R.W. 1973. Breeding biology of Magpies in Aberdeenshire. *Scottish Birds* 7: 399–403.

Lovegrove, R. 2007. *Silent Fields: the long decline of a nation's wildlife.* OUP, Oxford.

McGhie, H.A. 2000. Density and habitat association of Barn Owls in East Ross. *Scottish Birds* 21: 88–97.

MacGillivray, W. 1837. *A History of British Birds.* Volume 1. Scott, Webster & Geary, London.

MacGillivray, W. 1852. *A History of British Birds.* Volume 5. W.S. Orr & Co., London.

MacGillivray, W. 1855. *The Natural History of Deeside and Braemar.* Privately published, London.

McGinn, D. B. 1979. Status and breeding biology of Swallows in Banffshire. *Scottish Birds* 10: 221–229.

McGowan, G.M., Palmer, S.C.F., French, D.D., Barr, C.J., Howard, D.C., Smart, S.M., Mackey, E.C. & Shewry, M.C. 2002. *Trends in Broad Habitats: Scotland 1990–1998.* Scottish Natural Heritage Commissioned Report F00NB03. Available from www.snh.gov.uk/pdfs/strategy/ncms/CS2000-Scotlandresults.pdf

McKenzie, A.J., Petty, S.J., Toms, M.P. & Furness, R.W. 2007. Importance of Sitka Spruce *Picea sitchensis* seed and garden bird-feeders for Siskins *Carduelis spinus* and Coal Tits *Periparus ater*. *Bird Study* 54: 236–247.

Mackey, E.C. & Mudge, G. 2010. *Scotland's Wildlife: An assessment of biodiversity in 2010.* Scottish Natural Heritage, Inverness.

Mackey, E.C., Shewry, M.C. & Tudor, G.J. 1998. Land cover change: Scotland from the 1940s to the 1980s. Scottish Natural Heritage. Edinburgh, The Stationery Office.

Mackie, J. 1988. Distribution of Corn Bunting in Moray. *Moray & Nairn Bird Report* 1987: 46.

MacMillan, A.T. 1965. The Collared Dove in Scotland. *Scottish Birds* 3: 292–301.

Marchant, J. H. & Hyde, P. A. 1980. Aspects of the distribution of riparian birds on waterways in Britain and Ireland. *Bird Study* 27: 70–74.

Marquiss, M. 1989. Grey Herons *Ardea cinerea* breeding in Scotland: numbers, distribution and census techniques. *Bird Study* 36: 181–191.

Marquiss, M. 1993. *Herons.* Colin Baxter Photography Ltd. Grantown on Spey.

Marquiss, M. 2007. Seasonal pattern in hawk predation on Common Bullfinches *Pyrrhula pyrrhula*: evidence of an interaction with habitat affecting food availability. *Bird Study* 54: 1–11.

Marquiss, M. & Booth, C.J. 1986. The diet of Ravens *Corvus corax* in Orkney. *Bird Study* 33: 190–195.

Marquiss, M. & Duncan, K. 1993. Variation in the abundance of Red-breasted Mergansers *Mergus serrator* on a Scottish river in relation to season, year, river hydrography, salmon density and spring culling. *Ibis* 135: 33–41.

Marquiss, M. & Duncan, K. 1994a. Seasonal switching between habitats and changes in abundance of goosanders *Mergus merganser* within a Scottish river system. *Wildfowl* 45: 198–208.

Marquiss, M. & Duncan, K. 1994b. Diurnal activity patterns of goosanders *Mergus merganser* on a Scottish river system. *Wildfowl* 45: 209–221.

Marquiss, M. & Legge, G. 2003. Northern Goshawks in North-East Scotland. *North-East Scotland Bird Report* 2002: 127–131.

Marquiss, M. & Leitch, A. 1990. The diet of Grey Herons *Ardea cinerea* at Loch Leven, Scotland, and the importance of their predation on ducklings. *Ibis* 132: 535–549.

Marquiss, M. & Newton, I. 1982. The Goshawk in Britain. *British Birds* 75: 243–260.

Marquiss, M. & Newton, I. 2008. Stable isotope evidence for different regional source areas of common crossbill *Loxia curvirostra* irruptions into Britain *J. Avian Biology* 39: 30–34.

Marquiss, M. & Rae, R. 1994. Seasonal trends in abundance, diet and breeding of common crossbills (*Loxia curvirostra*) in an area of mixed species conifer plantation following the 1990 crossbill irruption. *Forestry* 67: 31–47.

Marquiss, M. & Rae, R. 2002. Ecological differentiation in relation to bill size amongst sympatric, genetically undifferentiated crossbills *Loxia* spp. *Ibis* 144: 494–508.

Marquiss, M., Carss, D.N., Armstrong, J.D. & Gardiner, R. 1998. *Fish-eating birds and salmonids in Scotland.* Report on fish-eating bird research (1990–1997) to the Scottish Office Agriculture, Environment and Fisheries Department. HSMO. Edinburgh.

Marquiss, M., Newton, I. & Ratcliffe, D.A. 1978. The decline of the Raven *Corvus corax* in relation to afforestation in southern Scotland and northern England. *Journal of Applied Biology* 15: 129–144.

Marquiss, M., Petty, S.J., Anderson, D.I.K. & Legge, G. 2003. Contrasting population trends of the Northern Goshawk (*Accipiter gentilis*) in the Scottish/English Borders and North-East Scotland. Pp 143–148 *in* Thompson, D.B.A., Redpath, S.M., Fielding, A.H., Marquiss, M. & Galbraith, C.A. (eds) *Birds of Prey in a Changing Environment*. Scottish Natural Heritage & The Stationary Office, Edinburgh, UK.

Marquiss, M., Rae, R., Harvey, P. & Proctor, R. 1995. Scottish Crossbill moves between Deeside and Strathspey. *Scottish Bird News* 37: 2–3.

Marren, P. 1982. *A Natural History of Aberdeen*. Published by R. Callander, Aberdeen People's Press, Aberdeen.

Massie, J. 2001. Tawny Owls in North-East Scotland 2000 - a Grampian Ringing Group report. *North-East Scotland Bird Report* 2000: 121–122. North-East Scotland Bird Club, Aberdeen.

Massie, J. & Walker, R. 2007. Tawny Owl Report 2007. A Grampian Ringing Group study into status, breeding and distribution 1978–2007. *Unpublished Report held in RSPB office*, Aberdeen.

Matthews, J. & North, S. 1989. Gannets breeding on mainland Scotland. *Scottish Birds* 15: 132–133.

Mavor, R. & Addlesee, H.A. 2007. *Common Standards Monitoring (CSM) of breeding seabirds at sites in Grampian*. Report to Scottish Natural Heritage re. Project No. 21529. JNCC, Aberdeen.

Mavor, R.A., Heubeck, M., Schmitt, S. & Parsons, M. 2008. *Seabird numbers and breeding success, 2006*, UK Nature Conservation No 31. JNCC, Peterborough.

Mavor, R.A., Parsons, M., Heubeck, M. & Schmitt, S. 2006. *Seabird numbers and breeding success in Britain and Ireland, 2005*. UK Nature Conservation Series No. 30. Joint Nature Conservation Committee, Peterborough.

Merritt, J. & Leslie, G. 2009. *Northeast Scotland: a landscape fashioned by Geology*. SNH/BGS, Battleby.

Meteorological Office (1989). *The Climate of Scotland: some facts and figures*. HMSO, London.

Millais, J.G. 1884. Note on the occurrence of the Parrot Crossbill in Perthshire, and probable nesting. *Proceedings of the Perthshire Society of Natural Science* 1881–1886: 182.

Milsom, T.P. & Watson, A. 1984. Numbers and spacing of summering Snow Buntings and snow cover in the Cairngorms. *Scottish Birds* 13: 19–23.

Mitchell, P.I. & Thompson, K.R. 1998. Survey of breeding common gulls *Larus canus* in the Mortlach and Correen Hills, Grampian. JNCC Seabirds and Cetaceans Branch, Aberdeen. (Summary in *Birds in Moray & Nairn* 1999: 92–97).

Mitchell, P.I., Newton, S.F., Ratcliffe, N. & Dunn, T.E. 2004. *Seabird populations of Britain and Ireland: results of the Seabird 2000 census*. T. & A.D. Poyser, London.

Moorcroft, D., Wilson, J.D & Bradbury, R.B. 2006. Diet of nestling Linnets *Carduelis cannabina* on lowland farmland before and after agricultural intensification. *Bird Study* 53: 156–163.

Moss, D. 1978. Song-bird Populations in Forestry Plantations. *Quarterly Journal of Forestry* 75: 5–14.

Moss, D., Taylor, P.N. & Easterbee, N. 1979. The Effects on Songbird Populations of Upland Afforestation with Spruce. *Forestry* 52: 129–150.

Moss, R. & Watson, A. 2001. Population cycles in birds of the grouse family (Tetraonidae). *Advances in Ecological Research* 32: 53–111.

Munro, J.H.B. 1975. Scottish winter Rook roost survey - central and northern Scotland. *Scottish Birds* 8: 309–314.

Murray, R.D. 1991. Quail in Scotland, 1989. *Scottish Bird Report* 1989: 45–50.

Murray, R.D., Holling, M., Dott, H.E.M. & Vandome, P. 1998. The Breeding Birds of South-east Scotland. Scottish Ornithologists' Club, Edinburgh.

Murray, S. 2009. 2009 breeding season news - North Rona. *Seabird Group Newsletter* 112: 8.

Murton, R.K. 1965. *The Woodpigeon*. Collins, London.

Nethersole-Thompson, D. 1966. *The Snow Bunting*. Oliver & Boyd, Edinburgh & London.

Nethersole-Thompson, D. 1975. *Pine Crossbills*. T. & A.D. Poyser, Berkhamsted.

Nethersole-Thompson, D. 1976. Recent distribution, ecology and breeding of Snow Buntings in Scotland. *Scottish Birds* 9: 147–162.

Nethersole-Thompson, D. & Nethersole-Thompson, M. 1979. *Greenshanks*. Poyser, Berkhamsted.

Nethersole-Thompson, D. & Watson, A. 1974. *The Cairngorms: their natural history and scenery*. Collins. (2nd edition 1981, The Melven Press, Perth).

Newson S.E., Woodburn R.J.W., Noble D.G., Baillie S.R. & Gregory R.D. 2005. Evaluating the Breeding Bird Survey for producing national population size and density estimates. *Bird Study* 52: 42–54.

Newton, I. 1972. *Finches*. Collins, London.

Newton, I. 1986. *The Sparrowhawk* T. & A.D. Poyser, Calton.

Norman, D. 2008. Birds in Cheshire and Wirral. A breeding and wintering atlas. Liverpool University Press, Liverpool.

Norman, R.K. & Saunders, D.R. 1969. Status of Little Terns in Great Britain and Ireland in 1967. *British Birds* 62: 4–13.

Norman, S.C. 1992. Dispersal and site fidelity in Lesser Whitethroats *Sylvia curruca*. *Ringing and Migration* 13: 167–174.

North East Scotland Biodiversity Steering Group Partnership 2000. *North East Scotland Local Biodiversity Action Plan*. The Moray Council. 129p. Available from: www.nesbiodiversity.org.uk/publications/plan.pdf

North-East Scotland Bird Reports 1974–2009. North-East Scotland Bird Club, Aberdeen.

O'Brien, M. 1994. *Survey of breeding waders on Scottish lowlands: interim report: includes site data for Grampian Region*. RSPB unpublished report, Edinburgh. March 1994.

O'Brien, M. 2005. Estimating the number of farmland waders breeding in the United Kingdom. In: Thorup, O. (ed.) Breeding waders in Europe 2000. *International Wader Studies* 14: 135–139. IWSG, UK.

O'Brien, M., Tharme, A. & Jackson, D. 2002. Changes in breeding wader numbers on Scottish farmed land during the 1990s. *Scottish Birds* 23: 10–21.

O'Brien, M., Green, R.E., & Wilson, J. 2006. Partial Recovery of the population of Corncrakes *Crex crex* in Britain 1993–2004. *Bird Study* 53: 213–224.

Ogilvie, M. & the Rare Breeding Birds Panel. 1999. Rare breeding birds in the United Kingdom in 1997. *British Birds* 92: 389–428.

Ogilvie, M. & the Rare Breeding Birds Panel. 2001. Rare breeding birds in the United Kingdom in 1999. *British Birds* 94: 344–381.

Parkin, D.T. & Knox, A. 2010. *The Status of Birds in Britain and Ireland*. Christopher Helm, London.

Parr, R. 1979. Sequential breeding by Golden Plovers. *British Birds* 72: 499–503.

Parr, R. 1992. The decline to extinction of a population of Golden Plovers in north-east Scotland. *Ornis Scandinavica* 23: 152–158.

Parslow, J.L.F. 1973. Breeding Birds in Britain and Ireland: A historical survey. T & A. D. Poyser, Berkhamsted.

Patterson, I. J. 1982. *The Shelduck: a study of behavioural ecology*. Cambridge University Press, Cambridge.

Pearce-Higgins, J.W., Stephen, L., Langston, R.H.W., Bainbridge, I.P. & Bullman, R. 2009. The distribution of breeding birds around upland wind farms. *Journal of Applied Ecology* 46: 1323–1331.

Pennant, T. 1771. *A Tour in Scotland 1769*. John Monk, Chester.

Pennington, M., Osborn, K., Harvey, P., Riddington, R., Okill, D., Ellis, P. & Heubeck, M. 2004. *The Birds of Shetland*. Helm.

Perkins, A.J., Maggs, H.E., Wilson, J.D. & Watson, A. 2008. Targeted management intervention reduces rate of population decline in Corn Buntings *Emberiza calandra* in eastern Scotland. *Bird Study* 55: 52–58.

Perrow, M.R., Tomlinson, M.L., Lines, P., Benham, K., Howe, R. & Skeate, E. 2003. 'Is food supply behind Little Tern *Sterna albifrons* colony location? The case of the largest colony in the UK at the North Denes/Winterton SPA in Norfolk'. Proceedings of a symposium on Little Terns *Sterna albifrons*. *The Royal Society for the Protection of Birds, Research Report 8*.

Petty, S.J. 1996. History of the northern goshawk *Accipiter gentilis* in Britain. In Holmes, J.S. & Simons, J.R. (eds.) *The Introduction and Naturalisation of Birds*. pp 95–102. The Stationary Office, London.

Phillips, I.M. 1997. *Rare and Scarce Birds in North East Scotland*. Privately Published.

Picozzi, N. 1975. A study of the Carrion/Hooded Crow in north-east Scotland. *British Birds* 68: 409–419.

Picozzi, N. 1976. Hybridization of Carrion and Hooded crows *Corvus c. corone* and *Corvus c. cornix* in north-eastern Scotland. *Ibis* 118: 254–257.

Picozzi, N. 1978. Dispersion, breeding and prey of Hen Harrier (*Circus cyaneus*) in Glen Dye, Kincardineshire. Ibis 120: 498–509.

Picozzi, N. 1986. *Black grouse Research in NE Scotland*. ITE Project 764: Report to the World Pheasant Association.

Picozzi, N., Catt, D.C. & Cummins, R. P. 1996. Breeding waders in the Cairngorms Straths ESA in 1995. *Scottish Birds* 18: 197–204.

Polunin, O. & Walters, M. 1985. *A guide to the vegetation of Britain and Europe*. Oxford University Press, Oxford.

Prater, A.J. 1989. Ringed Plover *Charadrius hiaticula* breeding population of United Kingdom in 1984. *Bird Study* 36: 154–160.

Presland, J. 2006. Reporting on local change. *BSBI Newsletter* 103: 16–18.

Proffitt, F., Newton, I., Wilson, J.D. & Siriwardena, G.M. 2004. Bullfinch *Pyrrhula pyrrhula* breeding ecology in lowland farmland and woodland: comparisons across time and habitat. *Ibis* 146 (Suppl. 2): 78–86.

Rae, R. 1999. Corn Buntings in north-east Scotland, 1998–1999. *North East Scotland Bird Report* 1999: 111–114.

Rae, R. & Watson, A. 1998. Minimal numbers and habitat of breeding Dunlin in north east Scotland. *Scottish Birds* 19: 185–194.

Rao, S. 2004. Classic wildlife sites: Mar Lodge Estate, Cairngorms. *British Wildlife* 16: 86–94.

Ratcliffe, D.A. 1993. *The Peregrine Falcon*. 2nd Edition. T. & A.D. Poyser, Calton.

Ratcliffe, D.A. 1997. *The Raven*. T. & A.D. Poyser. Calton.

Raven, M.J., Noble, D.G. & Baillie, S.R. 2007. *The Breeding Bird Survey 2006*. BTO/JNCC/RSPB Report. Also available on BTO website www.bto.org

RCAHMS (Royal Commission on the Ancient and Historical Monuments of Scotland) 2008. *In the Shadow of Bennachie: a field archaeology of Donside, Aberdeenshire*. RCAHMS, Edinburgh. 2nd edition.

Rebecca, G. W. 2001. The contrasting status of the Ring Ouzel in two areas of upper Deeside, north-east Scotland, between 1991 and 1998. *Scottish Birds* 22: 9–19.

Rebecca, G. W. 2006. The breeding ecology of the Merlin (*Falco columbarius aesalon*), with particular reference to north-east Scotland and land-use change. Unpublished Ph.D. thesis, The Open University.

Rebecca, G. W. & Bainbridge, I. P. 1998. The breeding status of the Merlin *Falco columbarius* in Britain in 1993–94. *Bird Study* 45: 172–187.

Rebecca, G. W. & Cosnette, B. L. 2003. Long-term monitoring of breeding Merlin (*Falco columbarius*) in Aberdeenshire, North-East Scotland 1980–2000. In Thompson, D.B.A., Redpath, S. M., Fielding, A., Marquiss, M. & Galbraith, C. A. (eds.) *Birds of Prey in a changing environment*. Chapter 14. The Stationery Office, Edinburgh.

Rebecca, G. W., Cosnette, B. L., Hardey, J. J. C. & Payne, A. G. 1992. Status, distribution and breeding biology of the Merlin in north-east Scotland, 1980–1989. *Scottish Birds* 16: 165–183.

Riddle, G. 1971. The breeding season in a rural colony of Feral Pigeons. *Scottish Birds* 6: 321–329.

Riley, H.T. 1992. *Reproductive success in martins (Hirundinidae). Studies on the behaviour and ecology of individuals using DNA fingerprinting*. Unpubl. Ph.D. thesis, University of Stirling.

Risely, K., Noble, D.G. & Baillie, S.R. 2008. *The Breeding Bird Survey 2007*. BTO/JNCC/RSPB Report. Also available on BTO website www.bto.org/bbs/results/bbsreport.htm

Risely, K., Noble, D.G. & Baillie, S.R. 2009. *The Breeding Bird Survey 2008*. BTO/JNCC/RSPB Report. Also available on BTO website www.bto.org/bbs/results/bbsreport.htm

Ritchie, J. 1920. *The influence of Man on Animal Life in Scotland*. Cambridge University Press, Cambridge.

Robinson, R.A. 2010. State of bird populations in Britain and Ireland. Chpt. 17 (pp. 281–318) in: Maclean, N. (ed.) *Silent Summer: the state of wildlife in Britain and Ireland*. Cambridge University Press.

Rogers, M.J. & the Rarities Committee. 1997. Report on rare birds in Great Britain in 1996. *British Birds* 90: 453–522.

Rogers, M.J. & the Rarities Committee. 1999. Report on rare birds in Great Britain in 1998. *British Birds* 92: 554–609.

Rowlands, I. & Cook, M. 1997. Little Ringed Plovers breeding at Speymouth - new to Moray & Nairn. *Moray and Nairn Bird Report* 1996: 79.

RSPB Scotland 2009. The illegal killing of birds of prey in Scotland in 2008. RSPB Scotland, Edinburgh. http://www.rspb.org.uk/Images/illegalkilling2008_tcm9-225981.pdf

Rutz, C., Bjilsma, R.G., Marquiss, M. & Kenward, R.E. 2006. Population limitation in the Northern Goshawk in Europe. *Studies in Avian Biology* 31: 158–197.

Sangster, G., Collinson, J.M., Knox, A.G., Parkin, D.T. & Svensson, L. 2007. Taxonomic recommendations for British birds: Fourth report. *Ibis* 149 (4), 853–857.

Sangster, G., Collinson, J.M., Knox, A.G., Parkin, D.T. & Svensson, L. 2010. Taxonomic recommendations for British birds: Sixth report. *Ibis* 152 (1), 180–186.

Sara, M. 2008. Breeding abundance of threatened raptors as estimated from occurrence data. *Ibis* 150: 766–778.

Scott, M. 2009. Climate change and the high Cairngorms: reality and hyperbole. *British Wildlife* 20: 389–397.

Scottish Aggregates Survey 2005. Scottish Government, November 2007.

Scottish Enterprise 2008. *Aberdeen City and Shire Economic Review*. Scottish Enterprise, Aberdeen.

Scottish Natural Heritage 2002. *Natural Heritage Futures - Cairngorms Massif; North East Glens; North East Coastal Plain; Eastern Lowlands; Moray Firth.* Scottish Natural Heritage, Battleby. (5 booklets).

Scottish Natural Heritage 2009. *Natural Heritage Futures updates - Cairngorms Massif; North East Glens; North East Coastal Plain; Eastern Lowlands; Moray Firth.* Scottish Natural Heritage, Battleby. (5 booklets). Available at: http://www.snh.org.uk/strategy/NHF00.asp

Scottish Natural Heritage/British Geological Survey 1994. *Cairngorms: a landscape fashioned by Geology.* SNH/BGS, Battleby.

Scottish Raptor Study Groups 1997. The illegal persecution of raptors in Scotland. *Scottish Birds* 19: 65–85.

Sharrock, J.T.R. 1976. *The Atlas of Breeding Birds in Britain and Ireland.* BTO/IWC. Tring, Herts. T. &. A.D. Poyser, London.

Sharrock, J. T. R. & the Rare Breeding Birds Panel. 1978. Rare breeding birds in the United Kingdom in 1976. *British Birds* 71: 11–13.

Shaw, G. 1990. Timing and fidelity of breeding for Siskins *Carduelis spinus* in Scottish conifer plantations. *Bird Study* 37: 30–35.

Shaw, K.D. 2009. The decline of the Whinchat as a breeding bird in mainland Fife. *Scottish Birds* 29: 38–39.

Shaw, P. & Thompson, D.B.A. (eds.) 2006. *The Nature of the Cairngorms: diversity in a changing environment.* The Stationery Office, Edinburgh.

Shaw, P., Thompson, D.B.A., Duncan, K. & Buxton, N. 2006. Chapter 18 in Shaw, P. & Thompson, D.B.A. (eds.): *The Nature of the Cairngorms: diversity in a changing environment.* The Stationery Office, Edinburgh.

Shepherd, K.B., Brown, A.F. & Harding, N.J. 1989. *Moorland Bird Surveys in Grampian, Tayside and Central Regions in 1989: site descriptions and preliminary results.* NCC Chief Scientist Directorate Commissioned Research Report No. 951. NCC, Peterborough.

Shewan R. 1998. Corn Bunting Census 1997. *Moray and Nairn Bird Report* 1997: 91–94.

Sim, G. 1903. *Vertebrate Fauna of 'Dee'.* Wyllie, Aberdeen.

Sim, I.M.W., Burfield, I.J., Grant, M.C., Pearce-Higgins, J.W. & Brooke, M. de L. 2007. The role of habitat composition in determining breeding site occupancy in a declining Ring Ouzel *Turdus torquatus* population. *Ibis* 149: 374–385.

Sim, I.M.W., Dillon, I.A., Eaton, M.A., Etheridge, B., Lindley, P., Riley H., Saunders, R., Sharpe, C. & Tickner, M. 2007. Status of Hen Harrier *Circus cyaneus* in the UK and Isle of Man in 2004, and a comparison with the 1988–89 and 1998 surveys. *Bird Study* 54: 256–267.

Sim, I.M.W., Eaton, M.A., Setchfield, R.P., Warren, P.K. & Lindley, P. 2008. Abundance of male Black Grouse *Tetrao tetrix* in Britain in 2005, and change since 1995–96. *Bird Study* 55: 304–313.

Sim, I.M.W., Gregory, R.D., Hancock, M. & Brown, A.F. 2005. Recent changes in the abundance of British upland breeding birds. *Bird Study* 52: 261–275.

Sim, I. M. W., Rebecca G. W. & Ludwig S. 2008. Glen Clunie Ring Ouzel Breeding Ecology Project. *North-East Scotland Bird Report* 2006: 117–119.

Sim, I., Rollie, C., Arthur, D., Benn, S., Booker, H., Fairbrother, V., Green, M., Hutchinson, K., Ludwig, S., Nicoll, M., Poxton, I., Rebecca, G., Smith, L., Stanbury, A. & Wilson, P. 2010. The decline of the Ring Ouzel in Britain. *British Birds* 103: 229–239.

Smart, J., Taylor, E., Amar, A., Smith, K., Bierman, S., Carpenter, J., Grice, P., Currie, F. & Hewson, C. 2007. *Habitat associations of woodland birds: implications for woodland management for woodland species.* RSPB Research Report No. 26. RSPB, Sandy.

Smiles, S. 1876. *Life of a Scotch Naturalist: Thomas Edward.* John Murray, London. 1st edition.

Smith, A. J. M. 1975. Studies of breeding Sandwich Terns. *British Birds* 68: 142–156.

Smith, K. W., Dee, C.W., Fearnside, J.D., Fletcher, E.W. & Smith, R.N. 1993. *The Breeding Birds of Hertfordshire.* Hertfordshire Natural History Society.

Smith, R.D. 1991. Monitoring of breeding Snow Buntings in 1988 and 1989. In Stroud, D. & Glue, D. (eds.) *Britain's Birds in 1989–90: the conservation and monitoring review.* Pp.112–113. BTO/NCC, Stretford.

Smith, R.D. 1996. Racial composition of breeding and wintering Snow Buntings *Plectrophenax nivalis* in the north-east Scottish uplands. *Ringing & Migration* 17: 123–136.

Smith, R.D. & Marquiss, M. 1994. Breeding seasons and nesting success of Snow Buntings in north-east Scotland. *Scottish Birds* 17: 223–234.

Smith, R.D. & Marquiss, M. 1995. Production and costs of nesting attempts in Snow Buntings *Plectrophenax nivalis*: why do they attempt second broods? *Ibis* 137: 469–476.

Smith, R.D. & Summers, R.W. 2005. Population size, breeding biology and origins of Scottish Purple Sandpipers. *British Birds* 98: 579–588.

Smith, R.D., Watson, A. & Marquiss, M. 2009. Whether a hen snow bunting pairs with the same cock for a second nest. *Scottish Birds* 29: (1) 34–45.

Snow, D.W. & Perrins, C.M. 1998. *The Birds of the Western Palearctic.* Concise Edition. Two volumes. Oxford University Press, Oxford.

Sparks, T.H., Huber, K., Bland, R.L., Crick, H.Q.P., Croxton, P.J., Flood, J., Loxton, R.G., Mason, C.F., Newnham, J.A. and Tryjanowski, P. 2007. How consistent are trends in arrival (and departure) dates of migrant birds in the UK? *Journal of Ornithology* 148: 503–511.

Spencer, R. & the Rare Breeding Birds Panel. 1986. Rare breeding birds in the United Kingdom in 1984. *British Birds* 79: 470–495.

St. John, C. 1863. *Natural History and Sport in Moray.* Edmonstone & Douglas. Edinburgh.

Standley, P., Bucknell, N.J., Swash, A. & Collins, I.D. 1996. *The Birds of Berkshire.* The Berkshire Atlas Group. Produced by Quetzal Communications, Basingstoke.

Stott, M., Callion, J., Kinley, I., Raven, C. & Roberts, J. 2002. *The Breeding Birds of Cumbria: a tetrad atlas 1997–2001.* Cumbria Bird Club.

Sullivan, M.A. 1982. Mew Gulls successfully nesting on a roof in Aberdeen. *Scottish Birds* 13: 229.

Summers, R.W. 1999. Swifts nesting in Scots Pines at Abernethy Forest. *Scottish Birds* 20: 27–45.

Summers, R.W. & Buckland, S.T. 2010. A first survey of the global population size and distribution of the Scottish Crossbill *Loxia scotica. Bird Conservation International* (in press), Cambridge University Press. doi:/10.1017/50959270909990323.

Summers, R.W., Jardine, D.C. & Dawson, R.J.G. 2004. The distribution of the Scottish Crossbill, 1995–2003. *Scottish Birds* 24 (2): 11–16.

Summers, R.W., Jardine, D.C., Marquiss, M. & Rae, R. 2002. The distribution and habitats of crossbills *Loxia* spp. in Britain, with special reference to the Scottish crossbill *Loxia scotica. Ibis* 144: 393–410.

Summers, R.W., Mavor, R.A., Buckland, S.T. & MacLennan, A.M. 1999. Winter population size and habitat selection of Crested Tits *Parus cristatus* in Scotland. *Bird Study* 46: 230–242.

Summers-Smith, J. D. 1988. *The Sparrows.* T. & A. D. Poyser, Calton.

Sweeney, J.J. 1998. An Investigation into the Polygynous Mating System of the Wren *Troglodytes troglodytes indigenus* (L). Unpublished PhD thesis, University of Paisley.

Tapper, S. 1999. *A Question of Balance*. Game Conservancy Trust, Fordingbridge.

Tasker, M.L., Webb, A. & Mathews, J.M. 1991. A census of the large inland Common Gull colonies of Grampian. *Scottish Birds* 16: 106–112.

Taylor, M.J., Sharp, E.A. & Giela, A. 2009. *Pesticide poisoning of animals in 2008: a report of investigations in Scotland*. SASA Chemistry Branch, Scottish Government. http://www.sasa.gov.uk/mediafiles/0492BD9C_D3C8_A2 F0_76A16789748A3CC0.pdf

Thaler, E. & Thaler, K. 1982. Feeding Biology of the Goldcrest and Firecrest and their Segregation by choice of food. *Ökol. Vögel*. 4: 191–204.

Thom, V. M. 1986. *Birds in Scotland*. T. & A. D. Poyser, Calton.

Thórarinsson, T.L., Petersen, A., Einarsson, Á., Stefánsson, H.W., Kolbeinsson, Y.R., Stefánsson, A., Þórisson, B. & Bragadóttir, Þ.V. (in press). Population size and distribution of the Horned Grebe in Iceland 2004–2005. *Bliki* (in press). (Icelandic, with English summary).

Vickery, J.A., Tallowin, J.R., Feber, R.E., Asteraki, E.J., Atkinson, P.W., Fuller, R.J. & Brown, V.K. 2001. The management of lowland neutral grasslands in Britain: effects of agricultural practices on birds and their food resources. *Journal of Applied Ecology* 38: 647–664.

Visit Scotland 2005. *The Official Guide to Golf in Aberdeen & Grampian Highlands*. Produced for Visit Scotland Aberdeen & Grampian and the Golf Tourism Partnership. For average area figures see: http://www.sac.ac.uk/consulting/services/f-h/farmdiversification/database/leisureandrec/golfcourse

Walsh, P.M., Halley, D.J., Harris, M.P., del Nevo, A., Sim, I.M.W. & Tasker, M.L. 1995. *Seabird monitoring handbook for Britain and Ireland*. JNCC/RSPB/ITE/ Seabird Group, Peterborough.

Wanless, S., Matthews, J. & Bourne, W.R.P. 1996. The Troup Head Gannetry. *Scottish Birds* 18: 214–221.

Wanless, S., Murray, S. & Harris, M.P. 2005. The status of Northern Gannet in Britain & Ireland in 2003/04. *British Birds* 98: 280–294.

Wanless, S., Frederiksen, M., Daunt, F., Scott, B.E. & Harris, M.P. 2007. Black-legged Kittiwakes as indicators of environmental change in the North Sea: evidence from long-term studies. *Progress in Oceanography* 72: 30–38.

Watson, A. 1965a. A population study of ptarmigan (*Lagopus mutus*) in Scotland. *Journal of Animal Ecology* 34: 135–72.

Watson, A. 1965b. Research on Scottish ptarmigan. *Scottish Birds* 3: 331–49.

Watson, A. 1966. Hill birds of the Cairngorms. *Scottish Birds* 4: 179–203.

Watson, A. 1967. The Hatton Castle rookery and roost in Aberdeenshire. *Bird Study* 14: 116–119.

Watson, A. 1973. Shore Larks summering and possibly breeding in Scotland. *British Birds* 66: 505–508.

Watson, A. 1992. *The Cairngorms*. Scottish Mountaineering Club District Guidebook. Scottish Mountaineering Club, Edinburgh.

Watson, A. 1992. Some post-war declines in Corn Bunting numbers in north-east Scotland. *Scottish Birds* 16: 273–275.

Watson, A. 1998. Inland Common Gull colonies in north east Scotland. *Scottish Birds* 19: 244.

Watson, A. 2001. Common Quail heard on north east Scottish farmland 1988–2001. *Scottish Birds* 22: 112–113.

Watson, A. 2007. Global warming and Scottish land birds. *Scottish Bird News* 84: 1–2, 5.

Watson, A. & Moss, R. 2004. Impacts of ski development on Ptarmigan (*Lagopus mutus*) at Cairn Gorm, Scotland. *Biological Conservation* 116: 267–275.

Watson, A. & Moss. R. 2008. *Grouse: the natural history of British and Irish species*. Collins New Naturalist, London.

Watson, A. & Rae, S. 1987. Dotterel numbers habitat and breeding success in Scotland. *Scottish Birds* 14: 191–198.

Watson, A. & Smith, R.D. 1991. Scottish Snow Bunting numbers in summer 1970–87. *Scottish Birds* 16: 53–56.

Watson, A., Duncan, D., Cameron, I. & Pottie, J. 2008. Nine Scottish snow patches survive until winter 2007/2008. *Weather* 63: 138–140.

Watson, A., Moss, R. & Rae, S. 1998. Population dynamics of Scottish rock ptarmigan cycles. *Ecology* 79: 1174–92.

Watson, A., Perkins, A.J., Maggs, H.E. & Wilson J.D. 2009. Decline of Corn Buntings *Emberiza calandra* on east Scottish study areas in 1989–2007. *Bird Study* 56: 213–220.

Watson, D. 1977. *The Hen Harrier*. T. & A. D. Poyser, Berkhamsted.

Weir, D.N. 1978. Effects of poisoning on Raven and raptor populations. *Scottish Birds* 10: 31.

Welch, D. 1993. *Flora of North Aberdeenshire. Botanical vice-county 93*. Privately published, D. Welch, Banchory.

Wernham, C.V., Toms, M.P., Marchant, J.H., Clark, J.A., Siriwardena, G.M. & Baillie, S.R. 2002. The Migration Atlas: movements of the birds of Britain and Ireland. T. &. A.D. Poyser, London.

Westerberg, S. & Bowey, K. (eds.) 2000. *The Summer Atlas of the Breeding Birds of County Durham*. Durham Bird Club.

Whitfield, D.P. 2002. Status of breeding Dotterel in Britain in 1999. *Bird Study* 49: 237–249.

Whitfield, D.P., MacLeod, D.R.A., Watson, J., Fielding, A.H. & Haworth, P.F. 2003. The association of grouse moor in Scotland with the illegal use of poisons to control predators. *Biological Conservation* 114: 157–163.

Whitfield, D.P., Fielding, A.H., McLeod, D.R.A., Morton, K., Stirling-Aird, P. & Eaton, M.A. 2007. Factors constraining the distribution of Golden Eagles *Aquila chrysaetos* in Scotland. *Bird Study* 54: 199–211.

Whitfield, D. P., Fielding, A. H., McLeod, D. R. A. & Haworth, P. F. 2008. *A conservation framework for golden eagles: implications for their conservation and management in Scotland*. Scottish Natural Heritage Commissioned Report No.193 (ROAME No. F05AC306).

Williamson, K. 1974. Breeding Birds in the Deciduous Woodlands of Mid-Argyll, Scotland. *Bird Study* 21: 29–44.

Wills, J. 2009. Seasonal distribution and population trends of waterfowl on Loch of Skene. *North East Scotland Bird Report* 2007: 113–123. North East Scotland Bird Club, Aberdeen.

Wilson, J.O. 1890. Bird life in the Huntly district. *Trans. Banffshire Field Club* Aug. 1890: 81–82.

Winspear, R. & Davies G. 2005. A management guide to birds of lowland farmland. The RSPB, Sandy.

Witherby, H.F., Jourdain, F.C.R., Ticehurst, N.F. & Tucker, B.W. 1938–41. *The Handbook of British Birds*. Four volumes. H.F. & G. Witherby, London.

Wotton, S.R., Langston, R.H.W. & Gregory R.D. 2002. The breeding status of the Ring Ouzel *Turdus torquatus* in the UK in 1999. *Bird Study* 49: 26–34.

Yalden, D.W. & Albarella, U. 2009. *The History of British Birds*. Oxford University Press, Oxford.

Young, A. & Cook, M. 2001. The breeding population of Water Rails in Moray & Nairn in 1995–2000. *Birds in Moray & Nairn* 2000: 100–105.

Annex 1.   *Acknowledgements and list of contributors, photographers and sponsors*

We are extremely grateful to all the observers and organisations listed below for contributing records to the atlas. The authors of species accounts are marked with an asterisk and in bold, and we extend a special thank you to them.

Aberdeen University Bird Club
Sheila Adair
Ian Addis
Hugh Addlesee *
Anne Alexander
Sam Alexander
Graeme Allen
Andy Amphlett
Vicky Anderson
Mark Ancliff
Martin Auld *
Lizzie Bacon
Jon Bailey
David Bain
David Bale
Clare Ballinger
Dawn Balmer
Paul Baxter
P. Bekier
Stuart Benn
Amanda Biggins
Rob Blackwell
Jacqueline Blackwood
Katie Bliss
Phil Bloor
Alison Borthwick
Bill Bourne *
Sheila Bousfield
Anne Boyle
Caroline Brearley
John Brighouse
Grahame Brind
Ian Broadbent *
Richard Brooker
Colin Brooks
Ken Brown
Margaret Brown
Steve Brown
Craig Buchan
Kenny Buchan
Alan Bull
Colin Bullough
Richard Burn
Simon Busuttil *
Di Butcher
Robin Callander
Oscar Campbell
Mick Canham
Shirley Carroll
Charlie Catto
Amanda Chadderton
Peter Chalmers
Michael Chandler
Paul Chapman *
Margaret Cindery
Richard Cindery *
S. Clark
Alister Clunas *
Robert Coleman
Tony Comerford
Forestry Commission

Ged Connell
J. Connell
Jenny Cook *
Martin Cook *
Graham Cooper
Nicola Cooper
Michael Copleston
Peter Cosgrove
Brian Cosnette *
Jim Craib *
Bill Craigie
Alan Crawford
Jackie Cumberbirch
R. Cumming
S. Cumming
Karen Cunningham
Stuart Cutts *
Kathy Dale
Matt Dale
James Darroch
James Davidson
Norman Davidson
Paul Davidson
Jane Davies
Llinos Davies
Margaret Dearman
Roy Dennis
Adrian Devonshire
Gill Devonshire
Leslie Dingwall
Gilbert Dinnie
Chris Donald
Harry Dott
Angela Douglas
David Douglas
Iain Downie
Ron Downing
Paul Doyle *
Annabel Drysdale *
Desmond Dugan
Alistair Duncan *
Iain Duncan
Judy Duncan *
Raymond Duncan *
Tom Dunn
David Dunstan
Alan Edward
Arthur Ewing
Isobel Fairclough
Henry Farquhar
Steff Ferguson
Tom Finnemore
Richard Firmin
Dave Flumm
Aoife Flynn
Gary Flynn
Gina Ford
Martin Ford
Susannah Ford
Dugie Foreman
Jenny Foreman
John Forster

Nicola Fowlie
Adam Francis
Ian Francis *
Raymond Fraser
Robert Fuchs *
Dominic Funnell *
Clare Geddes
Glenda George
Charlie Gervaise *
Duncan Gibson
Steve Gilbert
Dave Gill
Chris Goodman
James Gordon
Peter Gordon
Peter Gordon Smith *
Peter Gove
Grampian Ringing Group
Doug Grant
Stephen Gray
Flora Grigor-Taylor
Karen Guthrie
C. Hall
Ken Hall
Sharon Hall
T. Hall
Neil Hancock
Jon Hardey *
Maria Hardy
J. Hart
David Hartley
Penny Hartley
Eddie Harwood
Richard Hewitt
Ian Hill
Margaret Hill
Paul Hirst
A. Hogg
H. Holbrook
Liz Holden
Peter Holden
Erica Hollis
Jeremy Hopkins
James Imray
Mike Innes *
Gemma Insley
Hugh Insley *
Alastair Irvine
Ryan Irvine
Peter Jamieson
David Jenkins
Andy Jensen *
R. John
Martin Johnson
Bill Johnston
Emmett Johnston
Jimmy Johnston
Sheila Johnston
Chris Jones
Glyn Jones
Janet Jones
Trevor Jones

Alan Knox *
Kenny Kortland *
Daniel Kraushaar
David Landsman
Iain Landsman
John Latham
David Law *
Allan Lawrence
Simon Lawrence
Genevieve Leaper
Fiona Leckie
Gavin Legge
Doug Leith
Jenny Lennon *
Laurie Lerner
Roy Leverton
Bev Lewis
Jim Lister
Amanda Little
John Littlejohn
Nick Littlewood *
Norman London
David Lunney
Ben Macallum *
Frazer Macfarlane
Malcolm Macgarvin
Alison Macintyre
Neil Mackenzie
John Mackie
Hywel Maggs *
Mick Marquiss *
Dave Marshall
Fiona Marshall
Tim Marshall
John Massie
Jill Matthews
Anne Mavor
Bill Mavor
Roddy Mavor
William McBain
Colin McClean
Peter McCormack
J. McDonald
Hamish McIntosh
Clive McKay *
Ian Middleton
Jane Milloy
Fiona Milne
Morag Milne
Rob Minshull
Kathleen Mitchell
Margaret Mitchell
Ruth Mitchell
Ian Moig
S. Morgan
Pat Morrey
Melvin Morrison *
Robert Moss
Stan Moyes
Colin Munro
National Trust for Scotland Mar Lodge Estate

Glenys Neville
Philip Neville
David Newlands
Graham Ormerod
Peter Osborn
Emma O'Shea
Jimmy Oswald
Jenny Owen
Steve Palmer
David Parnaby *
Scott Paterson *
Ian Patterson *
Rodney Payne
Sandy Payne
Kevin Peace
James Pearce-Higgins
Richard Pelling
Nicky Penford *
Allan Perkins *
Alison Phillip
Ian Phillips
Ivan Phillips
Nick Picozzi
Jim Piggins *
Brian Pirie
Anne Porteous
David Potter
Alistair Pout
C. Powell
Simon Power
Carina Prigmore
Justin Prigmore
Bob Proctor *
Dave Pullan *
Katherine Puttick
Robert Rae *
Shaila Rao *
Graham Rebecca *
Hilary Redden
Alan Reid
Kaisa Reinius
Alistair Rendall
Jodie Rhodes
Aileen Ross
RSPB Abernethy Forest Reserve
Graeme Ruthven
Peter Rydall
Anne Saunders
Richard Schofield *
Harry Scott *
D. Selbie
I. Sharp
Kath Shaw
Ken Shaw *
Raymond Shewan
Eleanor Shield
Innes Sim *
Andrew Simkins
Lenny Simpson
Ronald Simpson
Mike Smedley

Alan Smith
Alistair Smith *
Angie Smith
Gordon Smith
Howard Smith
Rosemary Smith
Trevor Smith
Andrew Stalker *
Brian Stewart
Andy Stronach
Annie Sturgeon
Helen Summers
John Summerwill
Liz Summerwill
Dave Sutherland
Ian Suttie *
Mark Tasker
Andy Taylor
Bill Taylor
Helen Taylor
Ken Taylor
S. Taylor
Doug Thorn
Andy Thorpe *
Owen Vaughan
Hazel Veitch
D. Walker
Gordon Walker
Kay Walker
Peter Walker
Sarah Wanless
Adam Watson *
Ross Watson
D. Wawman
Andy Webb
Peter Webster
Andrew Wells
Ewan Weston *
Brian Whitlock
John Whittal
Mark Whitton
Ian Wilde
Stephen Willis
John Wills *
Deirdre Wilson
John Wilson
Esther Woodward
Alastair Young *
Mark Young
Gusdi Zulfendi

The following photographers kindly allowed us to use images in the atlas:

Allan Adam	Gavin Legge
Hugh Addlesee	Jenny Lennon
Sam Alexander	Dave Mackinnon
Bruce Anderson	Hywel Maggs
John Anderson	Micky Maher
Paul Baxter	John Massie
Gavin Bennett	Jill Matthews
Martin Bennett	Derek McGinn
Amanda Biggins	Joyce Moyes
Paul Bingham	Nicky Penford
Ann Burns	Maria Perera
Bill Burns	Allan Perkins
Walter Burns	Nick Picozzi
Gavin Chambers	Richard Pittam
John Chapman	Gina Prior
Paul Chapman	Dave Pullan
Martin Cook	Rab Rae
Roy Dennis	Stuart Rae
Ed Duthie	Graham Rebecca
John Edelsten	Mike Reid
Adam Francis	Harry Scott
Ian Francis	Alistair Smith
Chris Gibbins	Lewis Thomson
Duncan Goulder	Mike Thrower
Trevor Gunby	Robert Tribe
Andy Hay	Chris Upson
Ian Hay	Ewan Weston
Bob Humphreys	David Whitaker
Chris Jones	Bryan Wright
Kev Jones	Anne Young
Alan Knox	John Young

We thank the atlas steering group: together with Ian Francis and Martin Cook, this comprised Graham Cooper, Dave Gill, Nick Picozzi, Rab Rae, Richard Schofield, Andy Thorpe, John Wills and Alastair Young. Harry Scott became involved in the production stages. Paul Doyle kindly maintained the atlas website, and Rodney Payne managed the finances of the project. We thank Adam Watson for writing the Foreword.

We are most grateful to the following organisations, especially those which generously provided funding towards the atlas:

Funding partners:

Scottish Natural Heritage (Ewen Cameron, David Bale, Jim Dey). SNH funding allowed complimentary copies to be given to every library and secondary school in North-East Scotland.

Forestry Commission Scotland (Hugh Insley, John Thomson, Alastair Young and Jackie Cumberbirch)

Cairngorms National Park Authority (Will Boyd Wallis, David Hetherington)

RSPB Scotland (Martin Auld, Sheila Adair, Kathleen Mitchell and Anne Porteous)

East Grampian Coastal Partnership (Ian Hay, Emily Hastings)

Aberdeenshire Council (Judith Cox)

We are very grateful to the editors of the first local atlas, Steve Buckland, Mike Bell and Nick Picozzi, together with Mark Tasker, for their help and for donating funds from that project.

Other help:
BTO (Su Gough, Kate Risely) for allowing us to use previous atlas distribution data and for provision of Breeding Bird Survey data.

Grampian Ringing Group

Intermap (Mark Stanley)

Macaulay (now James Hutton) Institute (Alessandro Gimona and Nick Littlewood) for providing LC2000 and other data.

NESBReC (Iain Lawrie, Glenn Roberts) for considerable help with the base map and for hosting the atlas dataset.

North-East Scotland Raptor Study Group

Ordnance Survey (Janet Keep)

Rare Breeding Birds Panel (Mark Holling) for providing information.

Scottish Ornithologists' Club (Ian Andrews, Wendy Hicks, David Jardine)

University of Aberdeen archive (Andrew Macgregor)

We thank the following for commenting on draft species accounts, atlas texts, providing information or helping in other ways: Andy Amphlett, Bruce Anderson, Ian Andrews, Martin Auld, David Bale, Stuart Benn, Amanda Biggins, Bill Bourne, Thomas Bregnballe, Simon Busuttil, Di Butcher, John Calladine, Paul Chapman, Jim Craib, Chloe Denerley, Roy Dennis, Nicola Dixon, Norman Elkins, Pete Ellis, David Elston, Brian Etheridge, Richard Evans, Tony Fox, Gillian Gilbert, Estelle Gill, Jon Hardey, Mark Holling, David Jardine, David Jenkins, Stewart Johnston, Alan Knox, Alan Leitch, Jenny Lennon, Jim Lennon, Jill Matthews, Hywel Maggs, Mick Marquiss, John Massie, Roddy Mavor, Clive McKay, Eric Meek, Jane Milloy, Fiona Milne, Carl Mitchell, Hannah Morton, Keith Morton, Robert Moss, Karen Mustin, David Norman, Mark O'Brien, Ian Patterson, Nicky Penford, Aevar Petersen, Allan Perkins, Nick Picozzi, Robert Rae, Stuart Rae, Shaila Rao, Graham Rebecca, Jim Reid, John Risby, Richard Schofield, Mike Smedley, Ron Summers, Gary Templeton, Innes Thacker, Peter Twist, Sarah Wanless, Adam Watson, Andy Webb, Alastair Young, Matthew Young.

The co-ordination of a project like this and the editing of a book involving so many contributors is very time-demanding! We are especially grateful to Nicky Penford and Adam Francis, to Jenny Cook and to Jackie, Eain and Emma Scott, for their tolerance over the last eight years!

Annex 2. *Atlas facts and figures, North-East Scotland and some comparisons*

Table 1. North-East Scotland Breeding Bird Atlas 2002–06
- Some summary statistics

- Land area: 8,686 km² (11% of Scotland's and 3.6% of UK's land areas)
- Number of tetrads covered: 2,340 (=116 whole or part 10-km squares)
- Number of records submitted: Total of all records 116,878; Non-duplicated records of maximum breeding status = 82,231
- 80,783 records deposited with NBN: 1,448 confidential records excluded from this and held by editors
- Number of observers participating: 348
- 33% of records collected by top 10 recorders; 47% by top 20
- Estimated 17,000 hours of observer effort: Average of 7.7 survey hours per tetrad (see Figure 1)

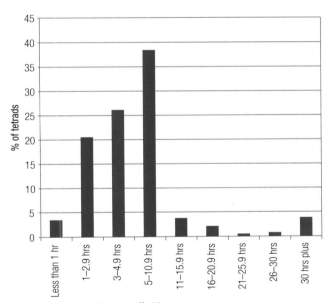

Figure 1. Frequency of survey effort hours.
Comparative figure for Hertfordshire (Smith *et al.* 1993); mean of 15.5 hours of survey effort per tetrad in 439 tetrads; over 7,600 hours of fieldwork effort in the atlas. These statistics are often not reported in published atlases.

Plate 1. Atlas covers - old and new.

Table 2. North-East Scotland Breeding Bird Atlas 2002–06 - breeding records statistics and comparison with some other atlases:

Area	Possible	Probable	Confirmed	Total records	Source
N-E Scotland 2002–06 (Max. status records)	22,738 (28%)	23,538 (29%)	32,319 (39%)	82,231	*n.b.* Plus 3,636 (4%) Observed (this atlas)
N-E Scotland 1981–84	20,887 (41%)	14,656 (29%)	15,448 (30%)	50,991	Buckland *et al.* 1990
S-e Scotland 1988–94	10,966 (15%)	24,599 35%)	29,149 (41%)	70,934	Murray *et al.* 1998 - data supplied by Ian Andrews: *n.b.* Plus 6,218 (9%) observed.
Berkshire 1987–89	4,926 (21%)	5,943 (26%)	12,120 (53%)	22,989	Standley *et al.* 1996
Cheshire & Wirral 2004–06	8,936 (26%)	7,045 (20%)	18,535 (54%)	34,516	Norman 2008

Table 3. Other comparative figures: Gibbons *et al.* (2007) presented a range of statistics for 411 bird atlases from 50 countries from 1951–2005. Comparison with our atlas (where relevant) shows:

Attribute	Average for atlases analysed and trend in attribute		North-East Scotland
Years of fieldwork	5.9	declining	5
Write up time (years)	3.7	declining	4.5
Area covered (km²)	7,317	declining	8,686
Years between repeats	16.7	increasing	21
No. of observers	404	declining	348
Observers/km²	0.08	increasing	0.04

Annex 3. *Further details of methods and coverage*

1. Examples of tetrad cards

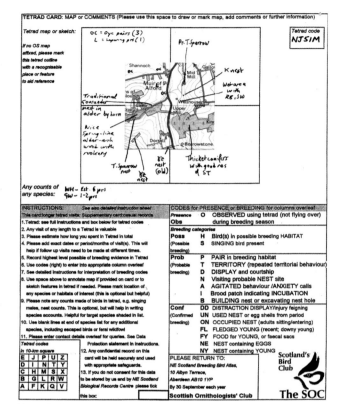

Figure 1. Main tetrad survey card (front).

Figure 2. Main tetrad survey card (reverse).

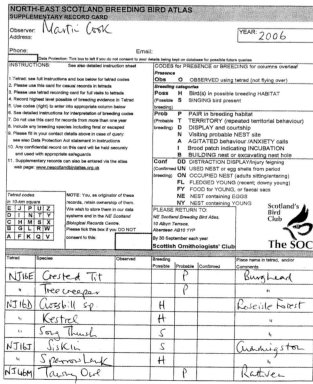

Figure 3. Supplementary record card.

2. Assessing the impacts of differing levels of observer effort between atlases

It is likely that differing levels of observer effort between atlases distorted the apparent changes in breeding distributions. This section sets out how we tried to take this factor into account.

A. Breeding distribution changes in Aberdeenshire and Aberdeen City between the two atlases 1981/84–2002/06

Effects of observer coverage levels

The problem of observer effort has been faced by several other 'repeat' UK bird atlases *e.g.* Bedfordshire - (Dazley & Trodd 1994); Hertfordshire (Smith *et al.* 1993) and in Ontario, Canada (Cadman *et al.* 2007; there, the observer survey hours in their second atlas were some 25% higher than in the first, but the method they developed for dealing with this does not translate to the differing recording units in our two atlases). Such variations in effort are potentially influential. As Smith *et al.* (1993) noted, "considerable care is needed when interpreting the changes in atlas distribution maps in relation to changes in bird populations. Each atlas record represents the presence of a species within a tetrad *and* the likelihood of it being recorded by an observer."

Are there indications, then, that levels of recording effort or effectiveness differed between our two atlases? Unfortunately, we have little direct evidence, as all possible measures of this are not very informative. Hours of survey effort were not recorded in 1981–84 and although they were (for most tetrads) during 2002–06 (see Chapter 1), comparison is clearly not possible. In any case, number of hours is only a crude method of measuring survey efficiency, as much depends on habitat and observer competence - and it is hard to take account of dedicated effort towards a particular species (for example, searching deliberately for Barn Owls but not necessarily all other species). In terms of the number of participating observers, there were 289 in 1981–84 and 258 for Aberdeenshire/Aberdeen City in 2002–06 (36 individuals took part in both!). But again, this is not very informative, as it depends on their level of partic-ipation; many of the 289 people in 1981–84 did not submit many breeding records, since this atlas was all year round (S. Buckland pers. comm.). The indication, then, is that despite more observers, there may have been less effort in the 1981–84 breeding seasons. Another variable that differed between the two atlases was the length of the survey period (the 1981–84 atlas covered four years; the 2002–06 atlas five years), and the recording units were very different (395 larger units in 1981–84 versus 1,772 component tetrads in the same recording area in 2002–06). These two factors may also affect any comparison.

Nevertheless, there was a general impression from the increases shown by most species that recording effort was greater in 2002–06, and supporting evidence for this comes from the total number of records gained for the same 395 recording units (when tetrad data were ascribed to a 1981–84 unit) in each atlas. The total number of records for all 154 species, adding all non-duplicated breeding code records for all units in the 1981–84 atlas, was 16,640, compared with 21,216 in 2002–06, a 27% increase. That is, if all the dots on the species comparison maps in Chapter 3 are counted, there were 27% more of them in the 2002–06 atlas.

We also used a method devised by the second Bedfordshire atlas (Dazley & Trodd 1994). We allotted values to breeding status in our 1981–84 atlas, so a possible breeding record in a unit was given a value of one, a probable breeding record two and a confirmed record three. These values were then summed. This was repeated for records for the same units derived from our 2002–06 atlas, and comparison made. In effect, this method measures recording intensity according to the effort needed to confirm breeding, rather than just to record presence. We looked at the 20 most widespread species, and also a random selection of ten scarcer species occurring in between ten and 50 old atlas recording units.

These 30 species together accounted for 41% of the old atlas unit records, and the summed values showed a 9% increase in 2002–06 compared with 1981–84. The increase was less for the 20 widespread species (only 4%) but very high for the ten scarce species (144% increase). Interestingly, two widespread waders in the 'top 20' (Lapwing and Curlew) actually *decreased* in summed breeding values, reinforcing the conclusion that they have declined in the area. This variation in increase in levels of breeding evidence implies that the widespread species were relatively well recorded and were harder to improve upon in terms of breeding status, but the less common birds showed bigger changes. It is commonly acknowledged that many of these more scarce species have truly become more widespread locally and that increases for some are unlikely to be solely or even mainly due to better recording. This method then suggests that increased effort was influential, but still cannot quantify its impact.

Allowing for the influence of an increased number of records

The issue of potentially more intensive recording was also faced by the 'Local Change' project of the Botanical Society of the British Isles (Braithwaite *et al.* 2006), where a large-scale, UK-wide repeat botanical survey experienced a similar large increase in number of records. They developed a complex method to correct for this, but we adopted a simpler alternative proposed by Presland (2006) for our atlas comparison. It calculates the proportion of the total number of records accounted for by each species in each survey, then examines how this changed. For this, we used 142 species of our original 154, excluding those with no unit occupancy data from 1981–84 (mostly rare breeding raptors) and those species which were absent in one of the two atlas periods (since a percentage calculation is involved).

Thus, we calculated, for each species in the 1981–84 atlas, the percentage of the total records it accounted for and did the same for each matching species in the 2002–06 atlas. For every species, this percentage in the second atlas was subtracted from the first, giving a 'relative species percentage change' value for each. If this was positive, then the species accounted for a greater proportion of the total records in the 2002–06 atlas than it did in 1981–84 - that is, a relative increase. If negative, the opposite was true - a relative decline. These proportions are not influenced by the total number of records. If the number of units occupied by a species had increased by around the same rate as the general increase in records, it would show a low value, and this would suggest that the apparent increase recorded in the raw data was only really what would have been expected given a higher overall number of records, and there may well have been little real change. Species with larger negative or positive figures are more likely to have experienced real declines or increases.

Summary of relative atlas distribution changes in species selected for analysis

Figures 4 and 5 show the comparative proportions of apparent increases and decreases based on the raw and then modified data. The very large proportion of species apparently showing an increase in occupied units (82%) reduces to nearer 54%, with around 46% of species actually experiencing a decline, as compared with the 18% in the original summary. This correction would be expected to show a roughly even split, but it also suggests that range increases were slightly more prevalent.

In summary, then, this relative change evidence suggests that recording effort was higher in 2002–06 and that this affected the apparent general increases shown in the raw data for many species. Proportionally, fewer species increased, but still there were indications of more species increasing than decreasing. Some of these increases will be real, but we cannot quantify this.

This analysis has considered only the degree to which *overall* changes may have been influenced by greater numbers of records. It is more difficult to find a meaningful measure that can be used for *individual* species, so in the species accounts in Chapter 3, the original raw figures have been retained. Nevertheless, in Chapter 5 we have compared the changes as measured by the two techniques and listed some species showing the greatest increases and decreases by both methods.

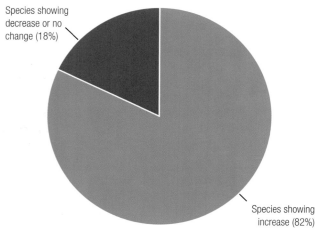

Figure 4. Change in distribution from raw data. Proportion of species showing increase or decrease of any magnitude between 1981–84 and 2002–06, based on the raw data - a simple count of the number of occupied units per species in each atlas. (*n.b.* - these two charts use slightly different categories to Figure 5.2 in Chapter 5, so the values are not identical).

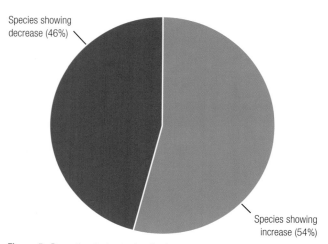

Figure 5. Proportional change in distribution. Species showing increase or decrease between the 1981–84 and 2002–06 atlases, expressed as the change in the proportion of total records that each species accounted for in each atlas.

B. Breeding distribution changes over the whole of North-East Scotland using atlas sources from 1968–72 to 2002–06

Effects of observer coverage levels

We suggested above that there was probably an increased level of observer effort in *local* atlas work in 2002–06 compared with 1981–84. There also appear to have been variations in effort and recording levels between the first two *national* atlases, when viewed together with our 2002–06 results. There is no definitive way of comparing observer coverage between the three atlases (see above for discussion of the issue locally), but anecdotal information was gained from discussions with local observers involved in both earlier national atlases and with others (*e.g.* J. Reid, pers. comm.). This suggests that the 1968–72 atlas experienced good levels of recording effort in our area, with enthusiasm high for the first ever national breeding bird atlas. Coverage was thorough, including of rarer species. The 1988–91 atlas, however, suffered from much poorer coverage levels. Changes in methods and the introduction of bird counting deterred many observers in North-East Scotland. This led to reduced coverage and many gaps. The 2002–06 atlas once again appeared to attract much support, and coverage was evidently much better.

This anecdotal picture is supported by an analysis of changes in the number of occupied 10-km squares over time. For each of 157 species that were present in 1968–72, the figure for 1968–72 was taken as 100, then the numbers in 1988–91 and 2002–06 were converted to percentages of this. All species were then sorted by shared patterns (simply grouped by differing trends in numerical change from the 100 start point) and these are shown in Figure 6.

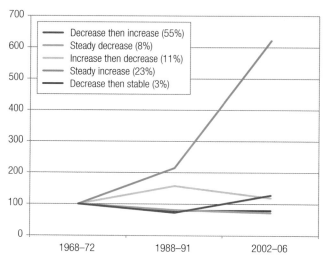

Figure 6. Index of % change in numbers of occupied 10-km squares between atlas periods for 157 species, taking 1968–72 as 100. The species are grouped according to five different patterns of change.

Over half of species showed a drop in 10-km square occupancy between the 1968–72 and 1988–91 atlases, followed by a rise to a level in 2002–06 higher than in 1988–91 (see Table 5.10 in Chapter 5 for some examples). Some of the species showing this 'trough' are common, widespread species that would not be expected to have experienced reduced populations sufficient to lead to absence in many 10-km squares in 1988–91. The degree of reduction is greater in more elusive and nocturnal species. Although 17 species (11%) showed an increase in occupancy in the 1988–91 atlas compared with the other two, these are mostly easily recorded coastal or farmland species. The 36 species (23%) that showed an increase over the whole period also showed an apparent slowing of the increase during 1988–91. This evidence suggests that there was a substantial reduction in recorder effort during the second national atlas in North-East Scotland. One consequence of this is that the contribution of 10-km squares in our area to national occupancy figures for declining species, calculated following the second UK atlas, must be regarded in many cases as spurious.

Annex 4. *Population estimates and status information*

Introduction

Table A summarises a wide range of status, population and trend information for each of the 190 species that at least possibly bred during 2002–06. **Table B**, following this, shows the importance of local breeding populations in a wider context. This is self-explanatory (see also the introduction to Chapter 3). Columns in the **Table A** are as follows:

Species

For each species, the 'Birds of Conservation Concern' status is shown in colour (see also Chapters 3 and 4)

Breeding status

This is a brief summary and matches that in the species accounts. The one Scottish endemic species and the three endemic subspecies that are found in our area are indicated. The breeding status is summarised first, followed by a summary of status at other times of year. We used standard categories to describe estimated breeding numbers (but not status at other times of year). These are:

Occasional: very rare birds that breed less than annually
Very rare: Usually 1–9 breeding pairs in the area
Rare: 10–99 breeding pairs
Scarce: 100–999 breeding pairs
Common: 1,000–9,999 breeding pairs
Very common: 10,000 breeding pairs or more

Breeding population estimates

Chapters 1 and 3 set out how we have produced estimates of the local breeding population for every species. Population figures in **bold** in the table are based on what we consider to be good information; these estimates are thought to be quite accurate. Other population estimates are calculated or derived from more indirect sources and are thought to be less accurate, but are still the best available for the area. These are given in *italics*.

The Cheshire & Wirral atlas (S.E. Newson in Norman 2008) used densities calculated within BBS squares to estimate county populations. This allowed population figures to be produced for *c.* 85 species. This would be useful for North-East Scotland, but BBS coverage in our area is not sufficient; contrast our 40 BBS squares usually covered per year with the 69 covered annually in around one quarter of the land area in Cheshire and Wirral. We used BBS data purely to provide some supporting information about trends in abundance, rather than absolute populations. Sara (2008) showed that within limits it is possible to estimate regional populations for some species (particularly rarer ones) using models based on atlas distribution data, exploiting the relationship between spatial occurrence and abundance. Such a modelling exercise was not undertaken in this project, but could also be a useful technique to be employed in future atlas surveys. Gibbons *et al.* (2007) showed that an increasing number of atlases are attempting to estimate populations by adopting appropriate methods. We recommend in Chapter 1 that this is worthwhile, despite initial doubts in our project leading to us not attempting this.

Atlas statistics (2002–06) for each species

These five columns present the figures for the numbers of Observed, Possible, Probable, Confirmed breeding tetrads and the total of occupied tetrads, for each species.

Distribution and population trend evidence

This summarises very briefly our assessment of evidence from all sources, and states our confidence in the reported trend (based on subjective evaluation). These are colour coded to clarify the trends; the colour codes are shown at the end of the table.

Atlas distribution change figures

For relevant species, this presents the local changes in occupied recording units between 1981–84 and 2002–06, again colour-coded for clarity. It also highlights where we consider there is most likely to be a strong influence of observer effort on this. The next column shows similar information for 10-km square changes from 1968–72 to 2002–06.

Breeding Bird Survey trends

Local and Scottish BBS trends are shown here (see Chapter 5), together, where relevant, with some other information such as changes in seabird counts. Trends are colour-coded for clarity.

Groups used for analysis

This indicates the species groups used for analysis in Chapter 5 (Section 6).

Plate 1. Chaffinch, Sutherland, May 2008. © *Ed Duthie* The Chaffinch is the most widespread breeding bird in North-East Scotland.

Table A. Summary of status, estimated breeding populations and trends in North-East Scotland. See key below for colour codes.

Species (Red, Amber, Green listing see Chapters 3 & 4). Black = not listed as above	Status in North-East Scotland	Breeding population estimate. See Key below.	Observed: No. of tetrads	Possible breeding: No. of tetrads	Probable breeding: No. of tetrads	Confirmed breeding 2002-06: No. of tetrads	Total no. occupied tetrads 02-06 (out of 2340)
Mute Swan	Scarce resident.	100	12	38	24	101	175
Whooper Swan	Occasional probable breeder. Winter visitor & passage migrant.	0	4	14	1		19
Greylag Goose	Rare resident feral breeder. Winter visitor & passage migrant.	75	24	23	10	16	73
Canada Goose	Very rare feral breeder. Passage migrant.	3	2	11	2	5	20
Barnacle Goose	Very rare feral breeder. Passage migrant & winter visitor.	1	5		1	1	7
Shelduck	Scarce resident & migrant breeder.	125	13	19	25	25	82
Mandarin	Very rare feral resident.	5	3	6		3	12
Wigeon	Rare breeder. Winter visitor & passage migrant.	38	15	24	13	12	64
Gadwall	Very rare breeder. Visitor at all seasons.	3		7	5	1	13
Teal	Scarce breeder. Winter visitor & passage migrant.	175	12	59	84	39	194
Green-winged Teal	Occasional in breeding habitat. Rare visitor, mostly in winter.	0	4	1			5
Mallard	Common resident. Winter visitor.	2600	14	268	334	425	1041
Pintail	Occasional breeder. Winter visitor & passage migrant.	0	1	3	3		7
Garganey	Occasional summer migrant breeder. Passage migrant.	1	2	8	5		15
Shoveler	Very rare breeder. Winter visitor & passage migrant.	3	4	6	4	5	19
Pochard	Very rare breeder. Winter visitor & passage migrant.	2	3	10	3	1	17
Tufted Duck	Scarce resident. Winter visitor & passage migrant.	175	6	30	63	50	149
Scaup	Occasional in breeding habitat. Winter visitor & passage migrant.	0	3	4	2		9
Eider	Common resident & migrant.	1750	9	43	28	28	108
Goldeneye	Rare breeder. Winter visitor & passage migrant.	30		31	8	12	51
Red-breasted Merganser	Rare breeder. Present on the coast all year.	35	14	20	6	5	45
Goosander	Scarce resident & migrant breeder.	100	15	80	50	46	191
Ruddy Duck	Occasional feral breeder. Summer visitor.	0	1	6	4		11
Red Grouse	Very common resident.	40000 i	1	137	209	385	732
Ptarmigan	Common resident. [Scottish Endemic ssp]	10000 i		14	19	78	111
Black Grouse	Scarce resident.	700 m		72	103	37	212
Capercaillie	Rare resident.	220 i		44	34	10	88
Red-legged Partridge	Rare resident breeder. Commonly released on shooting estates.	69		124	166	37	327
Grey Partridge	Common resident. Released on some shooting estates.	3525		120	264	160	544
Quail	Rare summer visitor & breeder. Passage migrant.	25		79	26	5	110
Pheasant	Very common resident. Commonly released on shooting estates.	40000	6	433	738	389	1566
Red-throated Diver	Very rare breeder. Present on the coast all year.	4	3	3	4	3	13
Black-throated Diver	Occasional breeder. Winter visitor & passage migrant.	1		3	2		5
Fulmar	Very common resident & migrant breeder. Passage migrant.	10000	13	11	3	64	91
Gannet	Common breeder, in one colony. Present offshore all year.	1800	27	3		1	31
Cormorant	Scarce resident & migrant breeder.	300	58	18	4	13	93
Shag	Scarce resident. Winter visitor.	849	15	19	7	21	62
Bittern	Occasional visitor in summer, more records in winter.	0		1			1
Little Egret	Occasional visitor, mostly in spring & summer.	0	2	1			3
Grey Heron	Scarce resident. Winter visitor.	420	152	393	22	48	615
Spoonbill	Occasional visitor in spring & summer.	0	3	3			6
Little Grebe	Scarce resident.	150	4	32	17	43	96
Great Crested Grebe	Very rare summer visitor & breeder. Few in winter.	4	1	4	1	3	9
Slavonian Grebe	Very rare breeder. Winter visitor.	1		2	3		5
Black-necked Grebe	Occasional probable breeder. Passage migrant.	0			2		2
Honey-buzzard	Very rare summer migrant breeder. Passage migrant.	1		6	1		7
Red Kite	Very rare re-introduced resident.	5	4	9			13
Marsh Harrier	Very rare migrant breeder. Passage migrant.	1	9	10	3	4	26
Hen Harrier	Rare breeder. Few in winter.	20	18	71	20	37	146
Goshawk	Rare resident.	55	5	52	12	12	81
Sparrowhawk	Scarce resident. Passage migrant.	750	28	452	107	143	730
Buzzard	Common resident.	2300	48	434	513	743	1738
Golden Eagle	Rare resident.	19	27	38	14	13	92
Osprey	Rare summer migrant breeder. Passage migrant.	30	59	73	13	36	181
Kestrel	Scarce resident. Passage migrant.	850	16	631	227	257	1131
Merlin	Rare resident. Passage migrant.	80	13	46	23	120	202
Hobby	Occasional probable breeder. Summer visitor & passage migrant.	0	4	7	2		13
Peregrine	Rare resident.	50	86	44	18	42	190
Water Rail	Scarce resident. Winter visitor & passage migrant.	150		18	19	5	42
Spotted Crake	Occasional probable summer migrant breeder. Passage migrant.	1		1	1		2
Corncrake	Occasional summer migrant breeder. Passage migrant.	0		3	3		6
Moorhen	Scarce resident. Winter visitor.	625	1	88	49	151	289
Coot	Scarce resident. Winter visitor & passage migrant.	150		33	11	53	97
Crane	Occasionally present in summer. Passage migrant.	0	2	3			5
Oystercatcher	Common resident & migrant breeder. Winter visitor.	7500	4	203	518	809	1534
Avocet	Occasional visitor, mostly in spring.	0	3	4	1		8

Best assessment of distribution /population trend late 1960s to now and confidence in trend: (H = High, M = Medium, L = Low or uncertain)	% change between local atlases 81-84 to 02–06 (where relevant) */** = Observer effort probably influential/very influential on this	10-km square occupancy 02-06 as % of 68-72	Local BBS trend 94-06 where information available	Scottish BBS trend 94-07, or other evidence e.g. seabird data, where available	Habitat group and African Migrant or non-AM (or Not Used) (Chpt 5) See key below
Slight to moderate increase (H)	38	119			WE
New probable breeder	1300	New			N
Big increase (H)	1033	725			WE
Big increase (H)	1300	1200			WE
New confirmed breeder		New			N
Slight to moderate increase (M)	40	110			WE
New confirmed breeder	500	New			N
Slight to moderate increase (M)	53	110			N
Big increase (H)		1000			N
No clear trend	10	94			WE
Trivial occurrence		New			N
Slight to moderate increase (L)	19	99	No tr/vari	7	WE
Trivial occurrence		100			N
New confirmed breeder		New			N
No clear trend	67	69			WE
No clear trend	400	57			WE
Slight to moderate increase (M)	94 *	126			WE
No clear trend		700			N
No clear trend	16	100			WE
Big increase (H)	625	3200			WE
Slight to moderate decrease (H)	-30	67			WE
Slight to moderate increase (M)	31	139			WE
Increase then decrease (H)	350	New			WE
Slight to moderate decrease (H)	4	84	Clear decr	6	UP
No clear trend	16	100			UP
No clear trend	21 *	100			UP
Big decrease (H)	-47	46			WO
Big increase (H)	555	1560	Clear incr		N
Slight to moderate decrease (H)	-9	84	Slight/poss		FM
Big increase (M)	2000 *	960			FM, Afri
No clear trend	7	100	No tr/vari	-6	GE
New confirmed breeder		New			WE
New confirmed breeder		New			N
No clear trend	-3	105		NCT	SB
Big increase (H)		New		Clear incr	N
Big increase (H)	300	243		Incr	SB
Increase then decrease (H)	35	107		Decrease	SB
Trivial occurrence		New			N
Trivial occurrence		New			N
Big increase (H)	55	109	No tr/vari	74	WE
Trivial occurrence		New			N
Big increase (M)	262	179			WE
No clear trend	40	86			WE
Increase then decrease (H)		250			N
Trivial occurrence		New			N
No clear trend		New			N
New confirmed breeder		New			N
Increase then decrease (H)		1100			N
Big decrease (H)	50	164			RA
Big increase (H)		4900			N
Slight to moderate increase (M)	92 *	116	Slight/poss		RA
Big increase (H)	254	172	Clear incr	36	RA
No clear trend		120			N
Big increase (H)		850			N
Slight to moderate decrease (M)	33	97	Slight/poss	-56	RA
Slight to moderate increase (H)	165	138			RA
Trivial occurrence		500			N
Increase then decrease (H)		252			N
Slight to moderate decrease (L)	229 **	208			WE
Increase then decrease (H)		200			N
Big decrease (H)		38			N
No clear trend	12	87	Clear incr		WE
No clear trend	18	94			WE
Trivial occurrence		New			N
Slight to moderate decrease (M)	-1	98	Clear decr	-27	WE
Trivial occurrence		New			N

Table A. Continued.

Species (Red, Amber, Green listing see Chapters 3 & 4). Black = not listed as above	Status in North-East Scotland	Breeding population estimate. See Key below.	Observed: No. of tetrads	Possible breeding: No. of tetrads	Probable breeding: No. of tetrads	Confirmed breeding 2002-06: No. of tetrads	Total no. occupied tetrads 02-06 (out of 2340)
Little Ringed Plover	Very rare summer migrant breeder.	6		4	1	5	10
Ringed Plover	Scarce resident & migrant breeder. Passage migrant.	140	4	31	25	54	114
Dotterel	Scarce summer migrant breeder. Passage migrant.	200	3	3	3	34	43
Golden Plover	Common resident & summer migrant breeder. Passage & winter visitor.	1600	20	67	143	120	350
Lapwing	Common resident & summer migrant breeder. Passage migrant.	3400	3	179	388	575	1145
Temminck's Stint	Occasional probable breeder. Passage migrant.	0	1				1
Pectoral Sandpiper	Passage migrant, may have bred.	0			1		1
Purple Sandpiper	Very rare breeder. Winter visitor & passage migrant.	1(2)			1		1
Dunlin	Scarce summer migrant breeder. Winter visitor & passage migrant.	425	32	14	13	18	77
Ruff	Occasional in breeding habitat. Passage migrant.	0	3	3	1		7
Snipe	Common resident & migrant breeder. Winter visitor & passage migrant.	2250	7	185	291	53	536
Woodcock	Common resident & migrant breeder. Winter visitor & passage migrant.	3000	6	126	237	28	397
Black-tailed Godwit	Occasional in breeding habitat. Passage migrant.	0	3	6			9
Whimbrel	Occasional in breeding habitat. Passage migrant.	0	3	2			5
Curlew	Common migrant breeder. Winter visitor & passage migrant.	4000	28	326	522	279	1155
Common Sandpiper	Common summer migrant breeder. Summer visitor & Passage migrant.	1150	13	95	185	109	402
Greenshank	Occasional in breeding habitat, former breeder. Passage migrant.	0	5	2			7
Redshank	Scarce resident & migrant breeder. Winter visitor & passage migrant.	150	27	66	59	38	190
Kittiwake	Very common resident & migrant breeder. Passage migrant.	70000	18	5		39	62
Black-headed Gull	Common resident & migrant breeder. Winter visitor, passage migrant.	1750	419	130	33	64	646
Mediterranean Gull	Occasional possible breeder. Visitor in other seasons.	0		1			1
Common Gull	Common resident. Winter visitor & passage migrant.	8000	528	209	100	179	1016
Lesser Black-backed Gull	Scarce summer migrant breeder. Passage migrant.	250	182	40	21	27	270
Herring Gull	Very common resident. Winter visitor & passage migrant.	16000	394	71	24	99	588
Great Black-backed Gull	Rare resident breeder. Winter visitor.	85	124	37	8	29	198
Little Tern	Rare summer migrant breeder.	28	4	2		5	11
Sandwich Tern	Scarce summer migrant breeder. Passage migrant.	810	42	11		2	55
Common Tern	Scarce summer migrant breeder. Passage migrant.	300	35	39	20	15	109
Roseate Tern	Occasional probable, & former, breeder. Summer visitor.	0		1	1		2
Arctic Tern	Scarce summer migrant breeder. Passage migrant.	525	15	6	1	7	29
Guillemot	Very common resident & migrant breeder.	100425	18	5		23	46
Razorbill	Very common resident & migrant breeder.	12100	13	7	2	28	50
Black Guillemot	Rare resident.	90	1	8	2	7	18
Puffin	Common summer migrant breeder.	2,500	5	9	7	16	37
Feral Pigeon	Common resident.	9750	3	251	294	424	972
Stock Dove	Locally common resident.	3000	3	188	221	87	499
Woodpigeon	Very common resident & migrant.	100000	18	299	578	936	1831
Collared Dove	Common resident.	2750	3	178	332	163	676
Cuckoo	Scarce summer migrant breeder.	375	1	458	112	22	593
Barn Owl	Scarce resident.	200		152	41	110	303
Tawny Owl	Common resident.	1750	1	337	310	264	912
Long-eared Owl	Scarce resident. Passage migrant.	225	1	66	25	90	182
Short-eared Owl	Rare resident & migrant breeder. Passage migrant & winter visitor.	45	7	79	33	57	176
Nightjar	Occasional summer visitor. Former breeder.	0		2			2
Swift	Common summer migrant breeder.	1000	207	257	91	108	663
Kingfisher	Rare resident.	50	1	36	6	8	51
Wryneck	Occasional in summer, has bred. Passage migrant.	0		5			5
Green Woodpecker	Rare resident.	95		73	15	15	103
Great Spotted Woodpecker	Common resident.	1125	1	292	207	259	759
Red-backed Shrike	Occasional possible, & former, summer migrant, breeder. Passage migrant.	0		4			4
Magpie	Common resident.	2625	7	315	312	249	883
Jay	Scarce resident.	830	1	221	132	61	415
Jackdaw	Very common resident.	20000	16	289	340	786	1431
Rook	Very common resident.	86000	153	395	95	628	1271
Carrion Crow	Very common resident.	18000	26	326	339	1036	1727
Hooded Crow/hybrid	Rare resident. Carrion x Hooded hybrids are scarce residents.	38	9	262	93	146	510
Raven	Rare resident.	15	59	72	30	7	168
Goldcrest	Very common resident. Passage migrant & winter visitor.	65000	2	396	487	299	1184
Blue Tit	Very common resident.	80000	1	280	302	898	1481
Great Tit	Very common resident.	40000	2	295	312	751	1360
Crested Tit	Scarce resident. [Scottish Endemic ssp]	575		21	12	30	63
Coal Tit	Very common resident.	60000		307	371	674	1352
Bearded Tit	Very rare resident.	3		2		1	3
Skylark	Very common resident & migrant breeder. Passage migrant.	50000		354	795	502	1651
Shore Lark	Occasional in breeding habitat. Passage migrant & winter visitor.	0		1			1
Sand Martin	Common summer migrant breeder. Passage migrant.	7000	102	203	46	186	537

Best assessment of distribution /population trend late 1960s to now and confidence in trend: (H = High, M = Medium, L = Low or uncertain)	% change between local atlases 81-84 to 02–06 (where relevant) */** = Observer effort probably influential/very influential on this	10-km square occupancy 02-06 as % of 68-72	Local BBS trend 94-06 where information available	Scottish BBS trend 94-07, or other evidence e.g. seabird data, where available	Habitat group and African Migrant or non-AM (or Not Used) (Chpt 5) See key below
New confirmed breeder		New			N
Slight to moderate increase (M)	122	133			WE
No clear trend	29	100			WE, Afri
Slight to moderate decrease (L)	-12	82		-5	WE
Slight to moderate decrease (H)	-8	94	Clear decr	-38	WE
Trivial occurrence	n/a	n/a			N
New probable breeder		New			N
New confirmed breeder		New			WE
No clear trend (L)	20 **	65			WE
Trivial occurrence		New			N
Slight to moderate increase (M)	41 *	100	No tr/vari	58	WE
No clear trend (L)	33 *	94			WE
Trivial occurrence		New			N
Trivial occurrence		200			N
Slight to moderate decrease (M)	-3	98	Clear decr	-48	WE
No clear trend	30	99		-14	WE
Big decrease (H)	-60	22			WE
Slight to moderate decrease (H)	-36	58			WE
Increase then decrease (H)	22	107			SB
No clear trend	15	95	Slight/poss	NCT	SB
Trivial occurrence		New			N
Big decrease (H)	65	98	Slight/poss	?	SB
No clear trend	69	112	Slight/poss	NCT	SB
Slight to moderate decrease (H)	96	127	No tr/vari		SB
Slight to moderate increase (L)	61	129			SB
Big decrease (H)	-75	57		NCT	SB, Afri
No clear trend	75	91		NCT	SB, Afri
Slight to moderate decrease (H)	14	66		NCT	SB, Afri
Trivial occurrence		50			N
Slight to moderate decrease (L)	-14	53		NCT	SB, Afri
Slight to moderate increase (H)	27	100			SB
Slight to moderate increase (H)	75	144			SB
Slight to moderate increase (M)	71	300			SB
Slight to moderate increase (M)	46	133			SB
No clear trend	26 *	136	No tr/vari	-31	GE
Slight to moderate increase (M)	180 *	139	Slight/poss		WO
No clear trend	4	97	Slight/poss	-11	WO
No clear trend	30	132	No tr/vari	-25	GE
No clear trend	16	85	Clear decr	39	GE, Afri
Big increase (M)	1488 **	269			GE
No clear trend	122 *	97			WO
Slight to moderate increase (L)	214 **	127			WO
No clear trend	47	79			UP
Trivial occurrence		100			N
Slight to moderate decrease (L)	21	107	Slight/poss	-53	N, Afri
Big increase (H)	3400	967			WE
Trivial occurrence		200			N
Slight to moderate increase (M)	22	543			WO
Big increase (H)	210	125	Clear incr	254	WO
Trivial occurrence		New		N	
Slight to moderate increase (H)	20	126	No tr/vari	14	GE
Big increase (H)	202	710	No tr/vari		WO
Slight to moderate increase (M)	0	95	Slight/poss	23	GE
Slight to moderate decrease (M)	-5	99	Clear decr	-12	GE
No clear trend	-2	100	No tr/vari	6	GE
Slight to moderate decrease (H)	-74	65	No tr/vari	-42	GE
Big increase (H)	367	111		155	UP
Slight to moderate increase (H)	42	107	No tr/vari	86	WO
Slight to moderate increase (M)	10	99	Slight/poss	16	GE
Slight to moderate increase (H)	21	106	Clear incr	87	GE
No clear trend	n/a	150			N
Slight to moderate increase (M)	9	104	Clear incr	14	WO
New confirmed breeder		New			N
No clear trend	1	96	Clear decr	2	FM
Trivial occurrence		New			N
No clear trend	107	102	No tr/vari		WE, Afri

Species (Red, Amber, Green listing see Chapters 3 & 4). Black = not listed as above	Status in North-East Scotland	Breeding population estimate. See Key below.	Observed: No. of tetrads	Possible breeding: No. of tetrads	Probable breeding: No. of tetrads	Confirmed breeding 2002-06: No. of tetrads	Total no. occupied tetrads 02-06 (out of 2340)
Swallow	Common summer migrant breeder. Passage migrant.	8250	62	171	288	1207	1728
House Martin	Common summer migrant breeder. Passage migrant.	5000	25	212	99	529	865
Long-tailed Tit	Common resident.	5500		165	138	199	502
Wood Warbler	Rare summer migrant breeder. Passage migrant.	30	1	27	9	4	41
Chiffchaff	Common summer migrant breeder. Passage migrant, few in winter.	1025	1	210	100	22	333
Willow Warbler	Very common summer migrant breeder. Passage migrant.	85000	3	437	639	664	1743
Blackcap	Common summer migrant breeder. Passage migrant & winter visitor.	3200		237	160	33	430
Garden Warbler	Scarce summer migrant breeder. Passage migrant.	250		82	43	10	135
Lesser Whitethroat	Occasional summer migrant breeder. Passage migrant.	3	1	4	1	1	7
Whitethroat	Common summer migrant breeder. Passage migrant.	7500		352	360	234	946
Grasshopper Warbler	Scarce summer migrant breeder. Passage migrant.	250		106	39	4	149
Sedge Warbler	Common summer migrant breeder. Passage migrant.	5025		301	307	227	835
Treecreeper	Common resident.	8500	1	338	166	204	709
Wren	Very common resident.	250000		425	634	824	1883
Starling	Very common resident. Winter visitor & passage migrant.	45000	9	166	144	1136	1455
Dipper	Scarce resident.	600	1	186	114	237	538
Ring Ouzel	Scarce summer migrant breeder. Passage migrant.	350	5	37	46	65	153
Blackbird	Very common resident. Winter visitor & passage migrant.	105000		275	354	1093	1722
Fieldfare	Occasional breeder. Winter visitor & passage migrant.	1	9	5		1	15
Song Thrush	Very common summer migrant breeder. Passage migrant, few in winter.	17500	1	432	401	695	1529
Redwing	Occasional breeder. Winter visitor & passage migrant.	1	4	4		1	9
Mistle Thrush	Common resident & migrant breeder.	7500	7	304	308	469	1088
Spotted Flycatcher	Common summer migrant breeder. Passage migrant.	2250		219	162	153	534
Robin	Very common resident & migrant breeder. Passage migrant.	115000		343	405	919	1667
Bluethroat	Probable breeder on one occasion. Passage migrant.	0			1		1
Redstart	Scarce summer migrant breeder. Passage migrant.	650	3	70	42	41	156
Whinchat	Scarce summer migrant breeder. Passage migrant.	165	4	64	21	52	141
Stonechat	Scarce resident & migrant breeder.	725	2	69	103	272	446
Wheatear	Common summer migrant breeder. Passage migrant.	2500	62	180	157	266	665
Pied Flycatcher	Very rare summer migrant breeder. Passage migrant.	2		5	1		6
Dunnock	Very common resident.	65000		411	501	480	1392
House Sparrow	Very common resident.	60000	4	129	217	885	1235
Tree Sparrow	Common resident.	3000		120	128	273	521
Yellow Wagtail	Occasional summer migrant breeder. Passage migrant.	1	1	3		2	6
Grey Wagtail	Common summer migrant breeder. Few in winter.	1350	1	241	235	370	847
Pied Wagtail	Common summer migrant breeder & resident.	17000	1	280	313	1111	1705
Tree Pipit	Common summer migrant breeder. Passage migrant.	1750	2	154	140	60	356
Meadow Pipit	Very common summer migrant breeder & resident. Passage migrant.	130000	2	290	520	1059	1871
Rock Pipit	Scarce resident.	525	2	19	20	49	90
Chaffinch	Very common resident. Winter visitor & passage migrant.	145000		269	698	937	1904
Brambling	Occasional possible, & former, breeder. Winter visitor, passage migrant.	0	6	2			8
Greenfinch	Very common resident. Winter visitor.	27500		377	506	444	1327
Goldfinch	Common resident & migrant breeder.	7500	4	324	534	307	1169
Siskin	Very common resident & migrant breeder. Winter visitor.	230000	4	375	358	172	909
Linnet	Very common resident. [Scottish Endemic ssp]	20000	5	290	606	365	1266
Twite	Scarce resident & migrant breeder. Winter visitor.	220	5	24	21	11	61
Lesser Redpoll	Common resident & migrant breeder.	1500	2	220	133	30	385
Common Crossbill	Common resident & irruptive migrant breeder.	2750	4	248	165	87	504
Scottish Crossbill	Common resident. [SCOTTISH ENDEMIC SP]	2000		14	11	11	36
Parrot Crossbill	Rare resident.	50			5	3	8
Common Rosefinch	Occasionally present in summer. Passage migrant.	0		1			1
Bullfinch	Common resident.	4000		223	287	106	616
Hawfinch	Very rare resident. Passage migrant.	3		5	1		6
Snow Bunting	Rare resident. Winter visitor & passage migrant.	18	1	9	5	12	27
Yellowhammer	Very common resident.	42500		399	642	536	1577
Reed Bunting	Common resident. Passage migrant.	3500		211	285	216	712
Corn Bunting	Scarce resident.	575		107	94	79	280
TOTAL			**3636**	**22738**	**23538**	**32319**	**82231**
%			**4.4**	**27.7**	**28.6**	**39.3**	

KEY to breeding population column
Bold figures = good estimate (see Chapter 3)
Italicised figures = less accurate estimate
All figures = estimated breeding pairs except:
i = individual birds; m = males

Best assessment of distribution /population trend late 1960s to now and confidence in trend: (H = High, M = Medium, L = Low or uncertain)	% change between local atlases 81-84 to 02–06 (where relevant) */** = Observer effort probably influential/very influential on this	10-km square occupancy 02-06 as % of 68-72	Local BBS trend 94-06 where information available	Scottish BBS trend 94-07, or other evidence e.g. seabird data, where available	Habitat group and African Migrant or non-AM (or Not Used) (Chpt 5) See key below
Slight to moderate increase (L)	3	104	Slight/poss	5	GE, Afri
Slight to moderate increase (M)	36	100	No tr/vari	152	GE, Afri
Slight to moderate increase (M)	90 *	114	No tr/vari		GE
Slight to moderate increase (M)	40	171			WO, Afri
Big increase (H)	189	411	No tr/vari	217	WO, Afri
Slight to moderate increase (M)	4	100	Clear incr	31	WO, Afri
Big increase (H)	281	405	No tr/vari	146	WO, Afri
Big increase (H)	109	225	No tr/vari		WO, Afri
Trivial occurrence	-20	250			N, Afri
Big increase (M)	30	105	Clear incr	85	GE, Afri
Slight to moderate increase (L)	200 **	180			N, Afri
Slight to moderate increase (M)	22	107	No tr/vari	28	N, Afri
Slight to moderate increase (H)	23	101	Clear incr	60	WO
Slight to moderate increase (M)	18	98	Clear incr	88	GE
Slight to moderate decrease (L)	1	92	Slight/poss	1	GE
Slight to moderate increase (L)	12	103		NCT	WE
Slight to moderate decrease (H)	-14	81			UP, Afri
No clear trend	-1	98	No tr/vari	25	GE
Trivial occurrence		100			N
Slight to moderate increase (M)	4	100	Clear incr	12	GE
Trivial occurrence	33	57			WO
Slight to moderate increase (M)	26	104	Clear incr	39	GE
No clear trend	-6	98	Clear incr		WO, Afri
Slight to moderate increase (L)	5	99	Clear incr	7	GE
Trivial occurrence		New			N
No clear trend	77 *	90			WO, Afri
Slight to moderate decrease (M)	0	102	Clear decr		N, Afri
Big increase (H)	695	254	No tr/vari	254	N
No clear trend	51 *	95	Slight/poss	24	UP, Afri
Slight to moderate decrease (L)		67			WO, Afri
Slight to moderate increase (M)	7	97	Clear incr	40	GE
Slight to moderate decrease (L)	-4	89	No tr/vari	30	GE
Slight to moderate increase (H)	174	149	Slight/poss		FM
Trivial occurrence	300	New			N, Afri
Slight to moderate increase (M)	52 *	104	No tr/vari	58	GE
No clear trend	3	99	No tr/vari	16	GE
Slight to moderate increase (L)	103 *	161	Slight/poss		WO, Afri
No clear trend	5	102	No tr/vari	-23	GE
Slight to moderate increase (L)	44	109			N
No clear trend	3	101	No tr/vari	10	GE
Trivial occurrence	-50	New			N
Slight to moderate increase (L)	7	100	No tr/vari	10	GE
Big increase (H)	193	231	Slight/poss	91	GE
Slight to moderate increase (H)	81	134	Slight/poss	0	WO
Slight to moderate increase (L)	40 *	99	No tr/vari	26	FM
No clear trend	30	66			UP
No clear trend	14	89	No tr/vari	3	WO
Big increase (H)	170	232	No tr/vari		WO
No clear trend	-13	n/a			WO
Big increase (H)		New			N
Trivial occurrence		New			N
Slight to moderate increase (L)	50 *	99	No tr/vari	46	WO
No clear trend		600			N
No clear trend		140			N
Slight to moderate decrease (M)	-8	89	Clear decr	15	FM
No clear trend	63 *	90	Slight/poss	56	FM
Big decrease (H)	-26	66	Clear decr		FM

FOR LOCAL ATLAS RANGE CHANGES:

Not present in earlier atlas, present 02–06

Big increase (range doubled or more)
Increase > 5%, but less than doubled
No change or less than 5% change
Decrease > 5%, but not halved
Big decrease (range halved or more)

Present in earlier atlas but not mapped

FOR BBS CHANGES:

ScotBBS >100%; local BBS clear increase
ScotBBS incr but <100%; local BBS slight increase
ScotBBS within 5% change; local BBS no clear trend
ScotBBS decr but not halved; local BBS slight decrease
ScotBBS more than halved; local BBS clear decrease

Key to Habitat Groups in Chapter 5:
African migrant - Afr
Farmland group - FM
General group - GE
Not used in analysis - N
Bird of Prey/Raptor - RA
Seabird - SB
Wetland group - WE
Woodland group - WO
Upland group - UP

Table B. Species whose estimated population in North-East Scotland is of importance at a wider geographic scale.

These percentages are approximate and should be seen only as a guide. In some cases they are based on differing information sources - see Table 6.1.

North-East Scotland's estimated breeding population accounts for approximately:

20% or more of the Scottish Population (31 species)	%	10% or more of the UK Population (22 species)	%	1% or more of the European Population (14 species)	%
Sandwich Tern	74	Purple Sandpiper	50	Scottish Crossbill	30
Corn Bunting	64	Parrot Crossbill	50	Siskin	8
Purple Sandpiper	50	Dotterel	35	Guillemot	5
Parrot Crossbill	50	Fieldfare	33	Oystercatcher	3
Tree Sparrow	47	Snow Bunting	33	Curlew	3
Quail	46	Ptarmigan	30	Kittiwake	3
Goshawk	42	Scottish Crossbill	30	Razorbill	3
Dotterel	35	Crested Tit	25	Rook	2
Fieldfare	33	Common Gull	<22	Herring Gull	2
Snow Bunting	33	Goldeneye	20	Common Gull	2
Ptarmigan	30	Kittiwake	18	Red/Willow Grouse	2
Scottish Crossbill	30	Quail	16	Meadow Pipit	1
Tawny Owl	29	Osprey	15	Wren	1
Grey Partridge	28	Black Grouse	14	Woodpigeon	1
Collared Dove	28	Goshawk	13		
Little Ringed Plover	27	Red Grouse	13		
Barn Owl	27	Siskin	12		
Linnet	25	Herring Gull	12		
Kittiwake	25	Water Rail	11		
Crested Tit	25	Capercaillie	11		
Garganey	25	Common Crossbill	10		
Stock Dove	24	Wigeon	10		
Yellowhammer	24				
Herring Gull	22				
Common Gull	22				
Rook	22				
Coal Tit	20				
Jackdaw	20				
Red-legged Partridge	20				
Goldeneye	20				
Black Grouse	20				

Annex 5. *Scientific names of species mentioned in the text*

Species mentioned in the text whose scientific names do not appear elsewhere. The pages where species are mentioned are also listed. Page number in *Italics* = mentioned in species account beginning on page listed.

Birds

Lesser Scaup	*Aythya affinis*	73
Lesser Spotted Woodpecker	*Dendrocopus minor*	473
Marsh Tit	*Poecile palustris*	473
Nightingale	*Luscinia megarhynchos*	473
Nuthatch	*Sitta europaea*	473
Redhead	*Aythya americana*	73
Ring-necked Duck	*Aythya collaris*	75
White-tailed Eagle	*Haliaeetus albicilla*	471
Willow Tit	*Poecile montana*	473

Mammals

Brown Rat	*Rattus norvegicus*	*110*
Field Vole	*Microtus agrestis*	148, *250, 256, 258,*
Fox	*Vulpes vulpes*	94, *92, 144, 202, 208, 216, 222, 258*
Mink	*Mustela vison*	110, *162, 202, 208, 212*
Mountain Hare	*Lepus timidus*	*144*
Otter	*Lutra lutra*	56, 70, *162*
Pine Marten	*Martes martes*	472
Red Deer	*Cervus elaphus*	88, 188, 202, *288,* 461
Red Squirrel	*Sciurus vulgaris*	*270*
Roe Deer	*Capreolus capreolus*	88, *144*
Rabbit	*Oryctolagus cuniculus*	52, 138, 142, 144, *366*

Amphibians

Frog	*Rana temporaria*	*120*

Fish

sandeels	*Ammomytidae*	469

Invertebrates

Large Black Slug	*Arion ater*	276
Prawn	*Nephrops norvegicus*	469
Sheep Tick	*Ixodes ricinus*	18, *88, 202*
wood ants	*Formica* spp.	266

Vascular Plants

Alder	*Alnus glutinosa*	31, *396, 398, 404*
Ash	*Fraxinus excelsior*	20
Aspen	*Populus tremula*	20
Barley	*Hordeum vulgare*	25, *102, 180, 457*
Beech	*Fagus sylvatica*	12, 20, 32, *130*
birches	*Betula* spp.	12, 19, 20, 22, *140, 266, 268, 270,* 296, *312, 314, 332, 346, 350, 354, 362, 368, 382, 390, 392, 394, 396, 398, 404, 414,* 463
Blackthorn	*Prunus spinosa*	26, *324*
Blaeberry	*Vaccinium myrtillus*	90, 94, *342*
Bracken	*Pteridium aquilinum*	12, *314, 362, 402*
Bramble	*Rubus fruticosus*	*320, 322, 324, 326*
Broom	*Cytisus scoparius*	22, 25
cherries	*Prunus* spp.	*418*
Chickweed	*Stellaria media*	*416*
Common Cottongrass	*Eriophorum angustifolium*	*94*
Common Reed	*Phragmites australis*	30, *118, 158*
Corsican Pine	*Pinus nigra*	21

cottongrass (see Common or Hare's-tail)	*Eriophorum* spp.	
Crowberry	*Empetrum nigrum*	90, *342*
cypresses	*Cupressaceae* sp.	*272*
Dandelion	*Taraxacum officinale*	396, *400*
Deer-grass	*Trichophorum germanicum*	17
docks	*Rumex* spp.	396, *416*
Dog-rose	*Rosa canina*	*324*
Douglas Fir	*Pseudotsuga menziesii*	21, *130*
European Larch	*Larix decidua*	21, *398, 408,* 410, *460*
Gorse	*Ulex europaeus*	22, *324, 326, 362, 364, 400, 422*
Hare's-tail Cottongrass	*Eriophorum vaginatum*	17
Hawthorn	*Crataegus monogyna*	*320, 324, 326*
Heather	*Calluna vulgaris*	9, 12, 13, 17, 18, 28, *88, 90, 342, 346, 356, 358, 362, 364, 384 402,* 462, 463
Ivy	*Hedera helix*	*348*
Japanese Larch	*Larix kaempferi*	21
Juniper	*Juniperus communis*	19, 20, 22, *266, 312, 342, 358, 362, 390,* 439
Kale	*Brassica oleracea viridis*	*104*
larches (see European or Japanese)	*Larix* spp.	*398, 408, 410*
Lodgepole Pine	*Pinus contorta*	21, *94,* 296, *410*
Marram Grass	*Ammophila arenaria*	*230*
Meadowsweet	*Filipendula ulmaria*	30
Nettle	*Urtica dioica*	*320, 326*
Norway spruce	*Picea abies*	21, *408, 410*
oaks	*Quercus* spp.	12, 20, *130, 314, 332, 346, 356, 360, 368, 418*
Oil-seed Rape	*Brassica napus oleifera*	25, *326, 330, 400, 456*
Reed Canary Grass	*Phalaris arundinacea*	*222*
Rhododendron	*Rhododendron ponticum*	316, *322, 350*
Rowan	*Sorbus aucuparia*	*266, 296, 362*
Scots Pine	*Pinus sylvestris*	10, 20, 21, *94, 136, 140, 150, 262, 266, 280,* 296, *332, 336, 342, 356, 360, 362, 398, 408, 410, 412,* 461
Sea Buckthorn	*Hippophae rhamnoides*	*324*
sedges	*Carex* spp.	156, *190*
Sitka Spruce	*Picea sitchensis*	21, *94, 244, 350, 398, 408, 410*
Soft Rush	*Juncus effusus*	*180*
Stiff Sedge	*Carex bigelowii*	*186*
Sycamore	*Acer pseudoplatanus*	32, *346*
thistles	*Cirsium* spp.	*396*
Three-leaved Rush	*Juncus trifidus*	176, *186*
Tufted Hair-grass	*Deschampsia cespitosa*	*328*
Turnip	*Brassica napus rapa*	25, *104, 181*
Wheat	*Triticum aestivum*	*385*
Whin – see Gorse		
willows	*Salix* spp.	30, 31, *158,* 296
Wood Sorrel	*Oxalis acetosella*	*416*
Yellow Flag iris	*Iris pseudacorus*	30, *118*
Yew	*Taxus baccata*	*418*
Yorkshire Fog	*Holcus lanatus*	*68*

Bryophytes

Woolly-hair Moss	*Racomitrium lanuginosum*	*176*

Annex 6. *Glossary*

Some definitions are taken from The Cambridge Illustrated Dictionary of Natural History *(R.J. Lincoln & G.A. Boxshall, CUP, 1987) and* A Dictionary of Birds *(B. Campbell & E. Lack, Poyser 1985).*

Agri-environment scheme Payments to land managers for environmental work, part-funded by the European Union under the Common Agricultural Programme. These are optional, competitive and usually under-funded in relation to demand.

Alpine See box on page 2 of Chapter 2 for definition.

Amber list species See 'Birds of Conservation Concern'.

Annex 1 (of EU 'Birds' Directive 1979, as codified 2009).

Benthic Associated with the bottom of lochs, rivers or the seabed.

Birds Directive EU Directive (1979) addressing the protection of a set of species across Europe. Annex 1 of the Directive includes those birds considered to be of special concern. Special Protection Areas and other measures are required to be designated and implemented in each member state to protect these species and their habitats.

Birds of Conservation Concern Birds assessed as being 'of conservation concern' in the UK. Using various criteria, species are listed as Red, Amber or Green, indicating the level of concern about their status. See Eaton *et al.* 2009.

Blanket bog Deep peatlands covering large areas of the uplands (sometimes extending to lower levels) and fed by rainwater only.

Boreal zone Cool or cool temperate regions of the northern hemisphere.

Breeding range Number of tetrads or recording units in which a species occurs (= breeding distribution).

Corvid A member of the crow family.

Dune slack Low-lying wetter areas between sand dunes in coastal areas.

Eclipse The plumage of ducks in late summer and autumn during moult, when the males become less colourful and may resemble females.

Eutrophic/eutrophication Enriched by nutrient influx by water or air (normally Phosphorus or Nitrogen).

Fen Low-lying areas in the landscape which receive water and which have a high water table all year. Usually dominated by sedges, rushes, grasses and sometimes reed or willow. Grades into reedbed in wetter conditions.

Feral Literally 'wild' but applied to populations of domesticated species that have reverted to a free existence.

Finishing cattle Rearing cattle for market that were born and raised elsewhere.

Forest Habitat Network A network of planting or regeneration designed to link up existing woodlands.

Green list species See 'Birds of Conservation Concern'.

Habitat See box on page 2 of Chapter 2 for definition.

Habitats Directive EU Directive 1992 on the Conservation of natural habitats and of wild fauna and flora. Deals with species other than birds and allows the designation of Special Areas of Conservation for certain priority habitats.

Irruptive A form of migration in which the proportion of birds leaving the breeding range, and the distance travelled, varies greatly from year to year, often in relation to availability of food.

Juncus Species of rush, usually Soft Rush *Juncus effusus*, forming large patches in fields with impeded drainage.

Land cover The habitats and land uses covering the surface of a defined area.

Littoral Pertaining to the shore of a loch or the sea.

Lowlands In our area, generally land below 200 m, but there is no strict definition.

Mesotrophic Intermediate in nutrient status between oligotrophic and eutrophic.

Muirburn The practice of burning Heather moorland in strips or patches, promoting new growth of Heather, as food for Red Grouse or deer.

Naturalised Birds that have either escaped from captivity or been introduced by humans but which are now successfully established and breeding regularly in the wild.

Neeps Turnips, usually grown to feed cattle and sheep.

Nominate race The subspecies of a bird that bears the same subspecific name as the species (*e.g. Carduelis flammea flammea*) rather than a subspecies with a different subspecific name (*Carduelis flammea rostrata*).

North-East Scotland The area covered by this atlas (Moray, Aberdeenshire & Aberdeen City).

North-east Scotland The SOC recording area covered by the Buckland *et al.* 1990 atlas (Aberdeenshire & Aberdeen City).

Oligotrophic Having low nutrient levels and primary productivity; usually applied to lochs and rivers.

Open General Licence Provision under the Wildlife & Countryside Act to allow the killing of certain birds for specified reasons. Primarily used to kill crows, pigeons and gulls.

Passerine The order or group of birds called 'Passeriformes', which in general includes the (usually) smaller 'perching' or 'song' birds.

Pelagic Living on the open sea.

Polyandrous A single female mating with several males.

Polygynous A single male bird mating with several females.

Raised bog Peatlands, often in lowland areas, where peat formation (fed by rain) has led to the build up of a peat dome above the surrounding land.

Ramsar site Wetlands designated under the Ramsar Convention 1971.

Red list species See 'Birds of Conservation Concern'.

Riparian Pertaining to the banks of rivers, burns or lochs.

Roding Display flight at dusk or dawn by Woodcocks.

SAC Special Area of Conservation (see Habitats Directive 1992).

SAC Scottish Agricultural College.

Schedule 1 (of Wildlife & Countryside Act 1981, as amended) - species listed in this schedule of the Act are given special protection during the breeding season.

Set-aside Farmland left uncropped as a production control measure. Largely ceased by around 2008 due to changes in EU rules.

SPA Special Protection Area (see Birds Directive).

Tetrad 2x2 km square of the Ordnance Survey national grid (see Chapter 1).

Uplands In our area, generally land above 200 m, but there is no strict definition.

Water Framework Directive (EU 2000). Implemented in Scotland by the Water Environment and Water Services (Scotland) Act 2003. Sets targets for improvement of water quality and creates a framework and local plans to achieve this.

Annex 7. *Gazetteer and index of sites mentioned in the text*

Page number in *Italics* = mentioned in species account beginning on page listed. Page number in **bold** = site profile.

Site Name	Grid ref	Page
Aberchirder	NJ625525	28, *110*
Aberdeen (city)	NJ935065	10, 11, 33, *52, 84, 88, 110, 116, 124, 132, 140, 142, 148, 154, 168, 172, 174, 194, 206, 208, 212, 214, 216, 224, 226, 232, 236, 252, 244, 248, 252, 262, 264, 268, 274, 280, 284, 290, 298, 302, 308, 318, 322, 324, 336, 338, 344, 370, 374, 376, 378, 388, 400, 414, 416, 418, 422, 426, 428, 429, 436, 458, 463, 464, 466, 467, 470*
Abergeldie	NO289952	*130*
Aberdour (house)	NJ910640	429
Aberlour	NJ265428	*368*
Aboyne	NO528984	21, *82, 240, 262, 314, 322, 360, 374, 392, 418*
Alford	NJ576161	11, 25, *100, 240, 280, 312, 346, 368, 374, 400,* 429, 459, 461
Allt a' Mharcaidh	NH890030	14
Alpity	NO788771	429
Altens, Aberdeen	NJ953023	*174, 212*
Altyre Estate	NJ025545	*270, 296,* 466
Alves	NJ135625	*282*
An Socach	NO090800	16
An Sgarsoch	NN935837	*188*
Arbuthnott	NO795755	429
Arnage Castle	NJ937370	*280*
Arnbarrow Hill	NO650780	*197*
Asloun	NJ542147	459
Auchenblae	NO725785	*418,*
Auchmacoy	NJ990308	*64, 172, 302*
Aultmore	NJ475575	*92, 212, 296*
Avonside	NJ00-NJ13	*320*
Baddoch	NO135827	*298*
Ballater	NO368958	20, *50, 54, 94, 140, 160, 202, 204, 258, 260, 262, 274, 280, 282, 314, 350, 364, 368, 372, 394, 396, 400, 418, 422, 426, 462*
Ballindalloch	NJ180365	*266,* 467
Balloch	NJ472495	*212, 214*
Ballochbuie Forest	NO200900	*94,* **254,** *412,* 461
Ballogie	NO570955	*130*
Balmedie	NJ976180	*98, 148,* 463
Balmoral (estate)	NO255950	*46, 164, 197, 400,* 464
Banchory	NO698955	28, *54, 94, 138, 140, 156, 252, 264, 290, 346, 392, 402, 418,* 457
Banchory-Devenick	NO910023	*54*
Banff	NJ685645	*52, 54, 110, 306, 374, 376, 388, 424*
Banffshire	NJ65-NJ00	*150, 296, 328*
Banff & Buchan (district)	NJ95 area	*110, 164, 216*
Barras	NO822802	*102 426*
Beinn a' Bhuird	NO090990	428
Beinn Mheadhoin	NJ025018	16
Ben Aigan	NJ310480	*88, 392*
Ben Avon	NJ135015	428
Ben Macdui	NN989989	10, *90,* **406,** 428
Ben Rinnes	NJ255355	*90*
Bennachie	NJ682223	*94, 150, 418*
Bieldside	NJ880025	*418*
Bin Forest, Huntly	NJ520430	*270, 332*
Black Moss, Dinnet	NJ460015	*156, 208*
Blackburn	NJ825125	*426*
Blackhall Forest	NO665955	*290*
Blackwater Forest	NJ305265	17
Blairs	NO885005	*350*
Bluemill	NJ412123	*212, 214*
Boar's Head Rock	NJ289680	*230*
Boddam	NK136423	*116, 206, 232, 234, 238, 418*
Boultenstone	NJ411109	*212, 214*
Bow Fiddle Rock	NJ495688	*236, 287, 388*
Boyndie	NJ640640	*376*
Braemar	NO149914	11, *82, 168, 180, 192, 202, 240, 250, 258, 268, 272, 276, 278, 280, 282, 284, 290, 310, 312, 320, 330, 342, 344, 358, 360, 368, 396, 402, 432,* 460

The Breeding Birds of North-East Scotland

Index of birds and subjects

The separate indexes below include main mentions of all bird species and subjects. Bird groupings mapped in Chapter 4 are excluded, as is Annex 4, Table A. Species other than birds are indexed in Annex 5 and place name references are indexed in the Gazetteer in Annex 7.

Page number in **bold** = main species account. Page number in *italics* = mentioned in species account beginning on page listed.

Index to scientific names of birds

Reference is made to the main species account only (or to other reference if no species account). See Annex 5 for index to scientific names of other animals and plants

Subject index

The Breeding Birds of North-East Scotland